CONTENTS

PART 1 – CALCULUS

PART 2 – STATISTICS

ANSWER KEY

PART 1 – CALCULUS

PART 2 – STATISTICS

1.1. – RATE OF CHANGE

In the world that surrounds us things change: the temperature, the direction and strength of the wind, the prices of products, the velocity of objects, population size, our height, weight etc.

Example 1: Oil prices, represented as a function of time P(t):

1. As you can see there have been periods of time in history in which the prices

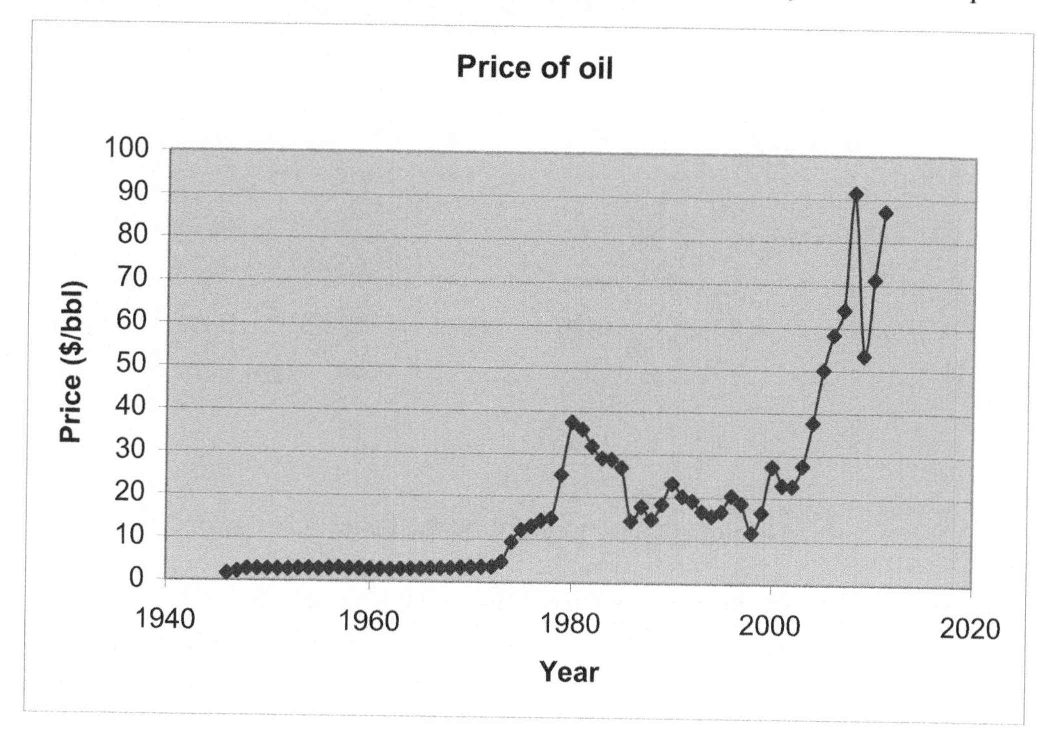

have changed slowly, Identify one of them: ____________________

2. In other periods the prices have been changing very quickly, identify one positive change: ________________ and one negative change: ____________

3. In this graph what are the units of the change of price: ______________

4. Find the average rate of change in oil prices between 1970 and 1985. Is this average similar to the real change in prices? Explain your answer.

5. Find the average rate of change between 1945 and 2005, how can this change be represented graphically?

Example 2: Population of 20 – 29 year olds in southern Europe for example, represented as a function of time P(t):

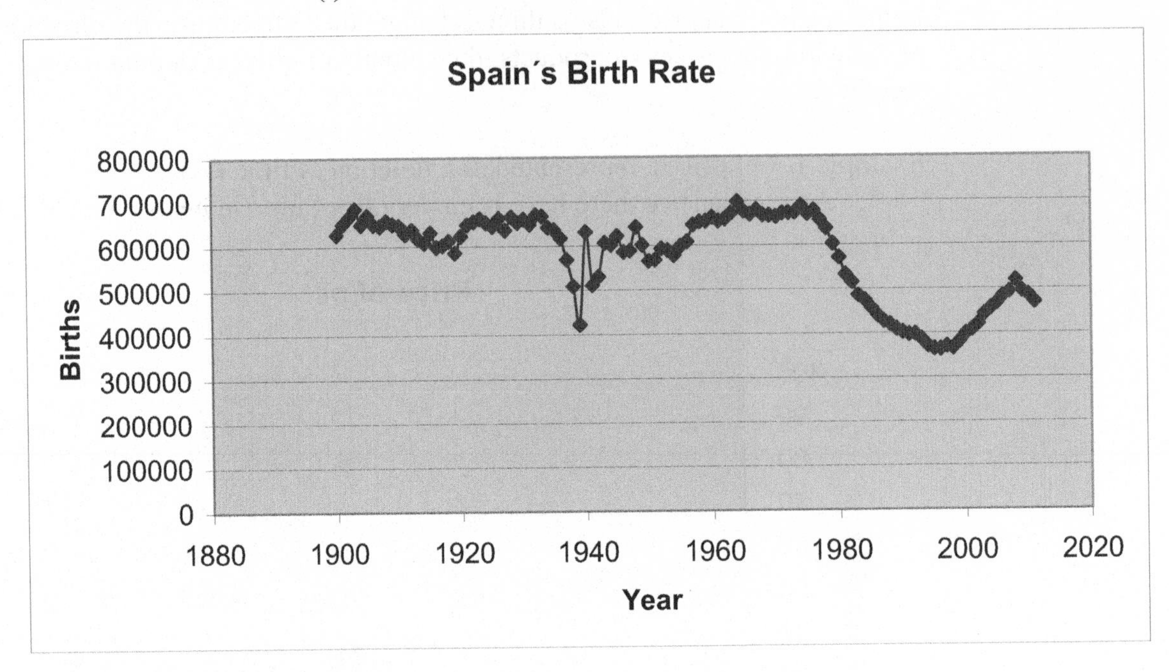

6. During what period of time the fastest change occurs? ________________

7. In this graph what are the <u>units</u> of the <u>change</u> of birth:________________

8. Find the <u>average rate of change</u> between 1960 and 2000. Is this average similar to the real change in births? Explain your answer.

9. Find the average rate of change between 2000 and 2010, how can this change be represented graphically?

1.2. – INTRODUCTION TO LIMITS

Introduction:

1. $x \to \infty$ means that ______________________________

2. $x \to -\infty$ means that ______________________________

3. $x \to 3$ means that ______________________________

4. $x \to 3^+$ means that ______________________________

5. $x \to 3^-$ means that ______________________________

6. $x \to 0^-$ means that ______________________________

7. $x \to 0^+$ means that ______________________________

GRAPHICAL INTERPRETATION OF LIMITS

1. Given the graph of the function:

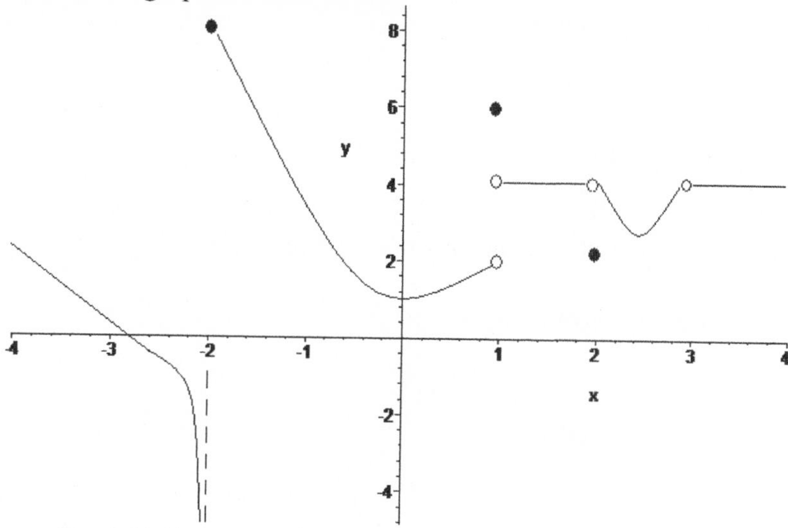

a. $\lim_{x \to 0^-}(f(x)) =$ $\lim_{x \to 0^+}(f(x)) =$ f(0) = $\lim_{x \to 0}(f(x)) =$

b. $\lim_{x \to -3^+}(f(x)) =$ $\lim_{x \to -3^-}(f(x)) =$ $f(-3) =$ $\lim_{x \to -3}(f(x)) =$

c. $\lim_{x \to -2^+}(f(x)) =$ $\lim_{x \to -2^-}(f(x)) =$ $f(-2) =$ $\lim_{x \to -2}(f(x)) =$

d. $\lim_{x \to 1^-}(f(x)) =$ $\lim_{x \to 1^+}(f(x)) =$ $f(1) =$ $\lim_{x \to 1}(f(x)) =$

e. $\lim_{x \to 2^+}(f(x)) =$ $\lim_{x \to 2^-}(f(x)) =$ $f(2) =$ $\lim_{x \to 2}(f(x)) =$

f. Using the graph find all the values of a for which f(a) does not exist: ________

2. Given the graph of the function:

a. $\lim_{x\to 0^-}(f(x))=$

b. $\lim_{x\to 0^+}(f(x))=$

c. $\lim_{x\to 0}(f(x))=$

d. $\lim_{x\to -3^+}(f(x))=$

e. $\lim_{x\to -3^-}(f(x))=$

f. $\lim_{x\to -3}(f(x))=$

g. $f(-3)=$

h. $\lim_{x\to -3^+}(f(x))=$

i. $\lim_{x\to -3^-}(f(x))=$

j. $\lim_{x\to -3}(f(x))=$

k. $f(3)=$

l. $\lim_{x\to -1^-}(f(x))=$

m. $\lim_{x\to -1^+}(f(x))=$

n. $\lim_{x\to -1}(f(x))=$

o. $f(-1)=$

g. State the equations of all the asymptotes: ____________________

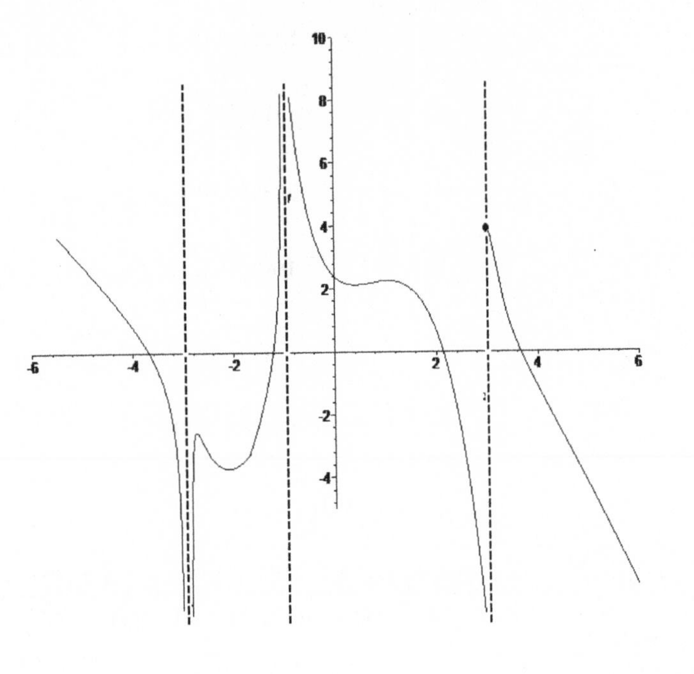

3. Find the following limits:

$\lim_{x\to\infty}(f(x))=$

$\lim_{x\to\infty}(f(x))=$

$\lim_{x\to\infty}(f(x))=$

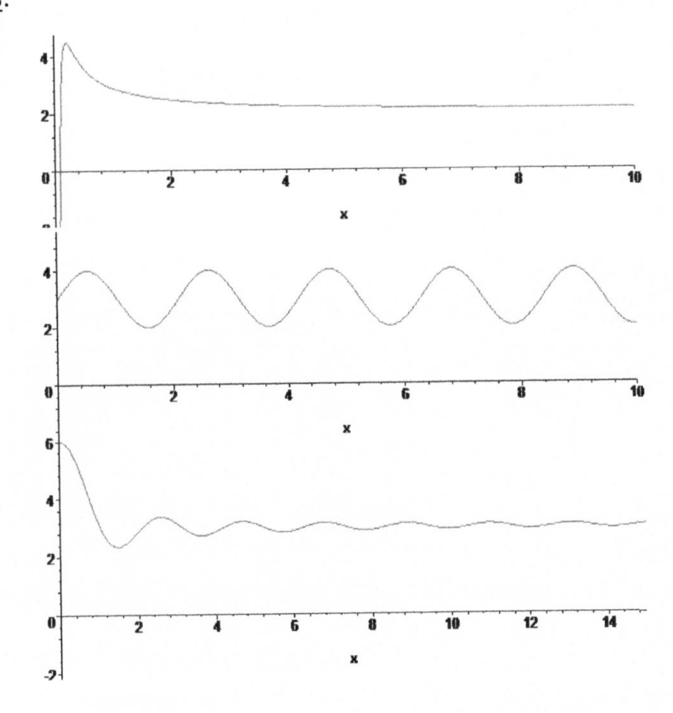

4. Find the limits:

$\lim_{x \to -\infty} (f(x)) =$

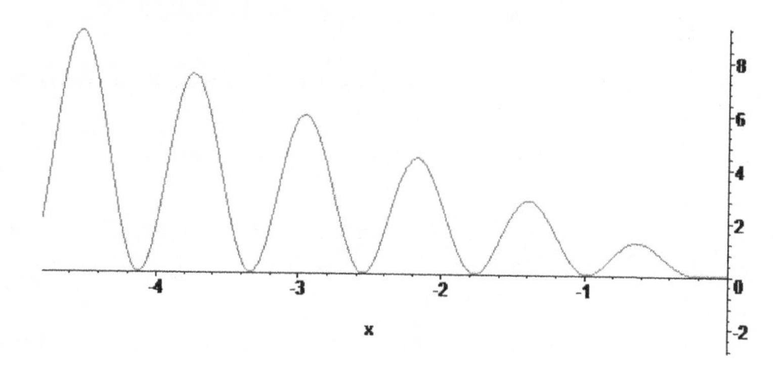

$\lim_{x \to \infty} (f(x)) =$

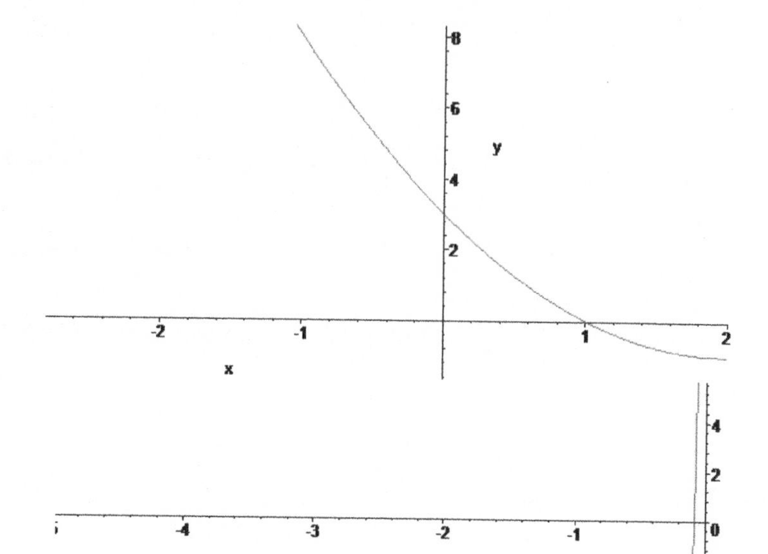

$\lim_{x \to -\infty} (f(x)) =$

$\lim_{x \to -\infty} (f(x)) =$

5. Given the following data for a certain function $f(x)$:

x	-17	-13	k	0	p	8	12	22	55
$f(x)$	0	1	1	8	2	11	N	-3	-7

a. Find the value of the following limits:
$Lim_{x \to -17}(f(x)) =$ ____ $Lim_{x \to -13}(f(x)) =$ ____ $Lim_{x \to p}(f(x)) =$ ____

b. Given that $Lim_{x \to -1}(f(x)) = 1$, write down the value of k.

c. Find $Lim_{x \to p}(f(x)) + Lim_{x \to 55}(f(x)) =$ ____

d. Given that $f^{-1}(-2) = 12$, write down the value of N.

6. Horizontal asymptotes appear ____________________, in case we look for them

   we need to check the limit of the function when x tends to _____ or _____

7. Vertical asymptotes appear ____________________. We check lateral limits to

   see the behaviour of the function next to it.

8. Given the following data for a certain function $f(x)$:

x	-7	-1	0	2	p	7	11	23	35
$f(x)$	4	0	4	8	2	11	N	5	5

   e. Find the value of the following limits:
      $Lim_{x\to 0}(f(x)) =$ ____ $Lim_{x\to 2}(f(x)) = 8$ $Lim_{x\to \_\_}(f(x)) = N$

   f. Given that $Lim_{x\to 11}(f(x)) = Lim_{x\to p}(f(x))$, write down the value of N.

   g. Find $Lim_{x\to -1}(f(x)) - Lim_{x\to 7}(f(x)) =$ ____

1.3. – DEFINITION OF DERIVATIVE

1. The derivative is the ______________________________

2. Given the function, sketch the tangent in each one of the points:

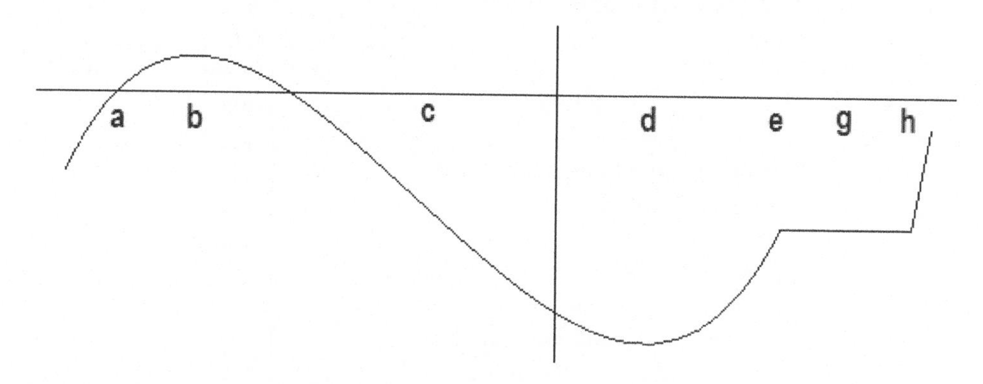

Fill the table with: Positive, negative, zero or doesn't exist.

	x = a	x = b	x = c	x = d	x = e	x = g	x = h
f(x)							
f'(x)							

3. Given the function, sketch the tangent in each one of the points:

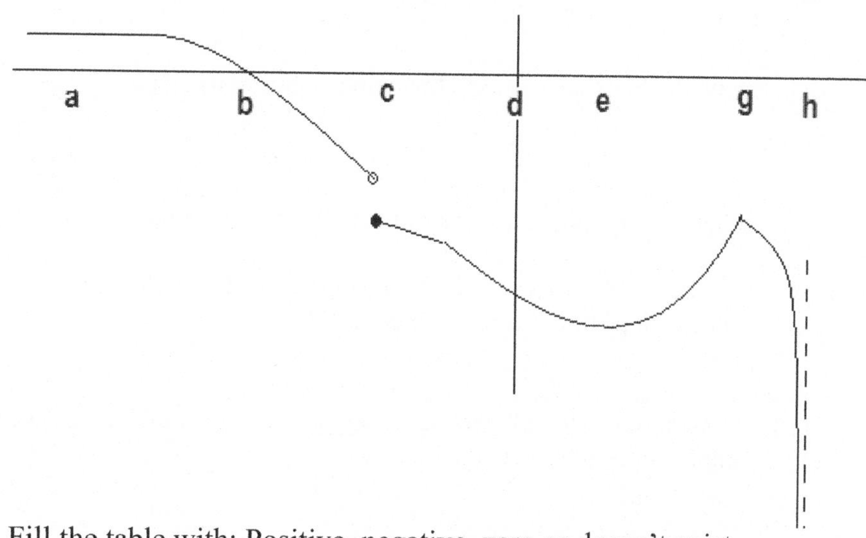

Fill the table with: Positive, negative, zero or doesn't exist.

	x = a	x = b	x = c	x = d	x = e	x = g	x = h
f(x)							
f'(x)							

4. Given the function $f(x) = -x^2$. f represents the temperature as the function of height x given in km:

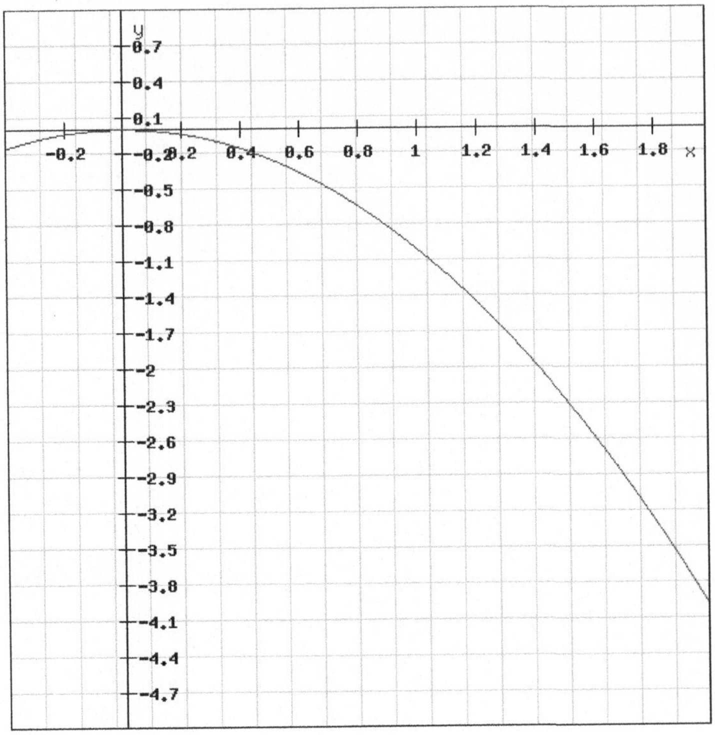

5. Fill the blanks and indicate the corresponding points on the graph:

   f(1) = ___ f(1.4) = ___

   Draw the line that connects the points and find its slope

   m = ___

6. Fill the blanks and indicate the corresponding points on the graph:

   f(1) = ___ f(1.2) = ___

   Draw the line that connects the points and find its slope

   m = ___

7. Fill the blanks and indicate the corresponding points on the graph:

   f(1) = ___ f(1.1) = ___ .

   Draw the line that connects the points and find its slope

   m = ___

8. What do you think the slope of the tangent at the point where x = 1 is? ____________

9. Looking at the process to find the slope at the point where x = 1, can you think how to find the slope of the tangent in general?

10. What does the slope **between 2 points** represent? Make reference to height and temperature and give units.

11. What does the slope of the tangent to the function **at a certain point** (the derivative) represent? Make reference to height and temperature and give units.

12. The slope between 2 points is ______________________________

13. The slope at a certain point is ______________________________

FORMAL DEFINITION OF DERIVATIVE

Definition: Let y = f(x) be a function. The derivative of f is the function whose value at x is the limit:

$$f'(x) = \lim_{h \to 0} \frac{f(x+h) - f(x)}{h}$$

Provided this limit exists. If this limit exists for each x in an open interval (a, b), then we say that f is differentiable on [a, b].

Differentiate the following functions, use the definition ONLY:

1. $f(x) = mx + b$

$$\frac{df}{dx} = f'(x) = \lim_{h \to 0} \frac{f(x+h) - f(x)}{h} = \lim_{h \to 0} \frac{\underline{\hspace{3cm}} - \underline{\hspace{3cm}}}{h} =$$

2. $f(x) = x^2 + k$

$$\frac{df}{dx} = f'(x) = \lim_{h \to 0} \frac{f(x+h) - f(x)}{h} = \lim_{h \to 0} \frac{\underline{\hspace{3cm}} - \underline{\hspace{3cm}}}{h} =$$

3. $f(x) = x^3 + k$

$$\frac{df}{dx} = f'(x) = \lim_{h \to 0} \frac{f(x+h) - f(x)}{h} = \lim_{h \to 0} \frac{\underline{\hspace{3cm}} - \underline{\hspace{3cm}}}{h} =$$

4. $f(x) = 4x - 3x^2$

$$\frac{df}{dx} = f'(x) = \lim_{h \to 0} \frac{f(x+h) - f(x)}{h} = \lim_{h \to 0} \frac{\underline{\hspace{3cm}} - \underline{\hspace{3cm}}}{h} =$$

5. $f(x)=\sqrt{x+1}$

$$\frac{df}{dx}=f'(x)=\lim_{h\to 0}\frac{f(x+h)-f(x)}{h}=\lim_{h\to 0}\frac{\underline{\qquad\qquad} - \underline{\qquad\qquad}}{h}=$$

6. $f(x)=\dfrac{1}{2x+1}$

$$\frac{df}{dx}=f'(x)=\lim_{h\to 0}\frac{f(x+h)-f(x)}{h}=\lim_{h\to 0}\frac{\underline{\qquad\qquad} - \underline{\qquad\qquad}}{h}=$$

7. $f(x)=\dfrac{-3}{-x+2}$

$$\frac{df}{dx}=f'(x)=\lim_{h\to 0}\frac{f(x+h)-f(x)}{h}=\lim_{h\to 0}\frac{\underline{\qquad\qquad} - \underline{\qquad\qquad}}{h}=$$

8. $f(x)=\sqrt{2x}+1$

$$\frac{df}{dx}=f'(x)=\lim_{h\to 0}\frac{f(x+h)-f(x)}{h}=\lim_{h\to 0}\frac{\underline{\qquad\qquad} - \underline{\qquad\qquad}}{h}=$$

9. $f(x) = \sqrt{3x-5} + 1$

$$\frac{df}{dx} = f'(x) = \lim_{h \to 0} \frac{f(x+h) - f(x)}{h} = \lim_{h \to 0} \frac{\rule{4cm}{0.4pt} - \rule{3cm}{0.4pt}}{h} =$$

10. $f(x) = \frac{4}{5x+1} + 2$

$$\frac{df}{dx} = f'(x) = \lim_{h \to 0} \frac{f(x+h) - f(x)}{h} = \lim_{h \to 0} \frac{\rule{4cm}{0.4pt} - \rule{3cm}{0.4pt}}{h} =$$

11. $f(x) = \sqrt{2x-3}$

$$\frac{df}{dx} = f'(x) = \lim_{h \to 0} \frac{f(x+h) - f(x)}{h} = \lim_{h \to 0} \frac{\rule{4cm}{0.4pt} - \rule{3cm}{0.4pt}}{h} =$$

12. $f(x) = \frac{1}{3x-4}$

$$\frac{df}{dx} = f'(x) = \lim_{h \to 0} \frac{f(x+h) - f(x)}{h} = \lim_{h \to 0} \frac{\rule{4cm}{0.4pt} - \rule{3cm}{0.4pt}}{h} =$$

13. Given the following function:

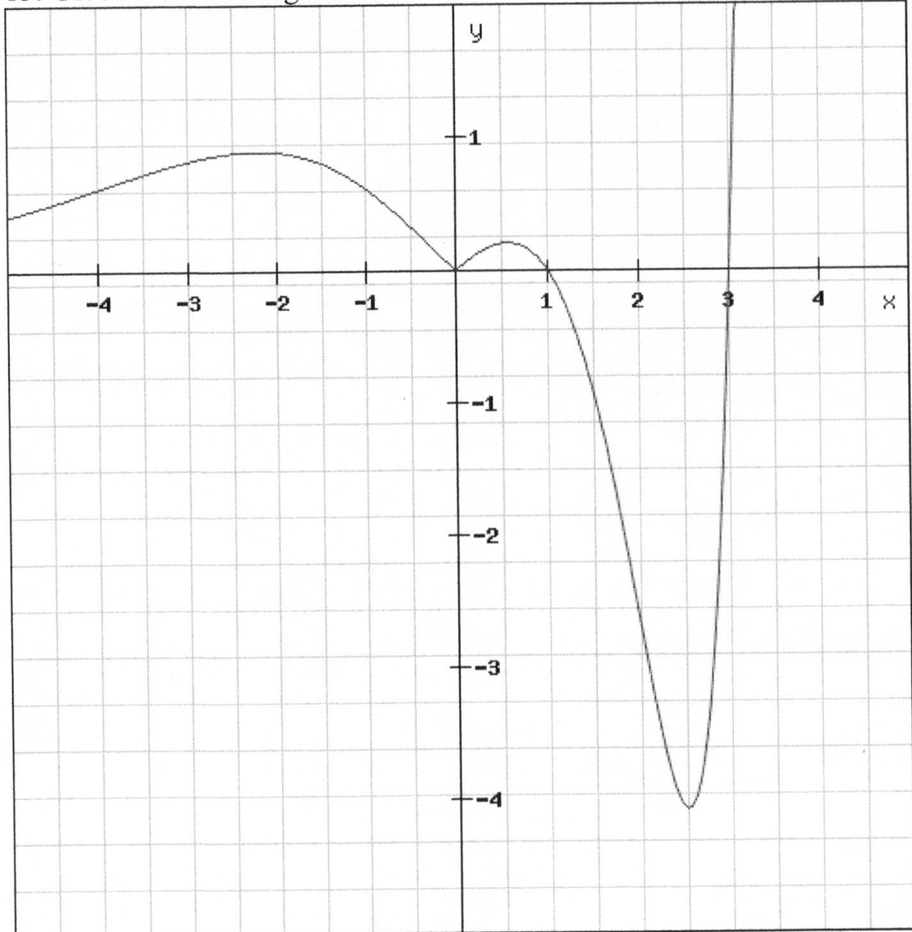

Find:

a. $f(-4) =$ __ $f'(-4) =$ __

b. $f(-3) =$ __ $f'(-3) =$ __

c. $f(-2.3) =$ __ $f'(-2.3) =$ __

d. $f(-1) =$ __ $f'(-1) =$ __

e. $f(0) =$ __ $f'(0) =$ __

f. $f(0.2) =$ __ $f'(0.2) =$ __

g. $f(0.6) =$ __ $f'(0.6) =$ __

h. $f(2) =$ __ $f'(2) =$ __

i. $f(2.5) =$ __ $f'(2.5) =$ __

j. $f(3) =$ __ $f'(3) =$ __

Use the information obtained to sketch the derivative on the same graph.

14. When the derivative is positive it means that the function is ______________.

15. When the derivative is __________ it means that the function is ____________.

16. When the derivative is zero it means that the function has__________________.

1.4. – GRAPHING THE DERIVATIVE (GRADIENT FUNCTION)

Draw the graph of the derivative of the following functions on the graph below:

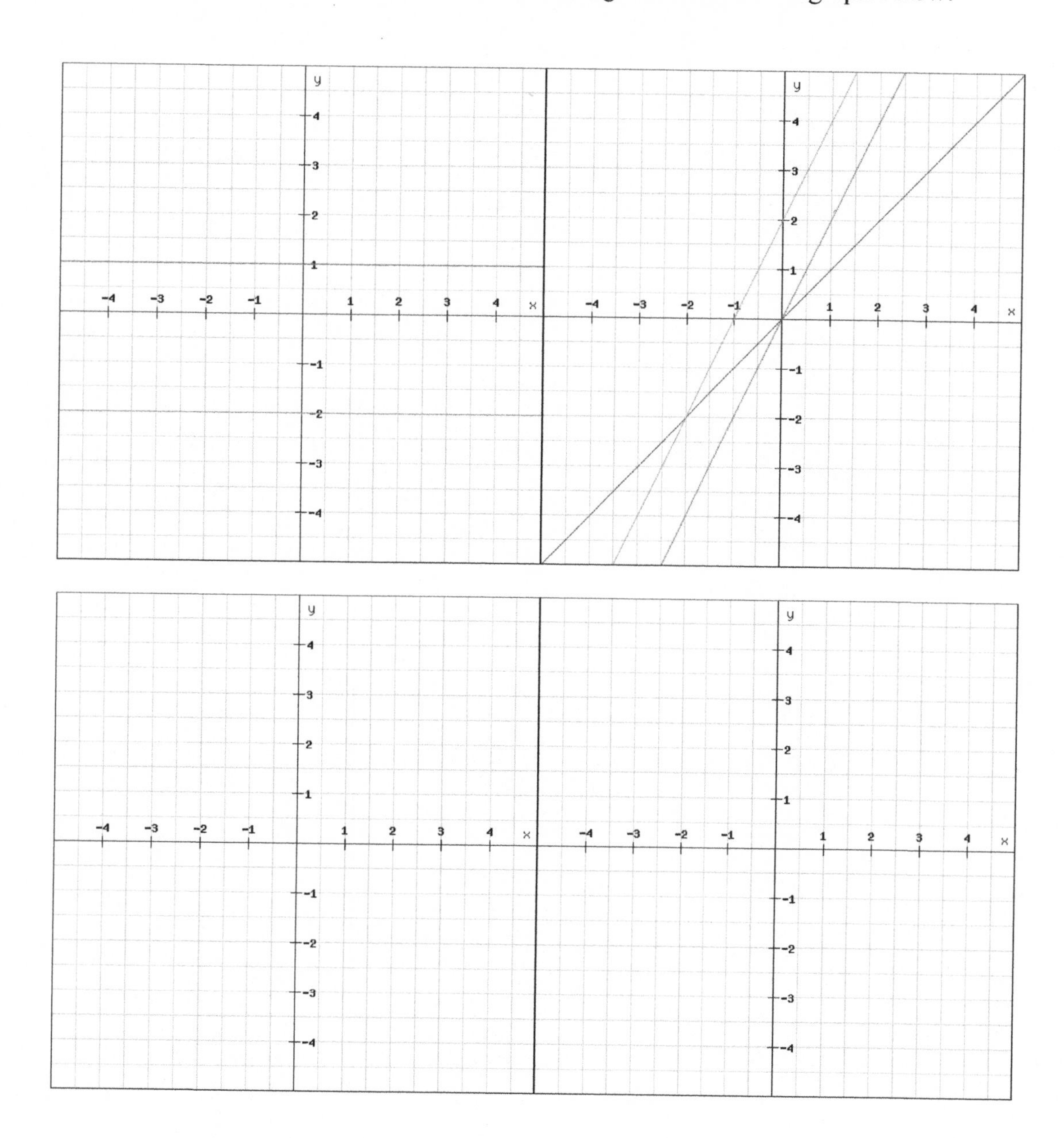

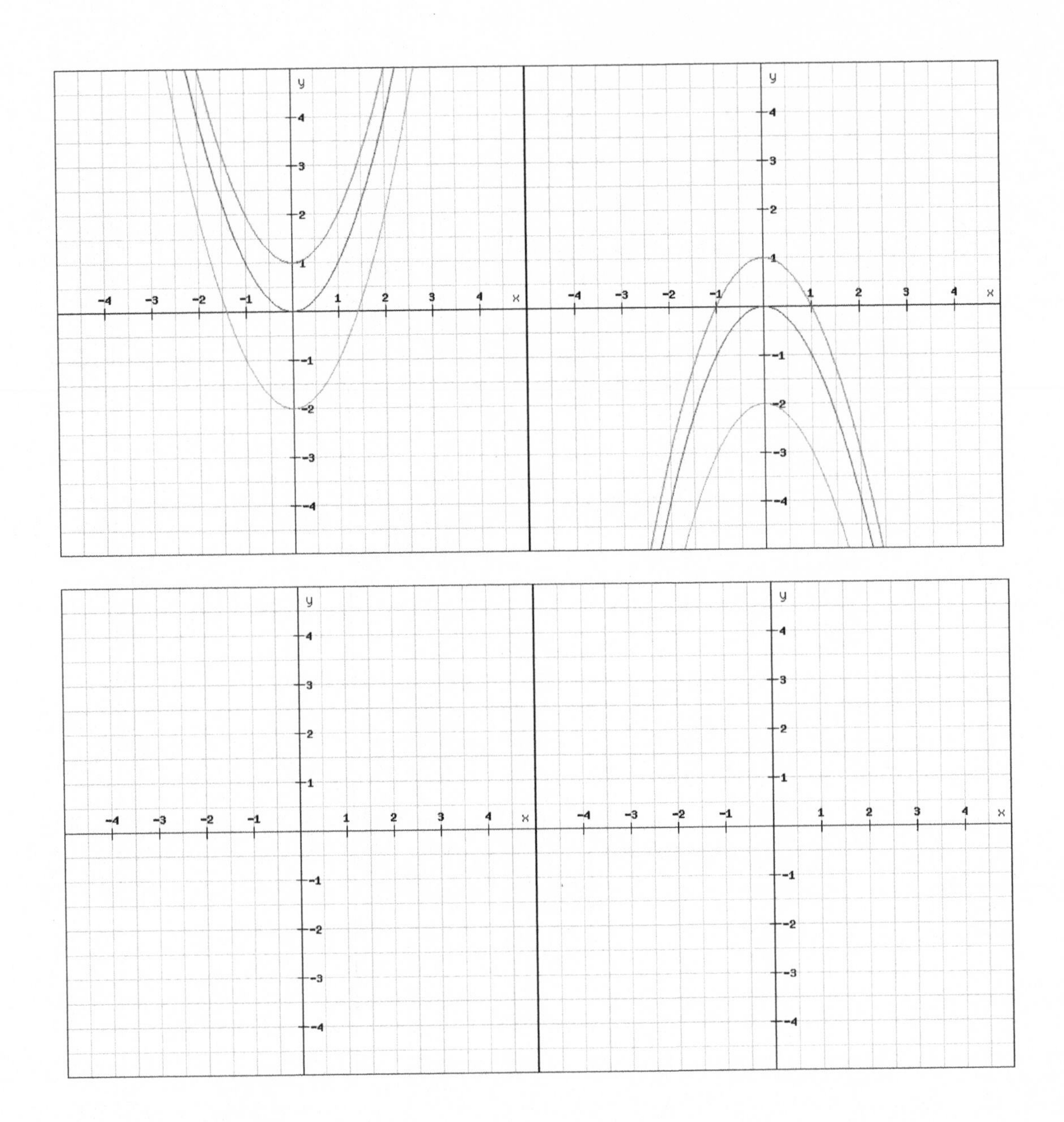

y
4
3
2
1
-4
-3
-2
-1
1
2
3
4
x
-1
-2
-3
-4

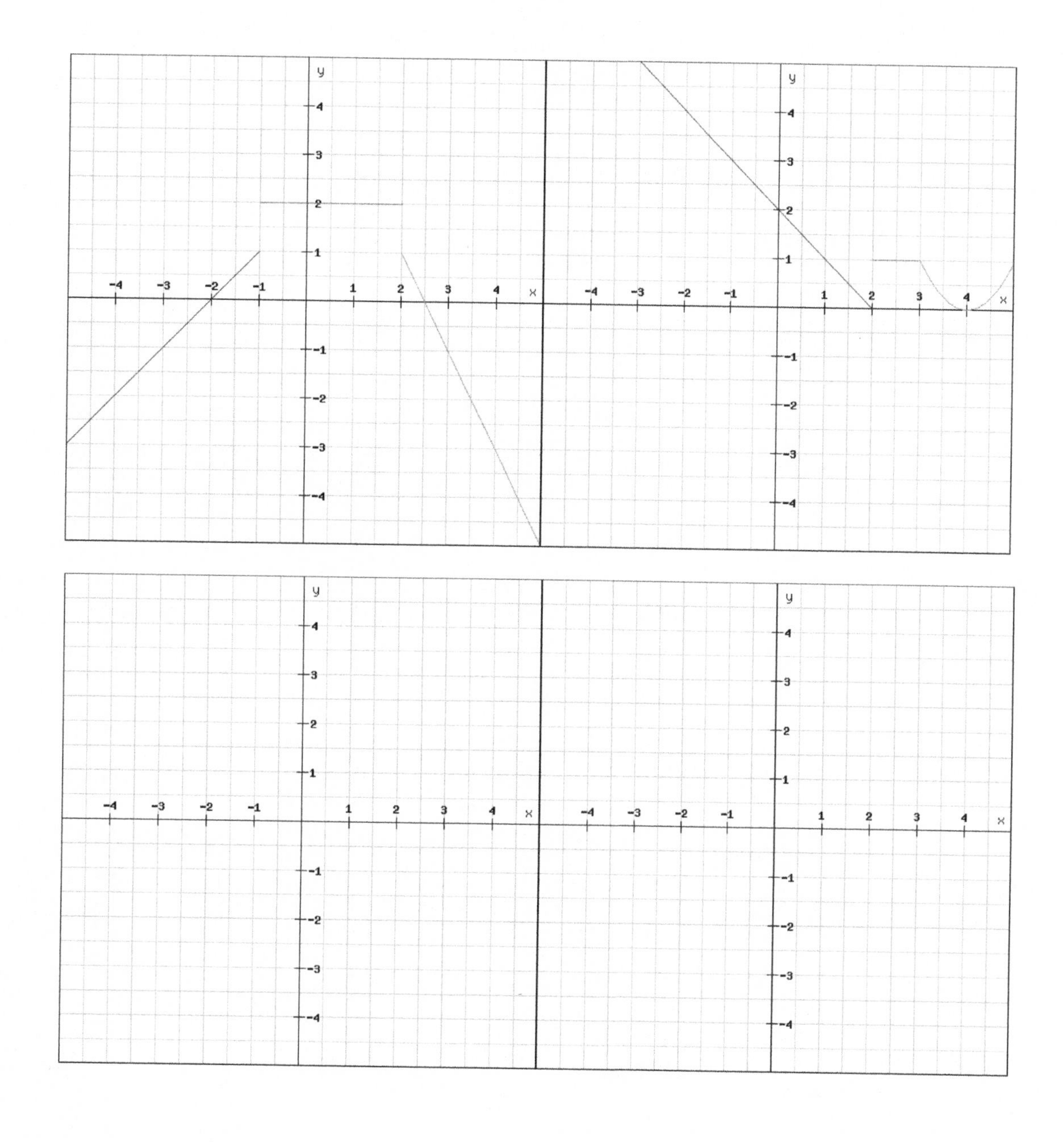

y
4
3
2
1
-4
-3
-2
-1
1
2
3
4
x
-1
-2
-3
-4

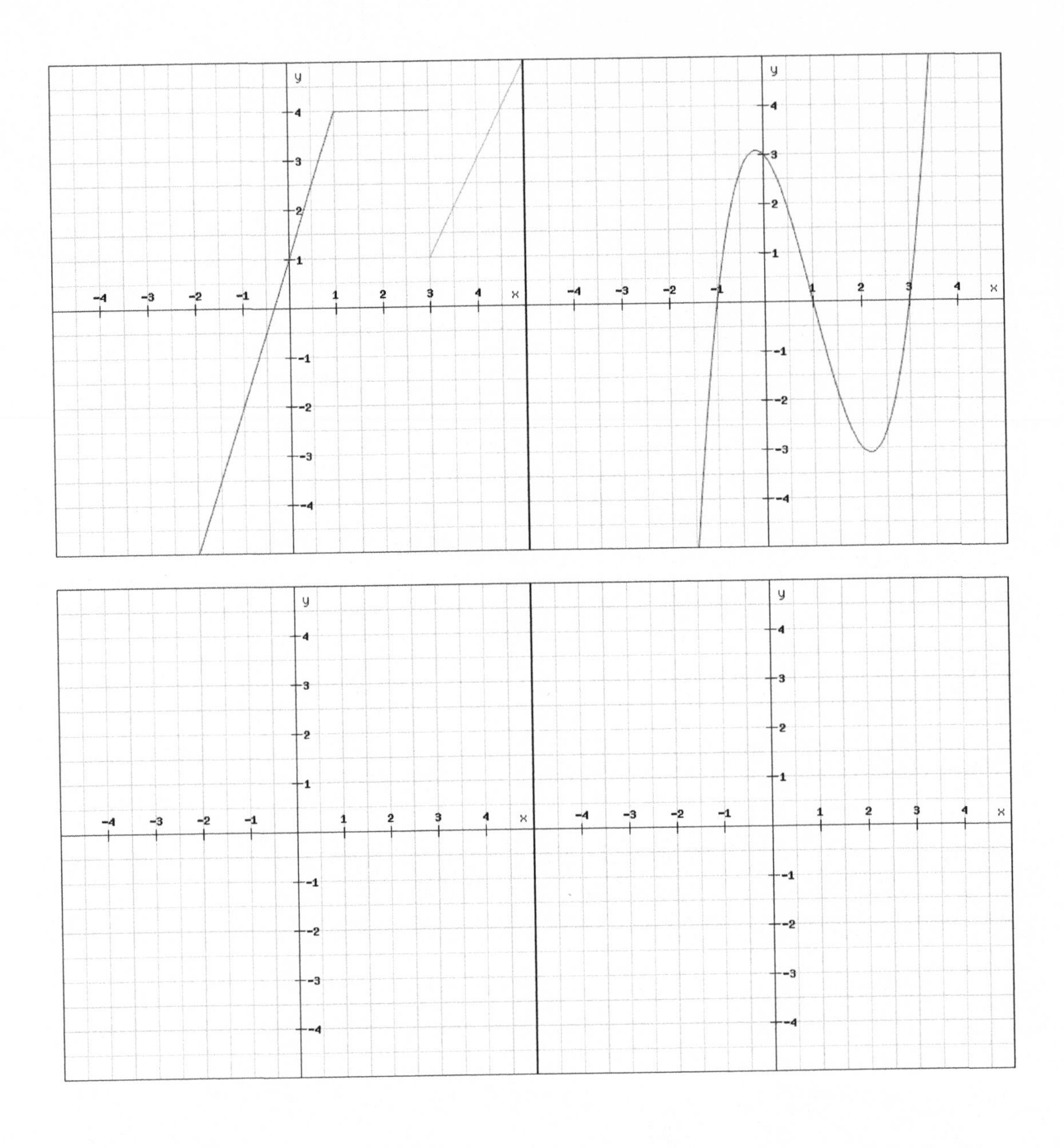

y
4
3
2
1
-4
-3
-2
-1
1
2
3
4
x
-1
-2
-3
-4

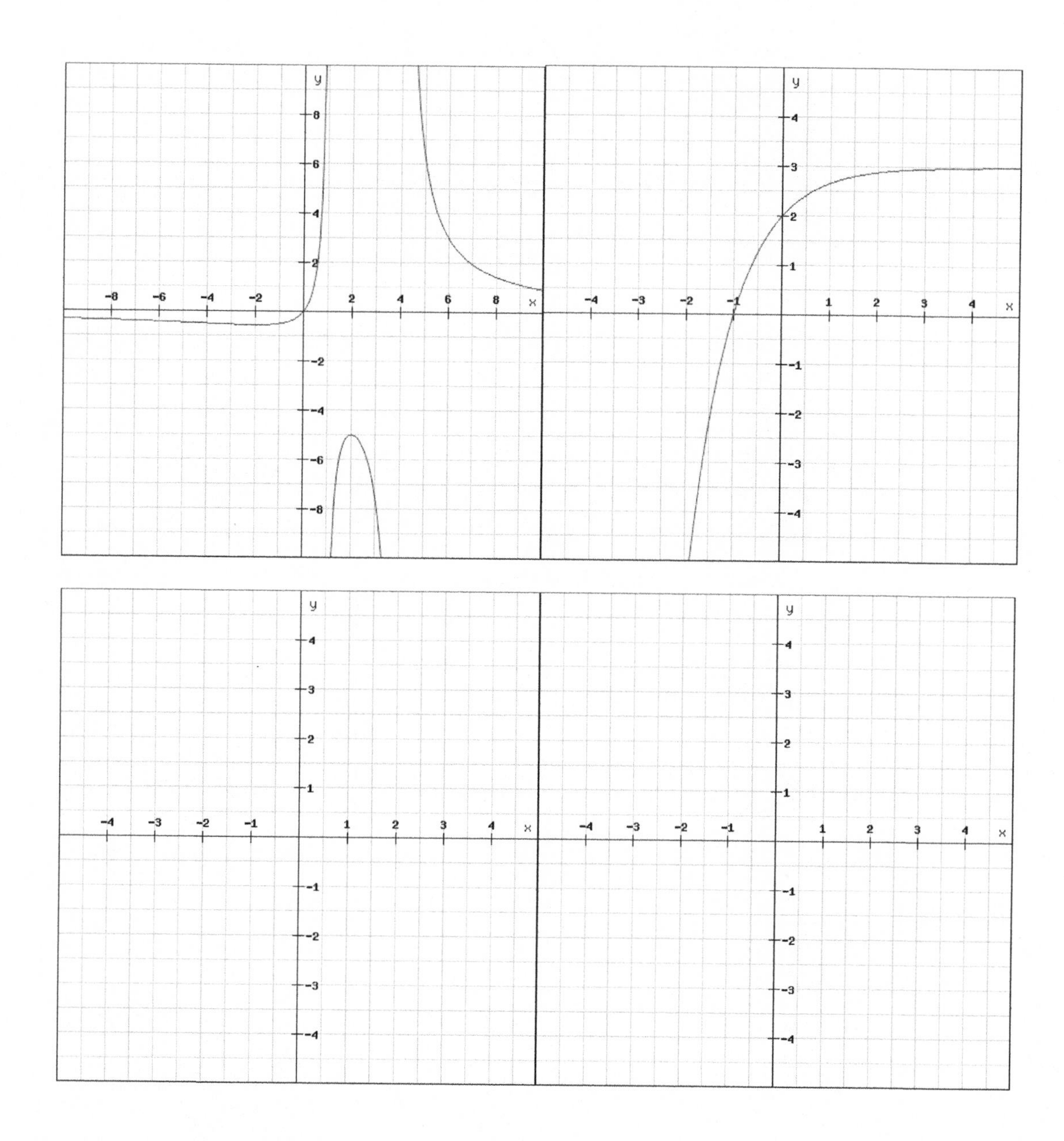

y
8
6
4
2
−8 −6 −4 −2 2 4 6 8 x
−2
−4
−6
−8
y
4
3
2
1
−4 −3 −2 −1 1 2 3 4 x
−1
−2
−3
−4
y
4
3
2
1
−4 −3 −2 −1 1 2 3 4 x
−1
−2
−3
−4
y
4
3
2
1
−4 −3 −2 −1 1 2 3 4 x
−1
−2
−3
−4

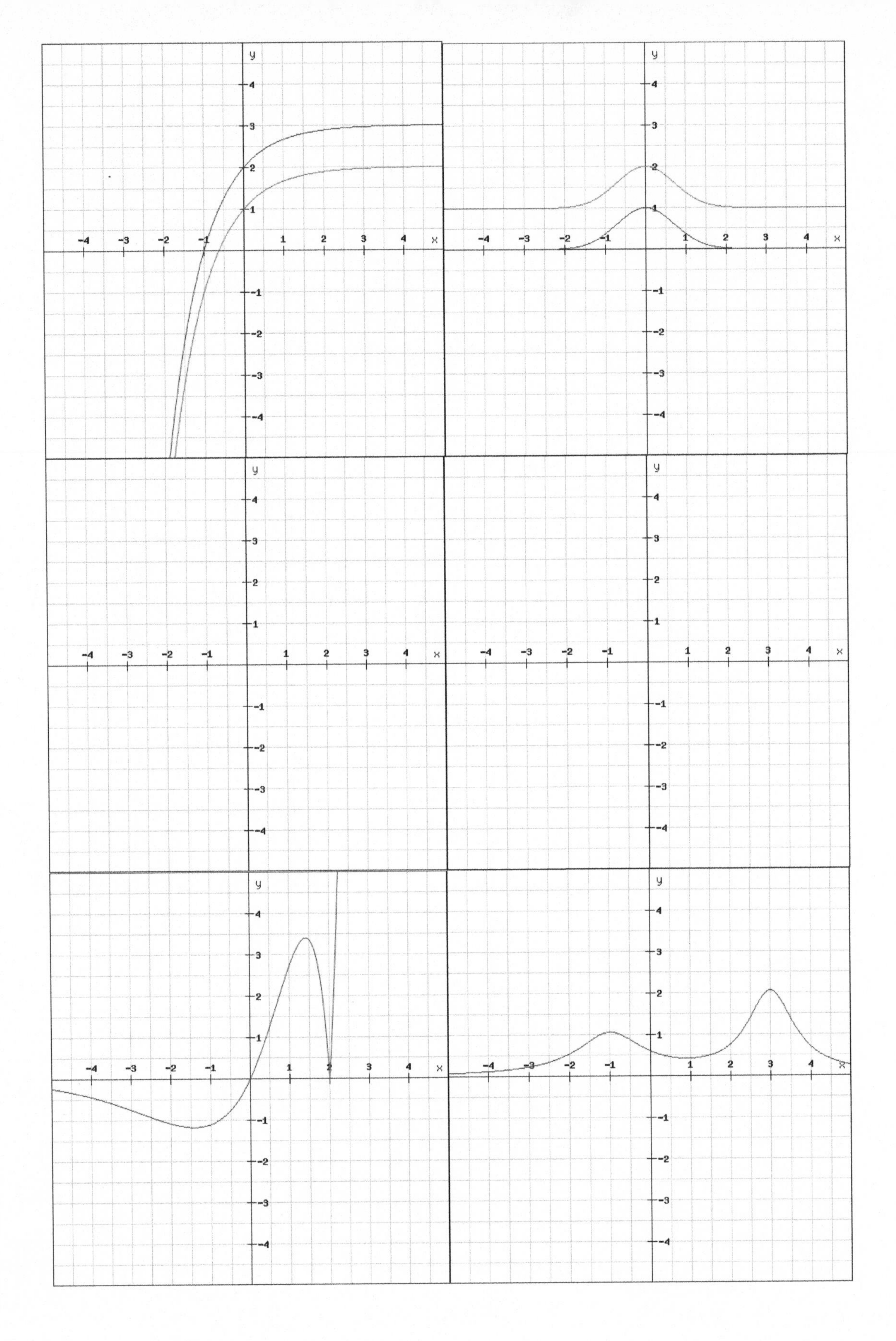

y
4
3
2
1
-4 -3 -2 -1 1 2 3 4 x
-1
-2
-3
-4
y
4
3
2
1
-4 -3 -2 -1 1 2 3 4 x
-1
-2
-3
-4
y
4
3
2
1
-4 -3 -2 -1 1 2 3 4 x
-1
-2
-3
-4
y
4
3
2
1
-4 -3 -2 -1 1 2 3 4 x
-1
-2
-3
-4
y
4
3
2
1
-4 -3 -2 -1 1 2 3 4 x
-1
-2
-3
-4
y
4
3
2
1
-4 -3 -2 -1 1 2 3 4 x
-1
-2
-3
-4

1.5. – GRAPHING THE ANTIDERIVATIVE

Draw the graph of the derivative of the following functions on the graph below:

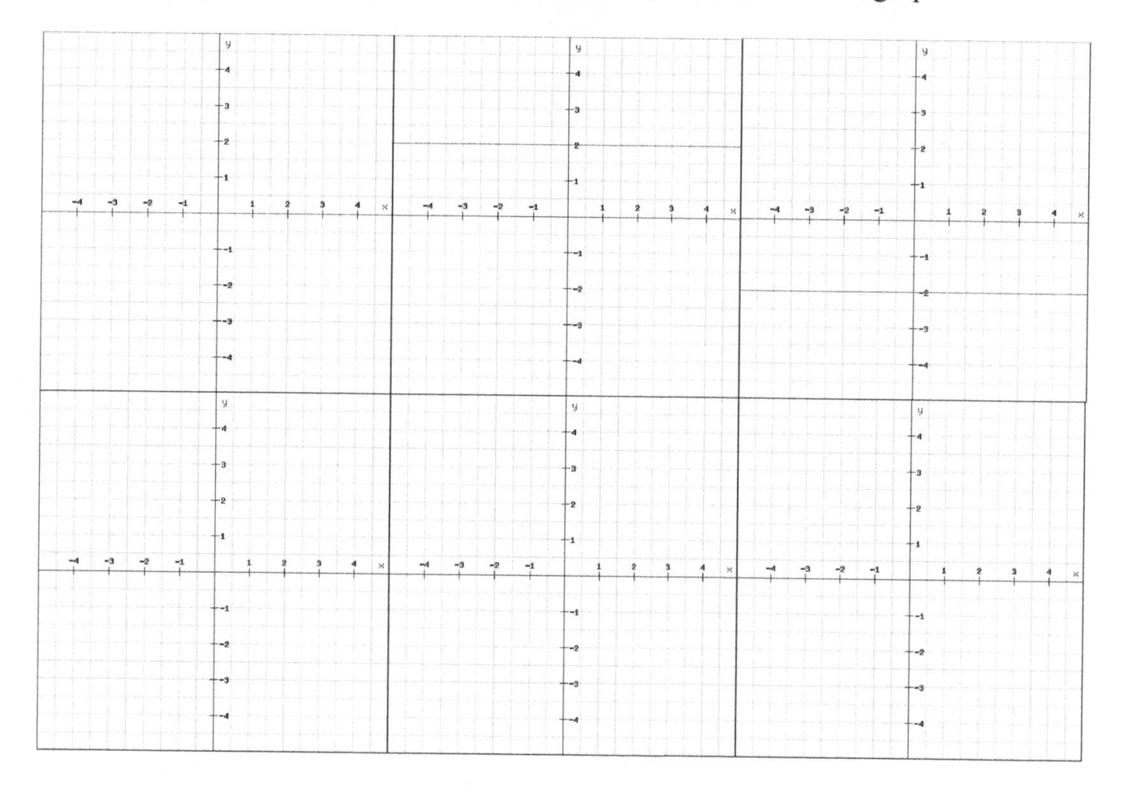

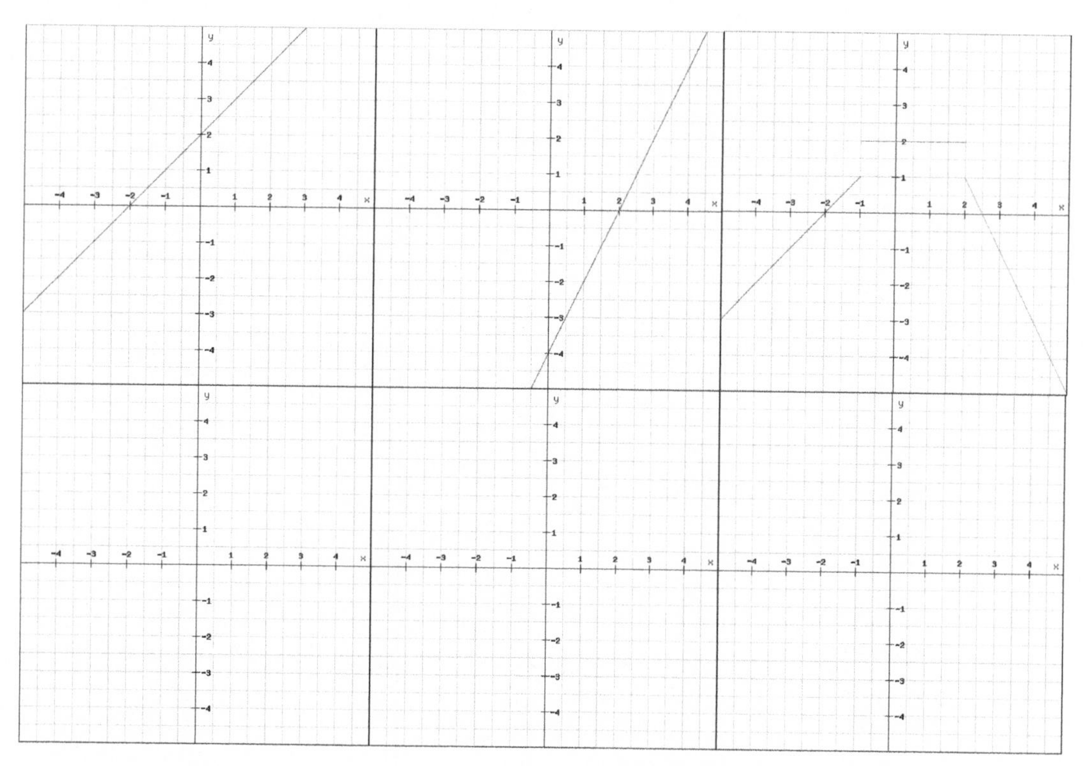

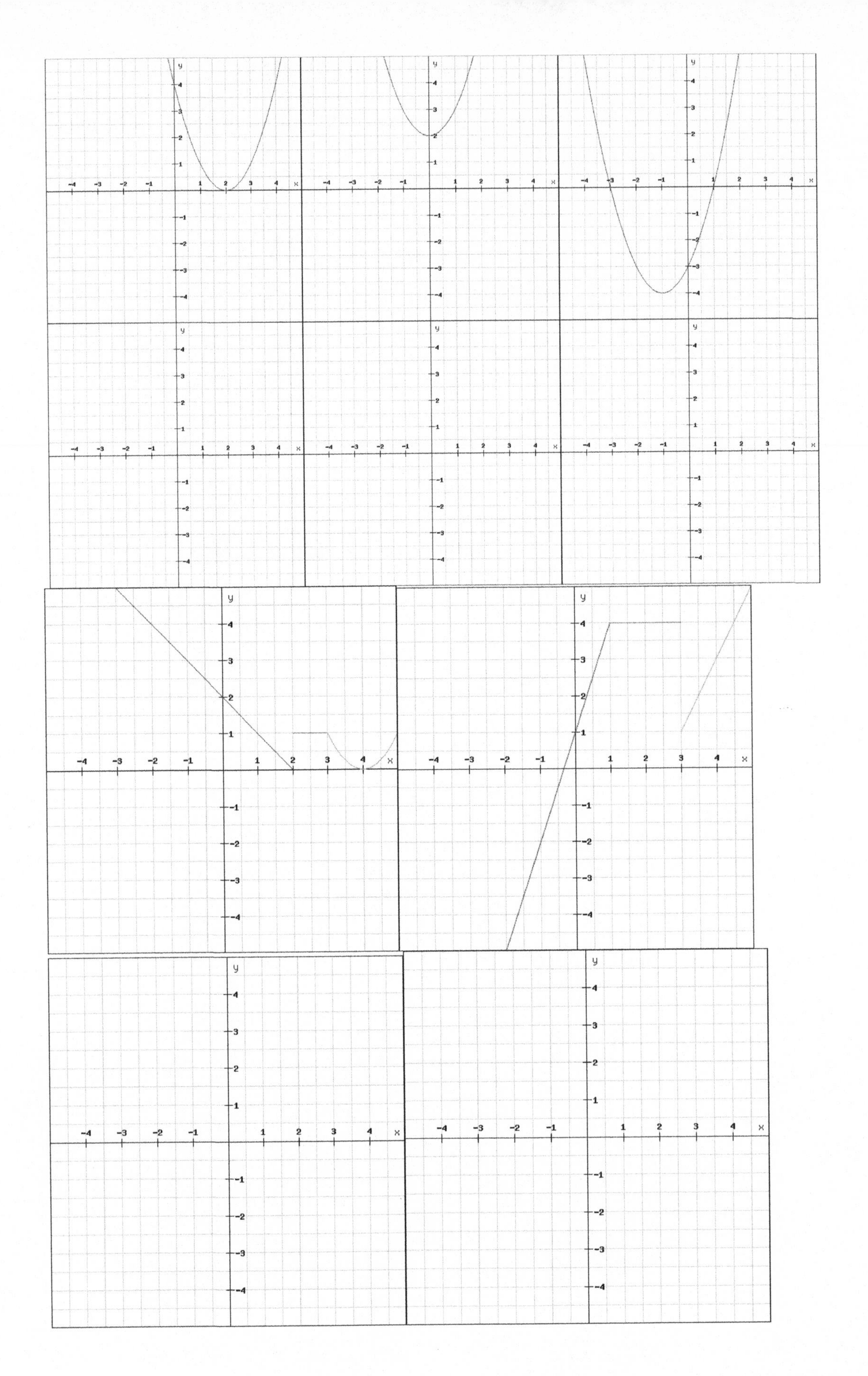

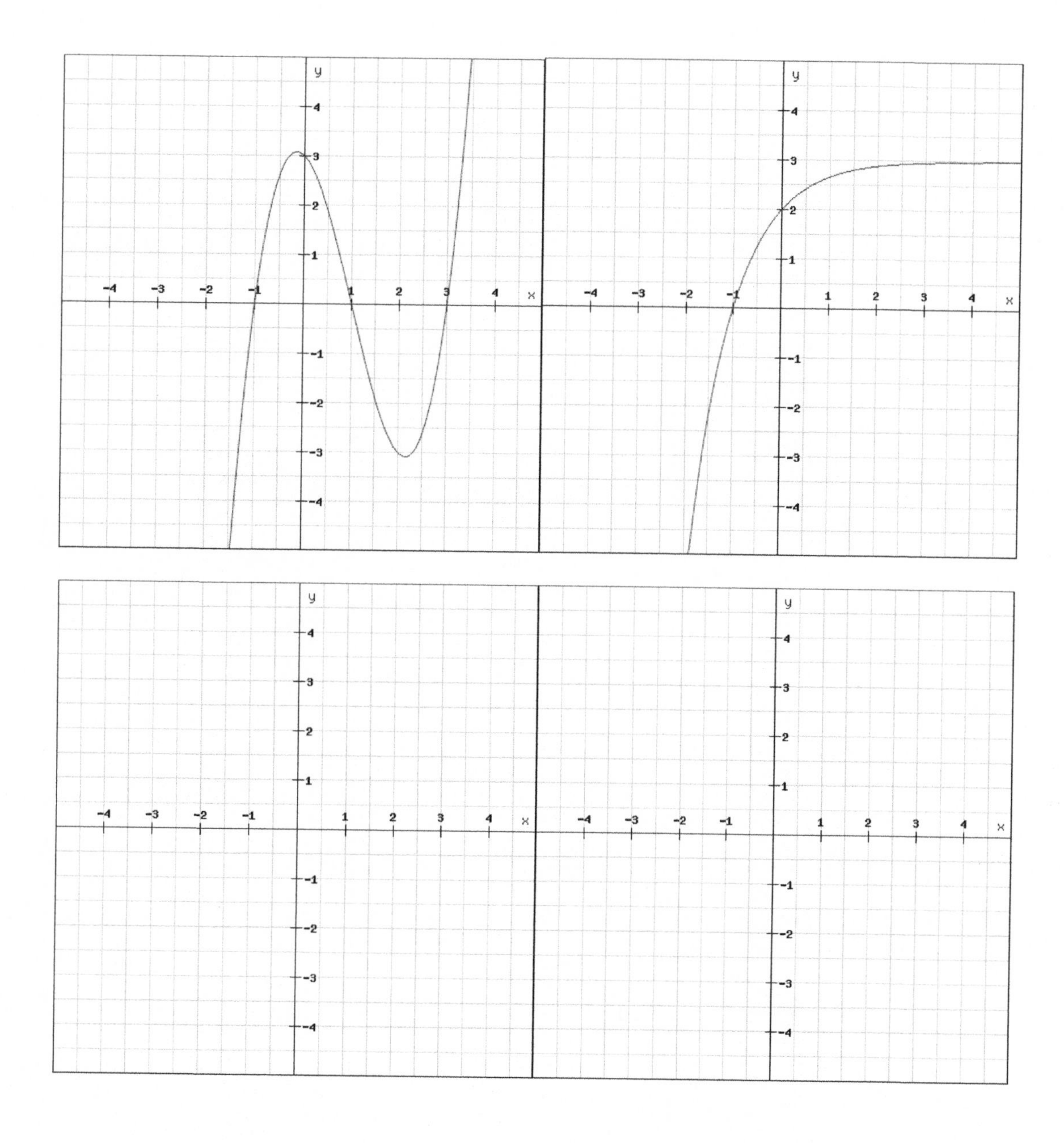
y
4
3
2
1
-4
-3
-2
-1
1
2
3
4
x
-1
-2
-3
-4

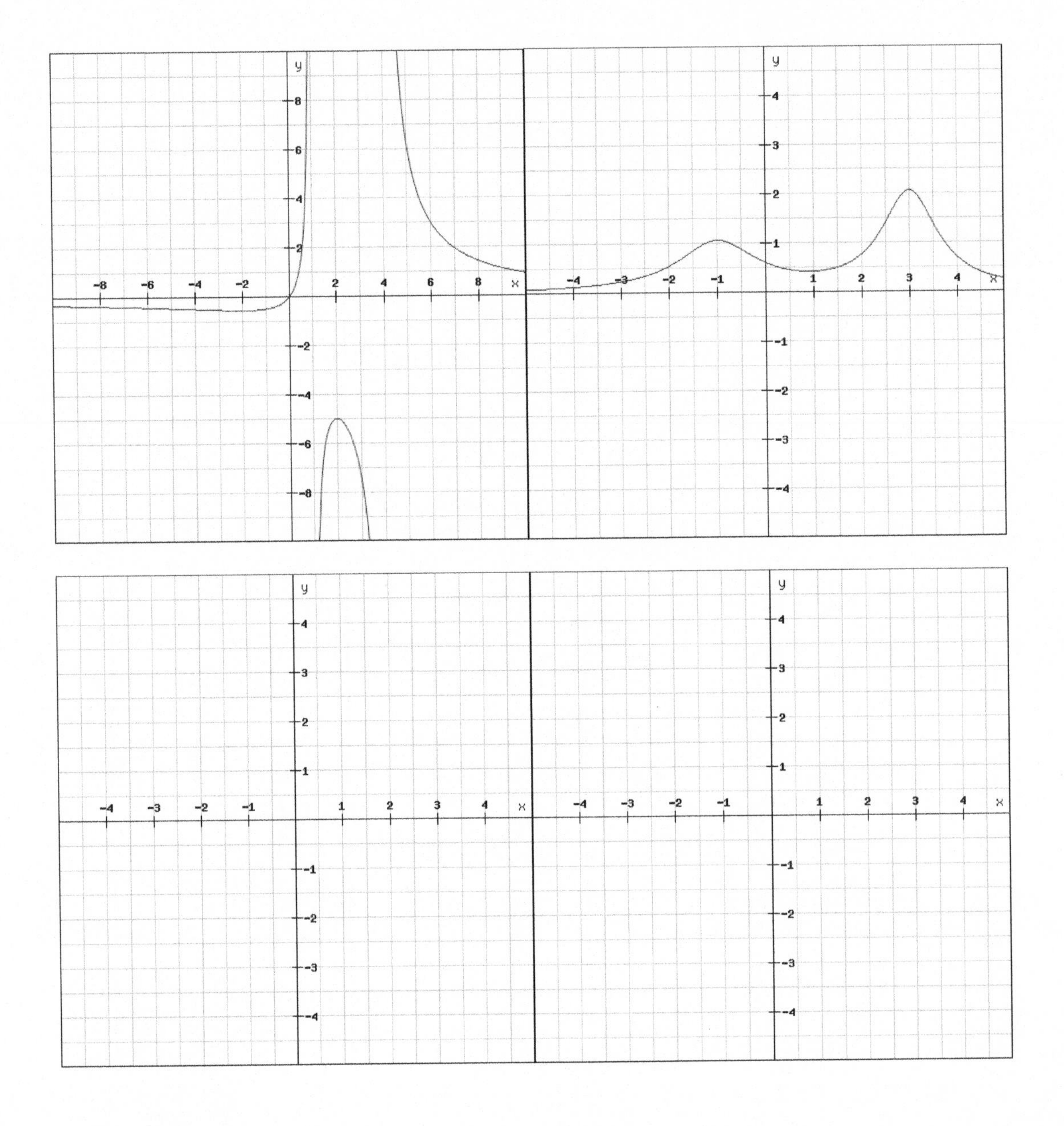
y
8
6
4
2
-8
-6
-4
-2
2
4
6
8
x
-2
-4
-6
-8
y
4
3
2
1
-4
-3
-2
-1
1
2
3
4
x
-1
-2
-3
-4
y
4
3
2
1
-4
-3
-2
-1
1
2
3
4
x
-1
-2
-3
-4
y
4
3
2
1
-4
-3
-2
-1
1
2
3
4
x
-1
-2
-3
-4

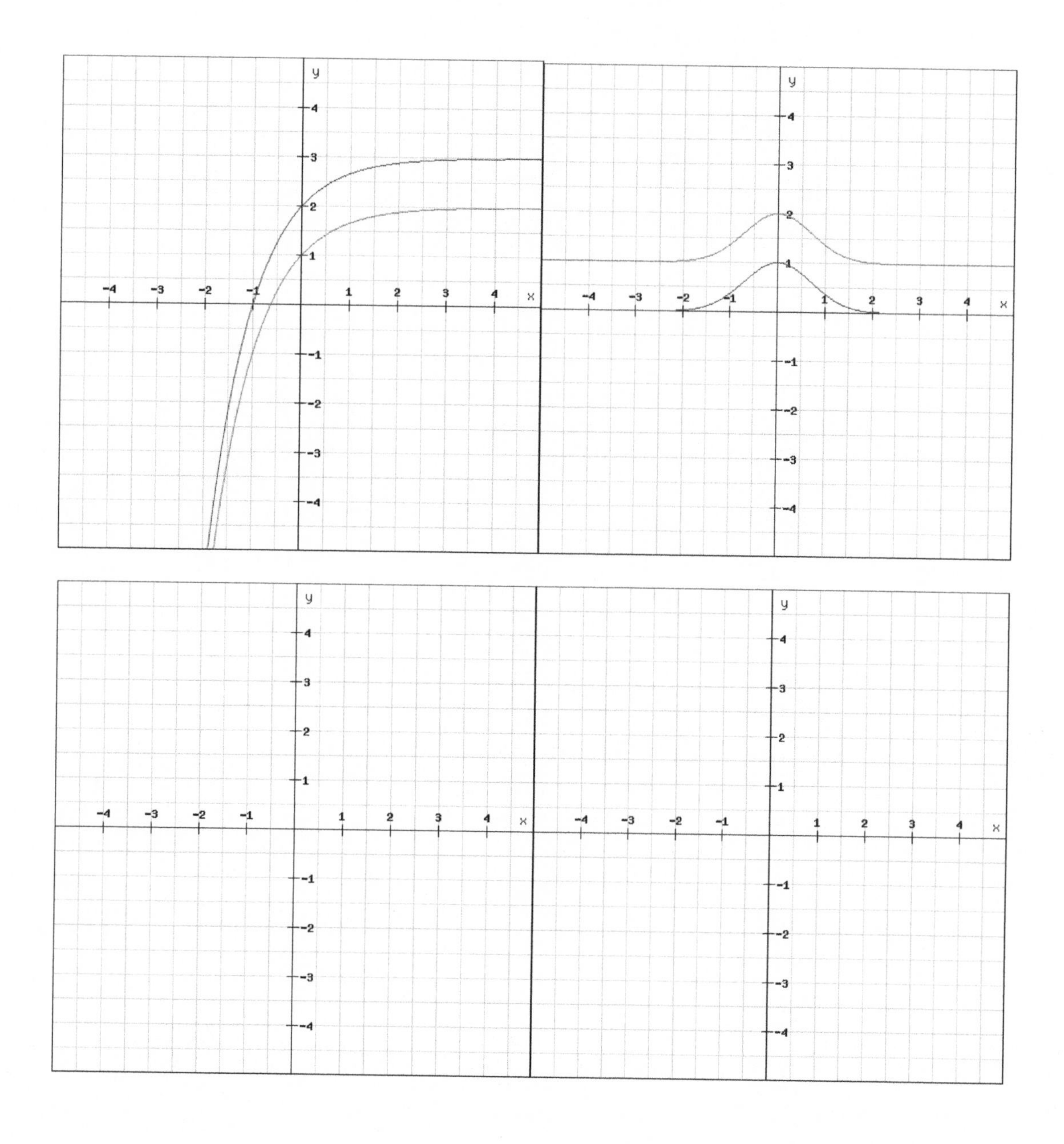

y
4
3
2
1
-4
-3
-2
-1
1
2
3
4
x
-1
-2
-3
-4

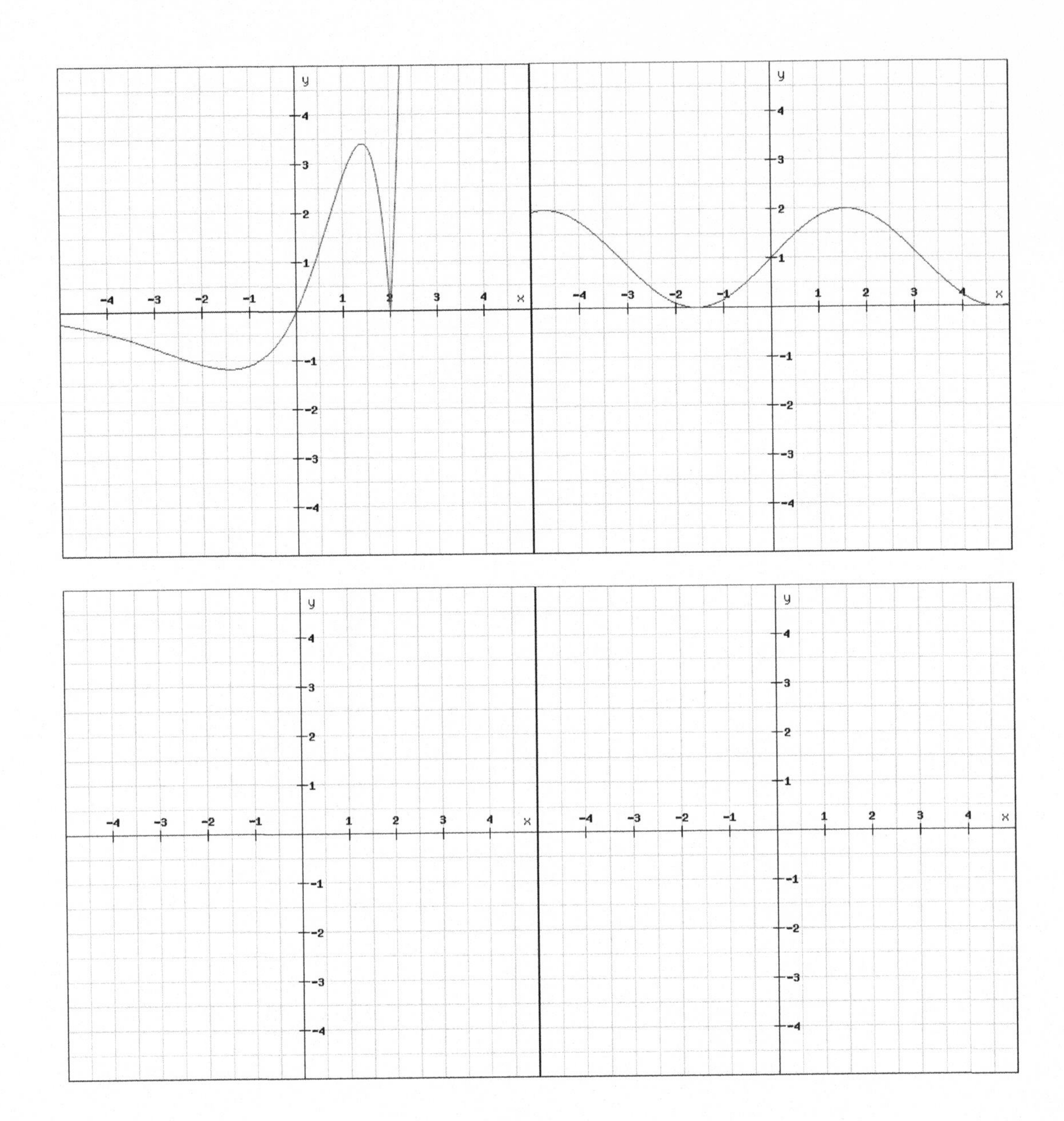

y
4
3
2
1
-4
-3
-2
-1
1
2
3
4
x
-1
-2
-3
-4

1.6. – TANGENTS AND NORMALS TO FUNCTIONS

1. Given the function $f(x) = 2x^2$. Sketch it.

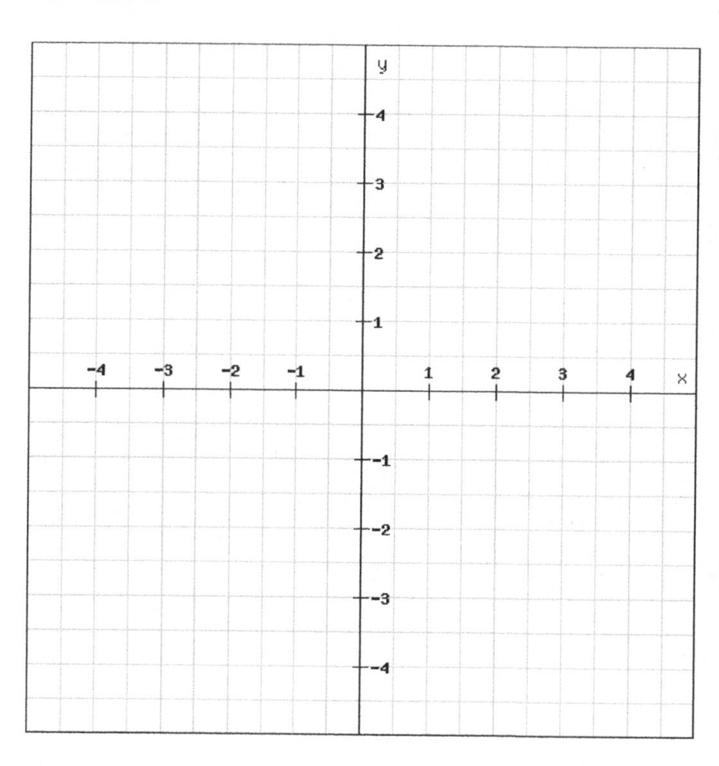

a. Find its derivative (use the definition).

$$f'(x) = \lim_{h \to 0} \frac{f(x+h) - f(x)}{h} = \lim_{h \to 0} \frac{\_\_\_\_\_\_ - \_\_\_\_\_\_}{h} =$$

b. Find the slope of the tangent to the function at the point with $x = 1$. Show the slope found on the graph.

c. Find the slope of the tangent to the function at the point with $x = 0$. Show the slope found on the graph.

d. Find the point in which the slope of the tangent to the function is 3. Show the point and slope on the graph.

e. Find the point in which the slope of the tangent to the function is -4. Show the point and slope on the graph.

f. Find the point in which the tangent to the function is parallel to the line $y = 2x + 3$. Show the point, the tangent and the line on the graph.

g. Find the point in which the tangent to the function is parallel to the line $y = -5x + 3$. Show the point, the tangent and the line on the graph.

h. Find the equation of the tangent to the function at the point with $x = 1$. Sketch the tangent on graph.

i. Find the equation of the tangent and normal to the function at the point with $x = 0$. Sketch the tangent and normal on graph.

j. Find the equation of the tangent and normal to the function at the point with $x = -2$. Sketch the tangent and normal on the graph.

2. Given the function $f(x) = -\frac{2}{x} + 1$. Sketch it.

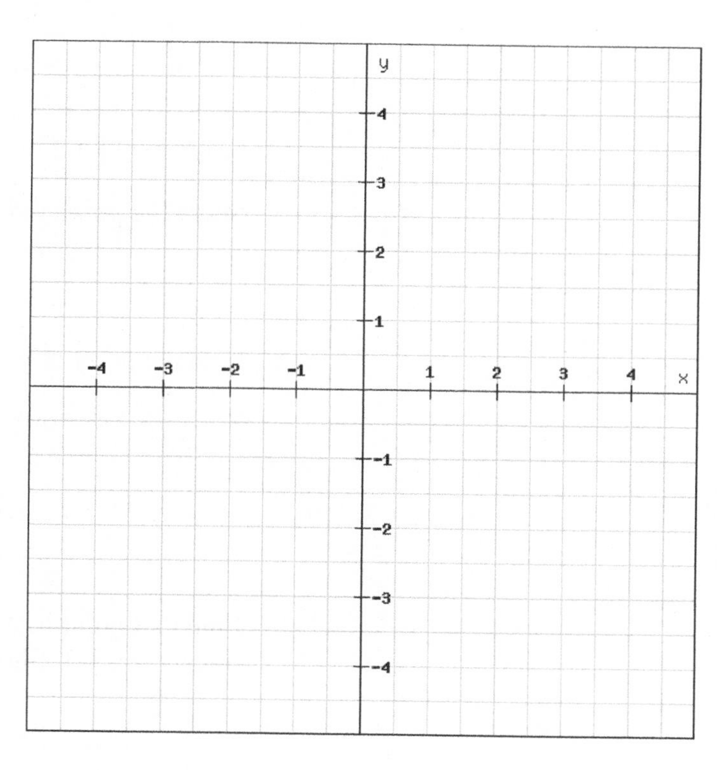

a. Find its derivative (use the definition).

$$f'(x) = \lim_{h\to 0} \frac{f(x+h)-f(x)}{h} = \lim_{h\to 0} \frac{\_\_\_\_\_\_\_\_ - \_\_\_\_\_\_\_\_}{h} =$$

b. Find the slope of the tangent to the function at the point with x = 1. Show the slope found on the graph.

c. Find the slope of the tangent to the function at the point with x = 0. Show the slope found on the graph.

d. Find the slope of the tangent to the function at the point with $x = \frac{1}{2}$.

Show the slope found on the graph.

e. Find the point in which the slope of the tangent to the function is -3. Show the point and slope on the graph.

f. Find the point in which the slope of the tangent to the function is $\frac{1}{2}$. Show the point and slope on the graph.

g. Find the point in which the tangent to the function is parallel to the line $y = -\frac{5}{3}x + 3$. Show the point, the tangent and the line on the graph.

h. Find that point in which the tangent to the function is parallel to the line $y = 6x + 3$. Show the point, the tangent and the line on the graph.

i. Find the equation of the tangent to the function at the point with $x = 1$. Sketch the tangent on graph.

j. Find the equation of the tangent and normal to the function at the point with $x = 0$. Sketch the tangent and normal on graph.

k. Find the equation of the tangent and normal to the function at the point with $x = \frac{1}{2}$. Sketch the tangent and normal on graph.

3. Given the function $f(x) = -x^2 - x$. Sketch it.

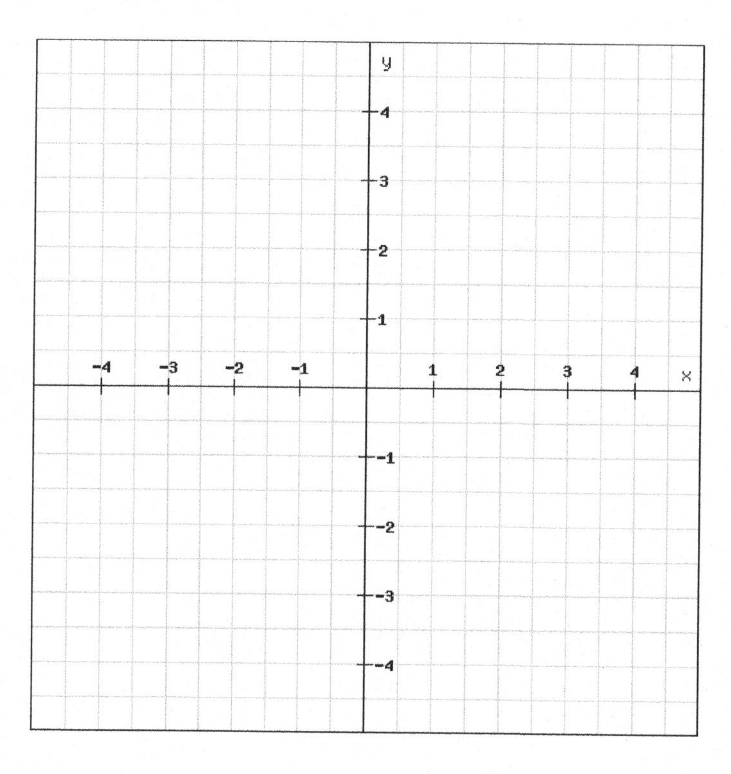

a. Find its derivative (use the definition).

$$f'(x) = \lim_{h\to 0} \frac{f(x+h) - f(x)}{h} = \lim_{h\to 0} \frac{\underline{\qquad\qquad} - \underline{\qquad\qquad}}{h} =$$

b. Find the slope of the tangent to the function at the point with x = –1. Show the slope found on the graph.

c. Find the slope of the tangent to the function at the point with x = 2. Show the slope found on the graph.

d. Find the slope of the tangent to the function at the point with x = –4. Show the slope found on the graph.

e. Find the point in which the slope of the tangent to the function is 2. Show the point and slope on the graph.

f. Find the point in which the slope of the tangent to the function is –2.3. Show the point and slope on the graph.

g. Find the point in which the tangent to the function is parallel to the line $y = 3x + 1$. Show the point, the tangent and the line on the graph.

h. Find the point in which the tangent to the function is parallel to the line $y = -5x + 3$. Show the point, the tangent and the line on the graph.

i. Find the equation of the tangent to the function at the point with $x = -1$. Sketch the tangent on graph.

j. Find the equation of the tangent and normal to the function at the point with $x = 2$. Sketch the tangent and normal on graph.

k. Find the equation of the tangent and normal to the function at the point with $x = -4$. Sketch the tangent and normal on graph.

4. Given the function $f(x) = -3x^2 + 1$. Sketch it.

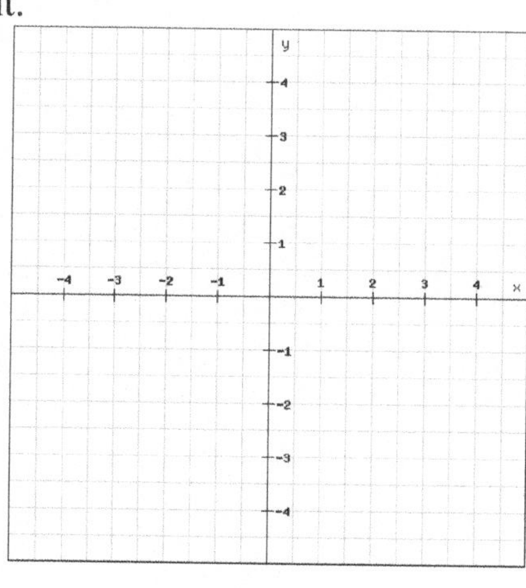

a. Find its derivative (use the definition).

$$f'(x) = \lim_{h \to 0} \frac{f(x+h) - f(x)}{h} = \lim_{h \to 0} \frac{\_\_\_\_\_\_\_\_ - \_\_\_\_\_\_\_\_}{h} =$$

b. Find $f'(1) =$____. Show it on the graph.

c. Find $f'(0) =$____. Show it on the graph.

d. Find $f'(2) =$____. Show it on the graph.

e. Given that $f'(x) = 3$, find x. Show it on the graph.

f. Given that $f'(x) = -4$, find x. Show it on the graph.

g. Find the point in which the tangent to the function is parallel to the line $y = -5x + 3$. Show the point and tangent on the graph.

h. Find the equation of the tangent and normal to the function at the point with $x = 0$. Sketch the tangent and normal on graph.

5. Given the function $f(x) = \frac{3}{x-2}$. Sketch it.

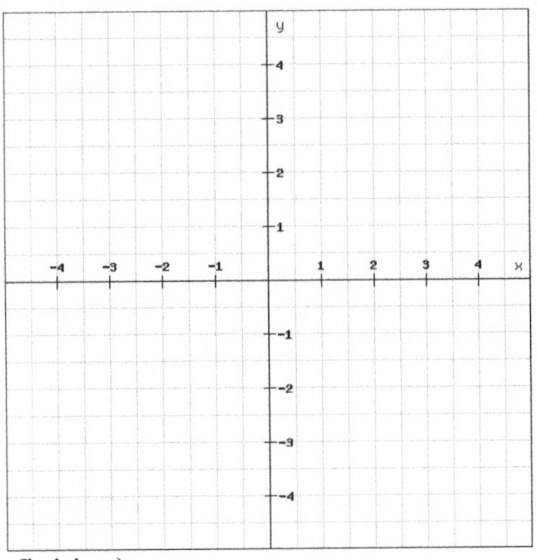

a. Find its derivative (use the definition).

$$f'(x) = \lim_{h \to 0} \frac{f(x+h) - f(x)}{h} = \lim_{h \to 0} \frac{\_\_\_\_\_\_ - \_\_\_\_\_\_}{h} =$$

b. Find $f'(1) =$____. Show it on the graph.

c. Find $f'(2) =$____. Show it on the graph.

d. Find $f'(\frac{1}{2}) =$____. Show it on the graph.

e. Given that $f'(x) = -3$, find x. Show it on the graph.

f. Given that $f'(x) = \frac{1}{2}$, find x. Show it on the graph.

g. Find the point in which the tangent to the function is parallel to the line $y = -\frac{5}{3}x + 3$. Show the point, the line and the tangent on the graph.

h. Find the equation of the tangent to the function at the point with $x = 1$. Sketch the tangent on graph.

i. Find the equation of the tangent and normal to the function at the point with $x = 2$. Sketch the tangent and normal on graph.

j. Find the equation of the tangent and normal to the function at the point with $x = \frac{1}{2}$. Sketch the tangent and normal on graph.

1.7. – DERIVATIVES

Polynomial Functions Differentiate the following functions:

$f(x) = x^n$

$f'(x) = nx^{n-1}$

1. $f(x) = 5$
2. $f(x) = 3$
3. $f(x) = x$
4. $f(x) = 5x$
5. $f(x) = 5kx+1$
6. $f(x) = -2x$
7. $f(x) = -2x - 3$
8. $f(x) = -2x + 3$
9. $f(x) = x^2 + 3x - 10$
10. $f(x) = x^2 + 7x - 1$
11. $f(x) = bx^6 + 2x + 7$
12. $f(x) = x^{22} + x - 1$
13. $f(x) = x^4 + 2x + 1$
14. $f(x) = x^5 + x$
15. $f(x) = x^{22} - \frac{1}{x}$
16. $f(x) = x^2 - 2x + \frac{1}{x^2}$
17. $f(x) = a\,x^5 - 2x^4 - \frac{5}{x^2} + \frac{1}{x^3}$

18. $f(x) = 5x^2 - 10x + \frac{1}{x^{\frac{2}{3}}} + \frac{1}{x^{-2}}$

19. $f(x) = -5x^{20} - \frac{1}{x^{-2}}$

20. $f(x) = -x^3 + 6x^2 - 8 - \sqrt{x} - \sqrt[3]{x}$

21. $f(x) = -x^5 - 6x^2 + 2x + \sqrt{x^6} - \sqrt[3]{x^4}$

22. $f(x) = -x^7 + x^2 - 5x - x\sqrt{x} - x\sqrt[3]{x} - \sqrt[3]{x^{-2}}$

23. $f(x) = -bx^4 - 4x^2 - 4$

24. $f(x) = -x^{-2} + 3x$

25. $f(x) = -15x^{-2} - 3x^{-5}$

26. $f(x) = \frac{5}{2}x^{-3} - b6x$

27. $f(x) = \frac{1}{6}x^3 - 3 + \frac{\sqrt{x}+3}{3} - \frac{1+x\sqrt{2}}{7}$

28. $f(x) = \frac{2}{3}x^{\frac{2}{3}} - 3x^{\frac{1}{2}} + 2e^2 - x\log(3)$

29. $f(x) = 3x^2 + \frac{2}{3}x^{\frac{4}{9}} - 5x^{\frac{2}{5}}$

30. $f(x) = x^2 + 3x + 4 + 3x^2 + b\frac{7}{6}x^{-\frac{4}{9}} - 5x^{\frac{3}{2}}$

31. $f(x) = -12x - 13 + 3bx + 4 + 3x^{-3} + \frac{7}{6}x^{-\frac{1}{9}} - 5x^{\frac{-7}{2}}$

32. $f(x) = -x^3 + 6x^2 - 8 - x\sqrt{x} - \sqrt[3]{x} + \cos(4)x^{-1}$

33. $f(x) = x^2 + 9x - 4 + 3x^2 + \frac{7}{6}x^{-\frac{4}{9}} - 5x^{\frac{3}{2}} + \ln(2)x^2$

34. $f(x) = 8x - x\sqrt{x} - \sqrt[3]{2x}$

35. $f(x) = -x^3 + 6x^{22} - 8 - x\sqrt{x} - \sqrt[3]{x}x^2$

Exponential functions

36. $f(x) = 8x - e^x$

37. $f(x) = 2e^x - x$

38. $f(x) = 5e^x - \sqrt{x} - \sqrt[3]{2x}$

39. $f(x) = -3e^x - x\sqrt{x} - \sqrt[5]{x^2}$

$f(x) = e^x$
$f'(x) = e^x$

Logarithmic functions

40. $f(x) = 2\ln(x) - \sqrt{x\sqrt{x}}$

41. $f(x) = \frac{1}{\sqrt[5]{x}} - \frac{\sqrt{x}}{2x} - \frac{\sqrt[5]{x^2}}{\sqrt{x}} - \ln(x)$

42. $f(x) = \frac{\sqrt{x}+3}{3} - \frac{1+x\sqrt{2}}{7} - \frac{2}{3x} + \log(x)$

43. $f(x) = 2e^x - \frac{\ln(5)}{\sqrt{2x}} - \log_2(x)$

44. $f(x) = \ln(7) - \frac{\cos(1)+\sqrt{2}}{7}e^x - x\sqrt{\frac{1}{2x}} - 2\log_e(x)$

$f(x) = \ln(x)$

$f'(x) = \frac{1}{x}$

Change of base:

$f(x) = \log_b(x) = \frac{\ln(x)}{\ln(b)}$

$f'(x) = \frac{1}{\ln(b)x}$

Trigonometric functions

45. $f(x) = \ln(8) - 2e^x + \cos(x)$

$f(x) = \sin(x)$

$f'(x) = \cos(x)$

$f(x) = \cos(x)$

$f'(x) = -\sin(x)$

46. $f(x) = \cos(2)x^2 - 23.7e^x - \sin(x)$

47. $f(x) = x^{-\frac{13}{9}} - 33^{\sqrt{2}} - 2\cos(x)$

48. $f(x) = (1+2^{\sqrt{2}})x - e^x + 5\cos(x)$

49. $f(x) = 2\sin(x) + \sin(8)\ln(6)x - e^x$

50. $f(x) = \cos(x) + \dfrac{5\sqrt{x}}{3x} - e^x$

51. $f(x) = 2\cos(x) - \ln(7) - \dfrac{x\ln(11)+\sqrt{2}}{\cos(7)} - \dfrac{\sin(1)}{3+\sqrt{2}}x + \log_9(x)$

PRODUCT RULE $(fg)' = f'g + fg'$

52. $f(x) = (x + 2)(x + 3)$

53. $f(x) = (x^2 - 2)(x^2 + 3)$

54. $f(x) = (2x + 2)(5x^2 - 3 + e^x)$

55. $f(x) = (-x + 2 - \cos(x))(5x^8 - 3x)$

56. $f(x) = (-x^9 + 2 + \sin(x))(x + 3x^2)$

57. $f(x) = (2\ln(x)+3x^2+\frac{7}{6}x^{-\frac{4}{9}}-5x^{\frac{3}{2}})(x^2-1-\cos(x))$

58. $f(x) = (2\log(x)-\frac{7}{6}\frac{2}{x^{\frac{2}{3}}}-5\frac{2}{x})(x^2-1)+\sin(x)$

59. $f(x) = (\log_3(x)+\frac{7}{6}\frac{2}{x^{\frac{2}{3}}}-5\frac{2}{x})(x^2-1+e^x-\sin(x))-e^x+\log_2(x)$

60. $f(x) = (\frac{1}{6}\frac{}{x^{-\frac{2}{3}}}-\frac{2}{x^5})(x^2-\sqrt{x})+\cos(x)$

61. $f(x) = (\frac{1}{6}x-\frac{2}{x^{\frac{1}{2}}})(x^2-\frac{1}{\sqrt[3]{x}}-\sin(x)+\cos(x)+e^x)+e^x+\cos(x)$

QUOTIENT RULE $$\left(\frac{f}{g}\right)' = \frac{f'g - fg'}{g^2}$$

62. $f(x) = \dfrac{x+1}{2x^2}$

63. $f(x) = \dfrac{2x^2 + x}{x^2}$

64. $f(x) = \dfrac{x^2 + \sqrt{x} + 1}{-x^4}$

65. $f(x) = \dfrac{x^{\frac{2}{3}} - x}{2x^2 + x}$

66. $f(x) = -4\dfrac{\sin(x) + x}{3x}$

67. $f(x) = \dfrac{x - \log(x)}{\log(x) + 1}$

68. $f(x) = \tan(x)$

69. $f(x) = 2\dfrac{x + e^x}{\cos(x)}$

70. $f(x) = \dfrac{\sin(x) + \ln(x)}{x^4}$

71. $f(x) = \dfrac{x^{-\frac{2}{5}} + \sin(x) + \ln(x)}{2x^{3.2} + 1}$

72. $f(x) = \dfrac{\sin(x)(x+1)}{2x^2}$

73. $f(x) = \dfrac{(3x+1)(2x+2)}{e^x}$

74. $f(x) = \dfrac{e^x}{2x}$

CHAIN RULE

$$(f(g))' = f'(g)g'$$

75. $f(x) = \sin(3x)$

76. $f(x) = -3\tan(-2x)$

77. $f(x) = 2\cos(6x^2)$

78. $f(x) = -(4x + 5)^2$

79. $f(x) = -3(6x - 1)^{-10}$

80. $f(x) = 2(3x^2 + 3)^{80}$

81. $f(x) = e^{4x} + 2^{2x}$

82. $f(x) = 5e^{4x} - 3^{4x}$

83. $f(x) = e^{\sin(x)}$

84. $f(x) = (5 - 3x^{2.3})^{-6}$

85. $f(x) = 5^x$

86. $f(x) = 5^{\sin(x)}$

87. $f(x) = 5^{\cos(2x)}$

88. $f(x) = (7 - x)^{-2}$

89. $f(x) = x\sin(2x)$

90. $f(x) = 4xe^{3x}$

91. $f(x) = 3x^2\cos(5x^2)$

92. $f(x) = e^x - 4^x$

93. $f(x) = -2^x + x$

94. $f(x) = 7^x - x^{10}$

95. $f(x) = 5e^x + 3^x$

96. $f(x) = \left(\frac{2}{3}\right)^x$

97. $f(x) = \left(\frac{1}{4}\right)^{x+1}$

98. $f(x) = -3x\log_2(3x + 2)$

99. $f(x) = 4x^5\log_4(5x^2 + x)$

100. $f(x) = (2 - 3x)(4 + 5x)^{-3}$

101. $f(x) = (5 - \ln(x))e^{\sin(x)}$

102. $f(x) = (\sin(3x))^3$

103. $f(x) = (4x^2 + 3x + 2 - e^x)^{\frac{5}{4}}$

104. $f(x) = \sqrt{(\sin(3x) + 2x)}$

105. $f(x) = \frac{3}{\sqrt{(\ln(x))}}$

106. $f(x) = x^2(\sin(3x^2 - 5x + 3) + 2x)$

107. $f(x) = \sqrt{\frac{2x+1}{2^x}}$

108. $f(x) = 3^{\sqrt{x}}$

109. $f(x) = 3^{\sqrt[3]{x}} + x$

110. $f(x) = (\ln(3x^2 + x))^{-2}$

111. $f(x) = \sin(\ln(x^2))$

112. $f(x) = 2^{\cos(x^2)}$

113. $f(x) = \ln(x + \cos(\sqrt{x})$

114. $f(x) = \dfrac{\sin(3x^2) - \ln(2x-1)}{e^{2x} + 4x}$

115. $f(x) = \dfrac{Ln(\sin((3x+1)^{-2}))}{\left(\dfrac{1}{\cos(2x)}\right)}$

HIGHER DERIVATIVES

Given the function fin the derivative indicated, $\frac{d^n f}{dx^n} = f^n(x)$ means the nth derivative.

1. $f(x) = x^2$

$$\frac{df}{dx} = f'(x) =$$
$$\frac{d^2 f}{dx^2} = f''(x) =$$

2. $f(x) = \ln(x)$

$$\frac{df}{dx} = f'(x) =$$
$$\frac{d^2 f}{dx^2} = f''(x) =$$

3. $f(x) = \sin(x)$

$$\frac{df}{dx} = f'(x) =$$
$$\frac{d^2 f}{dx^2} = f''(x) =$$

4. $f(x) = e^{2x}$

$$\frac{df}{dx} = f'(x) =$$
$$\frac{d^2 f}{dx^2} = f''(x) =$$
$$\frac{d^3 f}{dx^3} = f'''(x) =$$
$$\frac{d^n f}{dx^n} = f^{(n)}(x) =$$

5. $f(x) = xe^x$

$$\frac{df}{dx} = f'(x) =$$

$$\frac{d^2 f}{dx^2} = f''(x) =$$

$$\frac{d^3 f}{dx^3} = f'''(x) =$$

$$\frac{d^n f}{dx^n} = f^{(n)}(x) =$$

6. $f(x) = \sin(e^x)$

$$\frac{df}{dx} = f'(x) =$$

$$\frac{d^2 f}{dx^2} = f''(x) =$$

$$\frac{d^3 f}{dx^3} = f'''(x) =$$

$$\frac{d^4 f}{dx^4} = f^{(4)}(x) =$$

7. $f(x) = \ln(2x)$

$$\frac{df}{dx} = f'(x) =$$

$$\frac{d^2 f}{dx^2} = f''(x) =$$

$$\frac{d^3 f}{dx^3} = f'''(x) =$$

$$\frac{d^n f}{dx^n} = f^{(n)}(x) =$$

1.8. – STATIONARY POINTS

Functions may describe level of production, benefit, position, sugar level, efficiency of an engine, wind resistance or any other physical or other variable. Usually it is out interest to maximize benefit, efficiency or minimize lost. As a result we are usually interested in the maximum or minimum points of a function.

1. In a maximum or minimum point of a "smooth" function the slope of the tangent to the function is ________. Sketch an example:

2. There is one more situation in which the slope of the tangent to the function is ________, such point is called: ____________________. Sketch an example:

3. In order to find a stationary points′ x coordinate we equal the ________ to _____.
   For example the function $f(x) = 2x^2 + 2x$, $f'(x) =$, $x =$

4. To find the stationary points′ y coordinate we ________________________________.
   In the last example $f(\_\_) =$

5. Once we found the stationary point we have to decide if it's a ______________, ______________ or ______________.

6. We will discuss 3 methods to check if a function has minimum, maximum or horizontal inflection point at a certain point.

The 3 methods are:

1. Check the **value of the function** on both "sides" of the point and close to it. If both sides′ values are higher the point is ____________, if both sides are lower the point is ___________________ and if one side is higher and the other lower we have ___________________. Example: $f(x) = 2x^2 + 2x$

2. Build a diagram including all the zeros in the first derivative and all the places it is not defined, indicating **the sign of the derivative**. Example: $f(x) = 2x^4 + x^2$

3. Use the 2nd derivative. As you could see if the 2nd derivative, at the point in which the 1st derivative is 0, is positive the function is _______________ and the point would be a ____________, if the 2nd derivative, at the point in which the 1st derivative is 0, is negative the function is _______________ and the point would be a ____________, if the 2nd derivative is also 0 this test is ________________.

   Example: $f(x) = 2x^3 + x^2$

   Example: $f(x) = x^4$

SECOND DERIVATIVE

1. The 1st derivative of a function gives the ____.

2. In case $f(x) = x^2$, the first derivative is _____ and the 2nd derivative is _______. As you can see the second derivative is always ______________ and that means that the function is always ______________________________.

3. In case $f(x) = x^3 - 3x^2$:

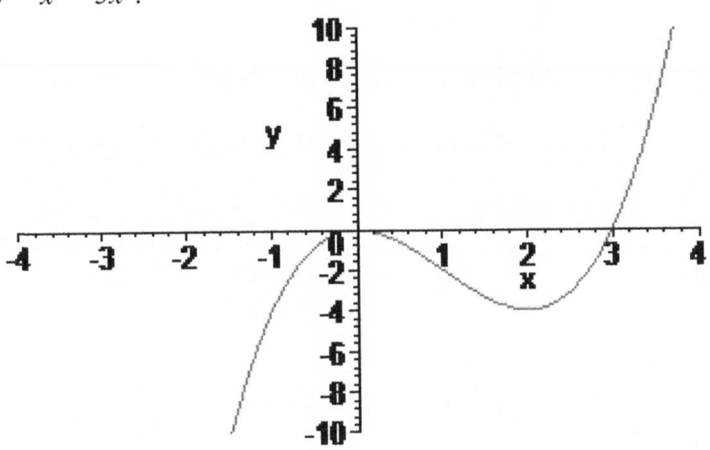

The first derivative is _________ and the 2nd derivative is _______. As you can see the second derivative is positive for ______________, negative for ___________ and exactly 0 for ____________. That means that when the 2nd derivative is positive the function is___________________ when the 2nd derivative is negative the function is__________________ and when the 2nd derivative is 0 the function might have ___________________.

4. In case $f(x) = x^4$

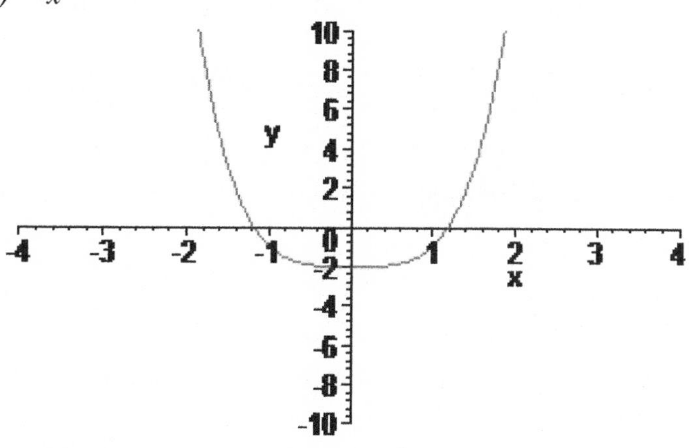

The first derivative is _______ and the 2nd derivative is _______. As you can see the second derivative is positive for _____________ , negative for __________ and exactly 0 for ___________. That means that when the 2nd derivative is positive the function is_________________ when the 2nd derivative is negative the function is_________________ and when the 2nd derivative is 0 the function might have _________________ but in this case it has a ___________.

5. If $f'(a) = 0$ it means the function has a ___________________________ at a.
6. If $f'(a) < 0$ it means the function is___________ at a.
7. If $f'(a) \neq$ and $f''(a) = 0$ it means the function ________________________ at a.
8. If possible, fill the following table with a sketch of the function around the point where $x = a$.

	$f''(a) = 0$	$f''(a) > 0$	$f''(a) < 0$
$f'(a)=0$			
$f'(a) > 0$			
$f'(a) < 0$			

4. A certain function satisfies the conditions:

   $f(a) = 2$ $\quad f'(a) = 1$ $\quad f''(a) < 0$

   Sketch a function that satisfies these conditions around a

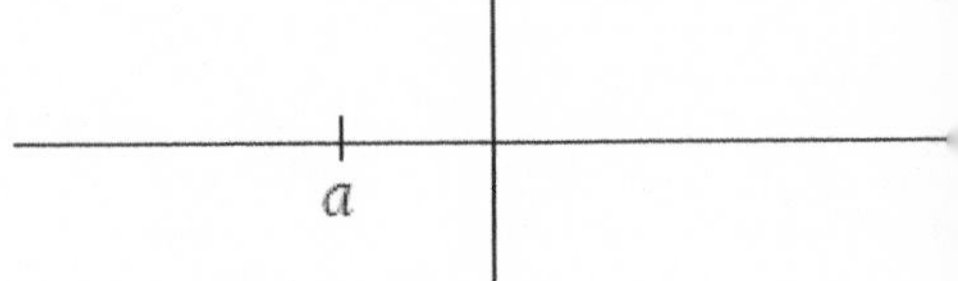

5. A certain function satisfies the conditions:

   $f(a) = -2$ $\quad f'(a) = -2$ $\quad f''(a) < 0$

   Sketch a function that satisfies these conditions around a

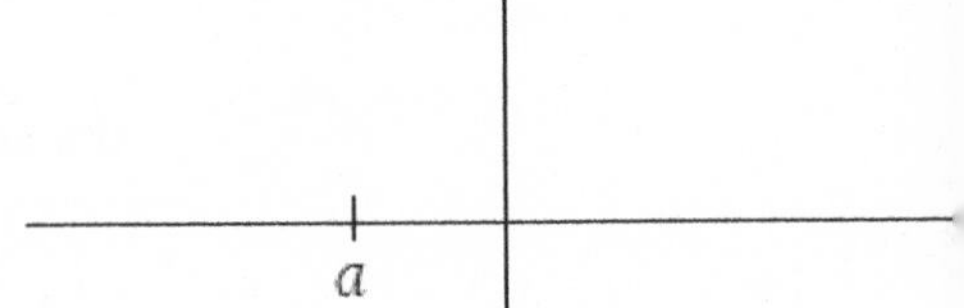

6. A certain function satisfies the conditions:

   $f(a) = 0$ $\quad f'(a) = -2$ $\quad f''(a) = 0$

   Sketch a function that satisfies these conditions around a

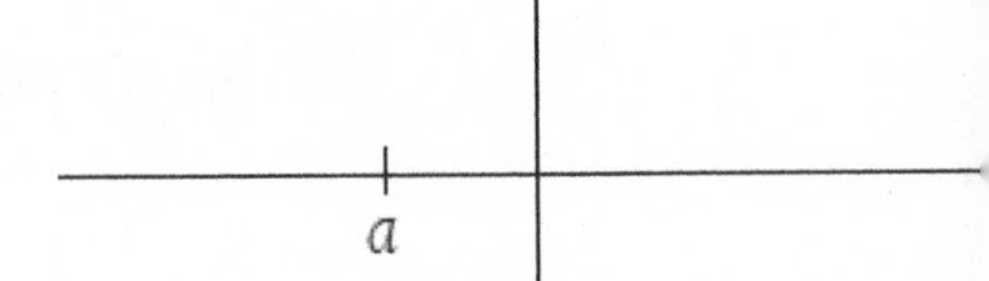

7. A certain function satisfies the conditions:

   $f(a) = 3$ $\quad f'(a) = 3$ $\quad f''(a) = 0$

   Sketch a function that satisfies these conditions around a

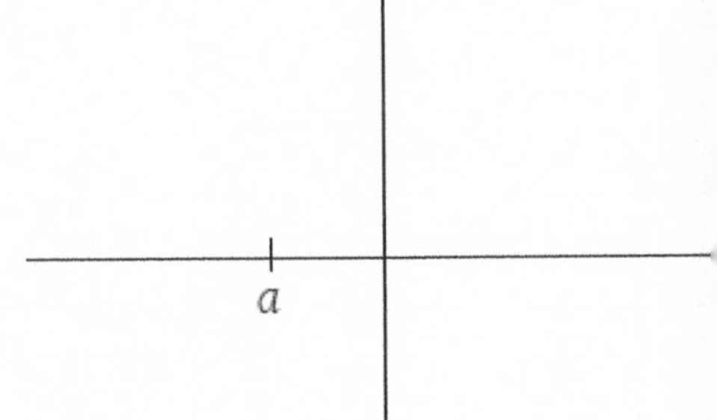

8. Sketch the graph of a function which has all the following properties:

a. $\lim_{x \to \infty} f(x) = -\infty$

b. $\lim_{x \to -\infty} f(x) = 1$

c. $f(1) = 2, f(3) = 1$

d. $f'(x) > 0$ if $x < 2$

e. $f'(x) < 0$ if $x > 2$

f. $f'(2) = 0$

g. $f''(x) > 0$ if $x < -1$

h. $f''(x) < 0$ if $-1 < x$

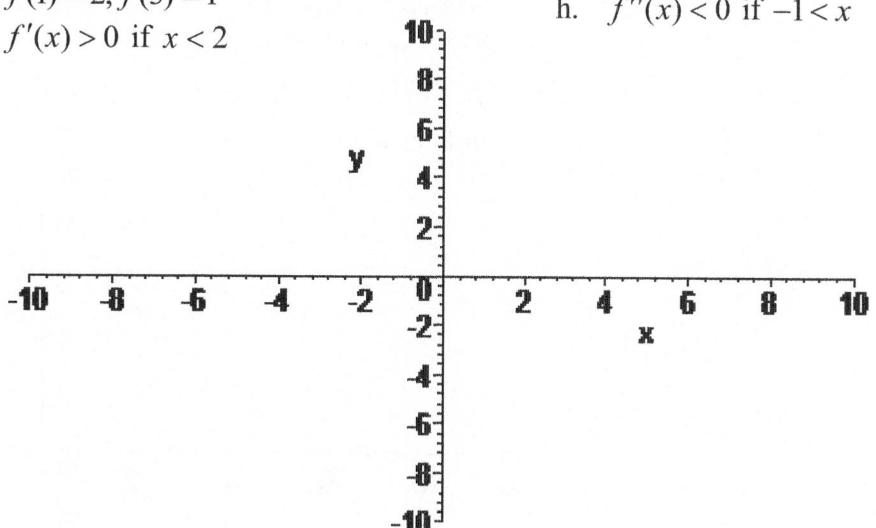

9. Sketch the graph of a function which has all the following properties:

a. $\lim_{x \to 2^-} f(x) = -\infty$

b. $\lim_{x \to 2^+} f(x) = \infty$

c. $\lim_{x \to -\infty} f(x) = 0$

d. $f(-2) = 2, f(5) = 1, f(0) = 0$

e. $f'(x) > 0$ if $x < -2$ or $x > 5$

f. $f'(x) > 0$ if $-2 < x < 2, 2 < x < 5$

g. $f'(5) = 0, f'(-2) = 0$

h. $f''(x) > 0$ if $x < -3$ or $x > 2$

i. $f''(x) < 0$ if $-3 < x < 2$

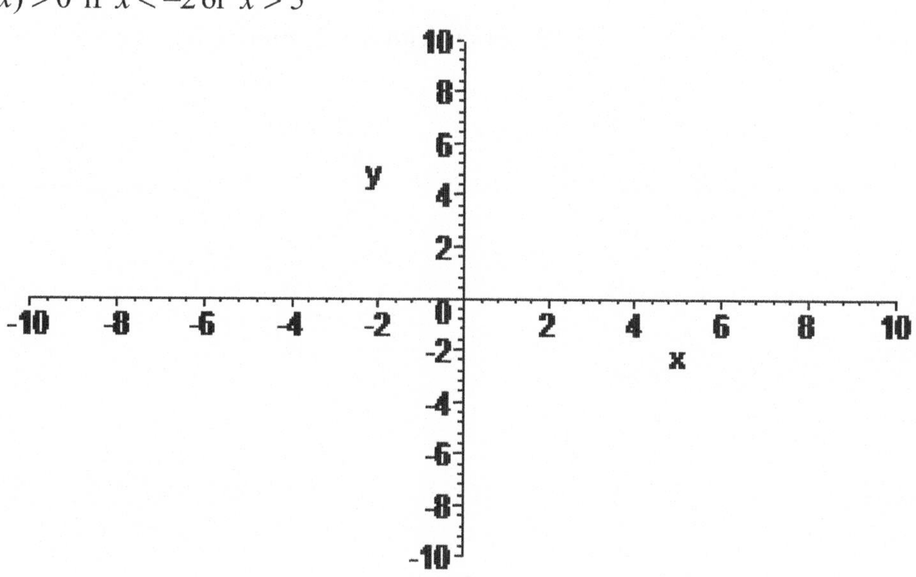

10. Sketch the graph of a function which has all the following properties:

a. g has domain $(-\infty,-2)\cup(-2,\infty)$
b. g has range $(-5,\infty)$
c. The graph of g has a vertical asymptote at x = –2
d. $\lim_{x\to-\infty} f(x)=2$
e. $\lim_{x\to\infty} f(x)=-5$
f. $\lim_{x\to3} f(x)=2$
g. G is discontinuous at x = 3
h. $g'(x)>0$ at $(-\infty,-2)$
i. $g'(x)<0$ at $(-2,3)$
j. $g'(4)$ does not exist. But g is continuous at 4.

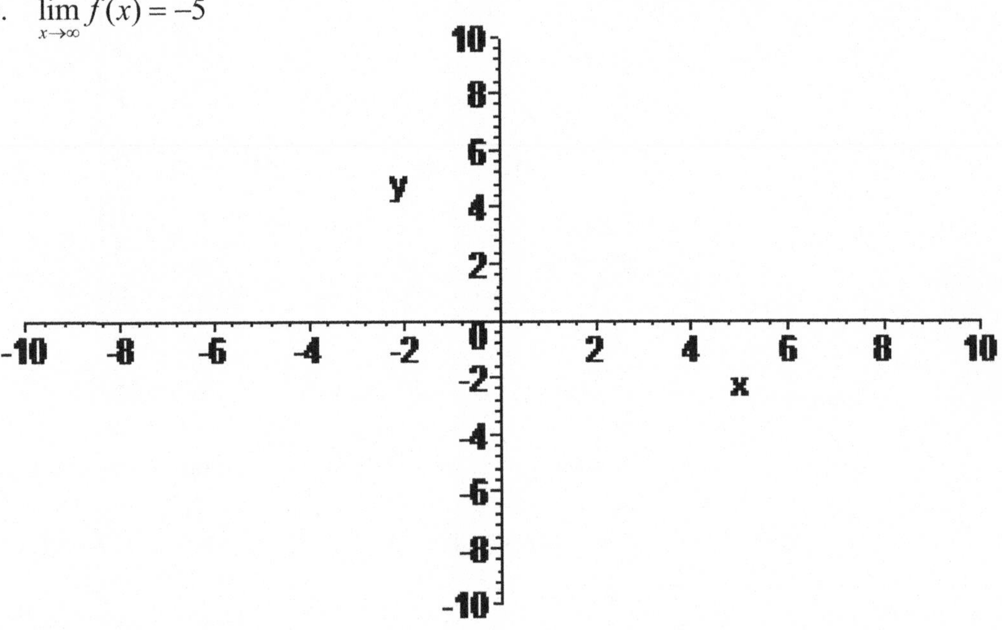

11. Given the function $f(x) = ax^2 + bx + c$. It is known the function has a maximum at the point (1, 1). It is also known that the line y = –2x is tangent to the function at the point with x = 2. Find a, b and c.

12. Given the function $f(x) = x^3 + ax^2 + bx + c$. It is known the function has a minimum at x = 1, passes throught the point (0, -1) and has an inflection point at the point where x = 2/3. Find a, b and c.

13. Given the function $f(x) = ax^3 + bx^2 + cx$. It is known the function has a critical point at (0, 0) and that the point (2, -16) is an inflection point. Find a, b and c.

14. Given the function $f(x) = \frac{a}{x} + bx^2$ find a and b knowing it has an extrema at (1, 3)

1.9. – FUNCTION ANALYSIS

Function analysis is an important idea in math. The steps indicated should be made in the analysis of the following functions. Order of the steps might change.

The steps are:

1. Find the domain.
2. Find the _________ asymptotes (in case they exist) and the corresponding limits.
3. Find the horizontal/slant asymptotes (in case they exist) and the corresponding limits.
4. Find __ intercept.
5. Find __ intercept(s).
6. Find extrema of the function (__________, minimum, __________ points) using the 1st and/or 2nd derivatives.
7. Sketch the function.
8. Discuss the concavity of the function
9. Dicuss the continuity of the function.
10. Indicate the range of the function.
11. Indicate the intervals of increase and decrease of the function.

The functions are classified in the following types:

a. Polynomial functions with natural powers.

b. Polynomial functions with rational powers.

c. Rational functions.

d. General functions.

A. POLYNOMIALS WITH NATURAL POWER

1. Graph the following functions. Obtain and indicate all x and y intercepts maximum, minimum and inflection points on the graph (include their coordinates)

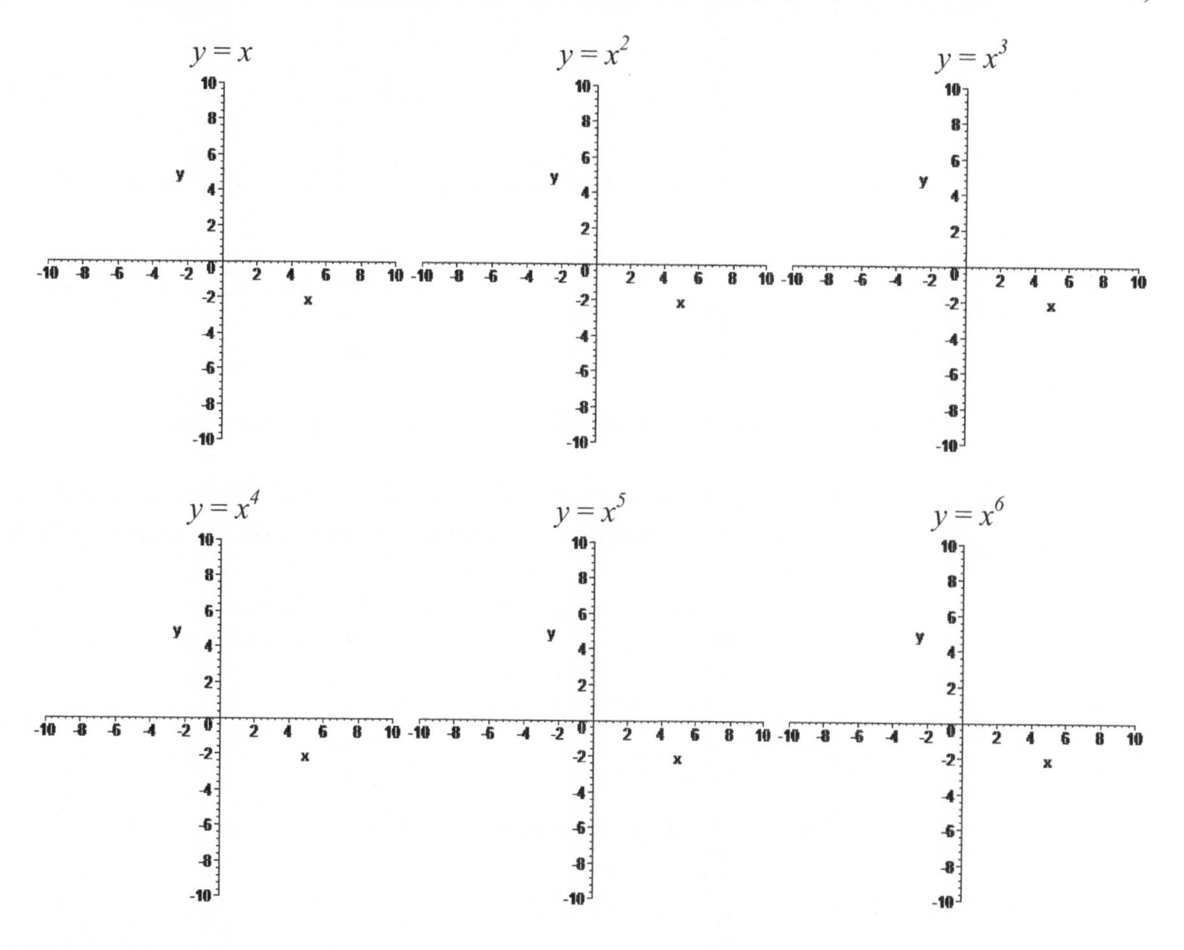

State at least one conclusion

2. Graph the following functions. Obtain and indicate all x and y intercepts maximum, minimum and inflection points on the graph (include their coordinates)

$y = (x+2)^2 + 1$ $\qquad$ $y = (x-2)^3 - 3$ $\qquad$ $y = (x+3)^4 - 6$

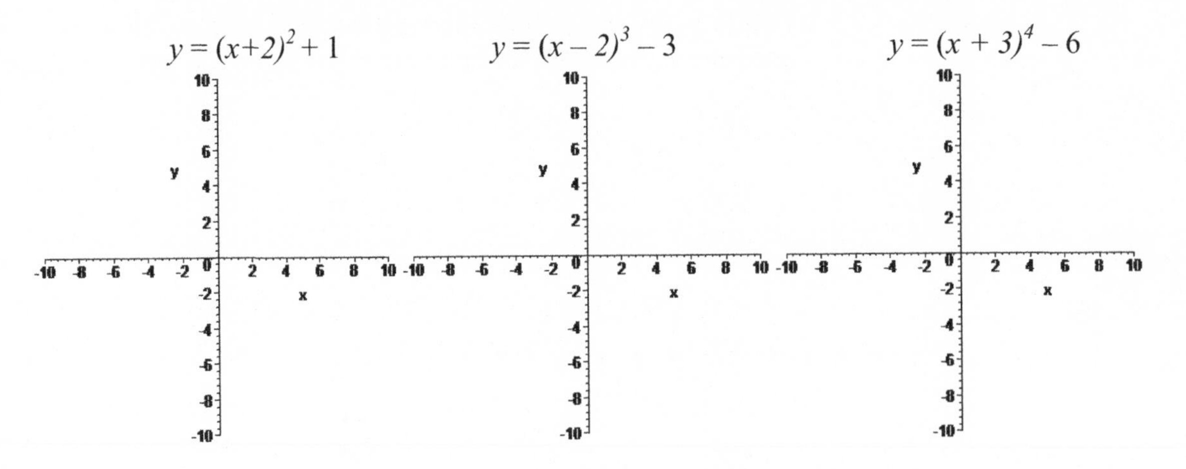

State at least one conclusión in relation to the previous part.

3. Graph the following functions. Obtain and indicate all x and y intercepts maximum, minimum and inflection points on the graph (include their coordinates)

$y = -(x+2)^2 + 1$ $\qquad$ $y = -(x-2)^3 - 3$ $\qquad$ $y = -(x+3)^4 - 6$

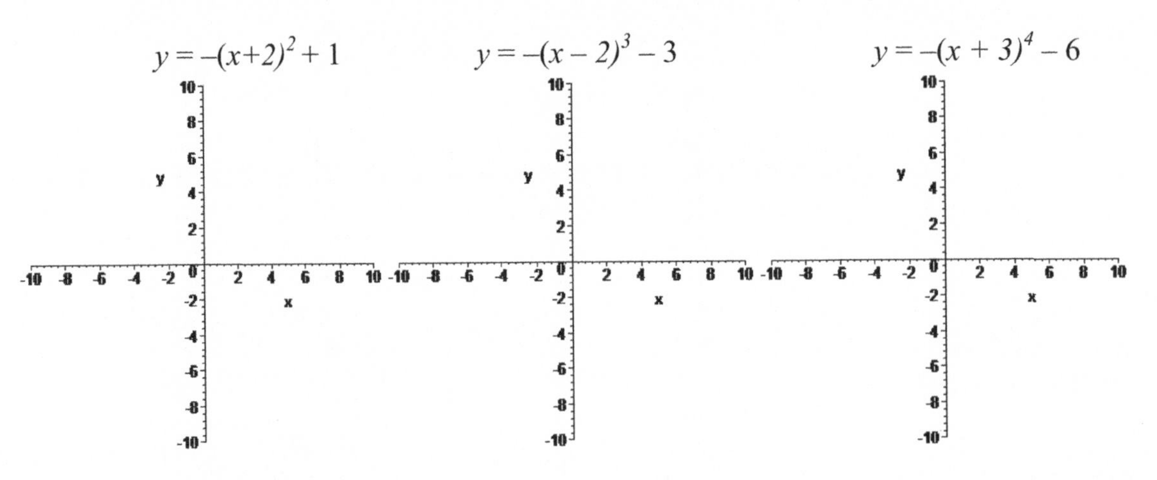

State at least one conclusión in relation to the previous part.

4. Graph the following functions. Obtain and indicate all x and y intercepts:

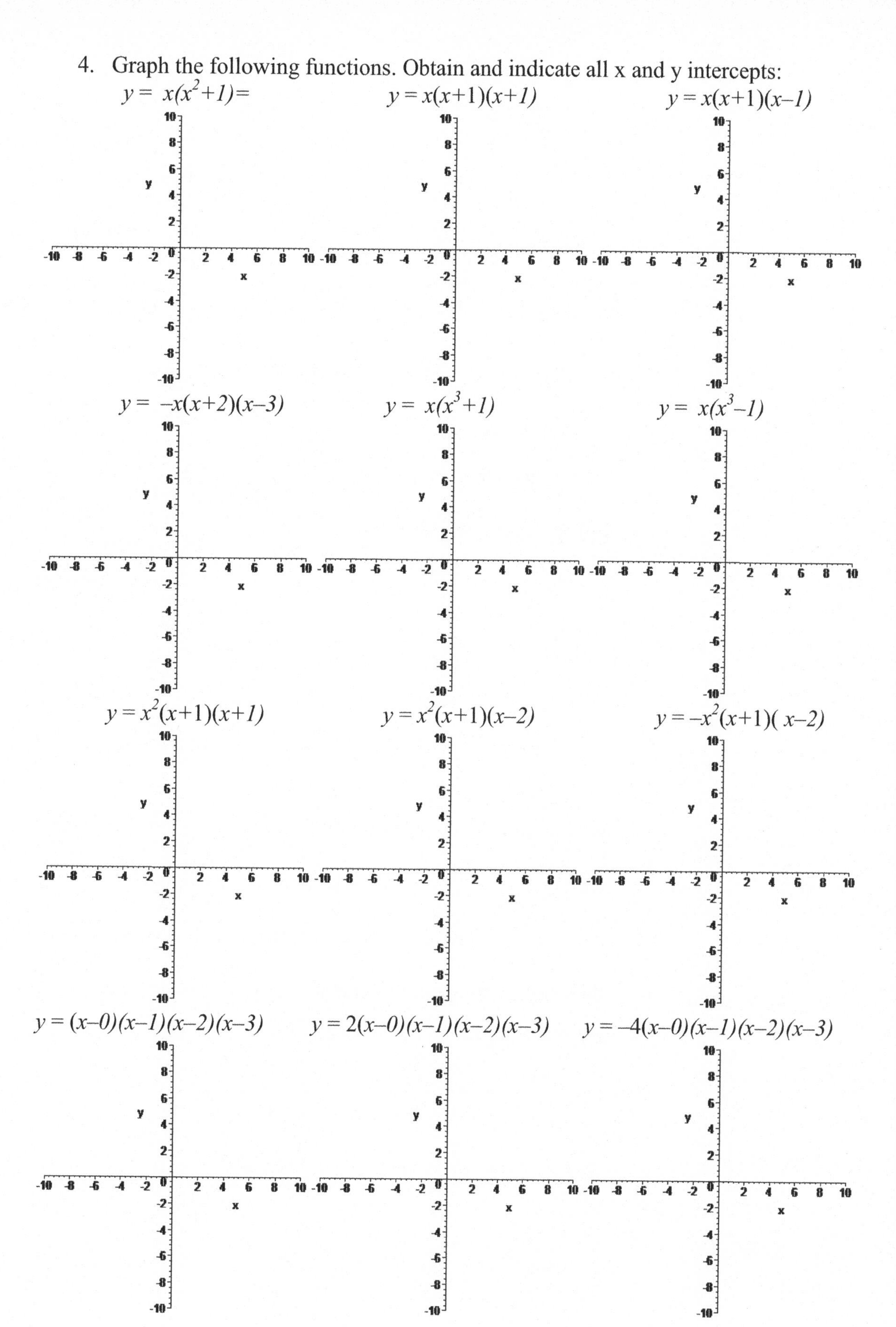

5. Fill the blanks (expand)

a) $y = x^3$

b) $y = x(x^2+1)=$ ___________

c) $y = x(x+1)(x+1)=$ __________

d) $y = x(x+1)(x-1)=$ __________

e) $y = -x(x+2)(x-3)=$ __________

f) $y = -(x-1)^3=$ __________

All the functions in this section are of the _____ degree. They all have an ____________. They all have at least 1 _____________. Sometimes they have ______________________________. If at one end the function tends to _____ then on the other end it will tend to __________.

6. Fill the blanks (expand)

a) $y = x^4$

b) $y = x(x^3+1)=$ ___________

c) $y = x(x^3-1)=$ ___________

d) $y = x^2(x+1)(x+1)=$ __________

e) $y = x^2(x+1)(x-1)=$ __________

f) $y = x^2(x+1)(x-2)=$ __________

e) $y = -x^2(x+1)(x-2)=$ __________

f) $y = -(x-2)^4$

All the functions in this section are of the _____ degree. They all have at least one ________ point. Sometimes they have two ______ and one ________ or two ________ and one ________. If on one end the function tends to _____ then on the other end it will tend to __________ as well.

7. Given the functions:

a) $y = (x-1)(x-2)(x-3)(x-4)$ b) $y = 2(x-1)(x-2)(x-3)(x-4)$

c) $y = 3(x-1)(x-2)(x-3)(x-4)$ d) $y = -4(x-1)(x-2)(x-3)(x-4)$

All the functions in this section are of the _____ degree. On multiplying a function by a number, the ____________________ stays the same. The ______ intercept changes. The general aspect of the function is similar/very different (circle the right answer)

8. Graph the following functions

$y = -(x-1)(x-2)^2(x-4)^3$ $y = -(x-2)^3(x-4)^4$ $y = (x-2)(x^2-1)(x^2+1)$

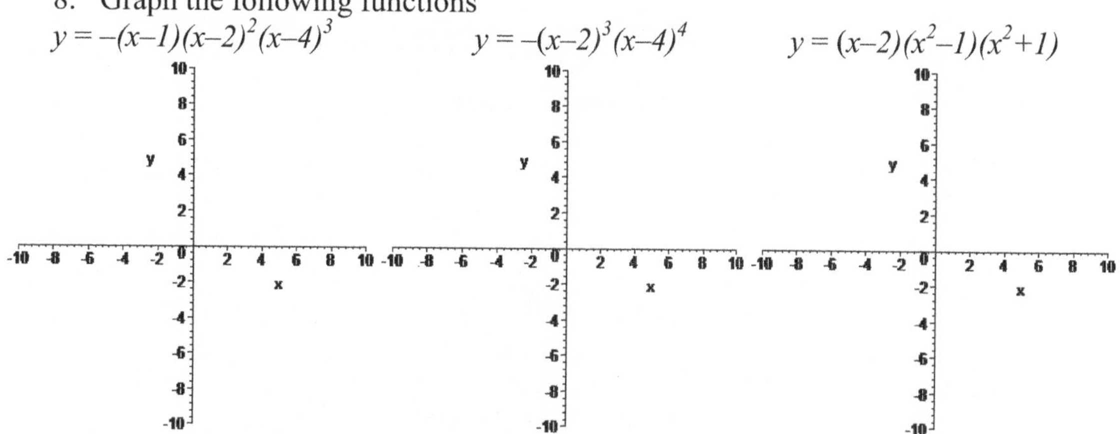

In case a factor is of 1st degree on the graph it will correspond an __________

In case a factor is of even degree on the graph it will correspond a _____ or _____

In case a factor is of odd (> 1) degree on the graph it will correspond an _________

9. Graph the following functions. Obtain and indicate all x and y intercepts on the graph (include their coordinates). Sketch a dashed line (use a pen or pencil) to indicate horizontal and/or vertical asymptotes.

a) $y = \dfrac{2x}{x-1}$

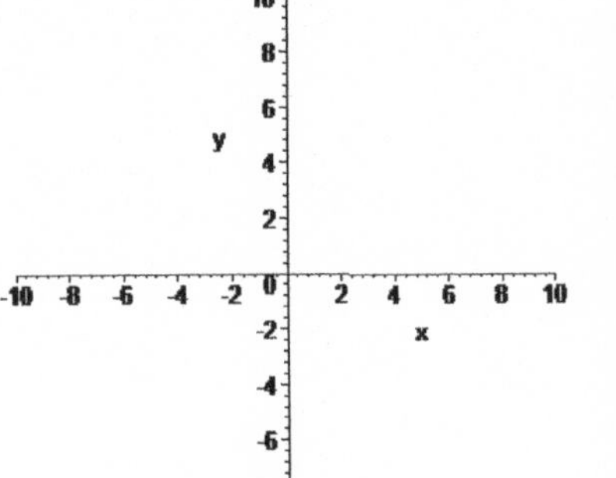

Vertical asymptote(s): _______________

Horizontal asymptote(s): _______________

b) $y = \dfrac{1}{(x+1)(x-2)}$

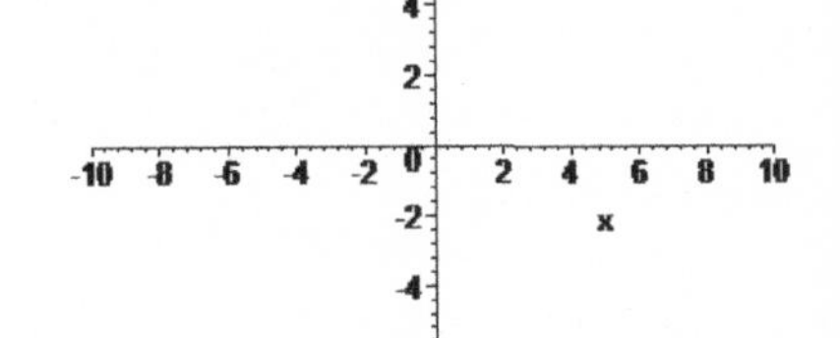

Vertical asymptote(s): _______________

Horizontal asymptote(s): _______________

c) $y = \dfrac{3x^2}{(x+1)(x-4)}$

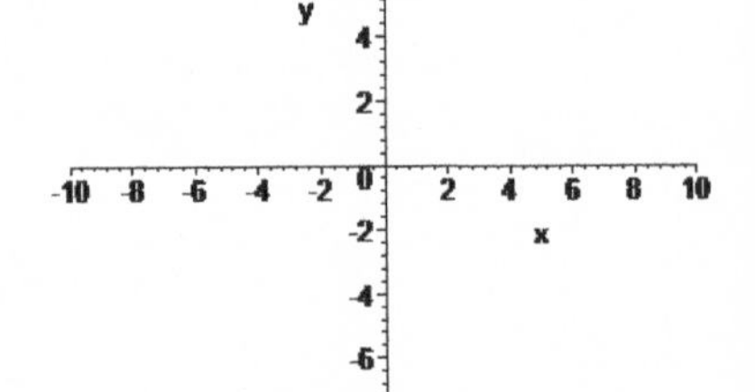

Vertical asymptote(s): _______________

Horizontal asymptote(s): _______________

d) $y = xe^x$

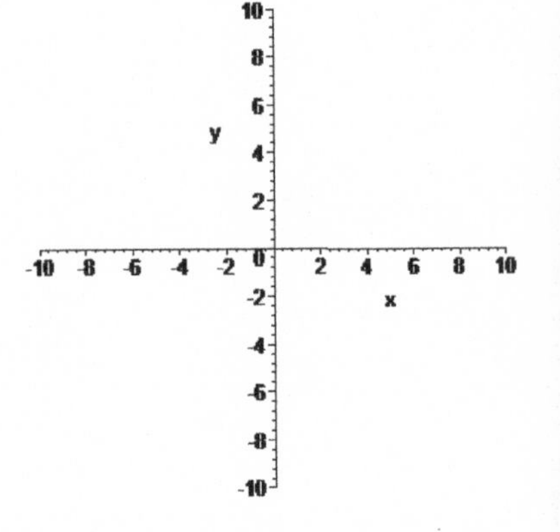

Vertical asymptote(s): _______________

Horizontal asymptote(s): _______________

10. Given the following function:

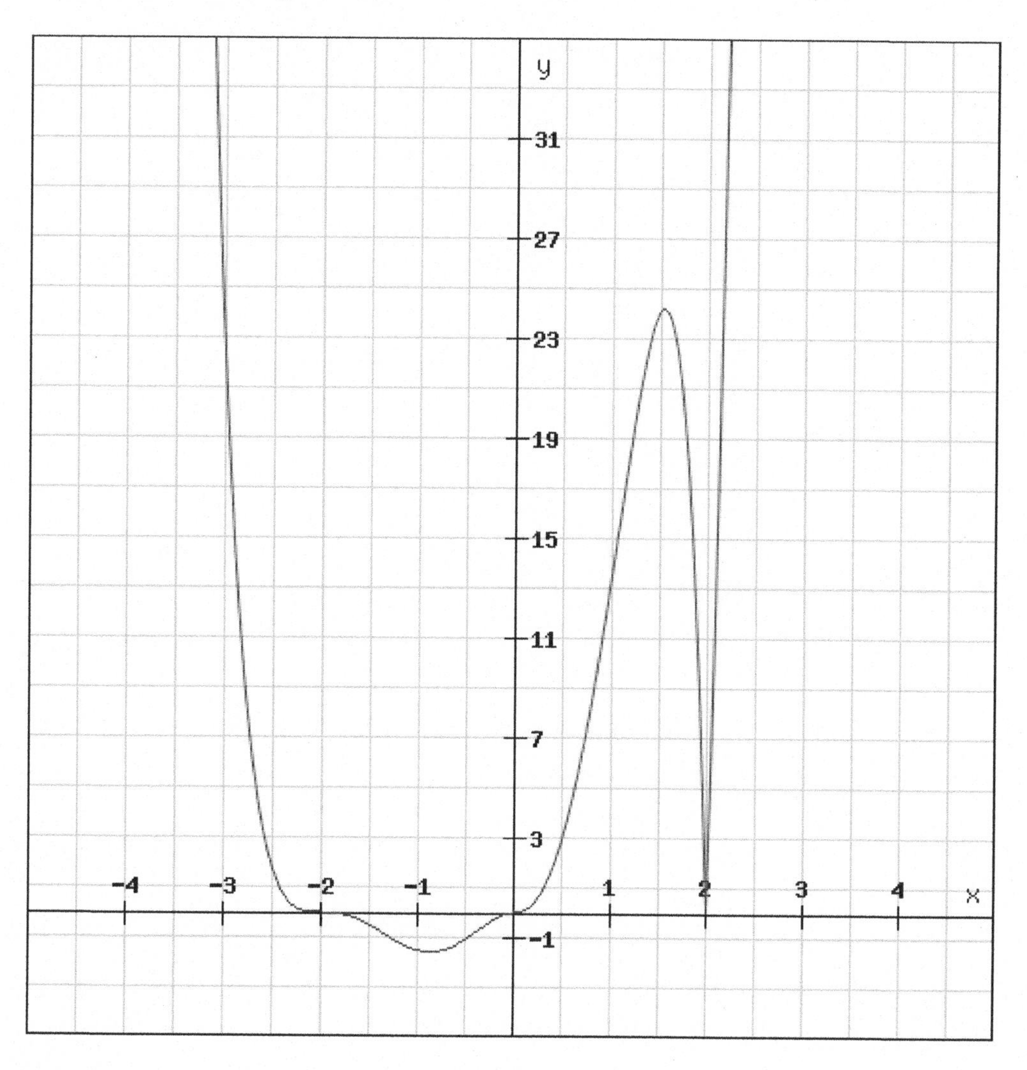

Fill the table:

x = a	x = –3	x = –2	x = – 1	x =–0.6	x = 0	x =1	x = 1.5	x = 2
f(x)								
f'(x)								
f''(x)								

Conclusions:

a. In a "smooth" maximum or minimum the ______________________________.

b. In a horizontal inflection point ______________________________.

c. In a non–horizontal inflection point ______________________________.

11. Use GDC to sketch the functions $f(x) = x^3$ and $g(x) = 4^x + 2^{-x} - 8$

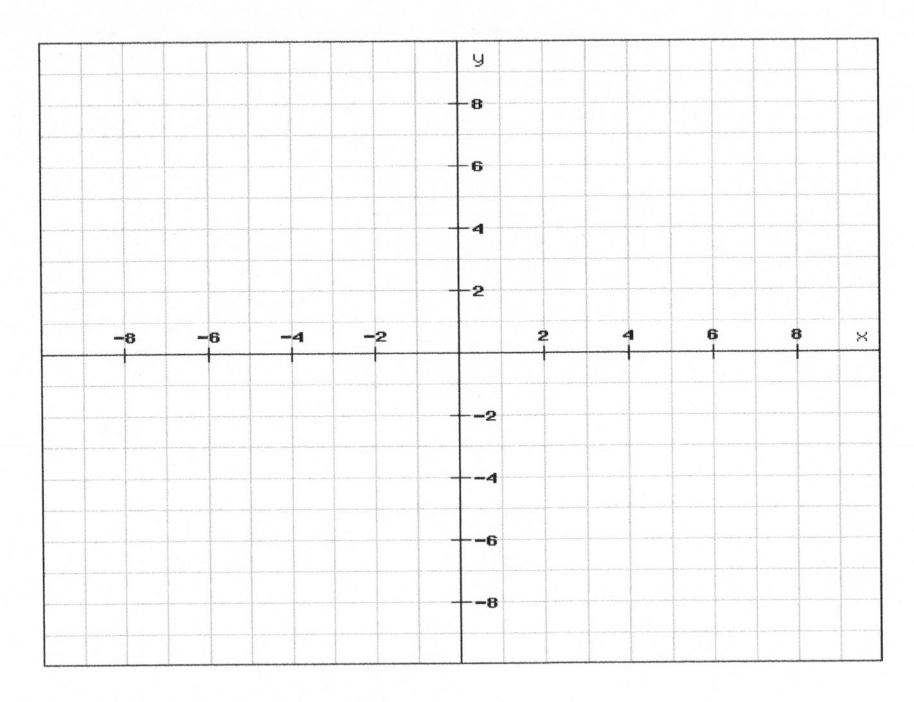

Find the values of x for which f(x) > g(x)

12. Use GDC to sketch the functions $f(x) = x^2$ and $g(x) = \ln(x)$

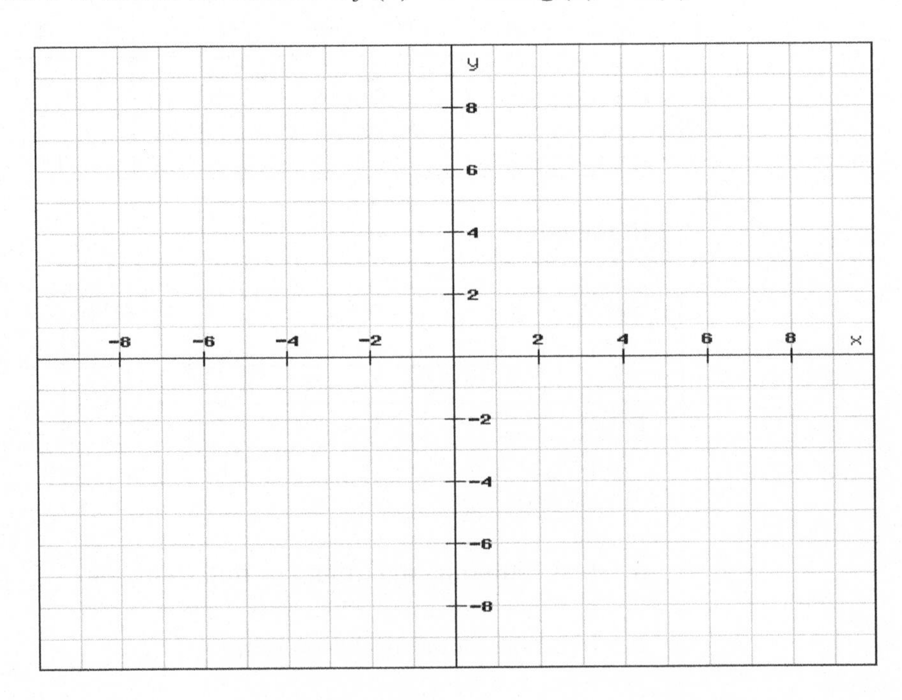

Find the values of x for which f(x) > g(x)

13. $f(x) = x^4, x \in [-1, 2]$

Domain: ______________________

Extrema (using the 1st and if needed 2nd derivatives)

Vertical asymptotes: ____________

Horizontal asymptotes: ___________

Range of the function: ___________

Slant Asymptotes: ____________

Function Increases: ____________

Function decreases: ____________

Concave up: ________________

y intercept: ____________________

Concave down: ______________

x intercept(s): __________________

Inflection point(s)______________

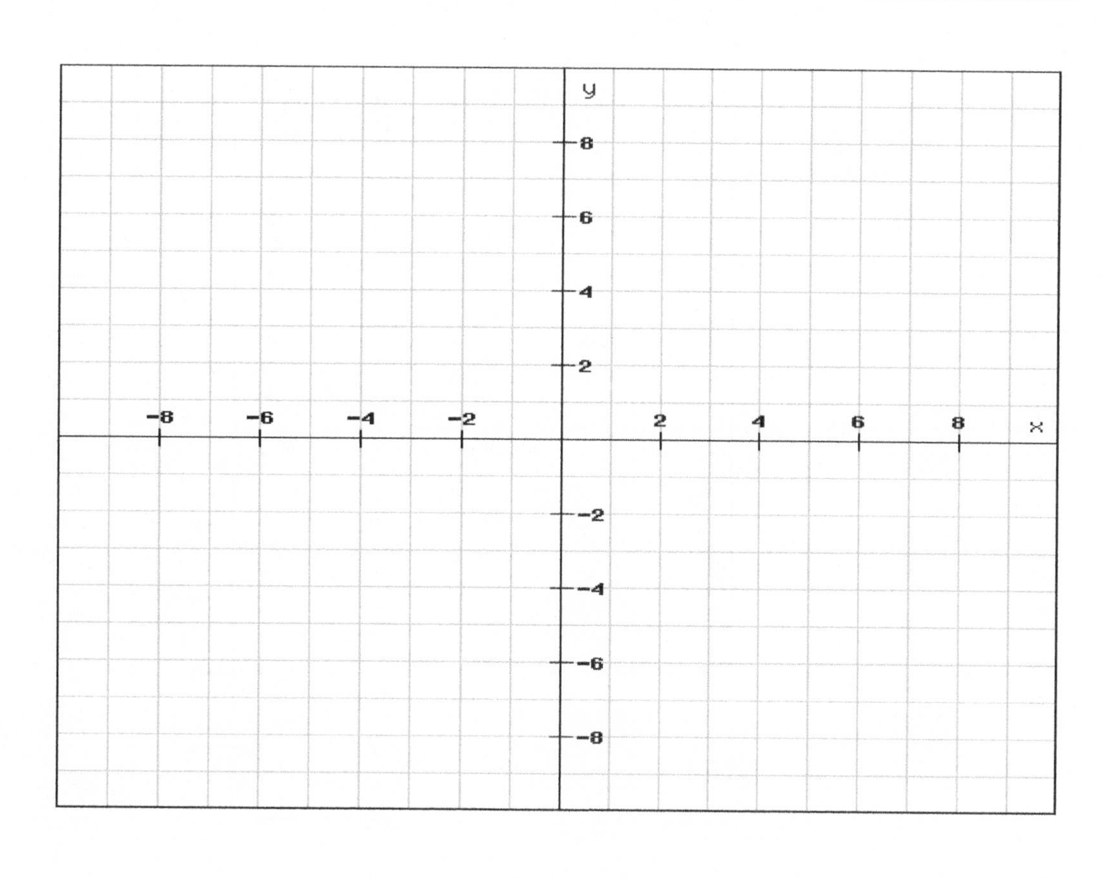

14. $f(x) = -x^6 + 6, x \in \mathbb{R}$

Domain: ___________________________

Extrema (using the 1st and if needed 2nd derivatives)

Vertical asymptotes: _______________

Horizontal asymptotes: ______________

Range of the function: _______________

Slant Asymptotes: ________________

Function Increases: _________________

Function decreases: _________________

Concave up: ________________________

y intercept: _________________________

Concave down: ______________________

x intercept(s): _______________________

Inflection point(s)____________________

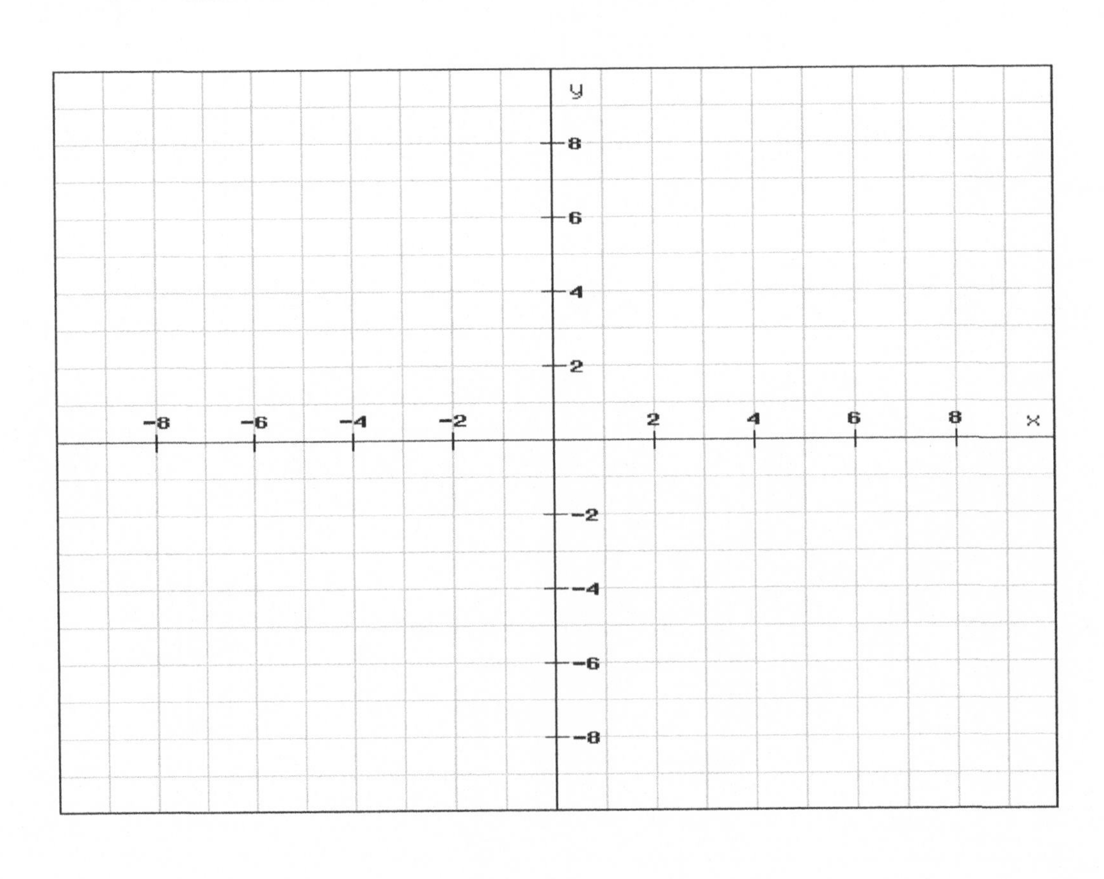

15. $f(x) = x^2(x+2), x \in [-\frac{3}{2}, \frac{1}{2}]$

Domain: ______________________

Vertical asymptotes: ______________

Horizontal asymptotes: ____________

Slant Asymptotes: ______________

y intercept: ______________________

x intercept(s): ____________________

Extrema (using the 1st and if needed 2nd derivatives)

Range of the function: ____________

Function Increases: ______________

Function decreases: ______________

Concave up: ____________________

Concave down: __________________

Inflection point(s)_________________

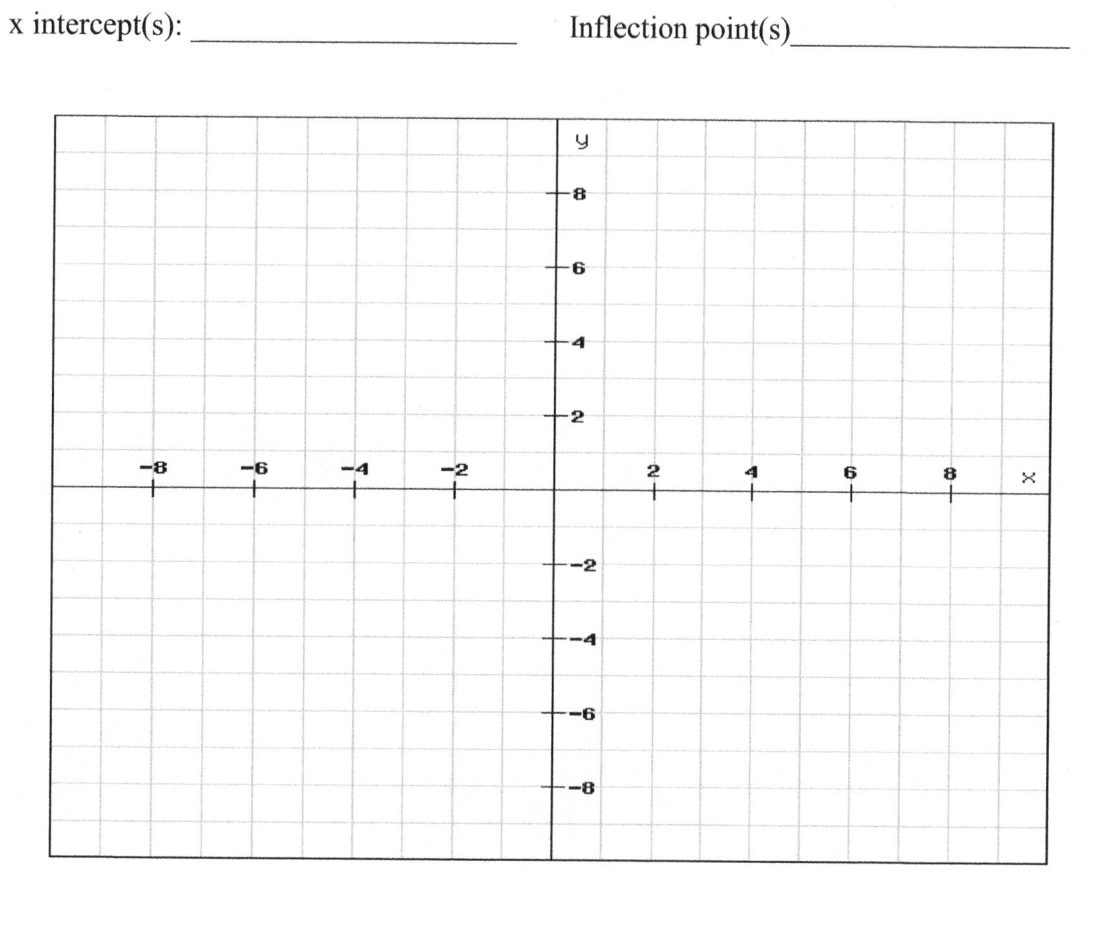

16. $f(x) = x(x+2)(x-1), x \in \mathbb{R}$

Domain: ______________________________

Vertical asymptotes: ________________

Horizontal asymptotes: _______________

Slant Asymptotes: _________________

y intercept: __________________________

x intercept(s): _________________________

Extrema (using the 1st and if needed 2nd derivatives)

Range of the function: _______________

Function Increases: __________________

Function decreases: __________________

Concave up: ________________________

Concave down: ______________________

Inflection point(s)____________________

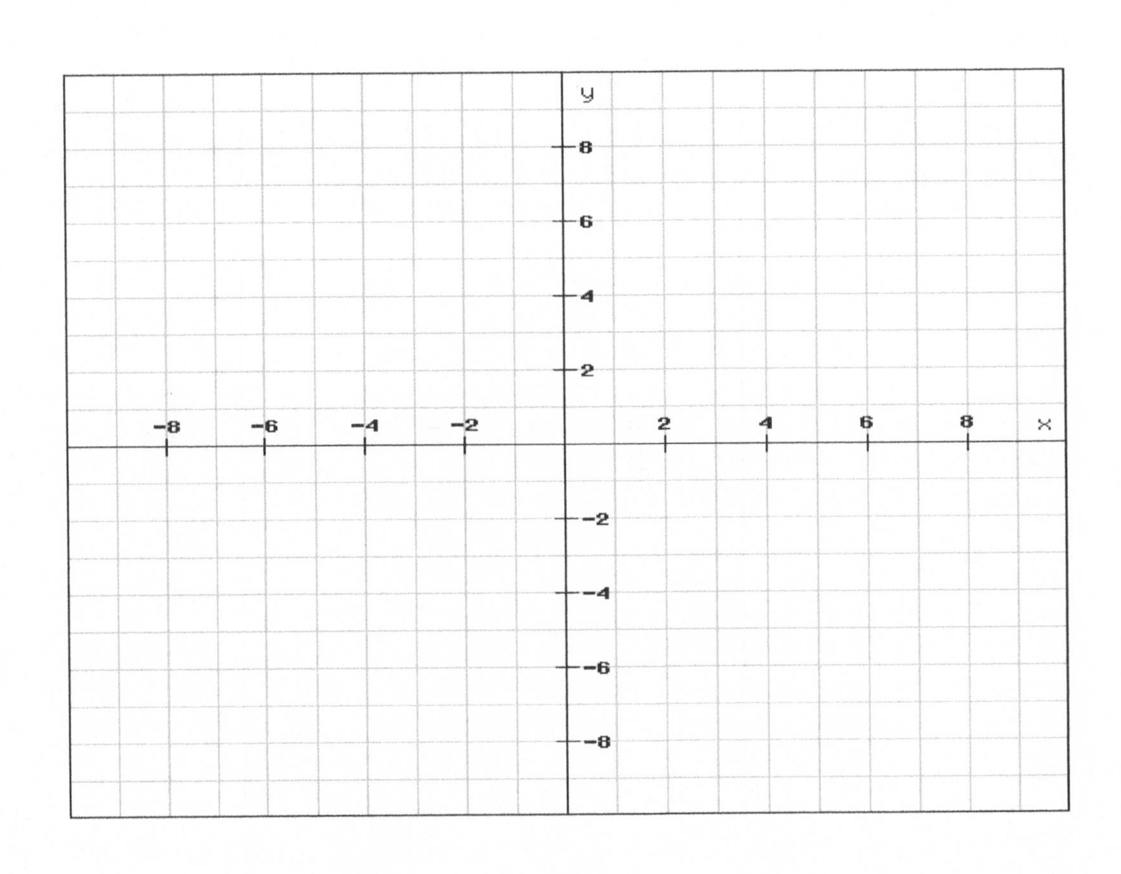

17. $f(x) = 2x^3 + 11x^2 + 10x - 8, x \in \mathbb{R}$

Domain: ___________________________

Vertical asymptotes: ________________

Horizontal asymptotes: ______________

Slant Asymptotes: ________________

y intercept: ______________________

x intercept(s): ____________________

Extrema (using the 1st and if needed 2nd derivatives)

Range of the function: ______________

Function Increases: _________________

Function decreases: ________________

Concave up: _______________________

Concave down: ____________________

Inflection point(s)___________________

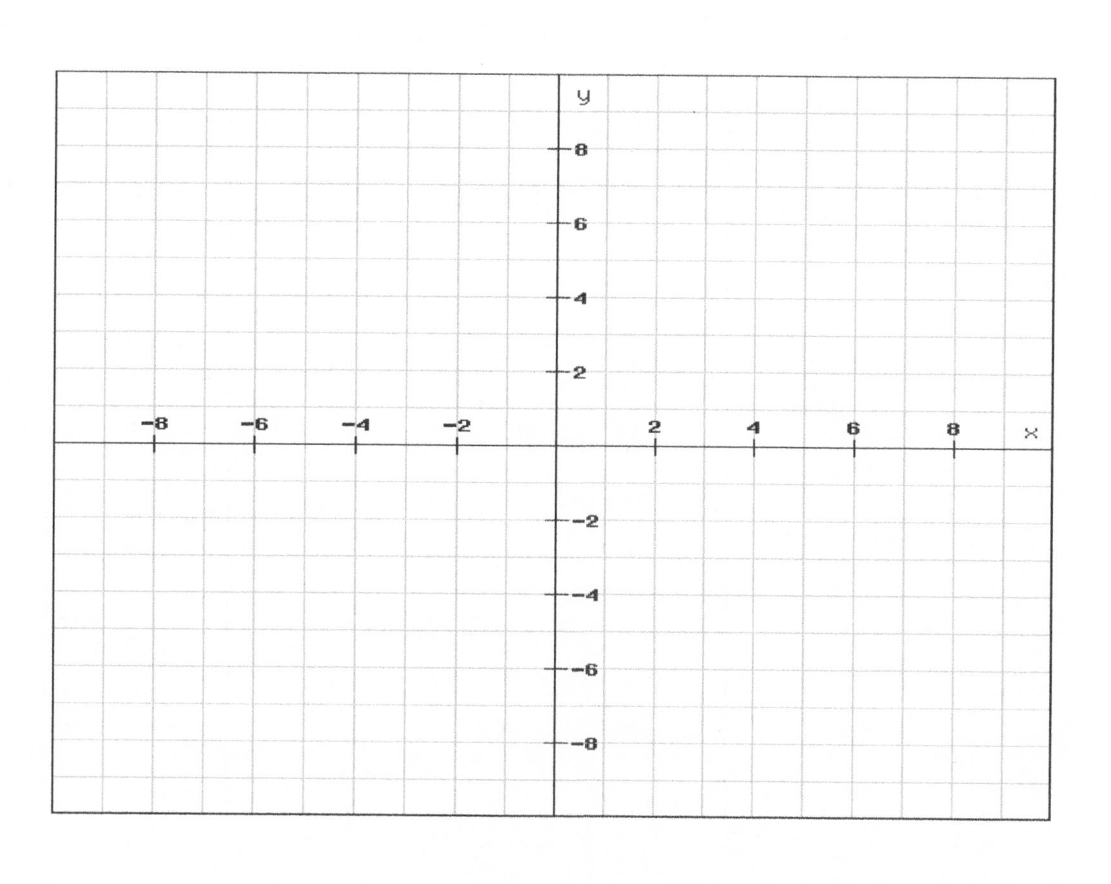

18. $f(x) = x^3 - x^2, x \in [0, 2]$

Domain: ________________________

Vertical asymptotes: ______________

Horizontal asymptotes: ____________

Slant Asymptotes: ______________

y intercept: ______________________

x intercept(s): ____________________

Extrema (using the 1st and if needed 2nd derivatives)

Range of the function: ______________

Function Increases: _______________

Function decreases: _______________

Concave up: _____________________

Concave down: __________________

Inflection point(s)_________________

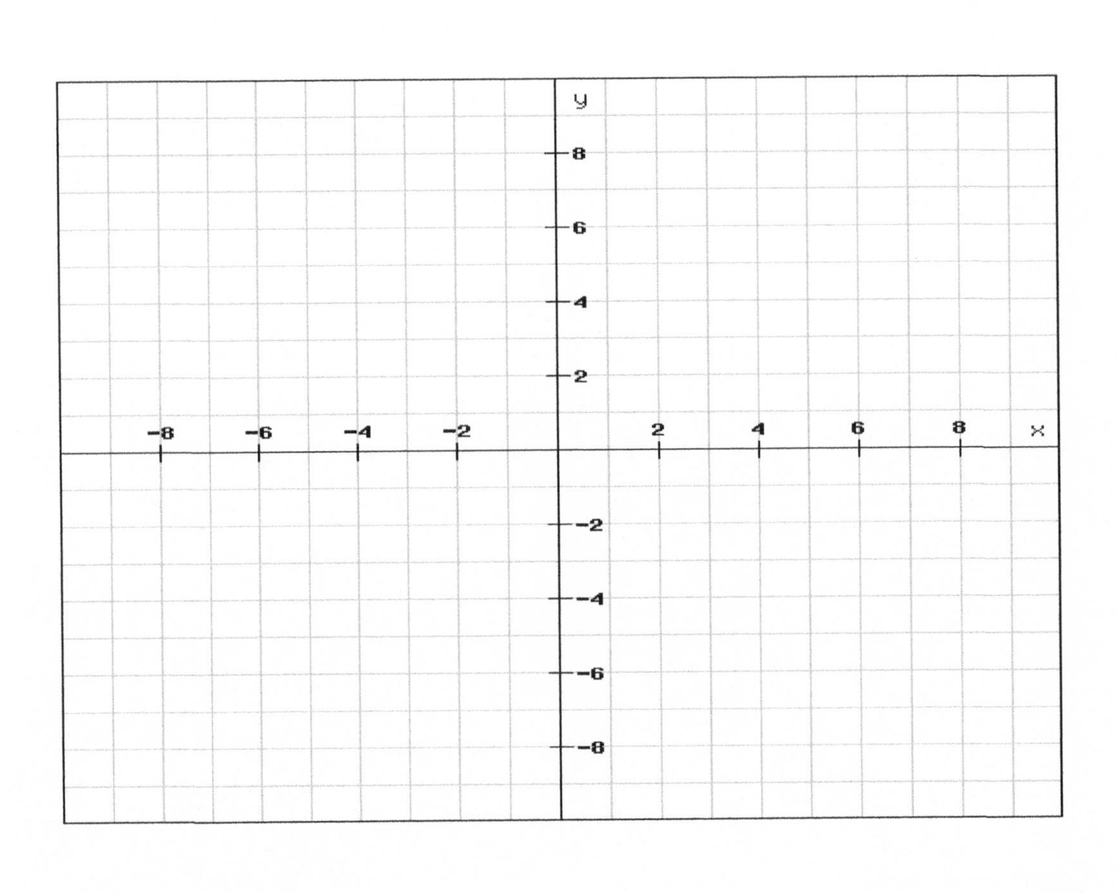

19. $f(x) = 2x^4 - 4x^2, x \in \mathbb{R}$

Domain: ______________________

Extrema (using the 1st and if needed 2nd derivatives)

Vertical asymptotes: ______________

Horizontal asymptotes: ____________

Slant Asymptotes: ______________

Range of the function: ____________

Function Increases: ______________

Function decreases: ______________

y intercept: ______________________

Concave up: ____________________

x intercept(s): ___________________

Concave down: __________________

Inflection point(s)______________

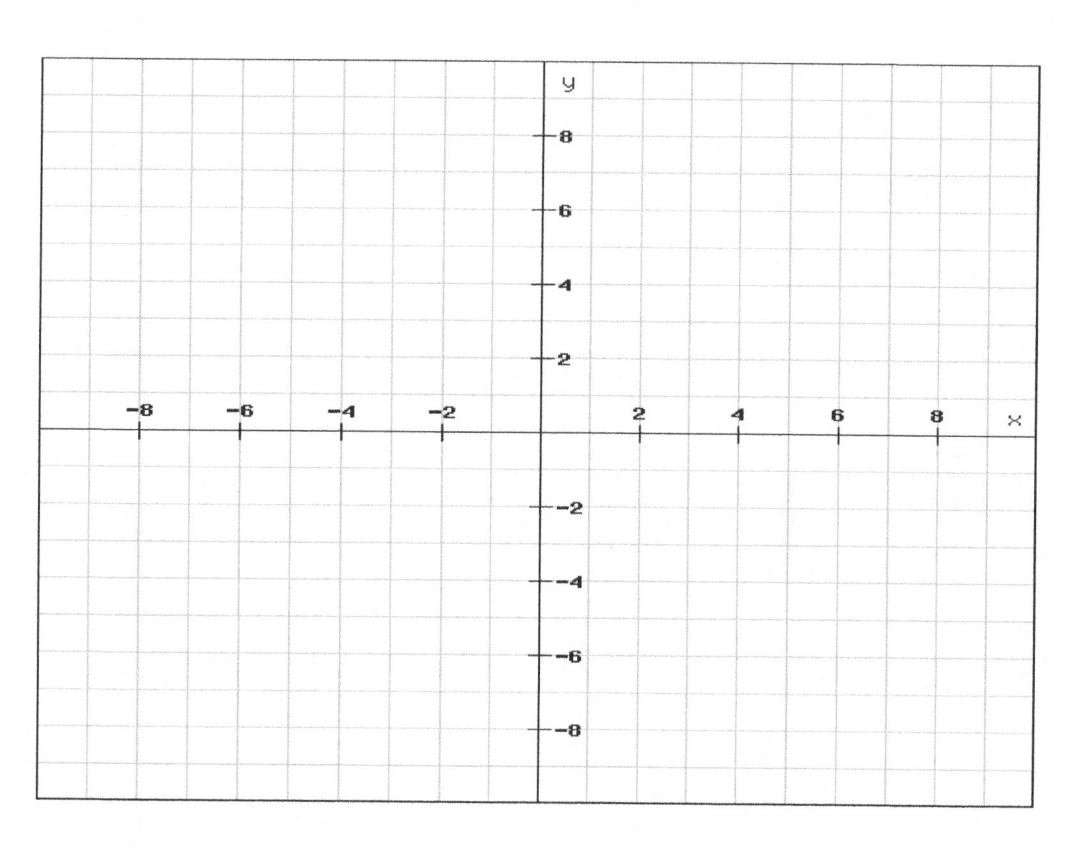

20. $f(x) = x^4 - 2x^3, x \in \mathbb{R}$

Domain: ___________________________

Extrema (using the 1st and if needed 2nd derivatives)

Vertical asymptotes: ________________

Horizontal asymptotes: _____________

Range of the function: _______________

Slant Asymptotes: ________________

Function Increases: ________________

Function decreases: ________________

Concave up: ______________________

y intercept: _______________________

Concave down: ___________________

x intercept(s): _____________________

Inflection point(s)___________________

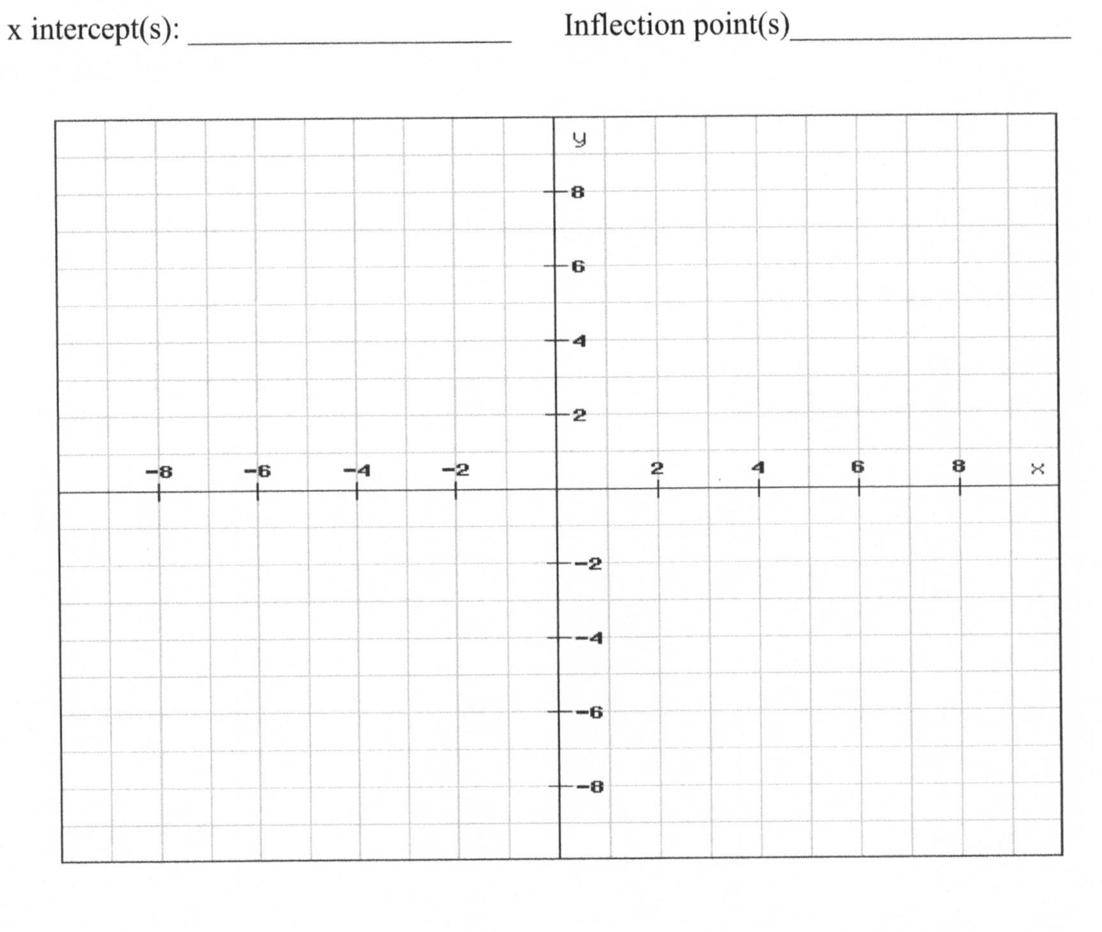

21. Write a possible expression of a function of the 3rd degree that intercepts the x axis at (2, 0), (–3, 0) and (–0.5, 0). Is it possible to make this function have a y intercepts (0, 10)? If yes, find the expression, if no explain why.

22. Write a possible expression of a function of the 4th degree that intercepts the x axis at (1, 0), (2, 0), (5, 0) and (–1, 0). Is it possible to make this function have a y intercepts (0, 5)? If yes, find the expression, if no explain why.

23. Write the expression of the function $f(x) = x^3$ shifted 2 positions to the right and 3 positions down.

24. Write the expression of the function $f(x) = x^4$ shifted 4 positions to the left and 6 positions up.

25. In case the first derivative of a function is 0 at a certain point, this point can be a

_______________ or a _______________ or a _______________.

26. In case the 1st derivative is 0 and the 2nd derivative is positive at a certain point, the point must be a _______________________________________.

27. In case the 1st derivative is 0 and the 2nd derivative is negative at a certain point, the point must be a _______________________________________.

28. In case the 1st derivative is 0 and the 2nd derivative is also 0 at a certain point, the point ____.

29. In the parts where $f'(x) > 0$ the function is ____________________.

30. In the parts where $f''(x) > 0$ the function is ____________________.

B. POLYNOMIALS WITH RATIONAL POWER

31. $f(x) = x^{\frac{2}{3}}, x \in$ □

Domain: ____________________

Vertical asymptotes: ____________

Horizontal asymptotes: ____________

Slant Asymptotes: ____________

y intercept: ____________________

x intercept(s): ____________________

Extrema (using the 1st and if needed 2nd derivatives)

Range of the function: ____________

Function Increases: ____________

Function decreases: ____________

Concave up: ____________

Concave down: ____________

Inflection point(s) ____________

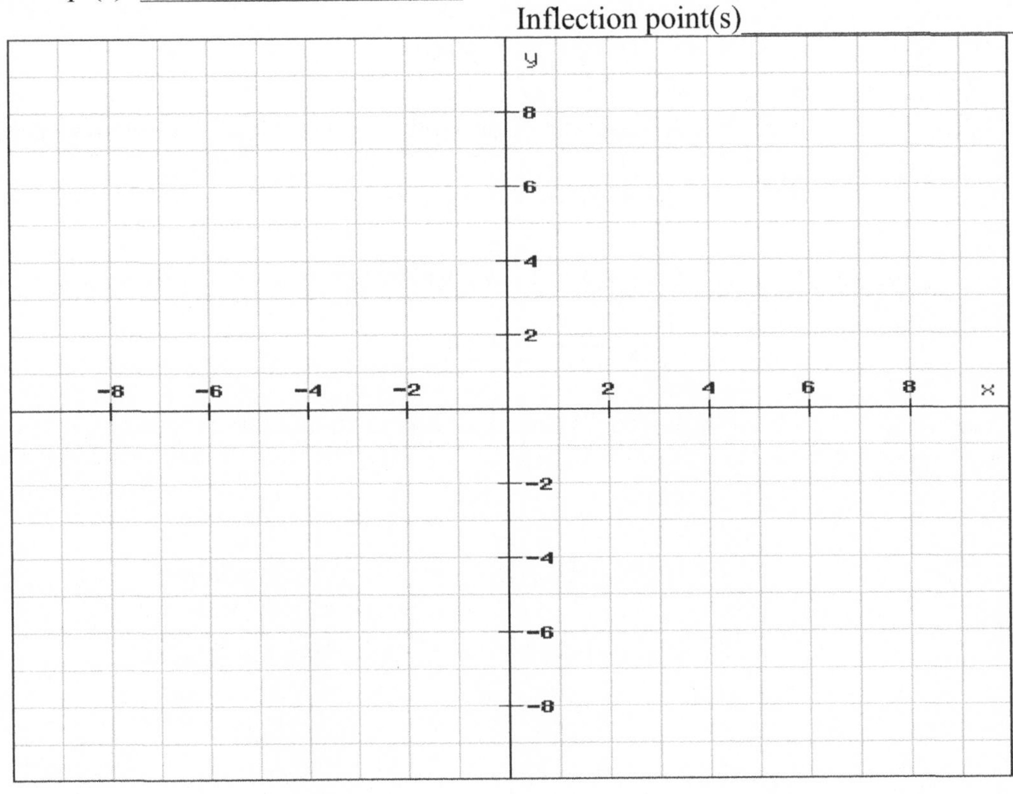

32. $f(x) = x^{\frac{4}{3}}, x \in$ □

Domain: ______________________

Vertical asymptotes: ______________

Horizontal asymptotes: ____________

Slant Asymptotes: ______________

y intercept: ______________________

x intercept(s): ___________________

Extrema (using the 1st and if needed 2nd derivatives)

Range of the function: ____________

Function Increases: ______________

Function decreases: ______________

Concave up: ____________________

Concave down: __________________

Inflection point(s)_______________

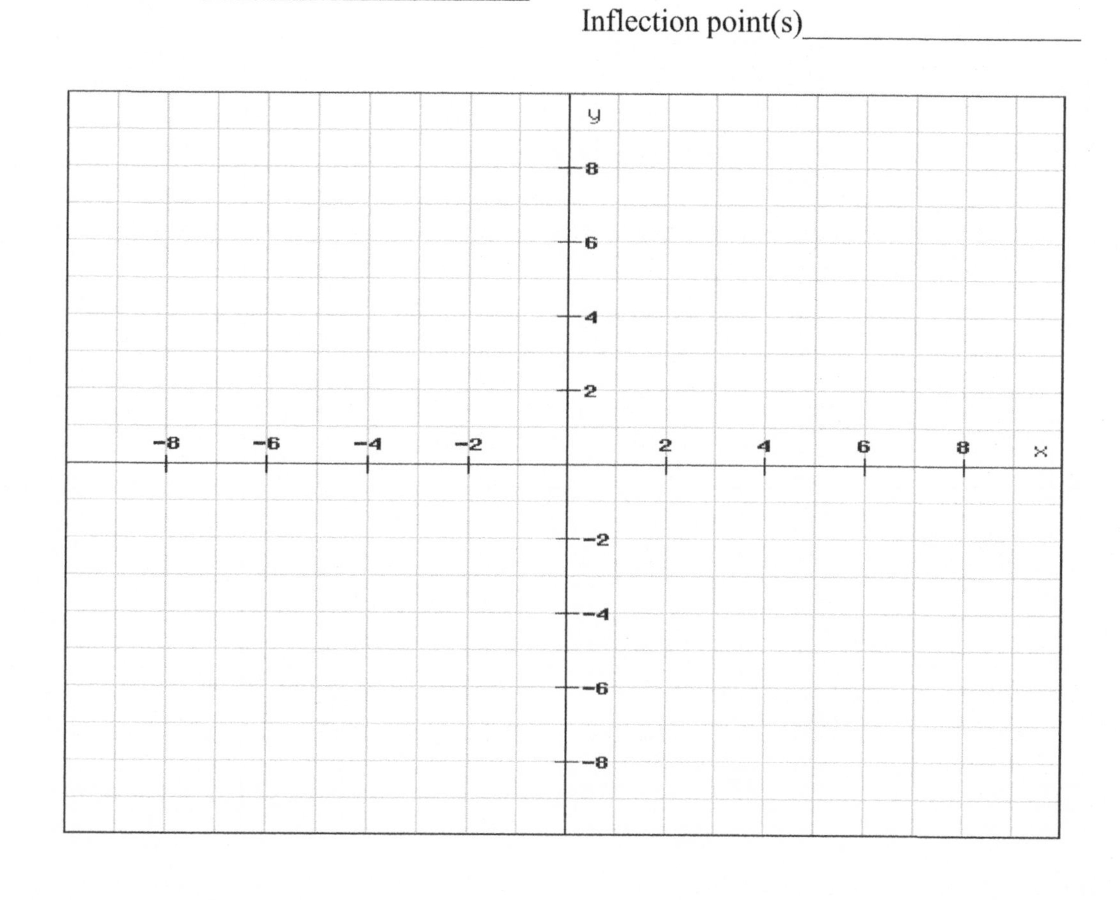

33. $f(x)=2x^{-\frac{4}{3}}, x\in \square$

Domain: ______________________

Extrema (using the 1st and if needed 2nd derivatives)

Vertical asymptotes: ______________

Horizontal asymptotes: ____________

Range of the function: ____________

Slant Asymptotes: ______________

Function Increases: ______________

Function decreases: ______________

Concave up: ____________________

y intercept: ____________________

Concave down: __________________

x intercept(s): __________________

Inflection point(s)________________

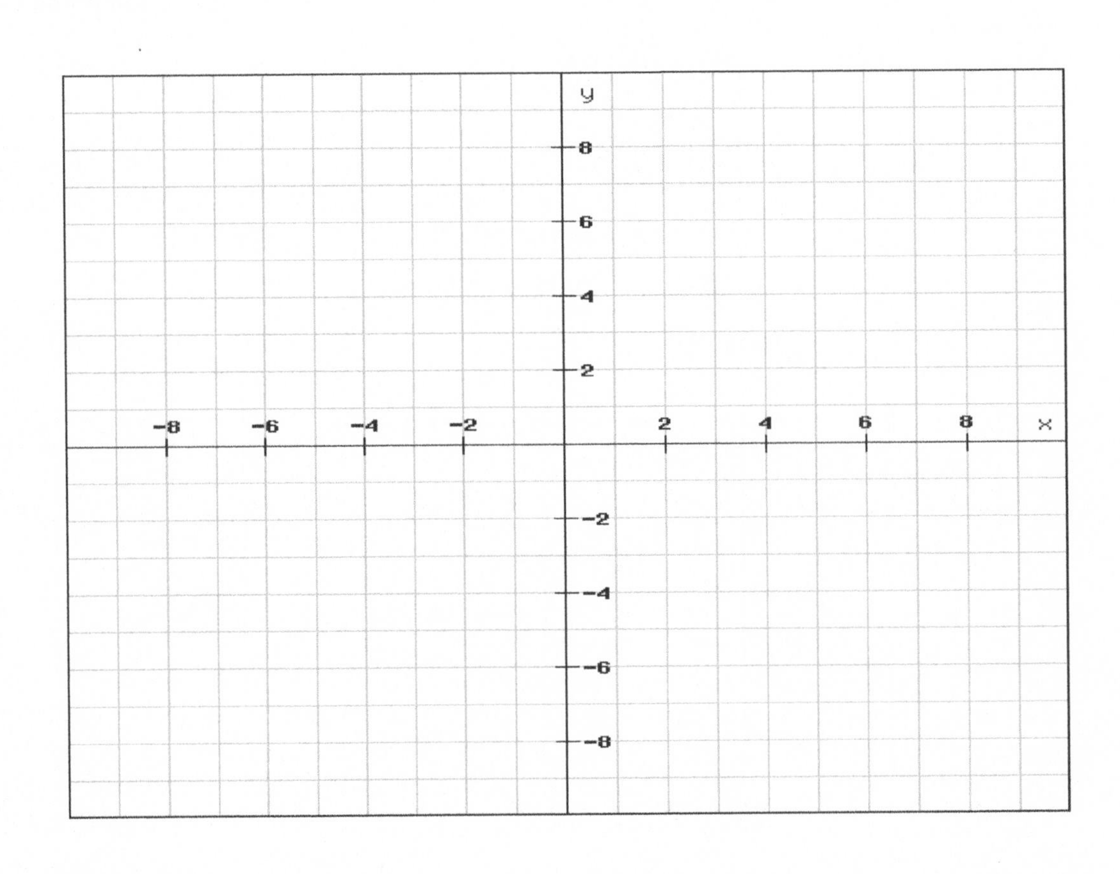

34. $f(x) = x - x^{\frac{2}{3}}, x \in \mathbb{R}$

Domain: ______________________

Extrema (using the 1st and if needed 2nd derivatives)

Vertical asymptotes: ____________

Horizontal asymptotes: ___________

Range of the function: __________

Slant Asymptotes: _____________

Function Increases: _____________

Function decreases: ____________

Concave up: ____________________

y intercept: ____________________

Concave down: _________________

x intercept(s): _________________

Inflection point(s)_______________

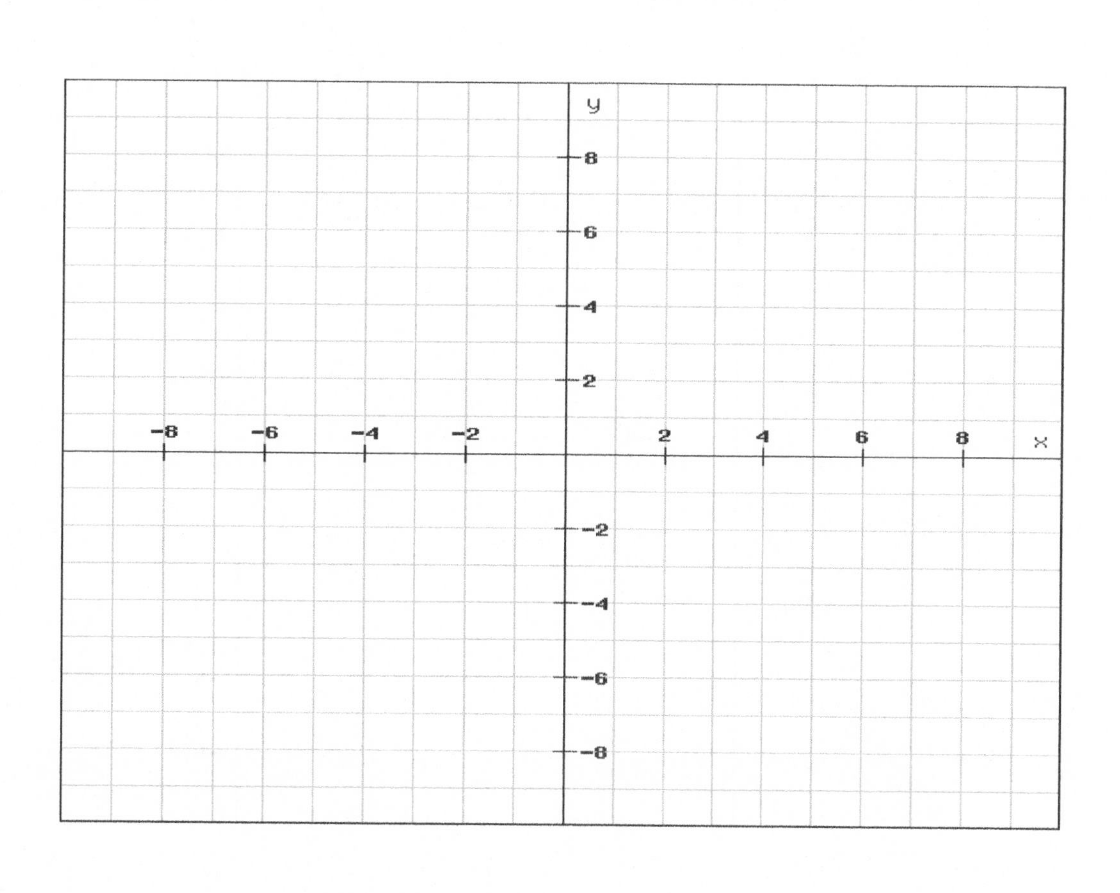

35. $f(x) = x + x^{-\frac{2}{3}}, x \in \square$

Domain: ____________________

Extrema (using the 1st and if needed 2nd derivatives)

Vertical asymptotes: ____________

Horizontal asymptotes: ____________

Range of the function: ____________

Slant Asymptotes: ____________

Function Increases: ____________

Function decreases: ____________

Concave up: ____________

y intercept: ____________________

Concave down: ____________

x intercept(s): ____________________

Inflection point(s)____________

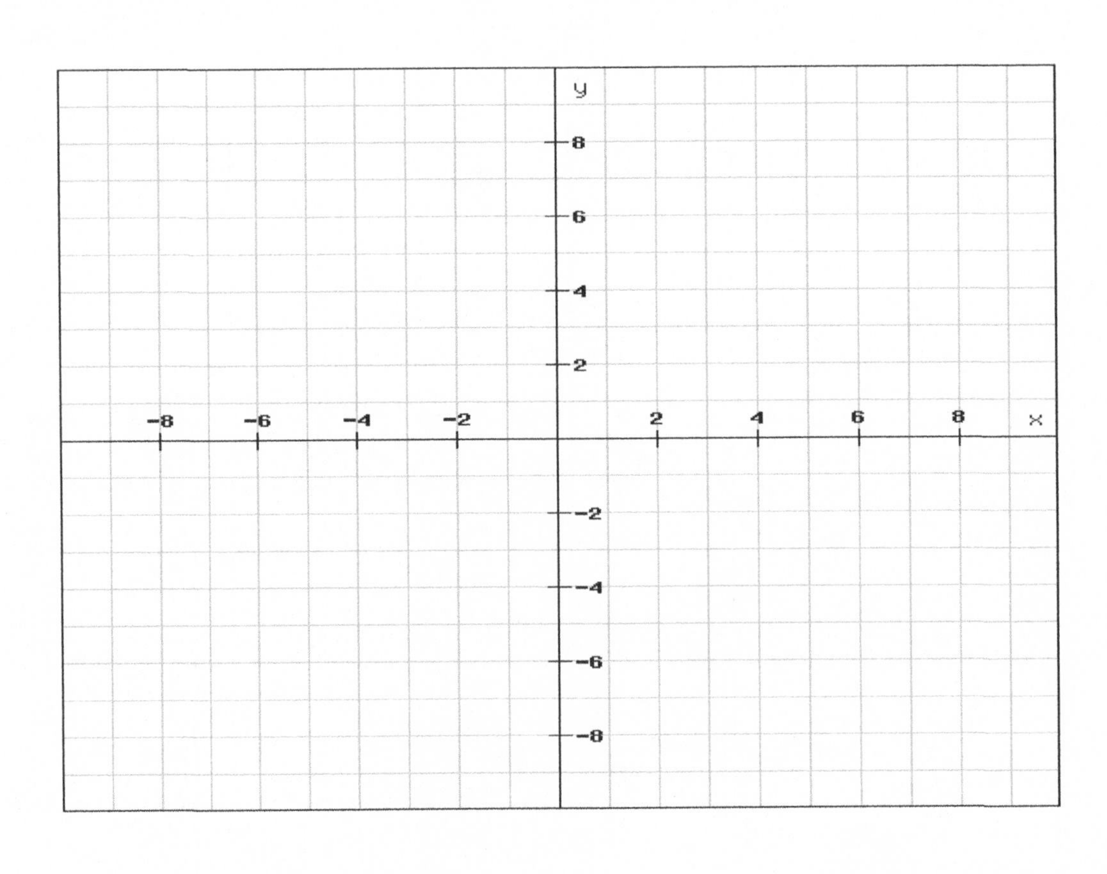

C. RATIONAL FUNCTIONS

36. $f(x)=\dfrac{3(x+2)}{(x-5)(x+2)}+4, x\in\mathbb{R}$

Domain: ____________________________

Vertical asymptotes: ________________

Continuity: _________________________

Horizontal asymptotes: ______________

y intercept: __________________________

x intercept(s): _______________________

Extrema (using the 1st and if needed 2nd derivatives)

Range of the function: ______________

Function Increases: _________________

Function decreases: _________________

Concave up: ________________________

Concave down: _____________________

Inflection point(s)____________________

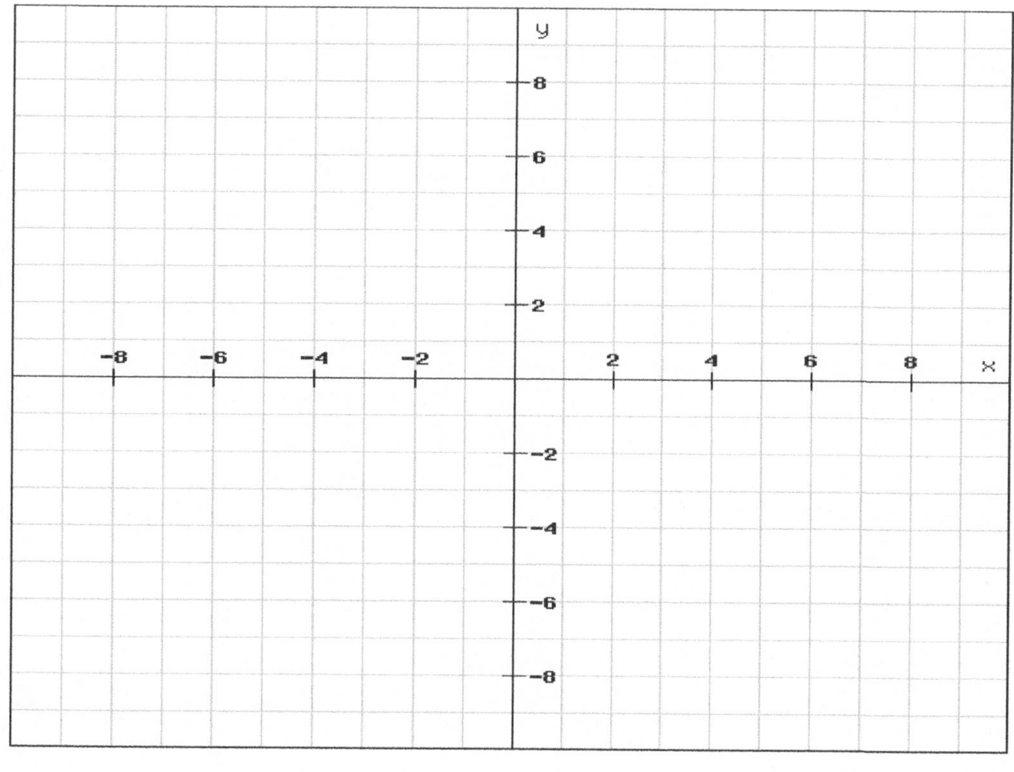

37. $f(x)=\dfrac{2x}{x+1}, x\in\mathbb{R}$

Domain: ______________________

Extrema (using the 1st and if needed 2nd derivatives)

Vertical asymptotes: ______________

Horizontal asymptotes: ____________

Range of the function: ____________

Function Increases: ______________

Continuity: _____________________

Function decreases: ______________

y intercept: _____________________

Concave up: ___________________

Concave down: _________________

x intercept(s): ___________________

Inflection point(s)________________

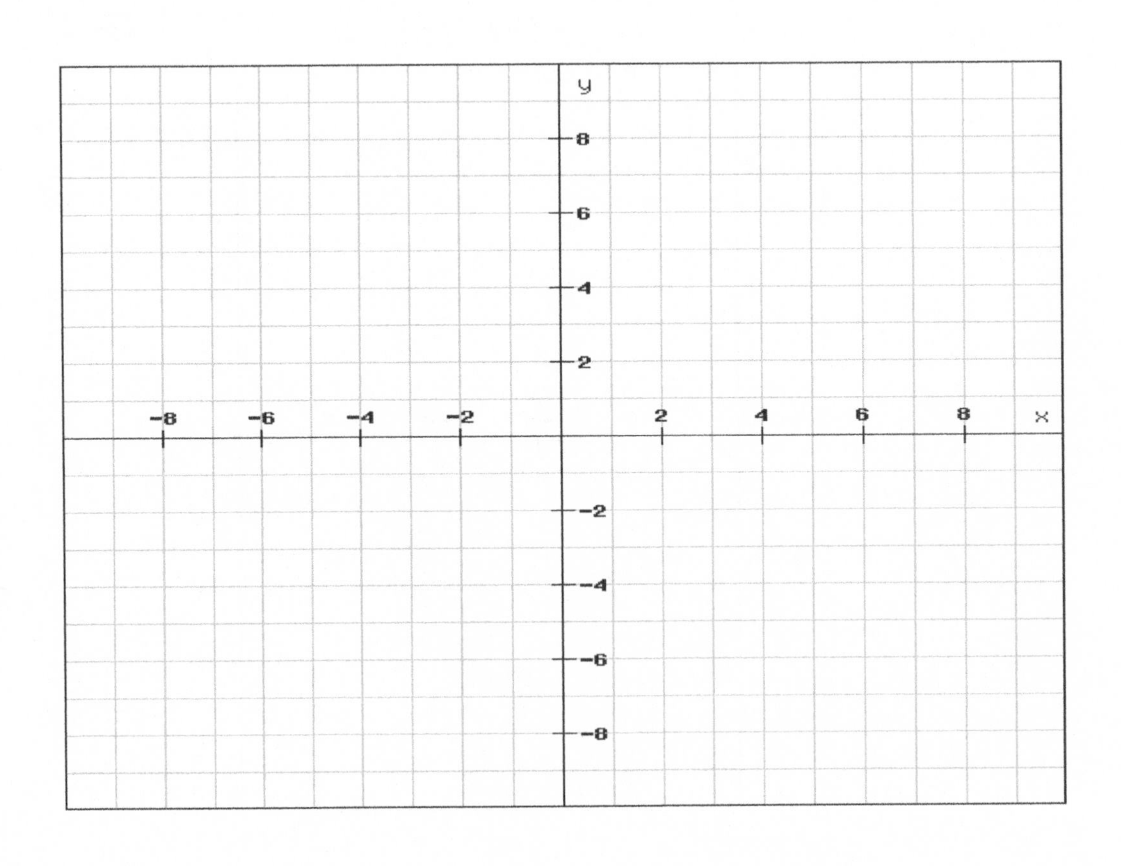

38. $f(x)=\dfrac{1}{x^2}, x \in \square$

Domain: ______________________

Vertical asymptotes: ______________

Horizontal asymptotes: ____________

Continuity: ______________________

y intercept: ______________________

x intercept(s): ___________________

Extrema (using the 1st and if needed 2nd derivatives)

Range of the function: ____________

Function Increases: ______________

Function decreases: ______________

Concave up: _____________________

Concave down: ___________________

Inflection point(s)________________

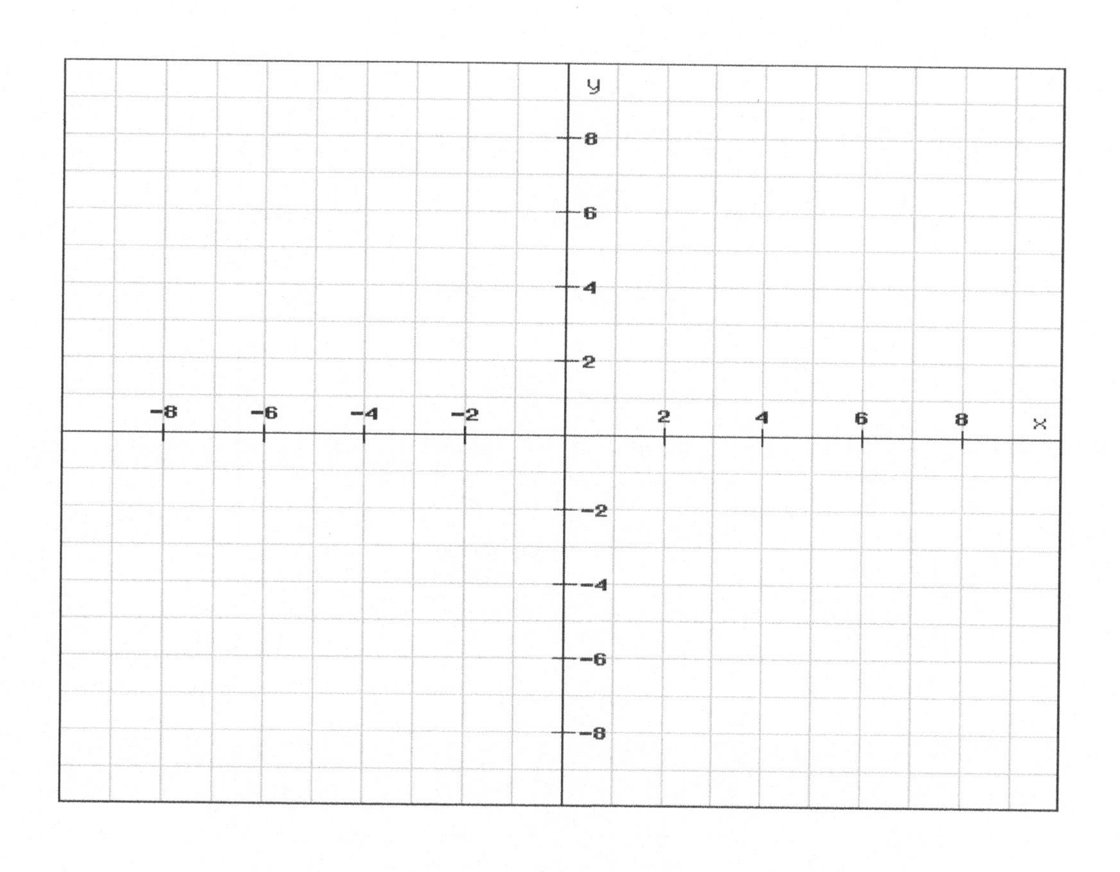

39. $f(x) = \dfrac{2}{(x-3)^2} - 4, x \in \square$

Domain: ______________________

Extrema (using the 1st and if needed 2nd derivatives)

Vertical asymptotes: ______________

Horizontal asymptotes: ____________

Range of the function: ____________

Continuity: ______________________

Function Increases: ______________

Function decreases: ______________

y intercept: ______________________

Concave up: ____________________

Concave down: __________________

x intercept(s): ____________________

Inflection point(s)________________

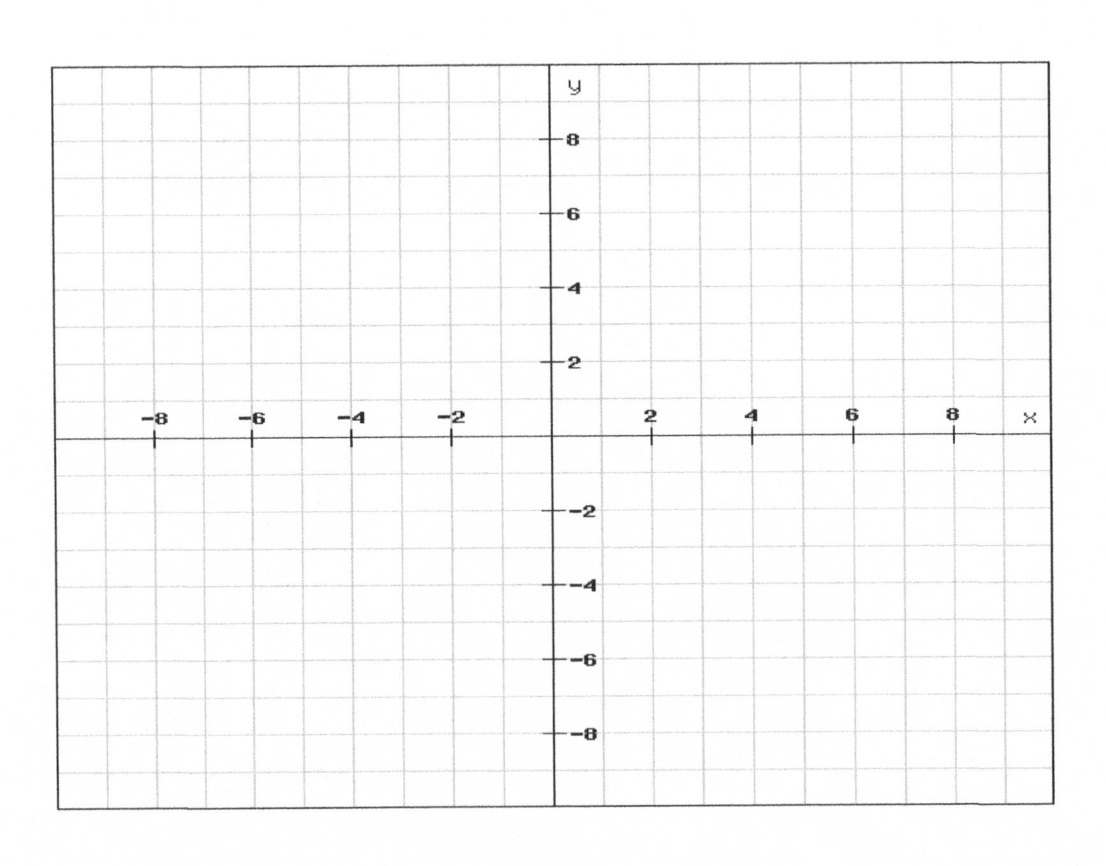

40. $f(x) = \dfrac{1}{x^2 + 1}, x \in$ □

Domain: ______________________

Extrema (using the 1st and if needed 2nd derivatives)

Vertical asymptotes: ____________

Horizontal asymptotes: ___________

Range of the function: ___________

Continuity: ____________________

Function Increases: ____________

Function decreases: ____________

y intercept: ___________________

Concave up: __________________

Concave down: ________________

x intercept(s): _________________

Inflection point(s)_______________

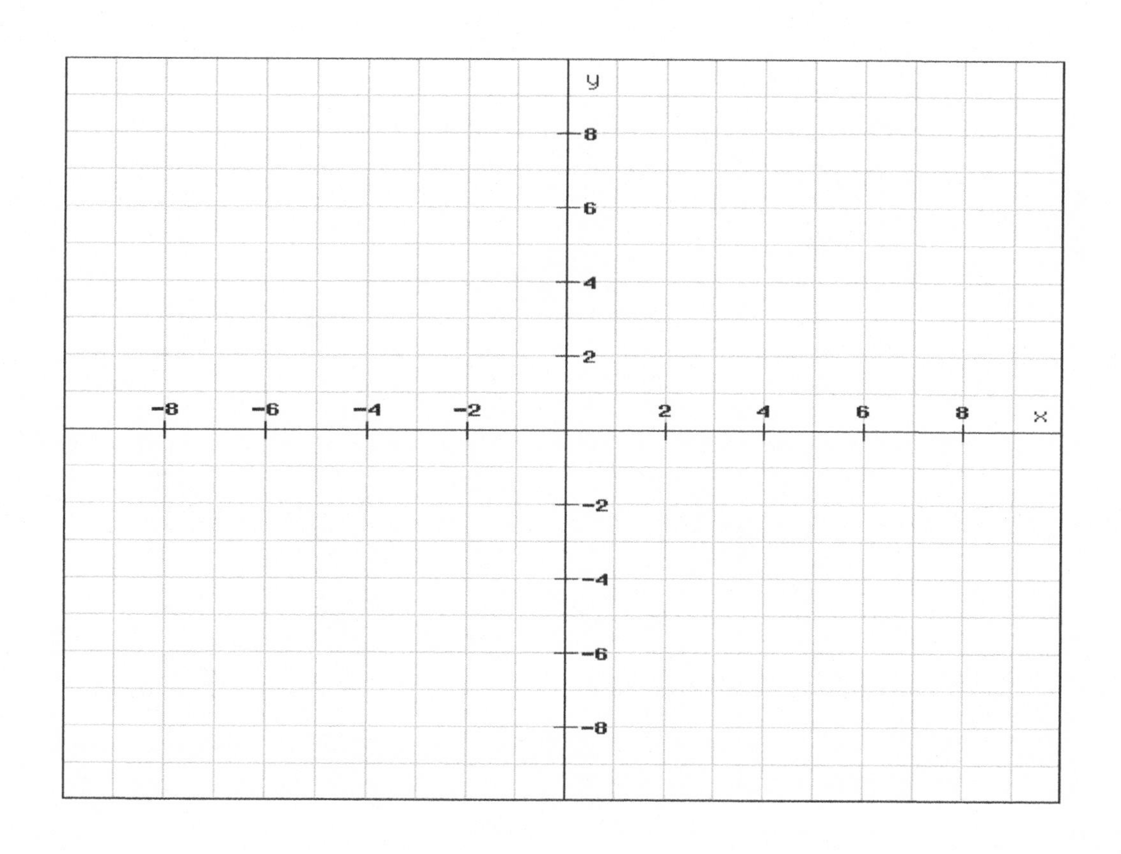

41. $f(x)=\frac{x}{x^2+2}, x\in\mathbb{R}$

Domain: ______________________

Extrema (using the 1st and if needed 2nd derivatives)

Vertical asymptotes: ______________

Horizontal asymptotes: ____________

Range of the function: _____________

Function Increases: _______________

Continuity: ____________________

Function decreases: _______________

Concave up: ____________________

y intercept: _____________________

Concave down: __________________

x intercept(s): ___________________

Inflection point(s)________________

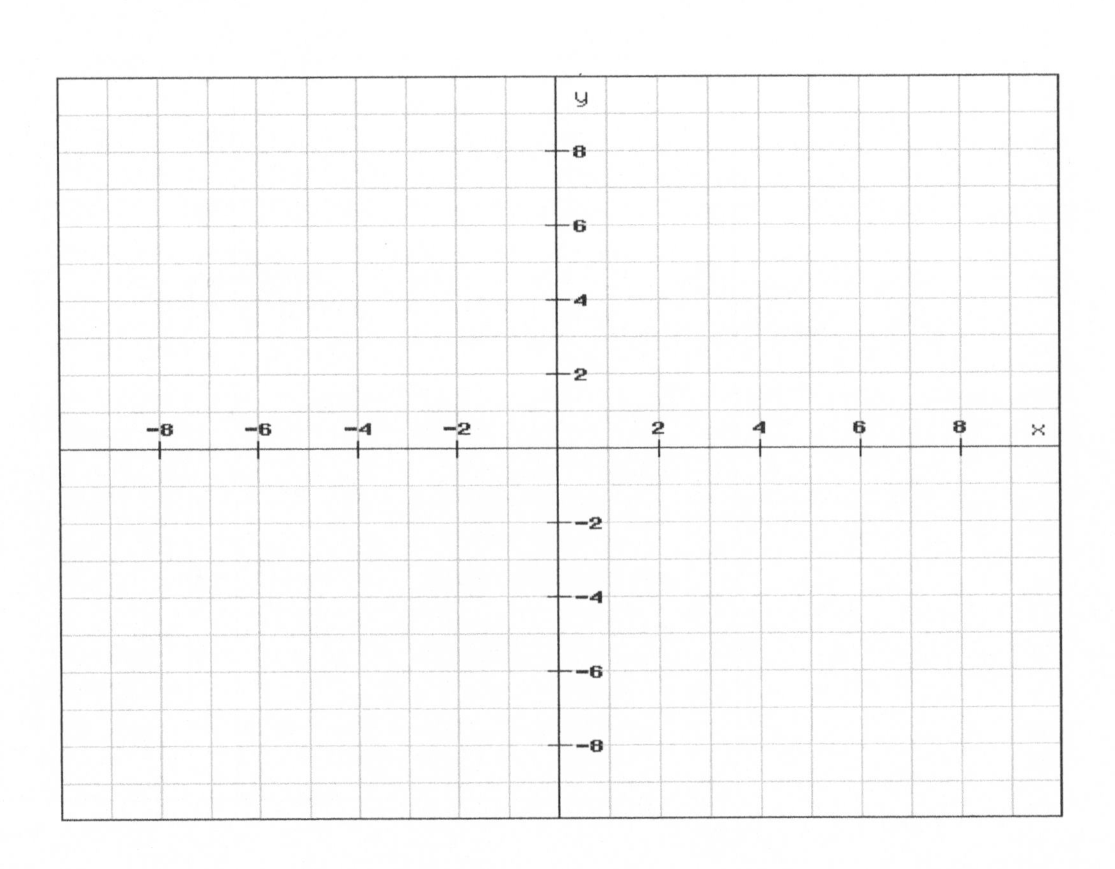

42. $f(x) = \dfrac{2}{(x-2)(x+3)}, x \in \square$

Domain: ____________________

Extrema (using the 1st and if needed 2nd derivatives)

Vertical asymptotes: ____________

Horizontal asymptotes: ____________

Range of the function: ____________

Continuity: ____________________

Function Increases: ____________

Function decreases: ____________

y intercept: ____________________

Concave up: ____________

Concave down: ____________

x intercept(s): ____________________

Inflection point(s)____________

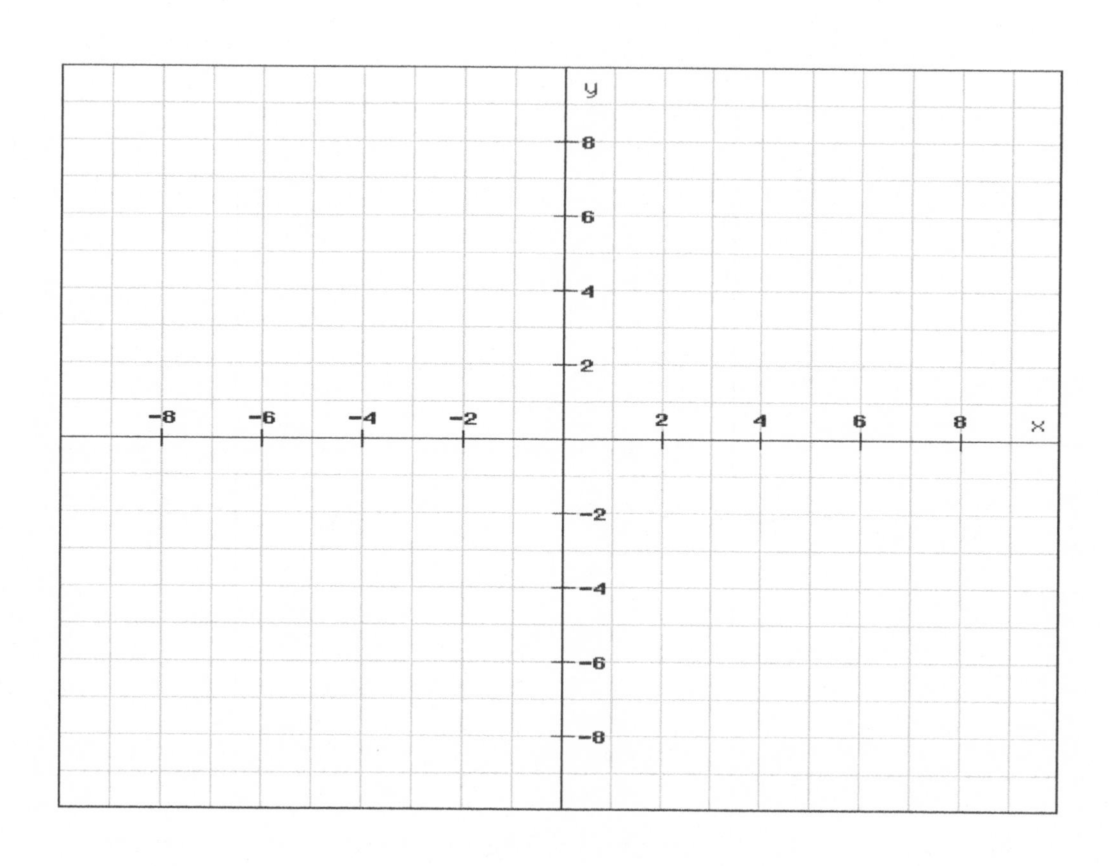

43. $f(x)=\dfrac{-3}{x^2-5x-6}, x\in \square$

Domain: ______________________

Extrema (using the 1st and if needed 2nd derivatives)

Vertical asymptotes: ______________

Horizontal asymptotes: ____________

Range of the function: _____________

Continuity: ____________________

Function Increases: _______________

Function decreases: _______________

y intercept: _____________________

Concave up: _____________________

Concave down: ___________________

x intercept(s): ___________________

Inflection point(s)_________________

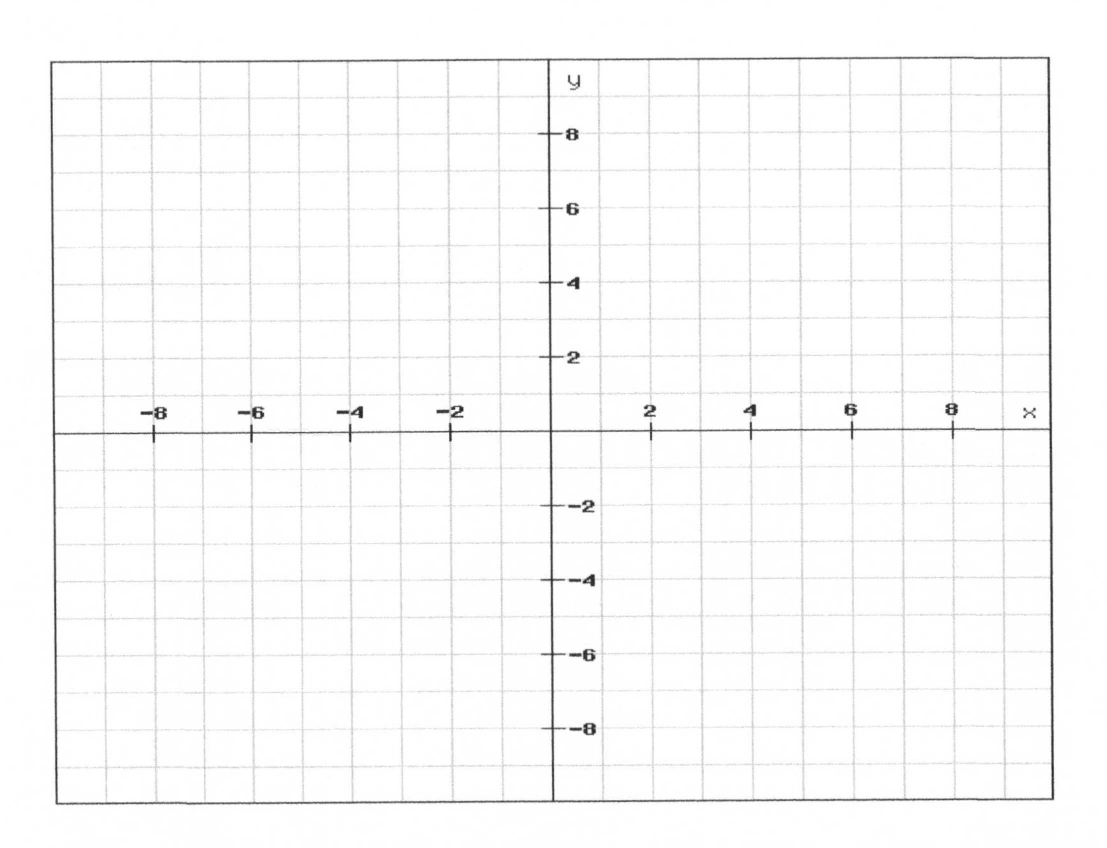

44. $f(x)=\dfrac{x^2}{x-1}, x \in \square$

Domain: ____________________________

Vertical asymptotes: _______________

Horizontal asymptotes: ______________

Slant Asymptotes: _______________

y intercept: ________________________

x intercept(s): ______________________

Extrema (using the 1st and if needed 2nd derivatives)

Range of the function: ______________

Function Increases: _______________

Function decreases: _______________

Concave up: ______________________

Concave down: ___________________

Inflection point(s)_________________

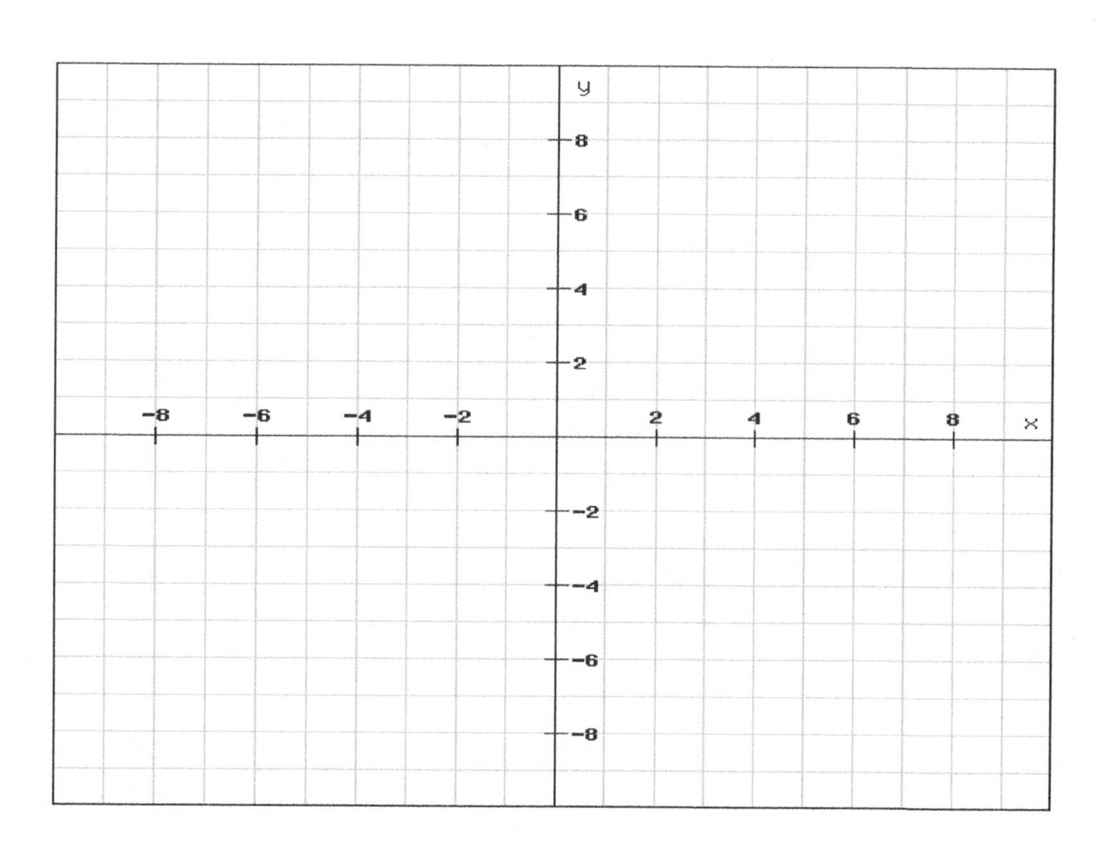

45. $f(x) = \dfrac{2x^2}{(x+3)(x-1)}, x \in \square$

Domain: ______________________

Vertical asymptotes: ______________

Horizontal asymptotes: ____________

Slant Asymptotes: ______________

y intercept: ______________________

x intercept(s): ___________________

Extrema (using the 1st and if needed 2nd derivatives)

Range of the function: ____________

Function Increases: _______________

Function decreases: _______________

Concave up: _____________________

Concave down: ___________________

Inflection point(s)_________________

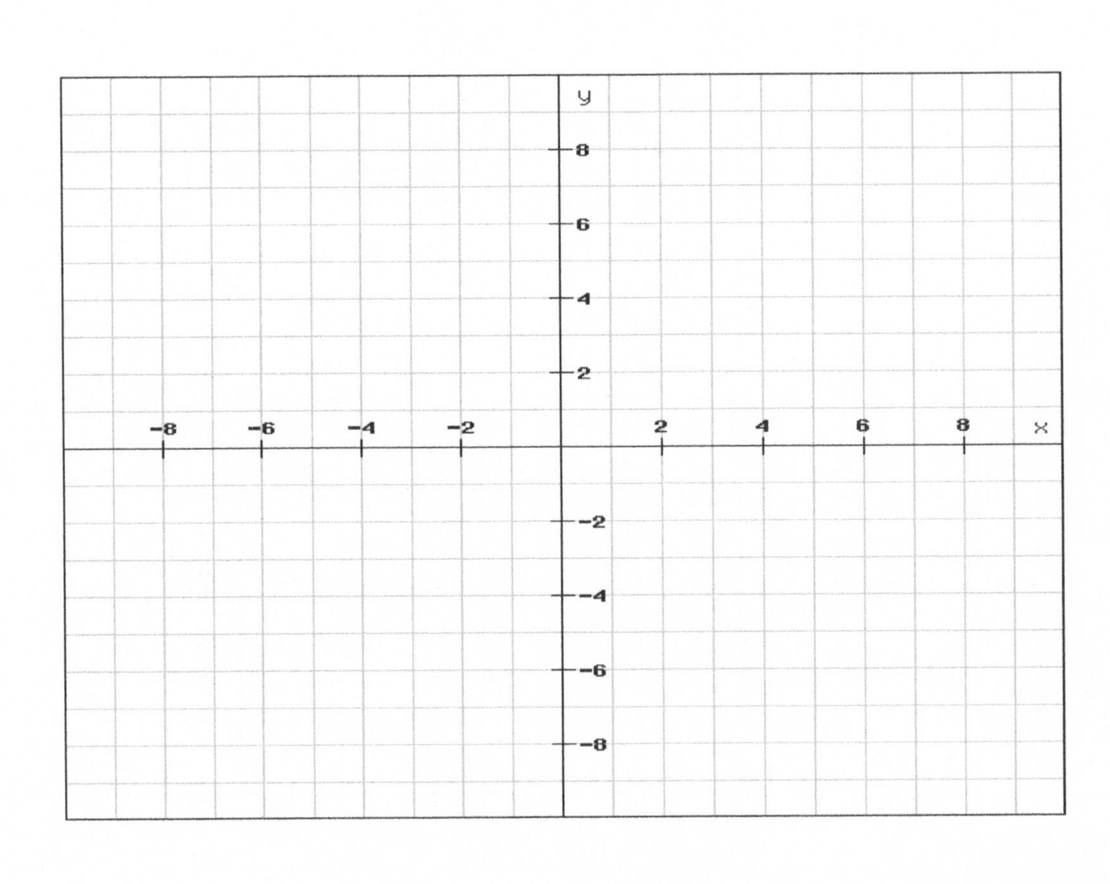

46. $f(x)=\dfrac{x^2+3}{x-1}, x\in \square$

Domain: ______________________________

Vertical asymptotes: __________________

Horizontal asymptotes: ______________

Slant Asymptotes: __________________

y intercept: ___________________________

x intercept(s): _________________________

Extrema (using the 1st and if needed 2nd derivatives)

Range of the function: ________________

Function Increases: ___________________

Function decreases: ___________________

Concave up: __________________________

Concave down: ________________________

Inflection point(s)______________________

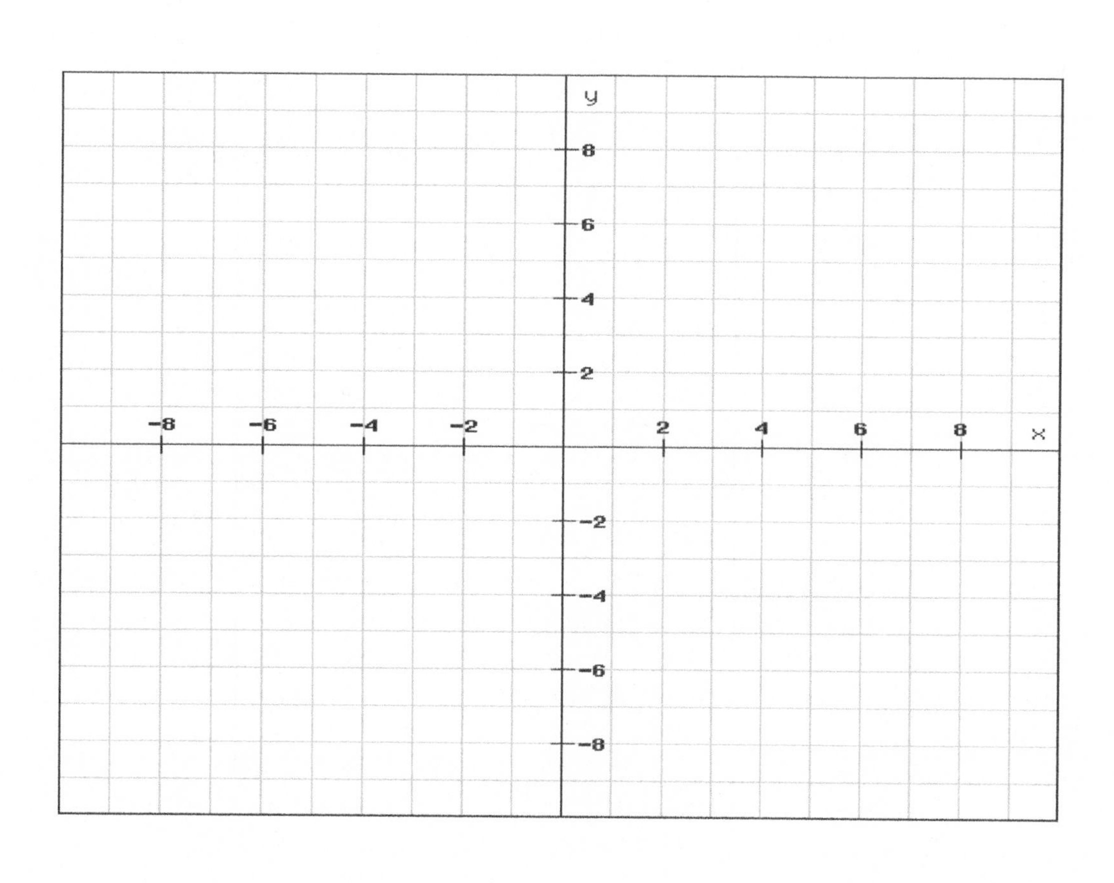

47. $f(x) = \frac{-1}{x^2 - x}, x \in \square$

Domain: ______________________

Extrema (using the 1st and if needed 2nd derivatives)

Vertical asymptotes: ____________

Horizontal asymptotes: ___________

Range of the function: ___________

Slant Asymptotes: ____________

Function Increases: ____________

Function decreases: ____________

y intercept: ____________________

Concave up: ____________________

Concave down: _________________

x intercept(s): __________________

Inflection point(s)_______________

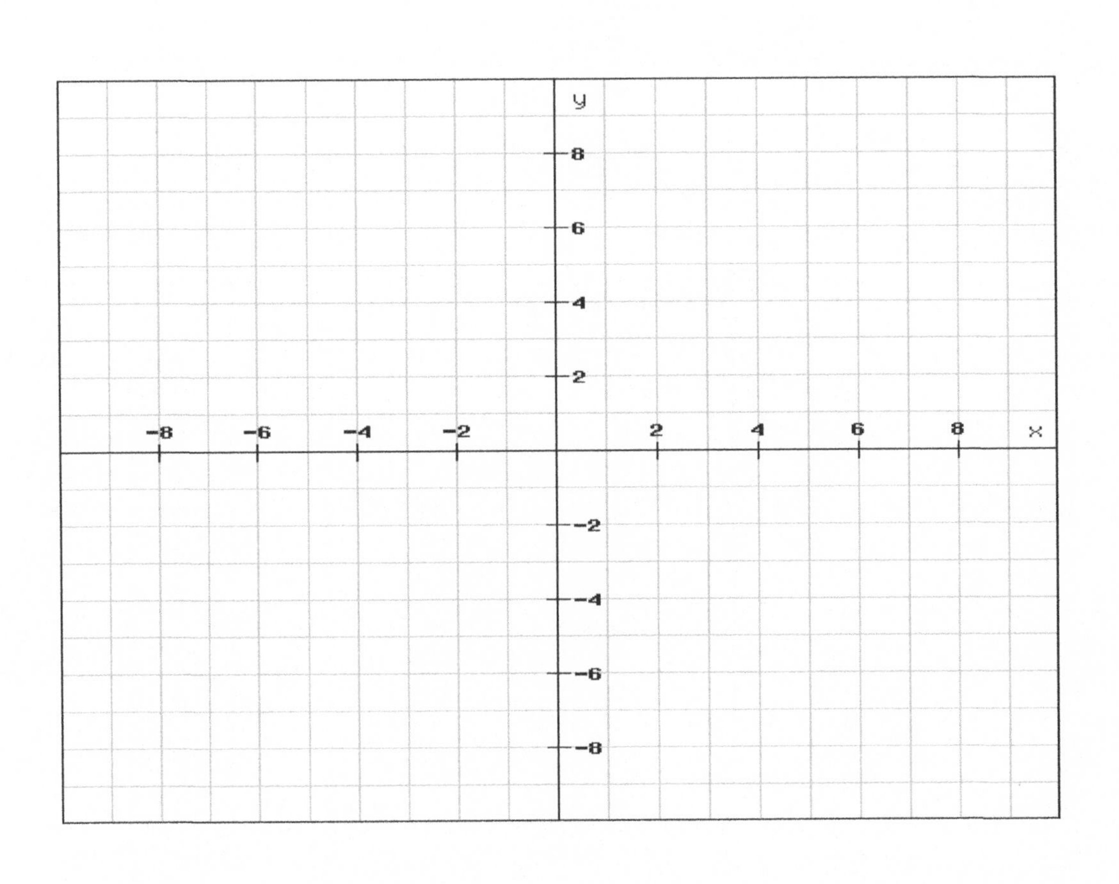

48. $f(x)=\dfrac{3x+1}{x^2-x}, x \in \square$

Domain: ______________________

Vertical asymptotes: ____________

Horizontal asymptotes: __________

Slant Asymptotes: ____________

y intercept: ____________________

x intercept(s): __________________

Extrema (using the 1st and if needed 2nd derivatives)

Range of the function: __________

Function Increases: ____________

Function decreases: ____________

Concave up: ________________

Concave down: ______________

Inflection point(s)______________

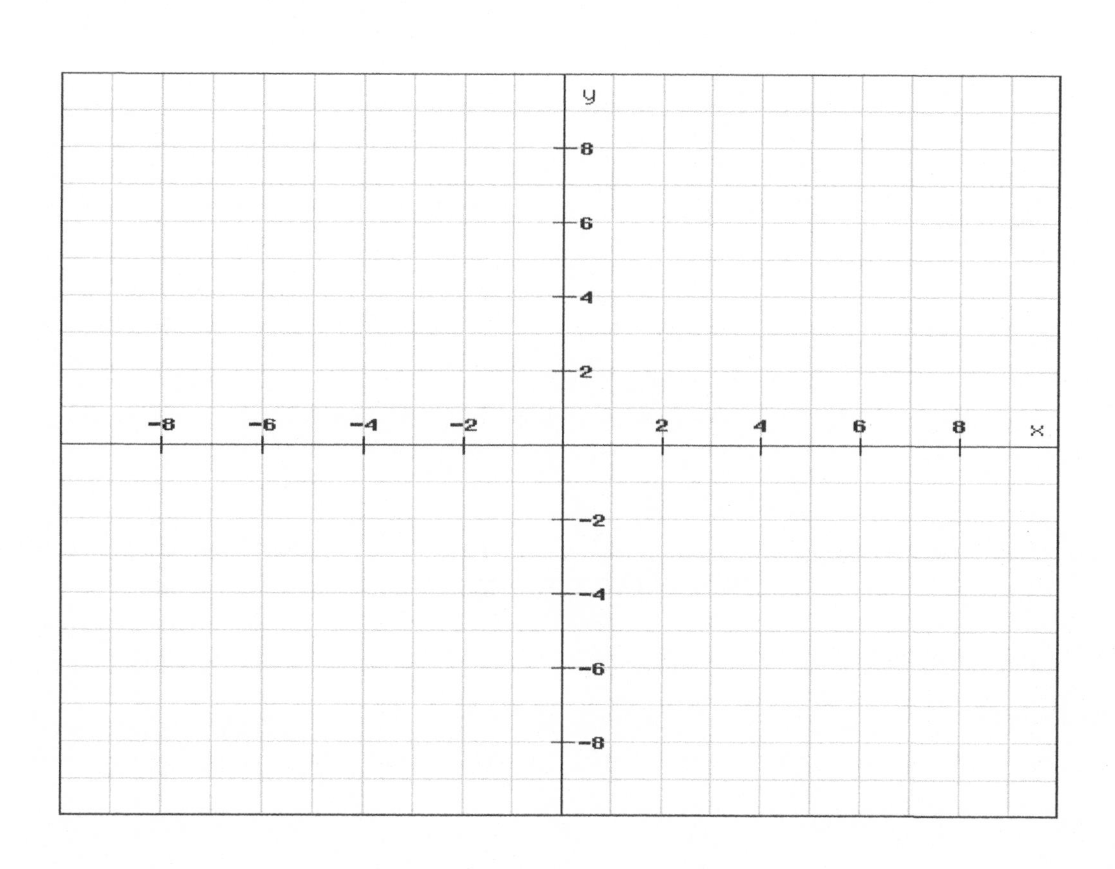

49. Sketch the following function $f(x) = 2x + 3$, on the 2nd graph, sketch the following: $f(x) = \dfrac{(2x+3)(x+1)}{(x+1)}$

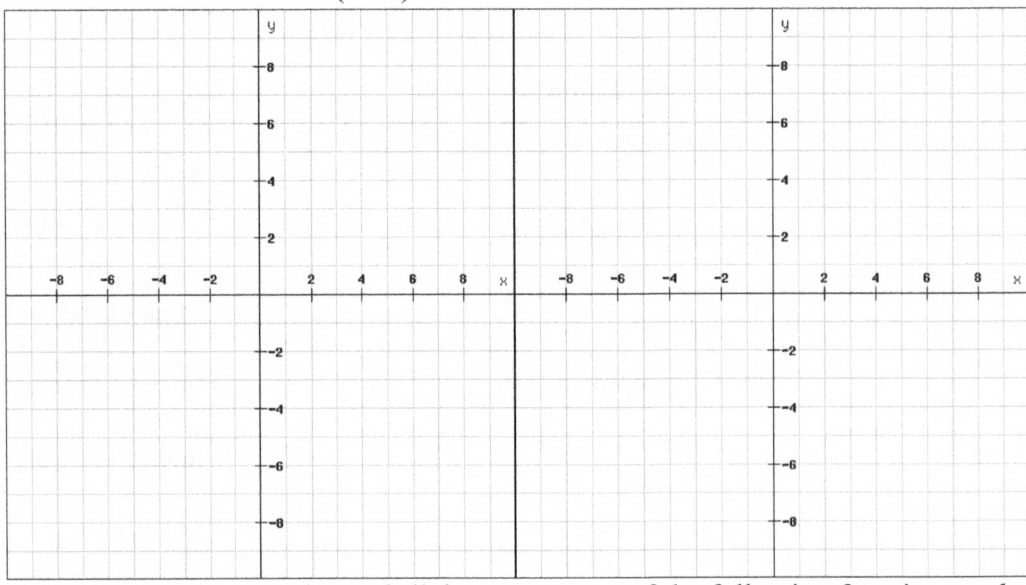

50. Determine the equations of all the asymptotes of the following functions and discuss their continuity:

a. $f(x) = \dfrac{2x^3 + 3x + 1}{x^3 - x}$

b. $f(x) = \dfrac{x^3 - x^2}{x^2 - 3x + 2}$

c. $f(x) = \dfrac{5x^3 + 3x^2 + 1}{x^2 - 2}$

d. $f(x) = \dfrac{x - 2x^2}{3x^2 - 9x + 6}$

51. Vertical asymptotes are of the form ____________. Their origin is a function in which a certain value of _____ makes the denominator of the function ____ and the numerator __________________.

52. Horizontal asymptotes are of the form ______________. Their meaning is significant for _______________and______________ of x. Sometimes a function can have a certain horizontal asymptote for ____________________ and a different horizontal asymptote for _________________________. In a rational function which is of the form ________________, when __________ the function will have a horizontal asymptote of the form ____________.

53. Slant (or oblique) asymptotes are of the form ______________. Their meaning is significant for _______________and______________ of x. Sometimes a function can have a certain horizontal asymptote for ____________________ and a different horizontal asymptote for _________________________. In a rational function which is of the form ________________, when __________ the function will have a slant asymptote.

54. (T/F) All functions must have at least one vertical asymptote.

55. (T/F) All functions must have at least one horizontal asymptote.

56. (T/F) All functions must have at least one slant asymptote.

57. (T/F) A function that has two vertical asymptotes cannot have a slant asymptote.

58. (T/F) A function that has two slant asymptotes cannot have a horizontal asymptote.

D. GENERAL FUNCTIONS

59. $f(x) = e^x - x, x \in □$

Domain: ______________________

Vertical asymptotes: ______________

Horizontal asymptotes: ____________

Slant Asymptotes: ______________

y intercept: ____________________

x intercept(s): __________________

Extrema (using the 1st and if needed 2nd derivatives)

Range of the function: ____________

Function Increases: ______________

Function decreases: ______________

Concave up: ____________________

Concave down: _________________

Inflection point(s)________________

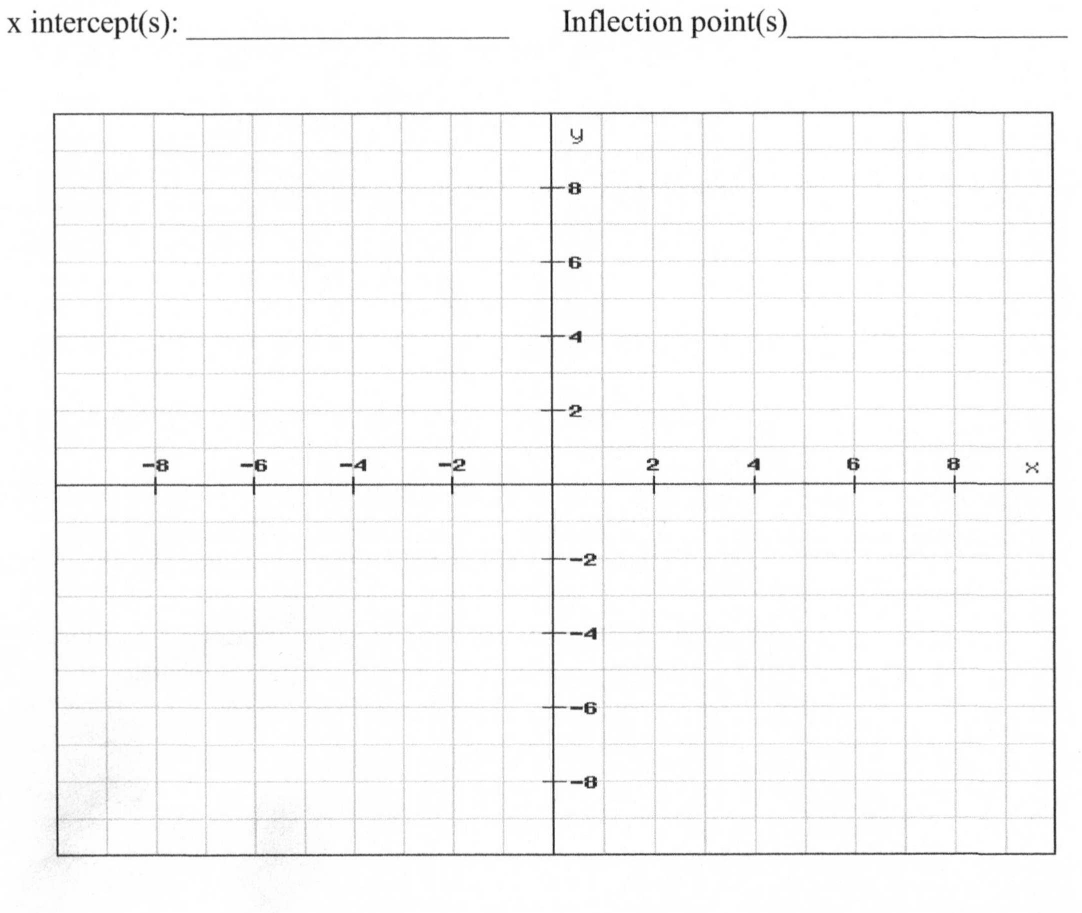

60. $f(x) = e^x + x, x \in$ □

Domain: ______________________

Extrema (using the 1st and if needed 2nd derivatives)

Vertical asymptotes: ______________

Horizontal asymptotes: ____________

Range of the function: ____________

Slant Asymptotes: ______________

Function Increases: ______________

Function decreases: ______________

y intercept: ______________________

Concave up: ______________________

Concave down: ________________

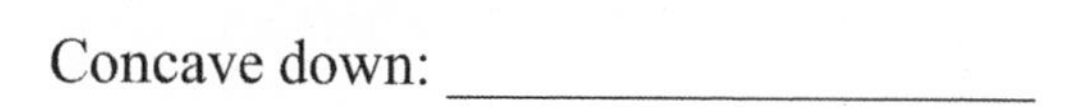

x intercept(s): ____________________

Inflection point(s)________________

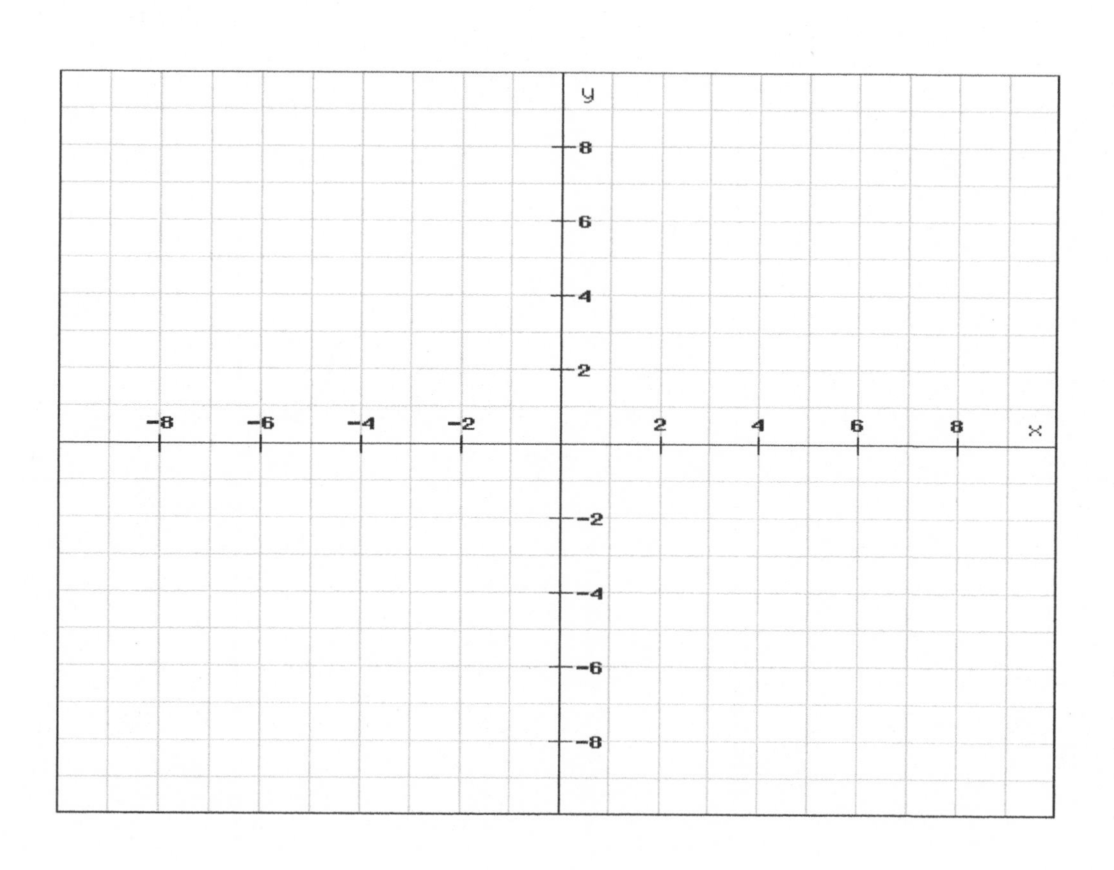

61. $f(x) = \dfrac{2}{1+e^x}$

Domain: ______________________

Extrema (using the 1st and if needed 2nd derivatives)

Vertical asymptotes: ____________

Horizontal asymptotes: ___________

Range of the function: ___________

Slant Asymptotes: ____________

Function Increases: ____________

Function decreases: ____________

y intercept: ____________________

Concave up: ____________________

Concave down: ________________

x intercept(s): __________________

Inflection point(s)______________

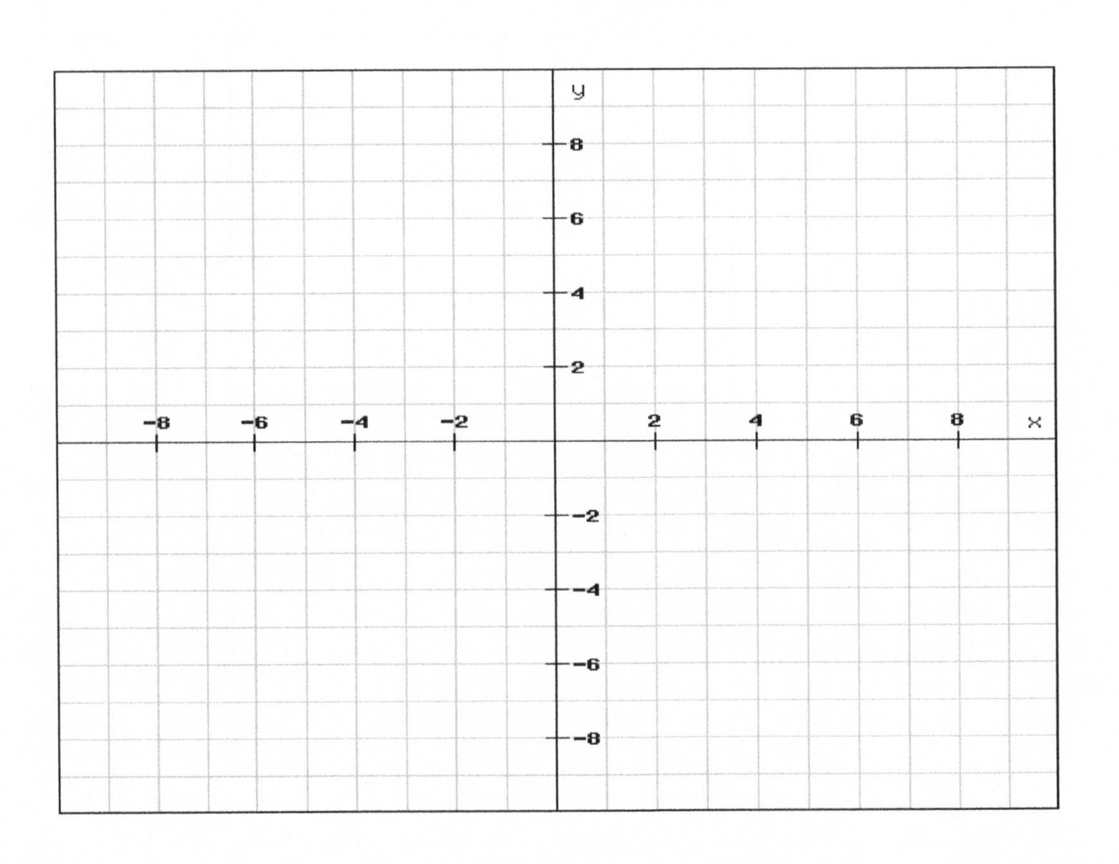

62. $f(x) = \dfrac{2}{2 - e^x}$

Domain: ___________________________

Vertical asymptotes: ______________

Horizontal asymptotes: ____________

Slant Asymptotes: ______________

y intercept: _______________________

x intercept(s): ____________________

Extrema (using the 1st and if needed 2nd derivatives)

Range of the function: ____________

Function Increases: ______________

Function decreases: ______________

Concave up: ____________________

Concave down: _________________

Inflection point(s)________________

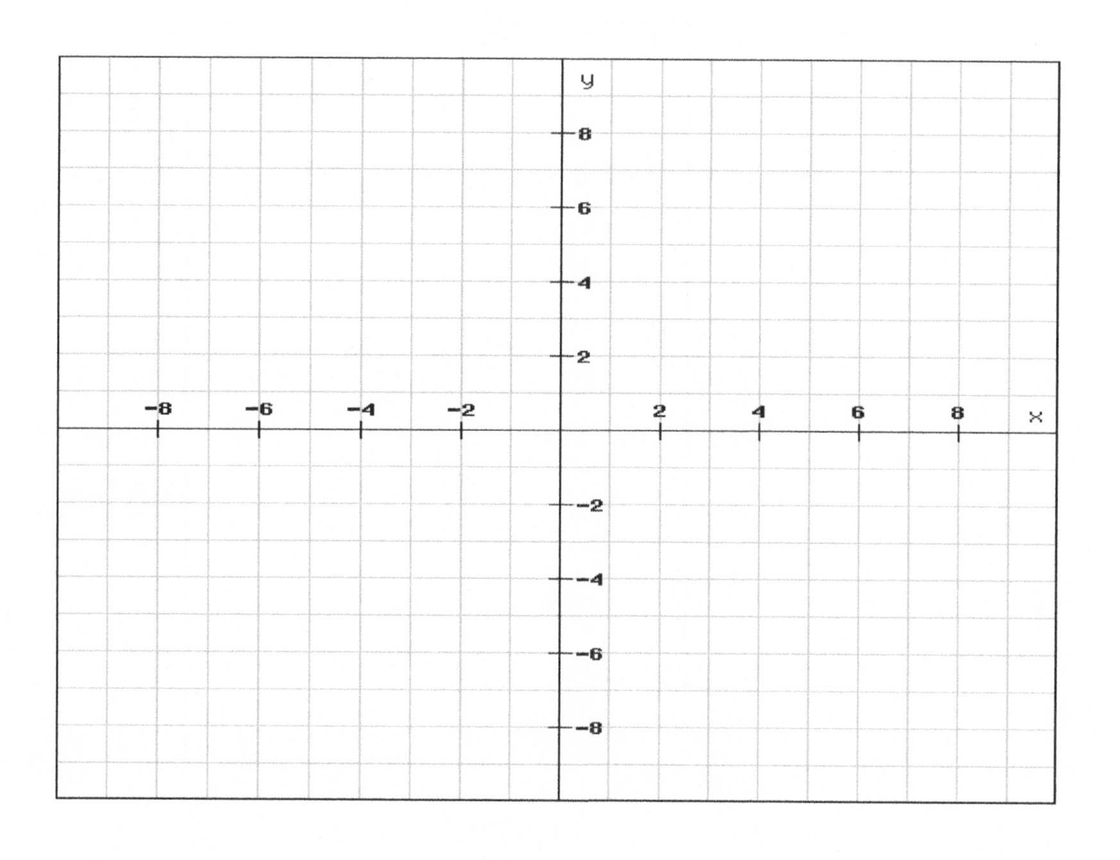

63. $f(x) = x\ln(x), x \in \square$

Domain: ______________________

Vertical asymptotes: ______________

Horizontal asymptotes: ____________

Slant Asymptotes: ______________

y intercept: ____________________

x intercept(s): __________________

Extrema (using the 1st and if needed 2nd derivatives)

Range of the function: ____________

Function Increases: ______________

Function decreases: ______________

Concave up: ____________________

Concave down: _________________

Inflection point(s)________________

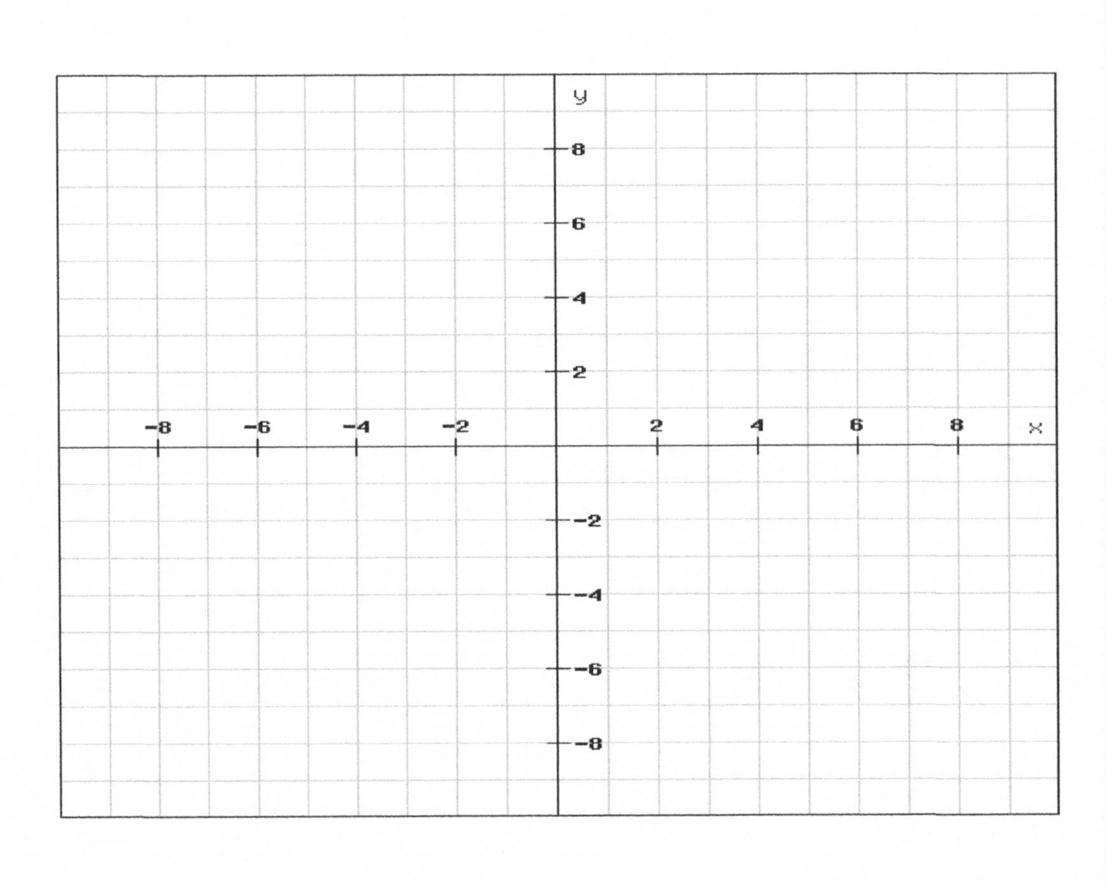

64. $f(x) = x\ln(x^2), x \in \square$

Domain: ______________________

Vertical asymptotes: _____________

Horizontal asymptotes: ___________

Slant Asymptotes: _____________

y intercept: ____________________

x intercept(s): __________________

Extrema (using the 1st and if needed 2nd derivatives)

Range of the function: ____________

Function Increases: ______________

Function decreases: ______________

Concave up: ___________________

Concave down: ________________

Inflection point(s)_______________

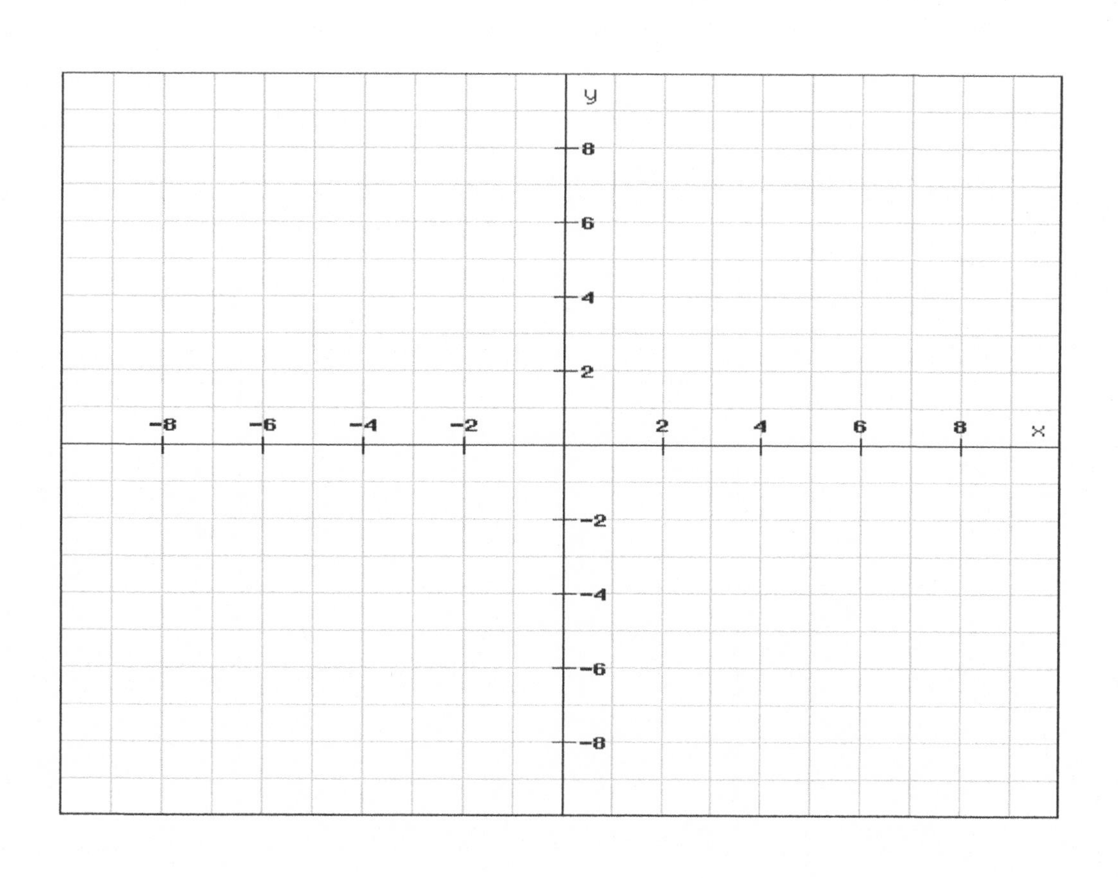

65. $f(x) = x^2 \ln(x), x \in$ □

Domain: ______________________

Extrema (using the 1st and if needed 2nd derivatives)

Vertical asymptotes: ______________

Horizontal asymptotes: ____________

Range of the function: ____________

Slant Asymptotes: ____________

Function Increases: ______________

Function decreases: ______________

y intercept: ____________________

Concave up: ____________________

Concave down: __________________

x intercept(s): ___________________

Inflection point(s)________________

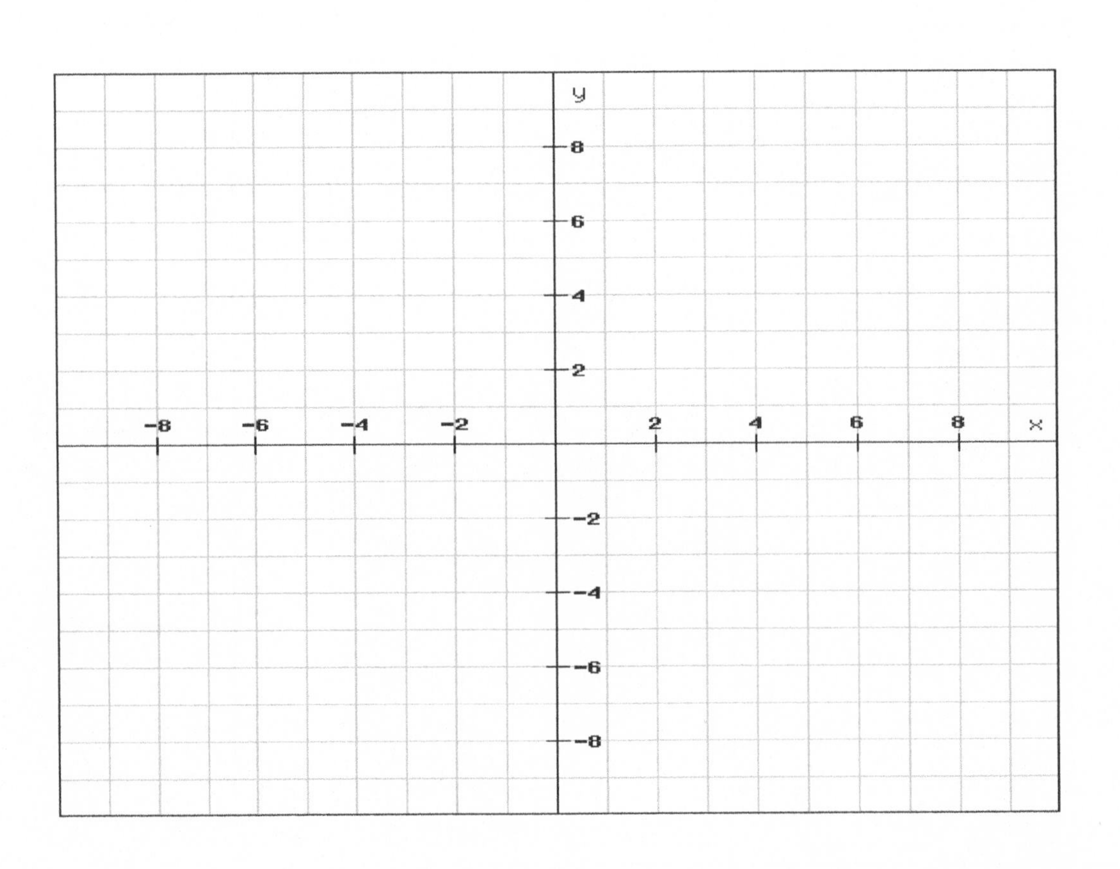

66. $f(x) = x(\ln(x))^2, x \in$ □

Domain: ______________________

Vertical asymptotes: ____________

Horizontal asymptotes: ____________

Slant Asymptotes: ____________

y intercept: ______________________

x intercept(s): ____________________

Extrema (using the 1st and if needed 2nd derivatives)

Range of the function: ____________

Function Increases: ______________

Function decreases: ______________

Concave up: ____________________

Concave down: __________________

Inflection point(s)________________

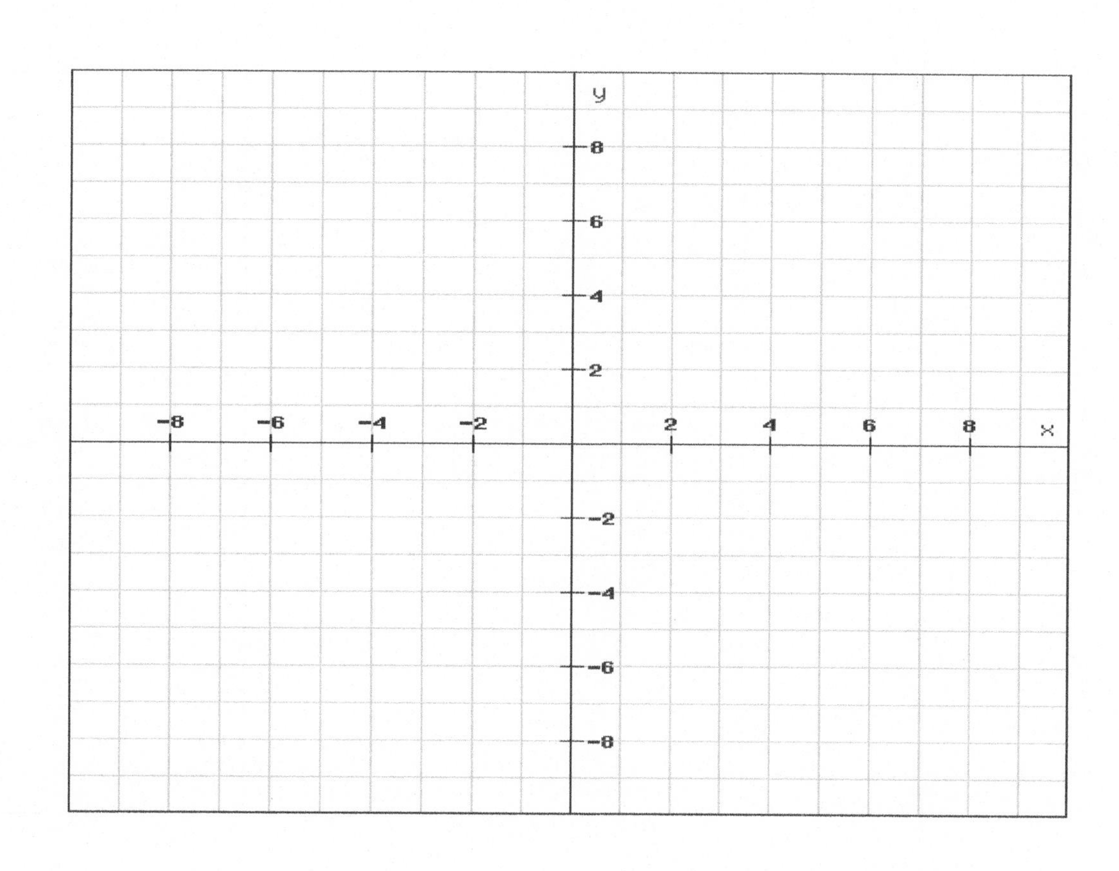

67. $f(x) = \dfrac{\ln(x)}{x}, x \in$ □

Domain: ______________________

Extrema (using the 1st and if needed 2nd derivatives)

Vertical asymptotes: ______________

Horizontal asymptotes: ____________

Range of the function: ____________

Slant Asymptotes: ______________

Function Increases: ______________

Function decreases: ______________

y intercept: ______________________

Concave up: ____________________

Concave down: _________________

x intercept(s): ___________________

Inflection point(s)_______________

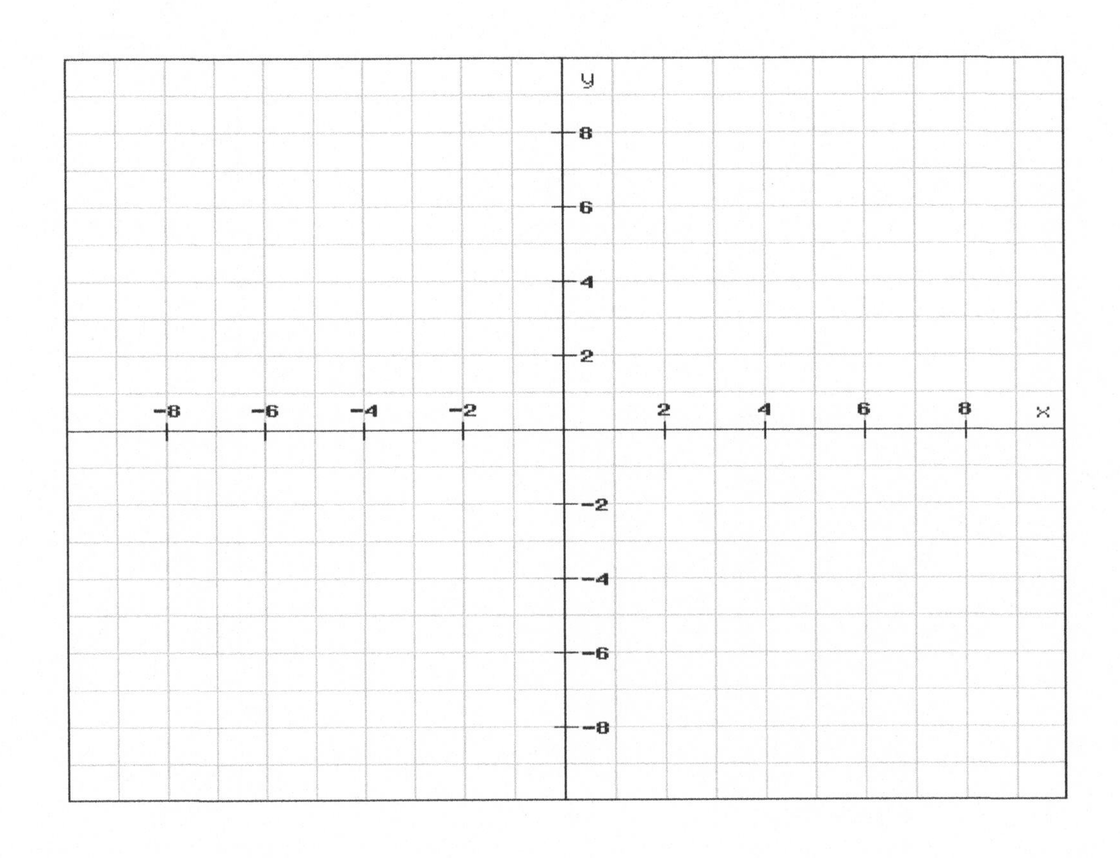

68. $f(x) = \sqrt{x} - x, x \in \square$

Domain: ______________________________

Vertical asymptotes: ________________

Horizontal asymptotes: ______________

Slant Asymptotes: ________________

y intercept: __________________________

x intercept(s): _______________________

Extrema (using the 1st and if needed 2nd derivatives)

Range of the function: ______________

Function Increases: _________________

Function decreases: _________________

Concave up: _________________________

Concave down: ______________________

Inflection point(s)____________________

69. $f(x) = x^2 - \dfrac{1}{x}, x \in \square$

Domain: ____________________________

Extrema (using the 1st and if needed 2nd derivatives)

Vertical asymptotes: ________________

Horizontal asymptotes: ______________

Range of the function: ______________

Slant Asymptotes: ________________

Function Increases: ______________

Function decreases: ______________

y intercept: ________________________

Concave up: ________________________

Concave down: ____________________

x intercept(s): ______________________

Inflection point(s)____________________

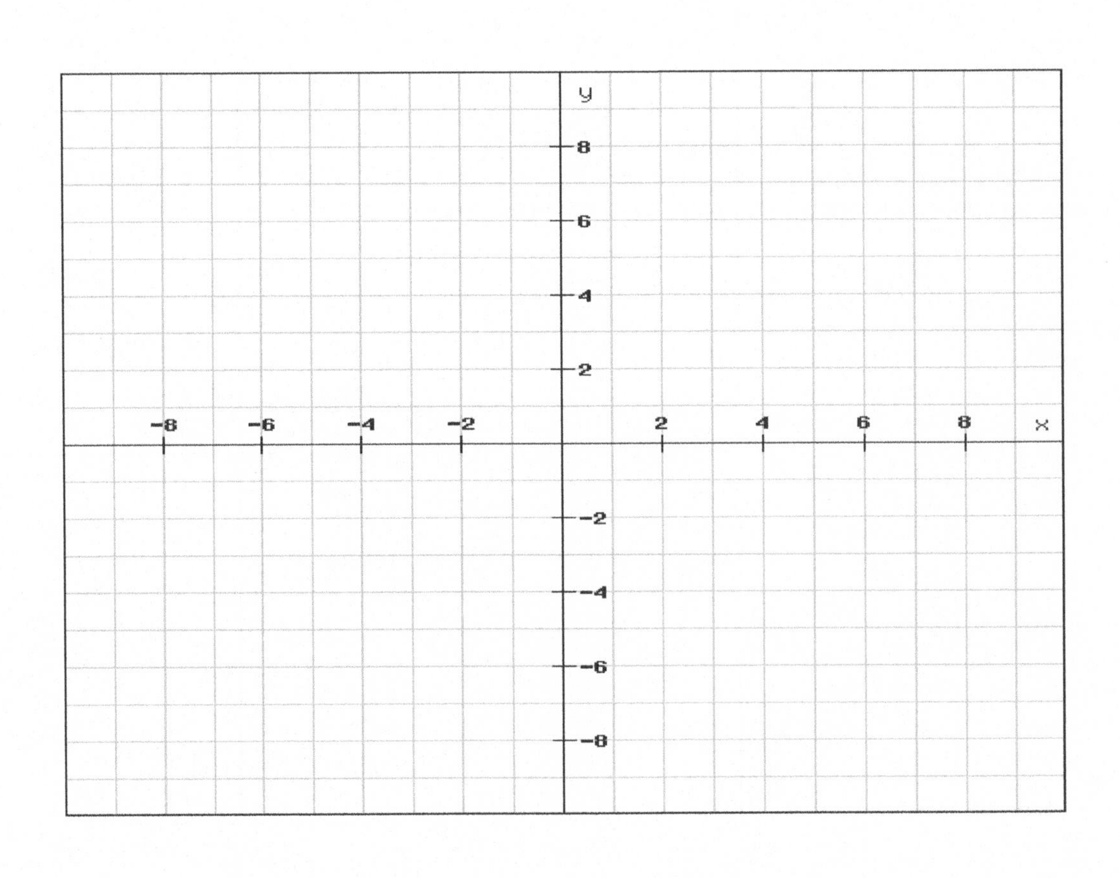

70. $f(x) = x^2 + \frac{2}{x}, x \in \mathbb{R}$

Domain: ___________________________

Extrema (using the 1st and if needed 2nd derivatives)

Vertical asymptotes: ______________

Horizontal asymptotes: ____________

Range of the function: ____________

Slant Asymptotes: ______________

Function Increases: ______________

Function decreases: ______________

y intercept: ______________________

Concave up: ______________________

Concave down: ___________________

x intercept(s): ___________________

Inflection point(s)________________

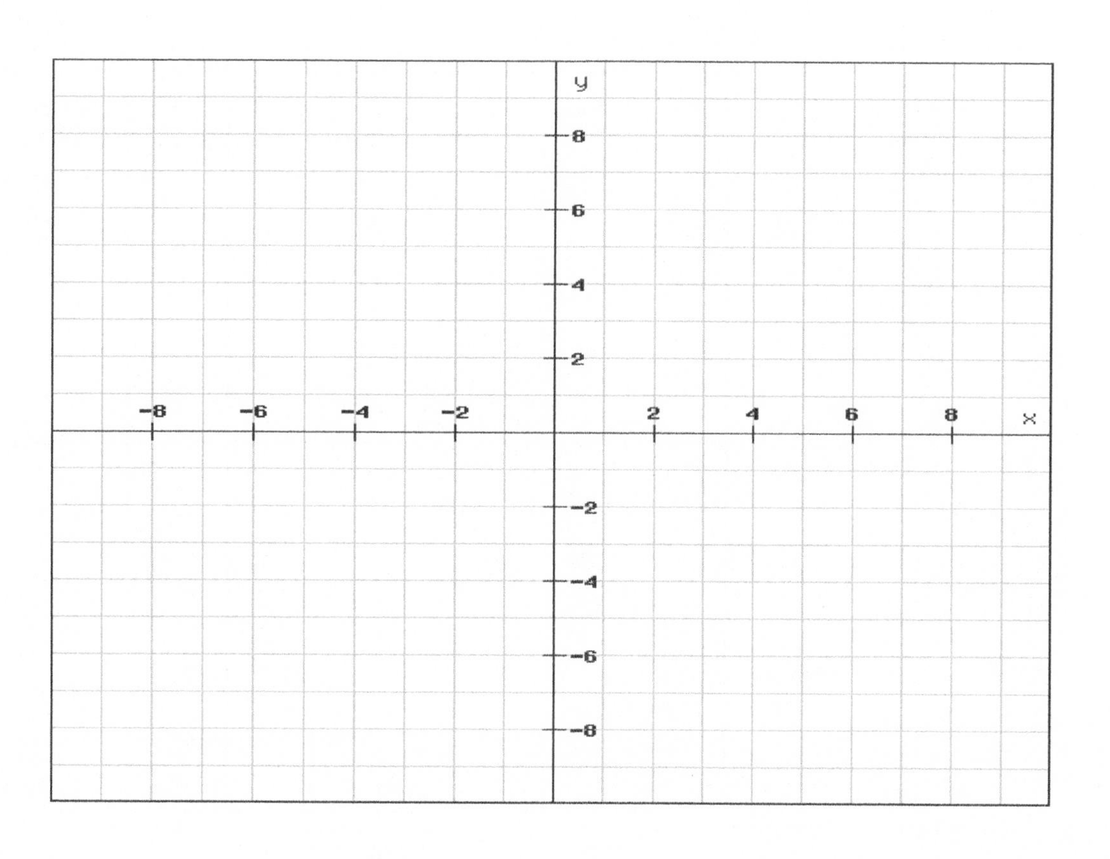

71. $f(x) = \sin(x^2), x \in$ □

Domain: ______________________

Extrema (using the 1st and if needed 2nd derivatives)

Vertical asymptotes: ______________

Horizontal asymptotes: ____________

Range of the function: ____________

Slant Asymptotes: ______________

Function Increases: ______________

Function decreases: ______________

y intercept: ______________________

Concave up: ______________________

Concave down: ___________________

x intercept(s): ___________________

Inflection point(s)________________

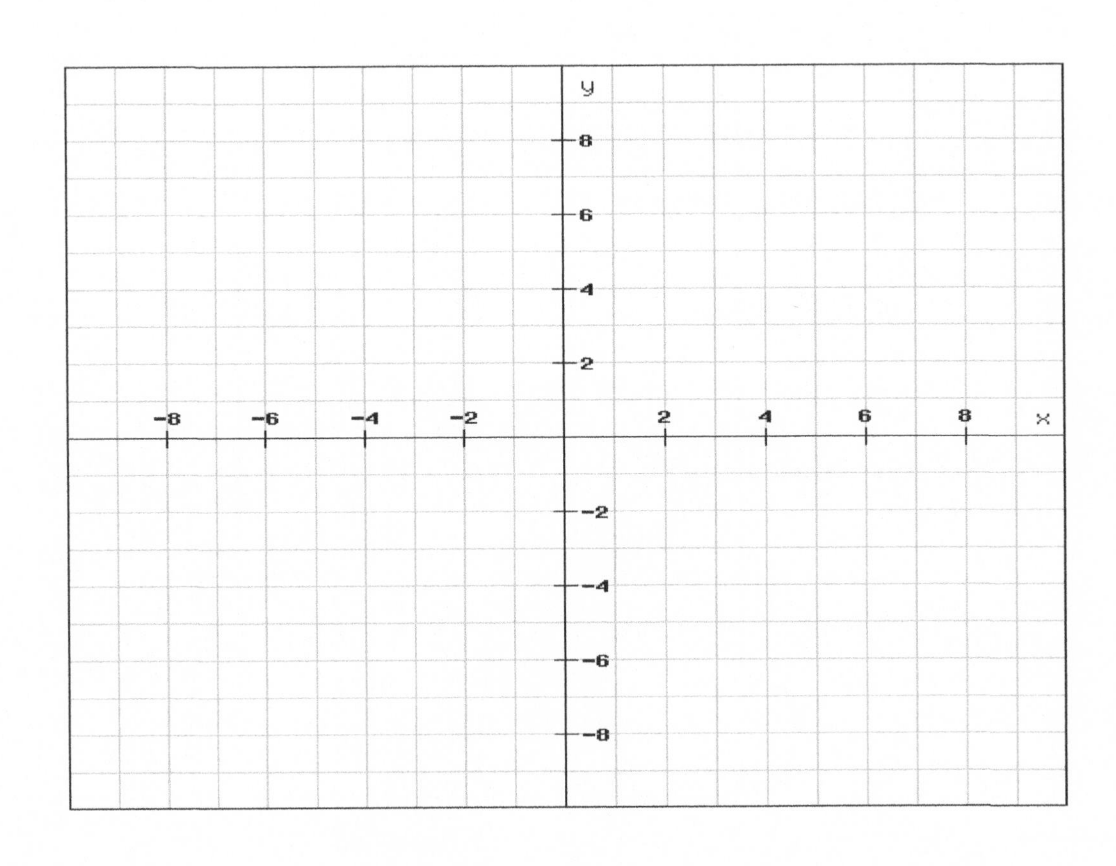

72. $f(x) = \sin(x) + x, x \in$ □

Domain: ________________________

Extrema (using the 1st and if needed 2nd derivatives)

Vertical asymptotes: ______________

Horizontal asymptotes: ____________

Range of the function: ____________

Slant Asymptotes: ______________

Function Increases: ______________

Function decreases: ______________

y intercept: ______________________

Concave up: ____________________

Concave down: _________________

x intercept(s): ____________________

Inflection point(s)_______________

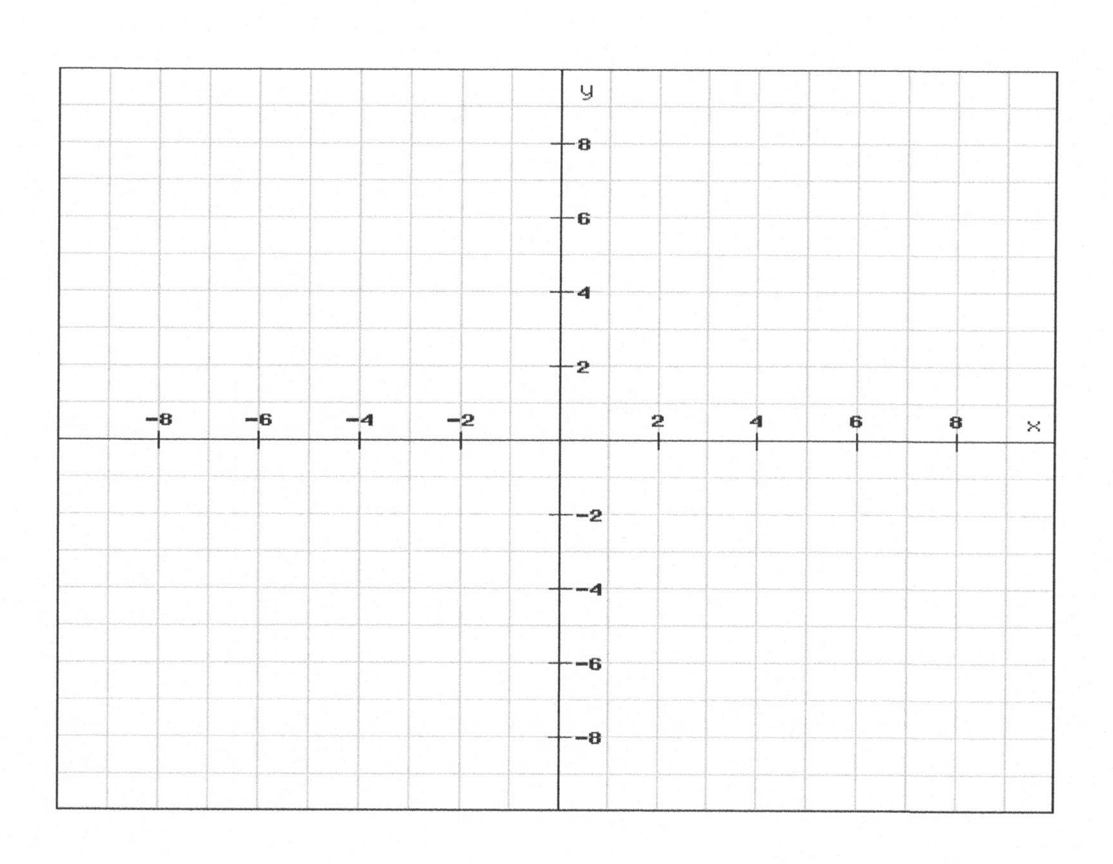

73. $f(x) = x(1 - \ln(x^2)), x \in \square$

Domain: ___________________________

Vertical asymptotes: ________________

Horizontal asymptotes: ______________

Slant Asymptotes: ________________

y intercept: ________________________

x intercept(s): ______________________

Extrema (using the 1st and if needed 2nd derivatives)

Range of the function: _______________

Function Increases: _________________

Function decreases: _________________

Concave up: ________________________

Concave down: _____________________

Inflection point(s)___________________

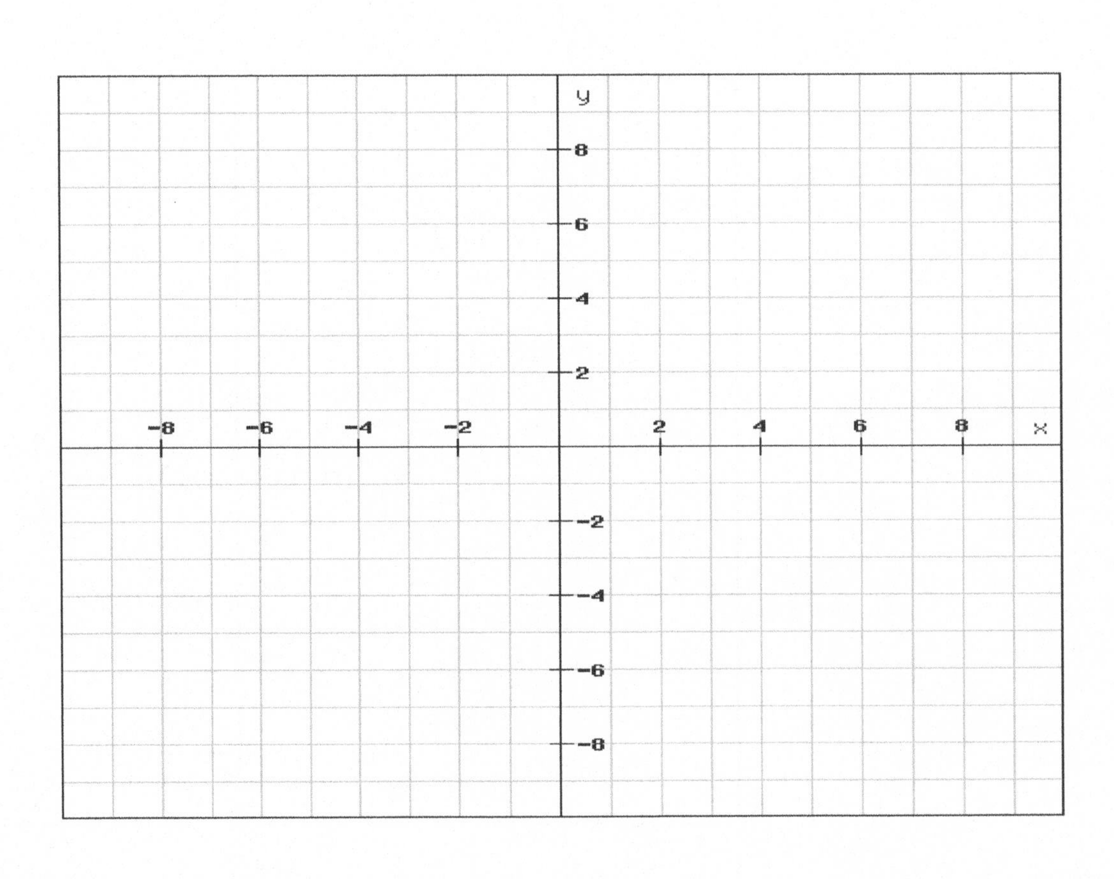

74. $f(x)=e^{x-x^2}, x \in$ □

Domain: ______________________

Extrema (using the 1st and if needed 2nd derivatives)

Vertical asymptotes: ____________

Horizontal asymptotes: ___________

Slant Asymptotes: ____________

y intercept: ____________________

x intercept(s): __________________

Range of the function: ___________

Function Increases: ______________

Function decreases: ______________

Concave up: ____________________

Concave down: __________________

Inflection point(s)________________

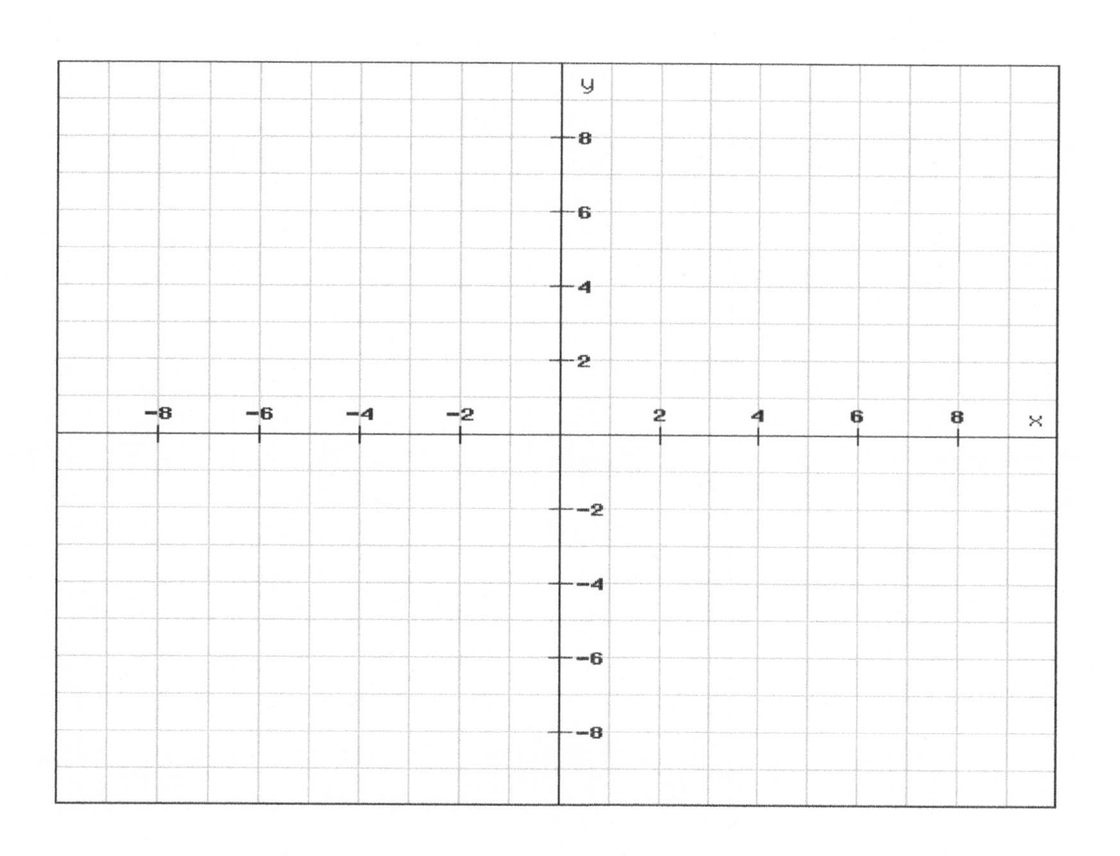

75. $f(x) = x^3(1 - \ln(x^2)), x \in \square$

Domain: ___________________________

Vertical asymptotes: ________________

Horizontal asymptotes: ______________

Slant Asymptotes: ________________

y intercept: _________________________

x intercept(s): ______________________

Extrema (using the 1st and if needed 2nd derivatives)

Range of the function: _______________

Function Increases: _________________

Function decreases: _________________

Concave up: _______________________

Concave down: ____________________

Inflection point(s)___________________

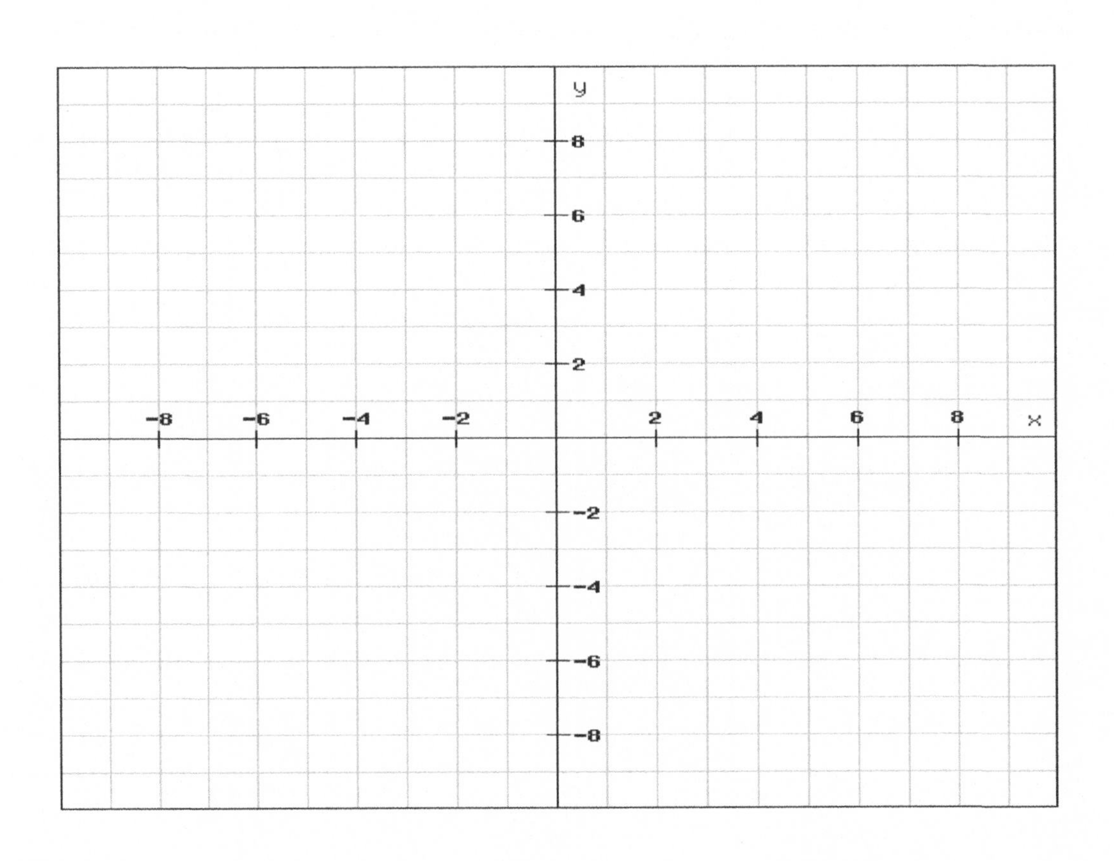

76. $f(x)=e^{x^3-x^2}, x\in\mathbb{R}$

Domain: ______________________

Extrema (using the 1st and if needed 2nd derivatives)

Vertical asymptotes: ______________

Horizontal asymptotes: ____________

Range of the function: ____________

Slant Asymptotes: ______________

Function Increases: ______________

Function decreases: ______________

y intercept: ____________________

Concave up: ____________________

Concave down: __________________

x intercept(s): __________________

Inflection point(s)________________

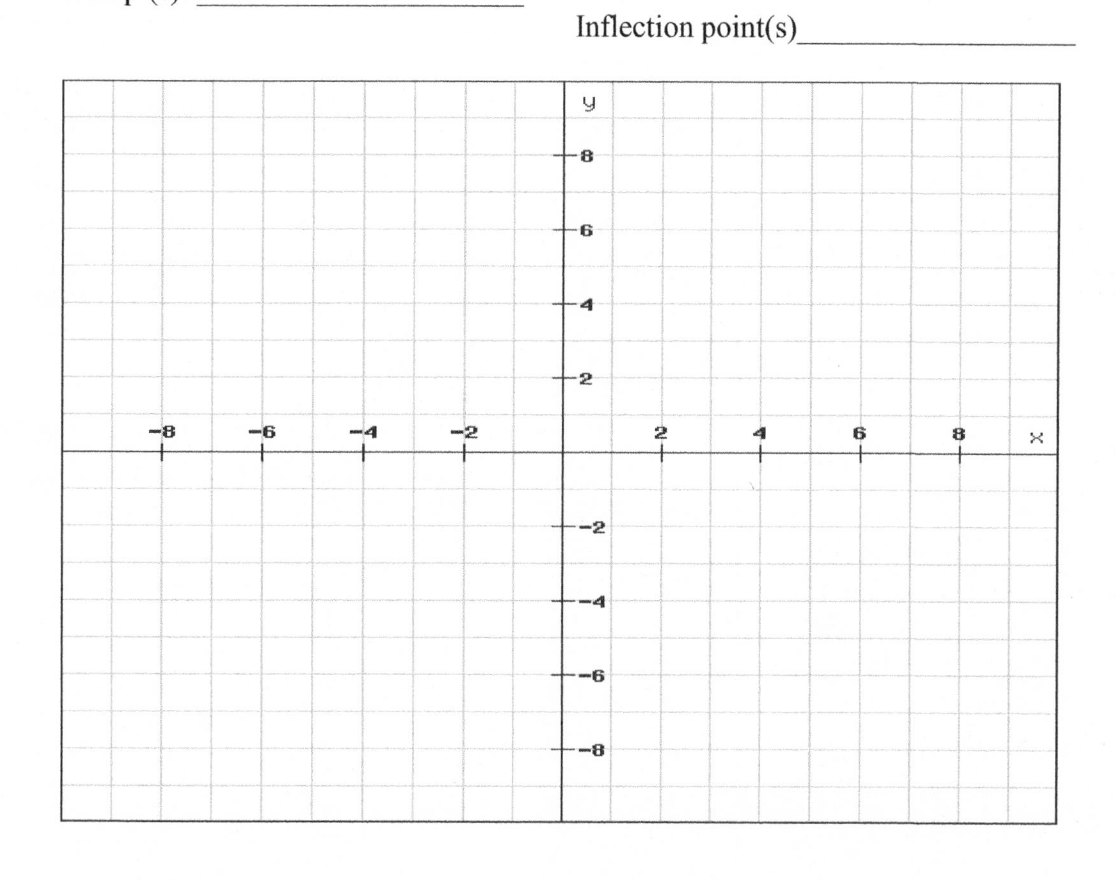

77. $f(x) = \ln(x^2 - 1), x \in \mathbb{R}$

Domain: ______________________

Extrema (using the 1st and if needed 2nd derivatives)

Vertical asymptotes: ______________

Horizontal asymptotes: ____________

Range of the function: ____________

Slant Asymptotes: ______________

Function Increases: ______________

Function decreases: ______________

y intercept: ______________________

Concave up: ______________________

Concave down: __________________

x intercept(s): ___________________

Inflection point(s)________________

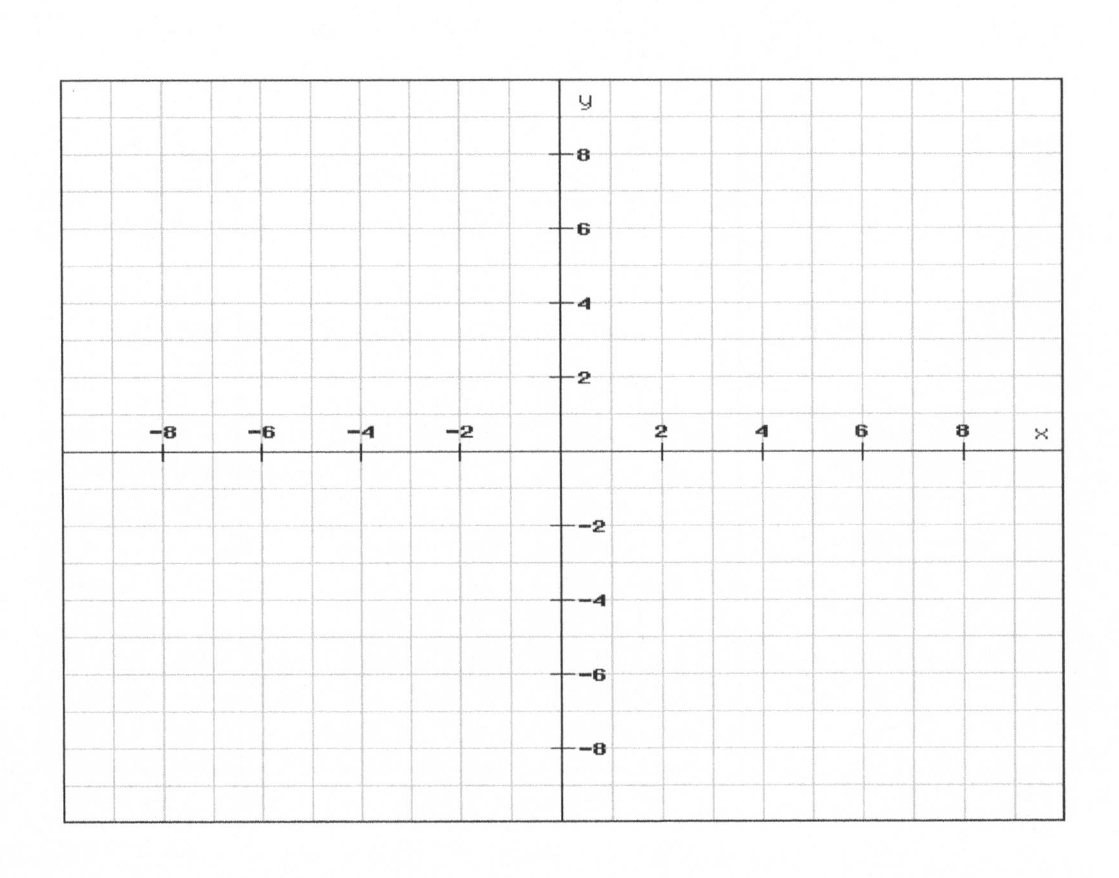

78. $f(x) = \ln(4 - x^2), x \in \mathbb{R}$

Domain: ____________________

Vertical asymptotes: ____________

Horizontal asymptotes: ____________

Slant Asymptotes: ____________

y intercept: ____________________

x intercept(s): __________________

Extrema (using the 1st and if needed 2nd derivatives)

Range of the function: ____________

Function Increases: ______________

Function decreases: ______________

Concave up: ____________________

Concave down: _________________

Inflection point(s)______________

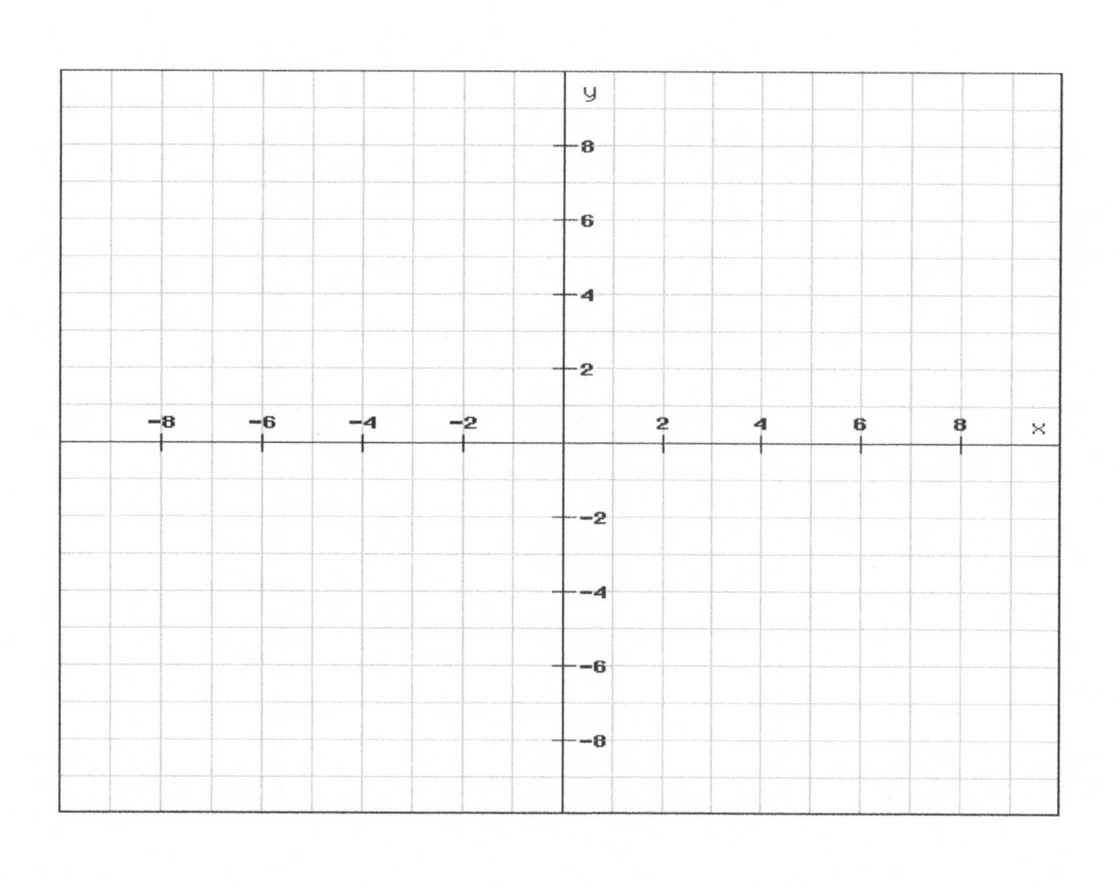

79. $f(x)=\sqrt{3x-x^2}$

Domain: ________________________

Vertical asymptotes: ______________

Horizontal asymptotes: ____________

Slant Asymptotes: ______________

y intercept: ______________________

x intercept(s): ____________________

Extrema (using the 1st and if needed 2nd derivatives)

Range of the function: ____________

Function Increases: _______________

Function decreases: _______________

Concave up: _____________________

Concave down: ___________________

Inflection point(s)_________________

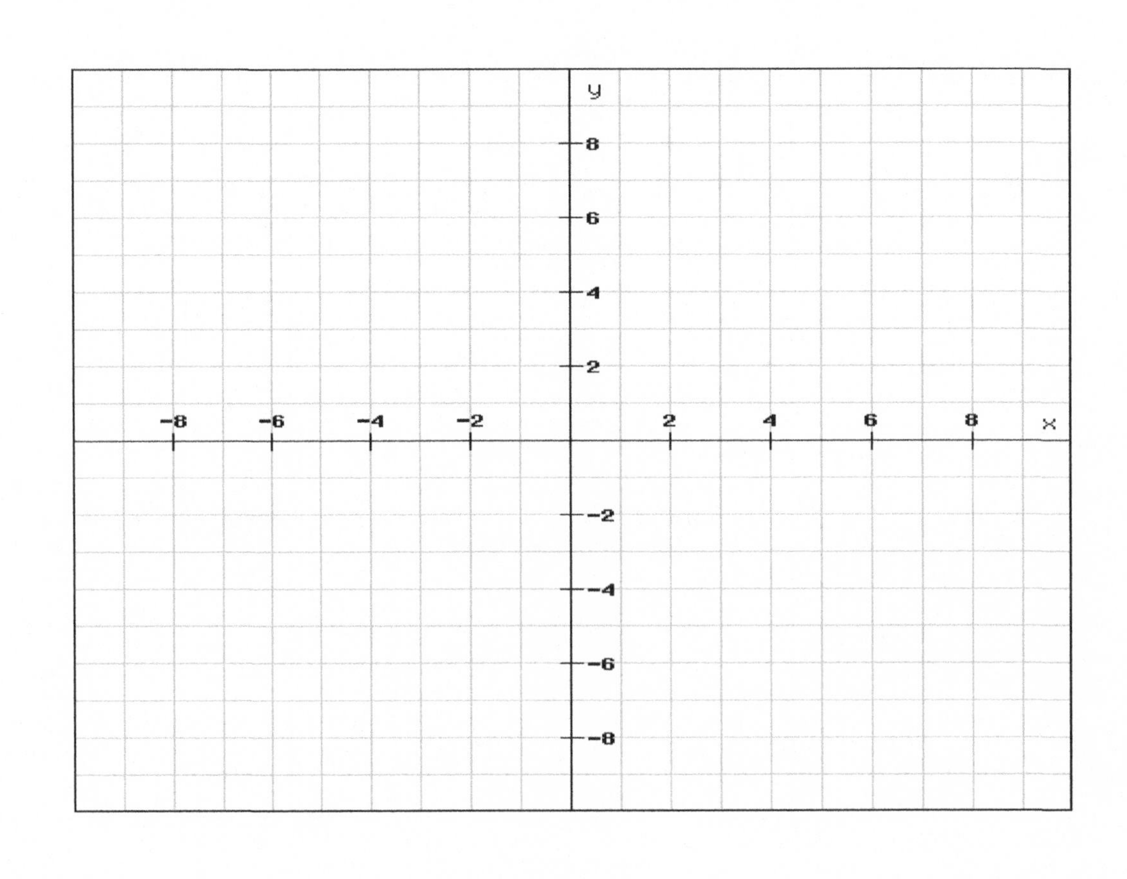

80. $f(x) = \dfrac{1}{\sqrt{3x - x^2}}$

Domain: ____________________________

Vertical asymptotes: ______________

Horizontal asymptotes: ____________

Slant Asymptotes: ______________

y intercept: ____________________________

x intercept(s): ______________________

Extrema (using the 1st and if needed 2nd derivatives)

Range of the function: ____________

Function Increases: ______________

Function decreases: ______________

Concave up: ____________________

Concave down: 

Inflection point(s) 

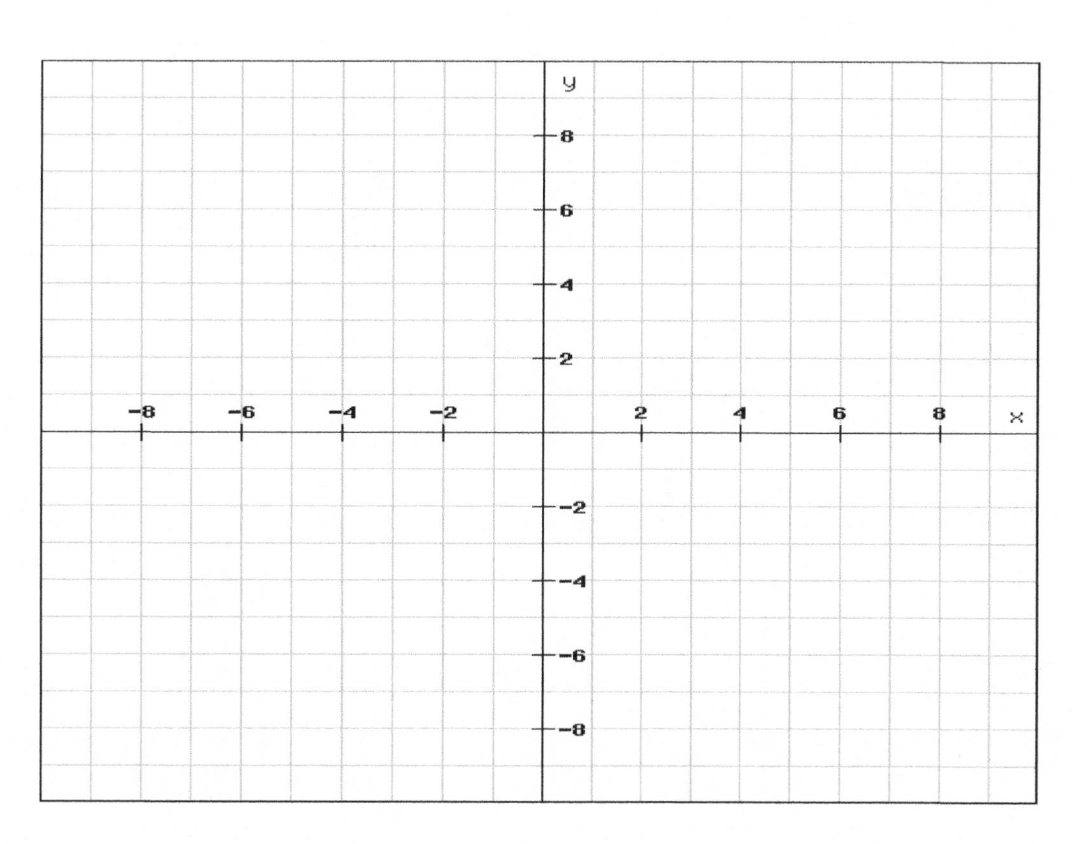

81. $f(x) = \dfrac{1}{\sin(x)+1}, x \in \mathbb{R}$

Domain: ___________________________

Vertical asymptotes: ________________

Horizontal asymptotes: ______________

Slant Asymptotes: ________________

y intercept: _________________________

x intercept(s): ______________________

Extrema (using the 1st and if needed 2nd derivatives)

Range of the function: _______________

Function Increases: _________________

Function decreases: _________________

Concave up: ________________________

Concave down: ______________________

Inflection point(s)___________________

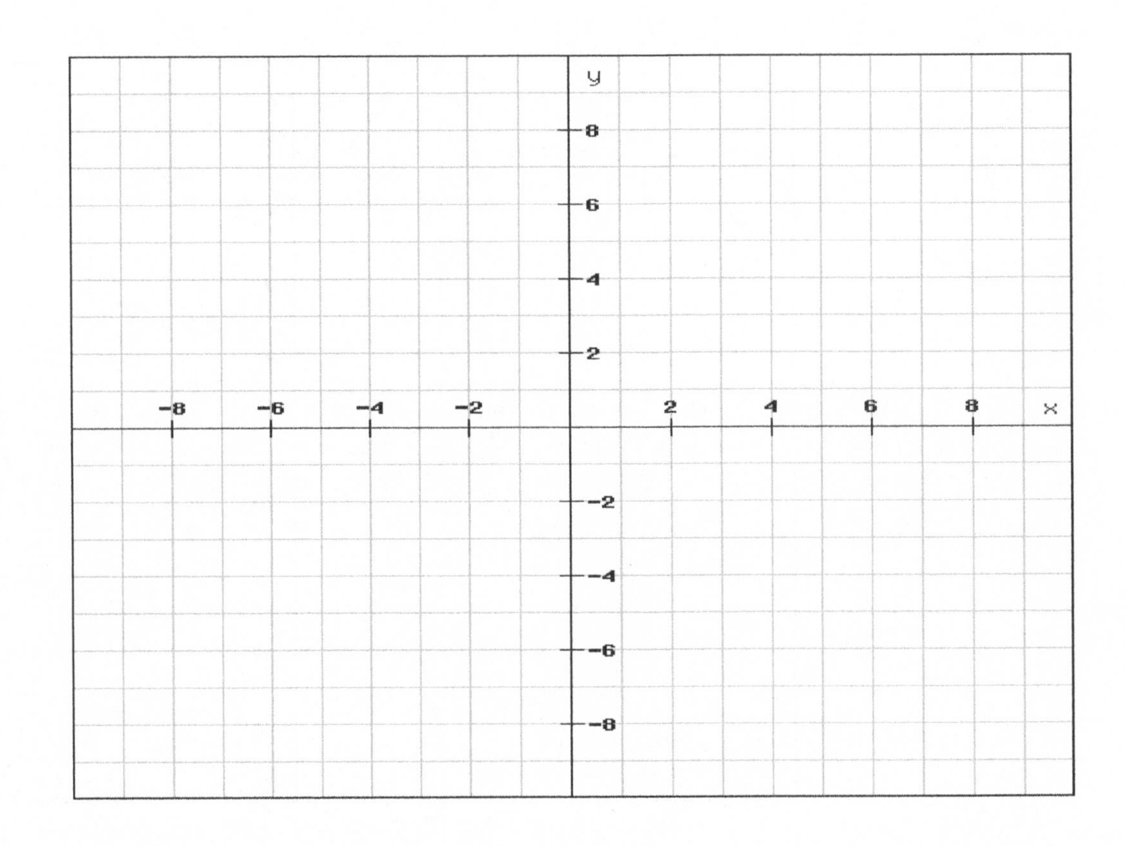

1.10. – INDEFINITE INTEGRATION

Integration is the inverse operation to differentiation. Its origin was the necessity to calculate areas and volumes of shapes that are not formed by straight lines (spheres, ellipsoids etc.)

Notation:

$\frac{dy}{dx} = f'(x) \rightarrow y = f(x) + c, c \in \mathbb{R}$, y is the antiderivative of f'(x)

The set of all antiderivatives is called the indefinite integral $\int f(x)dx$, f(x) is the integrand, x is the variable of integration, usually we write:

$$\int f(x)dx = F(x) + c$$

Example:

If $f(x) = x^2 + C$ then $f'(x) = 2x$

> Important: The "primitive function" means the integral.

Therefore

$\int (2x)dx = x^2 + C$

$$\int x^n \, dx = \frac{x^{(n+1)}}{n+1} + C \quad n \neq -1$$

Exercises:

$$\int \frac{1}{x} \, dx = \ln(x) + C$$

1. $\int x^{75} - 12x + 2dx =$

2. $\int \frac{1}{x^3} - 3x^{\frac{2}{3}} + 31xdx =$

3. $\int \sqrt[4]{\frac{1}{x^3}} - x + 1 + \pi + \cos(1) + edx =$

4. $\int \frac{1}{x^3} - 3x + 3dx =$

5. $\int \frac{1}{x^2} - \frac{3}{\sqrt{2x^3}}\, dx =$

6. $\int \frac{4}{x^5} - \frac{3}{2x^2}\, dx =$

7. $\int \frac{-5}{x^{55}} - \frac{5}{7x^{211}}\, dx =$

8. $\int \frac{2}{x} - \frac{5}{x}\, dx =$

9. $\int \frac{2}{x^3} + \frac{5}{3x^{10}} - \frac{2}{x}\, dx =$

10. $\int \frac{15}{x} - x^{12}\, dx =$

11. $\int \frac{2}{x^3} + \frac{5}{3x^{10}} - \frac{2}{x}\, dx =$

12. $\int \sqrt{\frac{a}{x}} + \frac{a}{x} + \frac{x}{a} - ae^x + \frac{1}{a} + x^a\, dx =$

13. $\int 0.1x - 0.2e^x\, dx =$

$$\int e^x\, dx = e^x + C$$

14. $\int \frac{1}{x} - 15e^x + 0.2dx =$

15. $\int \sqrt{\frac{2}{x}} + \frac{2}{3} - e^x\, dx =$

$$\int \sin(x)\,dx = -\cos(x) + C$$

$$\int \cos(x)\,dx = \sin(x) + C$$

16. $\int \frac{2}{x^{40}} + \frac{2}{7x^{12}} - 5e^{x}\,dx =$

17. $\int 7\cos(x) + 12x\,dx =$

18. $\int -\cos(x) - \sin(x) - \frac{2}{x} + \frac{2}{x^{2}} - e^{x}\,dx =$

19. $\int \cos(4) + 7e^{x} + \frac{3}{x^{12}}\,dx =$

20. $\int \cos(x) + \sin(x) + \frac{3}{x}\,dx =$

21. $\int \cos(4) + \sin(x) + \frac{3}{\sqrt{x^{7}}}\,dx =$

22. $\int 7 - \frac{a}{x} + \frac{b}{2x^{5}} + 4\,dx =$

23. $\int \frac{1}{3}\cos(x) + \frac{1}{2} - \sqrt{3}e^{x} + \sqrt{3} + \sqrt{2}x - \frac{2}{x} + \frac{1}{2x} + 1 + x\,dx =$

24. $\int \frac{1}{3}\sin(x) + \frac{5}{2} - \sqrt{3}e^{x} + \sqrt{7} + \sqrt{2}x - \frac{a}{x} + \frac{1}{bx} + 1 + x\,dx =$

More in general:

$$\int (g(x))^n g'(x)dx = \frac{g(x)^{n+1}}{n+1} + C, n \neq -1$$

Since integration is the inverse process to differentiation the following integrals are immediate: (See that if you differentiate right side you obtain the left side)

$$\int (ax+b)^n \, dx = \frac{(ax+b)^{(n+1)}}{a(n+1)} + C \quad n \neq -1$$

$$\int \frac{1}{ax+b} dx = \frac{\ln(ax+b)}{a} + C$$

$$\int e^{(ax+b)} dx = \frac{e^{(ax+b)}}{a} + C$$

$$\int \cos(ax+b)\, dx = \frac{\sin(ax+b)}{a} + C$$

$$\int \sin(ax+b)\, dx = -\frac{\cos(ax+b)}{a} + C$$

Worked examples

$$\int (3x^2+5x)^{-4}(6x+5)dx = \frac{(3x^2+5x)^{-3}}{-3} + C, n \neq -1$$

See that if you differentiate right side you obtain the left side.

$$\int (g(x))^{-1} g'(x)dx = Ln(|g(x)|) + C$$

$$\int (3x^2+5x)^{-1}(6x+5)dx = Ln(|3x^2+5x|) + C$$

See that if you differentiate right side you obtain the left side.

$$\int e^{g(x)} g'(x)dx = e^{g(x)} + C$$

$$\int e^{(3x^2+5x)}(6x+5)dx = e^{(3x^2+5x)} + C$$

See that if you differentiate right side you obtain the left side.

$$\int \cos(g(x))g'(x)dx = \sin(g(x)) + C$$

$$\int \cos(3x^2+5x)(6x+5)dx = \sin(3x^2+5x) + C$$

See that if you differentiate right side you obtain the left side.

$$\int \sin(g(x))g'(x)dx = -\cos(g(x)) + C$$

$$\int \sin(3x^2+5x)(6x+5)dx = -\cos(3x^2+5x) + C$$

See that if you differentiate right side you obtain the left side.

And in general:

$$\int (f(g(x))g'(x)dx = F(g(x)) + C$$

Exercises:

25. $\int 2x\cos(x^2)dx =$

26. $\int -2\sin(-x^3)x^2dx =$

27. $\int xe^{x^2+3}dx =$

28. $\int \cos(x^3+1)x^2dx =$

29. $\int \frac{4x}{x^2+2} dx =$

30. $\int x^3 \sin(x^4 + 5) dx =$

31. $\int \frac{4}{(3x+5)^7} dx =$

32. $\int e^{\frac{x}{2}} dx =$

33. $\int 2x \sin(3x^2 + 52) dx =$

34. $\int 5 \cos(3x + 5) dx =$

35. $\int \frac{20x+2}{5x^2+x} dx =$

36. $\int \frac{2}{5} \cos(\frac{x}{2} + 5) dx =$

37. $\int \frac{x^2}{x^3+3} dx =$

38. $\int (3x^2 - 4) e^{x^3-4x} dx =$

39. $\int 5x(x^2 - 4)^{-6} dx =$

40. $\int 15(e^x - 4)^{11} e^x dx =$

41. $\int x^2 e^{4x^3+17} dx =$

42. $\int e^{-5x+7} dx =$

43. $\int \frac{2x+3}{x^2+3x} dx =$

44. $\int \frac{4x+2}{2x^2+2x+7} dx =$

45. $\int \frac{4}{7} \cos(-7x + 11) dx =$

46. $\int \frac{4x}{3} \cos(3x^2 + 15) dx =$

47. $\int \frac{4}{7}\sin(3x+5)dx =$

48. $\int \frac{4x}{3(x^2-5)^4}\,dx =$

49. $\int \frac{2x-5}{(x^2-5x)^5}\,dx =$

50. $\int -\frac{2x^3}{(x^4-3)^5}\,dx =$

51. $\int -\frac{2x}{3(x^2-3)}\,dx =$

58. $\int \frac{3x^2+5x}{x}\,dx =$

59. $\int \frac{x^3+x^2-2\sqrt{x}+1}{\sqrt[3]{x}}\,dx =$

60. $\int \frac{\sqrt{x}}{x^4}\,dx =$

61. $\int (\sqrt{x}+\sqrt{\frac{1}{x}})dx =$

62. $\int \frac{\sqrt{x}+\sqrt[3]{x^2}}{\sqrt[6]{x^5}}\,dx =$

63. $\int \frac{x^2+\sqrt[3]{x^2}}{\sqrt{x}}\,dx =$

64. $\int \frac{dx}{x^2\sqrt[5]{x^2}} =$

65. $\int (3x+5)dx =$

66. $\int (5x-7)^{-3}\,dx =$

67. $\int (15x-7)^{-\frac{1}{2}}\,dx =$

68. $\int (12x+3)^{\frac{4}{7}}\, dx =$

69. $\int (12x+3)^{-\frac{1}{12}}\, dx =$

70. $\int 6x(3x^2+5)^2\, dx =$

71. $\int 18x(6x^3+5)^{-1}\, dx =$

72. $\int (60x^3-7)(15x^4-7x)^{-3}\, dx =$

73. $\int (\frac{1}{x}+1)(\ln(x)+x)^{-\frac{1}{2}}\, dx =$

74. $\int 3x^4(2x^5+3)^{\frac{4}{7}}\, dx =$

75. $\int (\frac{1}{\sqrt{x}}+2)(\sqrt{x}+x)^{\frac{2}{5}}\, dx =$

76. $\int x^{-1} dx =$

77. $\int x^{-2} dx =$

78. $\int e^{2x}(e^{2x}+2)^{-\frac{21}{4}}\, dx =$

79. $\int \frac{2}{x+1} dx =$

80. $\int \frac{1}{5x+1} dx =$

81. $\int \frac{x}{3x^2+5} dx =$

82. $\int \frac{2x}{x^2+1}dx =$

83. $\int \frac{x^2}{x^3-5}dx =$

84. $\int \frac{2x^3}{3x^4-5}dx =$

85. $\int \frac{x^{-\frac{1}{2}}-2}{x^{\frac{1}{2}}-x}dx =$

86. $\int \frac{3x^2+1}{x^3+x}dx =$

87. $\int \frac{3x^7}{2x^8+1}dx =$

88. $\int \frac{5x^{\frac{3}{2}}-4x}{x^{\frac{5}{2}}-x^2}dx =$

89. $\int \frac{-5e^x}{e^x-4}dx =$

90. $\int \frac{2e^{3x+1}}{e^{3x+1}-3}dx =$

91. $\int \frac{14e^{7x+2}-2}{e^{7x+2}-x}dx =$

92. $\int \frac{4x+1}{8x^2+4x+4}dx =$

93. $\int \frac{(\tan(x)+3)^{-2}}{(\cos(x))^2}dx =$

94. $\int \frac{\sin(x)}{\cos(x)}dx =$

95. $\int \frac{1-\sin(x)}{x+\cos(x)}dx =$

96. $\int \frac{1}{x\ln(x)}dx =$

97. $\int \frac{1}{x\ln(2x)}dx =$

98. $\int \frac{1}{(3x+1)\ln(3x+1)}dx =$

99. $\int \frac{3x^2+5x-1}{x}dx =$

100. $\int \frac{x^3+x^2-2\sqrt{x}+1}{\sqrt[3]{x}}dx =$

101. $\int \frac{\sqrt{\sqrt{x}}}{x^4}dx =$

102. $\int (x\sqrt{x}+\sqrt[5]{\frac{1}{x}})dx =$

103. $\int \frac{\sqrt{\sqrt{x}}+\sqrt[3]{x^2}}{\sqrt[6]{x^2}}dx =$

104. $\int \frac{2x^3+2\sqrt[3]{x^4}}{\sqrt{x}}dx =$

105. $\int \frac{\sqrt[3]{x^4}}{x\cdot\sqrt{x}}dx =$

106. $\int (\frac{1}{x^2}-\frac{1}{x+1})dx =$

107. $\int \left(\sqrt{x}+\frac{1}{\sqrt{x}}\right)^2 dx =$

108. $\int \left(x^2+\frac{1}{x}\right)^3 dx =$

109. $\int \left(\frac{1}{x^2}+\frac{1}{1+x^2}\right) dx =$

110. $\int\left(\sqrt{x}+\frac{1}{x}\right)^2 dx=$

111. $\int (nx)^{\frac{1-n}{n}}\,dx=$

112. $\int (a^{2/3}-x^{2/3})^3\,dx=$

113. $\int (\sqrt{x}+1)(x-\sqrt{x}+1)\,dx=$

114. $\int \frac{(x^2+1)(x^2-2)}{\sqrt[3]{x^2}}\,dx=$

115. $\int \sqrt{\frac{5}{x^3}}\,dx=$

116. $\int (x+\sqrt{x})^2\,dx=$

117. $\int \frac{5}{x+4}\,dx=$

118. $\int (x+\frac{1}{x^2})^3\,dx=$

119. $\int \frac{2}{2x+3}\,dx=$

120. $\int \frac{e^x}{e^x+4}\,dx=$

121. $\int \frac{x^2}{x^3+8}\,dx=$

122. $\int \frac{a\,dx}{a-x}=$

123. $\int \frac{e^{2x}}{e^{2x}+2}\,dx=$

124. $\int \frac{sin(x)}{2+\cos(x)}dx=$

125. $\int \frac{sin(Ln(x))}{x}dx=$

126. $\int \frac{dx}{tg\left(\frac{x}{5}\right)}=$

127. $\int \frac{tg\left(\sqrt{x}\right)}{\sqrt{x}}dx=$

128. $\int x\cot g(x^2+1)dx=$

129. $\int \frac{Ln^3(x)}{x}dx=$

130. $\int \frac{e^x}{e^x-1}dx=$

131. $\int \frac{\sqrt{x}+Ln^2(x)}{x}dx=$

132. $\int \frac{x}{\sqrt{x^2+1}}dx=$

133. $\int \sqrt{2-5x}\,dx=$

134. $\int \sqrt{5x^2-4x+3}(10x-4)dx=$

135. $\int \frac{x^2}{\sqrt{x^3+2}}dx=$

136. $\int \frac{3x^2}{\sqrt{1-2x^3}}dx=$

137. $\int 3x\sqrt{1-2x^2}\,dx=$

138. $\int \frac{x+3}{\sqrt{x^2+6x+4}} dx =$

139. $\int \frac{dx}{\sqrt{x+3}-\sqrt{x+2}} =$

140. $\int \frac{\sqrt{x^2+4}+x}{\sqrt{x^2+4}} dx =$

141. $\int \frac{dx}{\sqrt{x}\sqrt{1+\sqrt{x}}} =$

142. $\int \frac{e^x}{\sqrt{1+e^x}} dx =$

143. $\int (\cos(x) - sin(x))dx =$

144. $\int \frac{2-2sin^2(x)+3\cos(x)}{\cos(x)} dx =$

145. $\int sin(x)\cdot\cos(x)\, dx =$

146. $\int \frac{sin^2(x)-1+5sin^3(x)}{2sin^2(x)} dx =$

147. $\int 4^x dx =$

148. $\int 7^x dx =$

149. $\int 5^{2x} dx =$

150. $\int x\cdot 6^{x^2} dx =$

151. $\int (\cos 3x)2^{\sin 3x} dx =$

152. $\int e^x \cdot 9^{e^x} dx =$

153. $\int x^2 \cdot 6^{4x^3+1} dx =$

154. $\int \frac{4^{\sqrt{x}}}{\sqrt{x}} dx =$

155. $\int e^{3x} dx =$

156. $\int xe^{3x^2} dx =$

157. $\int \frac{e^x + e^{-x}}{\left(e^x - e^{-x}\right)^2} dx =$

158. $\int \frac{e^{3x} + e^x + 2}{e^x} dx =$

159. $\int e^x \left(e^x + 2\right)^2 dx =$

160. $\int \cos(x) \cdot e^{\sin(x)} dx =$

161. $\int \frac{e^{\frac{1}{x}}}{x^2} dx =$

162. $\int e^x \sqrt{1 - e^x} dx =$

163. $\int \left(x^2 - 2\right) e^{x^3 - 6x + 5} dx =$

164. $\int \left(e^x - e^{-x}\right)\left(e^x + e^{-x}\right)^4 dx =$

165. $\int \frac{1}{2x + 3} dx =$

166. $\int \frac{1}{2-3x} dx =$

167. $\int \frac{x^2+2x+3}{x} dx =$

168. $\int \frac{e^x}{1+e^x} dx=$

169. $\int \frac{(\ln(x))^3}{x} dx =$

170. $\int \frac{x+2}{x-1} dx =$

171. $\int \frac{x^2+2x+3}{x+1} dx =$

172. $\int (e^x - e^{-x})^2 dx=$

173. $\int \frac{\cos(x)}{\sin(x)} dx =$

174. $\int \frac{\ln(x)}{x} dx =$

175. $\int \frac{xdx}{x+1} =$

176. $\int x^2 e^{x^3} dx =$

177. $\int \frac{x-2}{x+1} dx =$

178. $\int \frac{2x-3}{x+1} dx =$

1.11. – DEFINITE INTEGRTION

The result of indefinite integration is a: ________ $= F(x) = \int f(x)dx$

The result of definite integration is __________ $= \int_a^b f(x)dx = F(b) - F(a)$

Definite integration represents the "**area under the graph**".

1. Above the x axis definite integrals have a ______________________.
2. Below the x axis definite integrals have a ______________________.
3. $\int_2^3 \frac{1}{x} + 2xdx =$
4. $\int_{\pi}^{\frac{3\pi}{2}} \cos(x) + xdx =$
5. $\int_1^e (\ln(x))dx =$

   (Use GDC)

6. $\int_2^6 x^2 + 1dx =$

7. $\int_0^2 3^x dx =$

8. $\int_1^{\sqrt{2}} x \cdot 2^{-x^2} dx =$

9. $\int_0^{\frac{\pi}{6}} (\cos\theta) 4^{-\sin\theta} d\theta =$

10. $\int_{-3}^{-1} 10^{-x} dx =$

11. $\int_0^{\frac{1}{2}} \frac{1}{\sqrt{1-x^2}} dx =$

Use GDC

12. $\int_{\sqrt{2}}^{2} \frac{1}{x\sqrt{x^2-1}} dx$

Use GDC

13. $\int_{-1}^{1} \frac{1}{1+x^2} dx$

Use GDC

14. $\int_{0}^{3} e^{3-x} dx$

15. $\int_{0}^{1} \frac{x^3}{x^4+1} dx$

16. $\int_{\frac{\pi}{6}}^{\frac{\pi}{2}} \frac{\cos(x)}{\sin(x)} dx$

17. $\int_{0}^{\frac{1}{6}} \frac{1}{\sqrt{1-9x^2}} dx$

Use GDC

18. $\int_{\sqrt{3}}^{3} \frac{1}{9+x^2} dx$

Use GDC

19. $\int_{1}^{e^2} \frac{3}{x} dx$

BOUNDARY CONDITION

20. Given that $\int \frac{1}{x} dx = F(x)$ and that $F(1) = 2$ find $F(x)$.

21. Given that $\int \sin(2x) dx = F(x)$ and that $F(\pi) = 1$ find $F(x)$.

22. Given that $\int e^{2x} + (x-1)^6 dx = F(x)$ and that $F(0) = 1$ find $F(x)$.

23. Given that $\int \sqrt{x} + x dx = F(x)$ and that $F(1) = 1$ find $F(x)$.

FINDING AREAS

24. Find the area enclosed between the functions $f(x) = x^2 - x$ and the x axis. Make a sketch to show the mentioned area.

25. Find the area enclosed between the function $f(x) = x^3 - 6x^2 + 8x$ and the x axis. Make a sketch to show the mentioned area.

26. Find the area enclosed between the function $f(x) = -x^3 + 3x^2 - 4$ and the axes
Make a sketch to show the mentioned area.

27. Find the area enclosed between the functions $f(x) = x^2 + x$ and $g(x) = x + 2$.
Make a sketch to show the mentioned area.

28. Find the area enclosed between the functions $f(x) = x^2 + 2$ and $g(x) = -x^2 + 3$. Make a sketch to show the mentioned area.

29. Find the area enclosed between the functions $f(x) = x^4 - 2x + 1$ and $g(x) = -x^2 + 1$. Make a sketch to show the mentioned area.

30. Find the area enclosed between the functions $f(x) = 2 - x^2$ and $g(x) = |x|$. Make a sketch to show the mentioned area.

31. Find the area enclosed between the function $f(x) = x^2 + 2x + 2$, the tangent to $f(x)$ at its extrema and the tangent to $f(x)$ with a slope 6. Make a sketch to show the mentioned area.

32. Find the area enclosed between the functions $f(x) = 5 - x^2 + 4x$ and $g(x) = 5$. Make a sketch to show the mentioned area.

33. Find the area enclosed between the functions $f(x) = x^2 - 2x$ and $g(x) = x$. Make a sketch to show the mentioned area.

34. The area enclosed between the curve $y = a(1 - (x - 2)^2)$ with $a > 0$ and the x axis is 12. Find a. Make a sketch to show the mentioned area.

35. Given the function $f(x) = ae^{\frac{x}{3}} + \frac{1}{x^2}, x \neq 0$, find:

a. $\int_1^2 f(x)dx$ in terms of a.

b. If F(x) is a primitive of f(x) find a knowing that $F(1) = 0$ and $F(2) = \frac{1}{2}$

36. Find the area bounded by: $y = e^{-x}$; $x = 0$; $y = 0$ and $x = 1$. Make a sketch to show the mentioned area.

37. Find the area enclosed between the function $f(x) = 1 - e^{-x}$, the tangent to f(x) at the point where x = 0 and the line x = 2. Make a sketch to show the mentioned area.

VOLUMES OF REVOLUTION

One possible way to create a Volume of Revolution is by spinning a certain area around the x axis.

For example, the volume of revolution formed by spinning the function $f(x)=x^2$ around the x axis between 0 and 2 is the following:

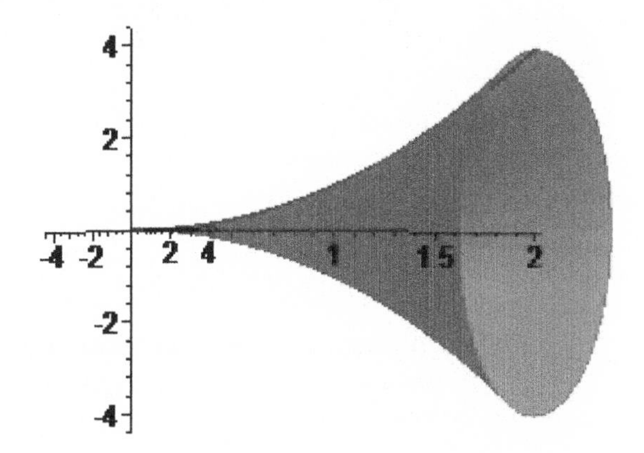

Since a volume o f revolution can be seen as the sum of the areas of infinite circles with changing sizes and can be calculated by (in this case):

$$V=\int_0^2 \pi x^2 dx=\left[\pi \frac{x^3}{3}\right]_0^2=\frac{8\pi}{3}$$

In general it is given by:

$$V=\int_a^b \pi\left(f(x)\right)^2 dx \text{ (spinning around the x axis)}$$

1. Find the volume of revolution formed by the function $f(x)=x+1, x\in[0,5]$

2. Find the volume of revolution formed by the function $f(x) = e^x, x \in [0,1]$

3. Find the volume of revolution formed by the function $f(x) = \sqrt{\sin(2x)}, x \in [0, \frac{\pi}{6}]$.

4. Find the volume of revolution formed by the function $f(x) = \sqrt{x-1}, x \in [2,3]$

1.12. – KINEMATICS

1. The displacement of an object is measure in ________________.

2. The velocity of an object is the __________________________ and it is measured in ________________. Mathematically it is the __________ of the displacement.

3. The acceleration of an object is the __________________________ and it is measured in ________________. Mathematically it is the __________ of the velocity or the ____________________ of the displacement.

4. An object accelerates from rest with a = 2 m/s^2 during 4 seconds, write down its velocity: ______________.

5. An object moves at 12 m/s and accelerates with a = –3 m/s^2 during 2 seconds, write down its final velocity: ______________.

6. If the distance run by an object after t seconds is given by $d(t) = 2t^2 + 3t + 5$, find:

   a. Its initial position.

   b. Its position after 2 seconds.

   c. Its velocity after 2 seconds.

   d. Its acceleration after 2 seconds.

7. The velocity of an object after t seconds is given by $v(t) = 2s\text{in}(3t)$, find:

    a. Its initial velocity.

    b. Its initial acceleration.

    c. The period of its motion.

8. The velocity of an object after t seconds is given by $v(t) = e^{-\frac{t}{a}}$, find:

    a. Its initial velocity.

    b. Given that its initial acceleration is –3 m/s^2, find a.

    c. Given that the initial displacement of the object is 2m, find its displacement after 3 seconds.

9. The acceleration of an object is given by $a(t) = \frac{1}{(t+1)^2}$, find:

   a. Given that v(0) = 0, find its velocity as a function time.

   b. Given that d(0) = 0, find its displacement as a function time.

   c. Write the acceleration and the velocity of the object after a long period

10. The acceleration of an object is given by $a(t) = 3\cos(2t)$, find:

   a. Given that v(0) = 0, find its velocity as a function time.

   b. Given that d(0) = 0, find its displacement as a function time.

2.1. – INTRODUCTION TO STATISTICS

In Statistics we try to obtain some conclusions by observing and/or analyzing data.

1. The set of objects that we are trying to study is called ______________, the number of elements in the population can be __________ or___________.
2. Usually the _____________ is too big and therefore we obtain a ___________. This process is called ________________.
3. We use the _______________ to obtain conclusions about the ____________.

Types of DATA

1. ___________ data.
2. ___________ data that can be divided to _____________ or ________________.
3. _____________ can be counted while __________ data can be ____________.
4. Give 5 examples of ____________ data:
5. Give 3 examples of __________ _________ data:
6. Give 3 examples of __________ _________ data:

OUTLIERS

7. An outlier is a data item which is more than _____________ from the nearest quartile.

8. Given that for certain data $Q_1 = 10$, $Q_3 = 22$. Find the range of values for k so that k is considered an outlier.

9. Given that for certain data $Q_1 = 7$, $Q_3 = 11$. Find the range of values for k so that k is considered an outlier.

10. Given that for certain data $Q_1 = p$, $Q_3 = 20$. It is known that $k = 28$ is an outlier. Find the possible values for p.

11. Given that for certain data $Q_1 = 5$ $Q_3 = c$ It is known that $k = 1$ is an outlier. Find the possible values for c.

SAMPLING TECHNIQUES

1. When sampling a population if not all objects are equally likely to be selected the results obtained may be biased (different)

2. For example: sampling the masculine football team of a school and using the sample to draw conclusions about the school.

3. **Simple Random Sampling**: Each element has the same ___________ of being selected. For example assigning a number to each element, writing it on a piece of paper and picking a number out of the bag. This method should be used when no prior information is known about the target population.

4. **Convenience Sampling**: When sampling "close" to the population target, for example waiting outside of the cinema and asking the spectators about the movie. Should be used when a specific target is studied, it is quick and easy.

5. **Systematic Sampling**: We split the population N to n groups with k elements in each group. We chose the first element in group 1, later first element in group 2 etc. This should be applied when the population is homogeneous, for example when sampling a yogurt produced from every 1000.

6. **Stratified Sampling**: This means we divide the elements in the population to groups (strata) based on a certain characteristic. For example by grade level in a school. This should be used when the population presents division into natural groups.

7. **Quota Sampling**: It is a type of stratified sampling; it should be used when the population is divided into groups in a certain proportion. For example in case in a certain population there are 30% men and 70% women then our sample should reflect that proportion.

3.2. – FREQUENCY DIAGRAMS

1. In a certain math class the following grades were obtained:

   68, 79, 75, 89, 54, 81, 88, 62, 67, 75, 64, 85, 97, 77, 79, 90, 75, 89, 76, 68

   a. State the number of elements in the set: ___________

   b. What kind of data is this? ___________________

   c. Fill the table:

Grade	Mid – Grade (Mi)	Frequency (fi)	fi x Mi	Cumulative Frequency (Fi)	Fi (%)
51 – 60					
61 – 70					
71 – 80					
81 – 90					
91 – 100					
Total					

   d. Is this the only possible choice for the left column of the table? Why? Discuss the advantages and disadvantages of organizing information in such a way.

   e. Design a new table with a different ____________________

Grade	Mid – Grade (Mi)	Frequency (fi)	Fi x Mi	Cumulative Frequency (Fi)	Fi (%)

f. Obtain the mean in both cases:

g. State a formula for the mean:

h. The mean of the <u>population</u> is denoted with the Greek letter mu: _____

and typically it is _____________. The mean of the <u>sample</u> is denoted by

_____

i. State the mode of the set: ____________

j. Find the modal interval in both cases:

k. Find the Median using the original data: _____________

l. Find the median using the tables, discuss your answer.

m. In general this method of organizing information is called __________

n. The 1st column is called ____________ with upper interval boundary and

_____________ interval boundary.

o. The 2nd column is called ____________

p. On the following grid paper sketch the corresponding points.

Cumulative frequency

Variable: _____

q. This graph is called cumulative frequency curve or _______________

r. Find the median using the graph: __________________

s. Find the first quartile (Q_1) using the graph: Q_1 = ___________________

t. Find the first quartile (Q_1) using the original data: Q_1 = ______________

u. Find the third quartile (Q_3) using the graph: Q_3 = ___________________

v. Find the first quartile (Q_3) using the original data: Q_3 = _____________

w. Find P_{30} using the graph: ________Find P_{65} using the graph: ________

x. The Inter Quartile Range is in general ________ in this case it is_______

y. Find the answers to all the different parts using your GDC.

2. In a certain class the following heights (in m) of students were collected:

1.77, 1.60, 1.89, 1.54, 1.77, 1.65, 1.86, 1.51, 1.67, 1.94, 1.73, 1.70, 1.66

a. State the number of elements in the set: ___________

b. What kind of data is this? _________________

c. Fill the table:

Grade	Mid – Grade (Mi)	Frequency (fi)	fi x Mi	Cumulative Frequency (Fi)	Fi (%)
[1.50 – 1.60)					
[1.60 – 1.70)					
[1.70– 1.80)					
[1.80 – 1.90)					
[1.90 – 2.00)					
Total					

d. Obtain the mean: ___________

e. State the mode of the set: ____________

f. Find the modal interval: ________________

g. Find the Median using the original data: _____________

h. Find the median using the table, discuss your answer.

i. On the following grid paper sketch the corresponding points.

Cumulative frequency

Variable: _____

j. This graph is called cumulative frequency curve or _______________

k. Find the median using the graph: __________________

l. Find the first quartile (Q_1) using the graph: Q_1 = ___________________

m. Find the first quartile (Q_1) using the original data: Q_1 = ______________

n. Find the third quartile (Q_3) using the graph: Q_3 = ___________________

o. Find the first quartile (Q_3) using the original data: Q_3 = _____________

p. Find P_{20} using the graph: ________Find P_{80} using the graph: ________

q. The Inter Quartile Range is in general ________ in this case it is_______

r. Find the answers to all the different parts using your GDC.

3. In a certain class students eye color was collected:

   Brown, Black, Brown, Blue, Brown, Blue, Green, Brown, Black, Green

   a. State the number of elements in the set: ___________

   b. What kind of data is this? _________________

   c. Fill the table:

Eye Color	Mid – Color (Mi)	Frequency (fi)	fi x Mi	Cumulative Frequency (Fi)	Fi (%)
Brown					
Blue					
Green					
Black					
Total					

   d. Obtain the mean: ___________

   e. State the mode of the set: ___________

   f. Find the modal interval: _______________

   g. Find the Median using the original data: _____________

   h. Find the median using the table, discuss your answer.

   i. Find the answers to all the different parts using your GDC.

   j. Represent the information in a histogram:

BOX AND WHISKER DIAGRAM

1. The following diagram shows a BOX AND WHISKER Diagram:

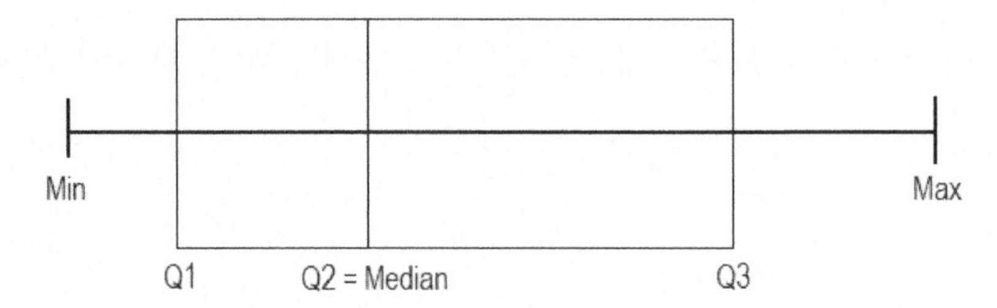

2. The results for 100 m dash competition are displayed in the following diagram: Use the Box and Whisker diagram to answer:

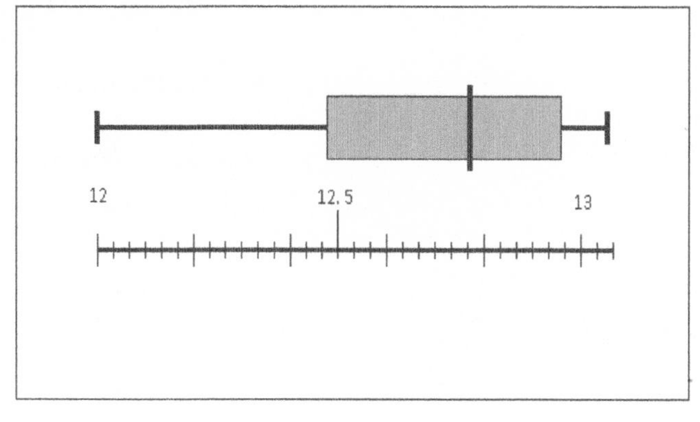

a. Min = ___________

b. Max = ___________

c. Q_1 = ___________

d. Q_2 = Med = _______

e. Q_3 = ___________

f. Range = ___________

g. Inter quartile range = ___________

3. Use the Box and Whisker diagram to answer:

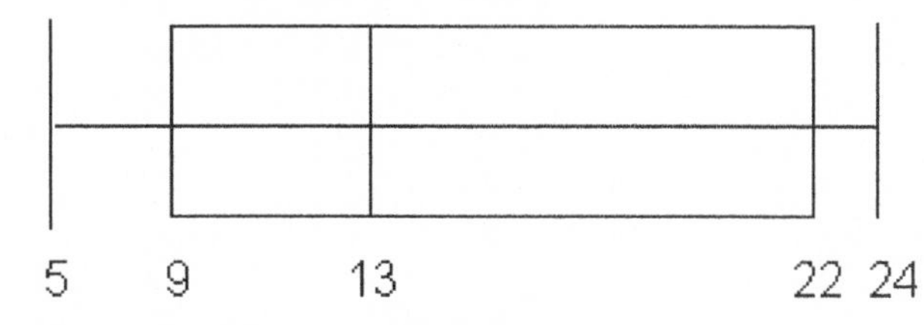

Use the Box and Whisker diagram to answer:

a. Min = ___________ Max = ___________

b. Q_1 = ___________ Q_2 = Med = ___________ Q_3 = ___________

c. Range = ___________

d. Inter quartile range = ___________

4. Given that in a certain classroom the heights of the students in cm are: 168, 178, 166, 191, 188, 181, 174, 159, 179, 173, 171, 166, 185, 184, 169. Draw a box-and-whisker Diagram.

2.3. – MEASURES OF DISPERSION

1. In a certain Biology test the following results were obtained: 80, 80, 80, 80,

   a. Obtain the mean: m = ____________

   b. Represent the results using a histogram:

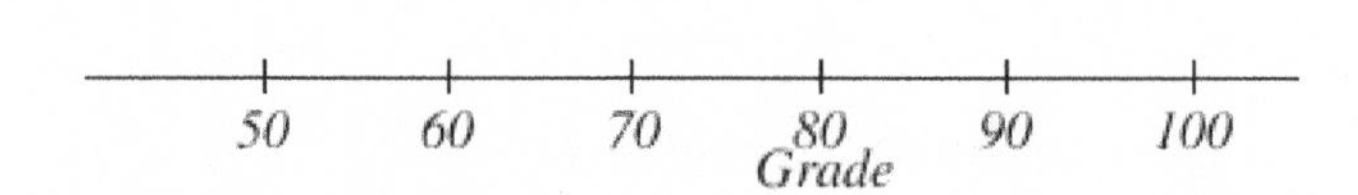

   c. The standard deviation of a set of numbers is defined by:

$$\sigma = \sqrt{\sum_i f_i(x_i - \mu)^2} = \sqrt{f_1(x_1 - \mu)^2 + f_2(x_2 - \mu)^2 + \ldots}$$

   In this case $\sigma =$ ____

   d. How spread is this group of grades?

2. In a certain Physics test the following results were obtained: 70, 80, 80, 90

   a. Obtain the mean: m = ____________

   b. Represent the results using a histogram:

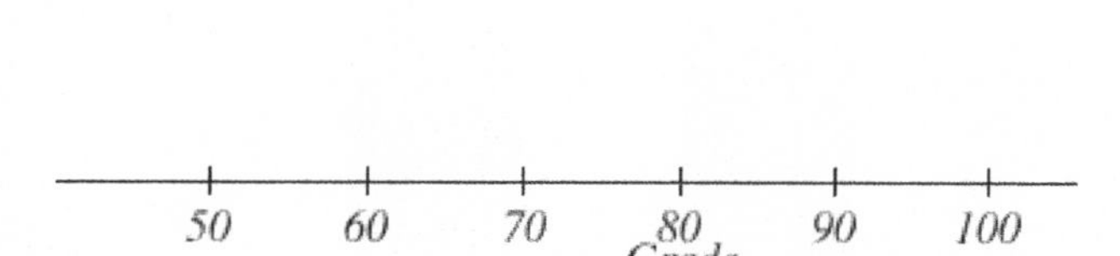

   c. The standard deviation of a set of numbers is defined by:

$$\sigma = \sqrt{\frac{\sum_{i=1}^{i=N} f_i (x_i - \mu)^2}{N}} = \sqrt{\frac{f_1(x_1-\mu)^2 + f_2(x_2-\mu) + f_3(x_3-\mu) + \ldots}{N}}$$

   In this case $\sigma =$ ______________________________

   d. How spread is this group of grades? Is it more spread than the previous one?

3. The weights in kg of 6 different classes (A, B, C, D, E, F) was collected and represented in the following histograms:

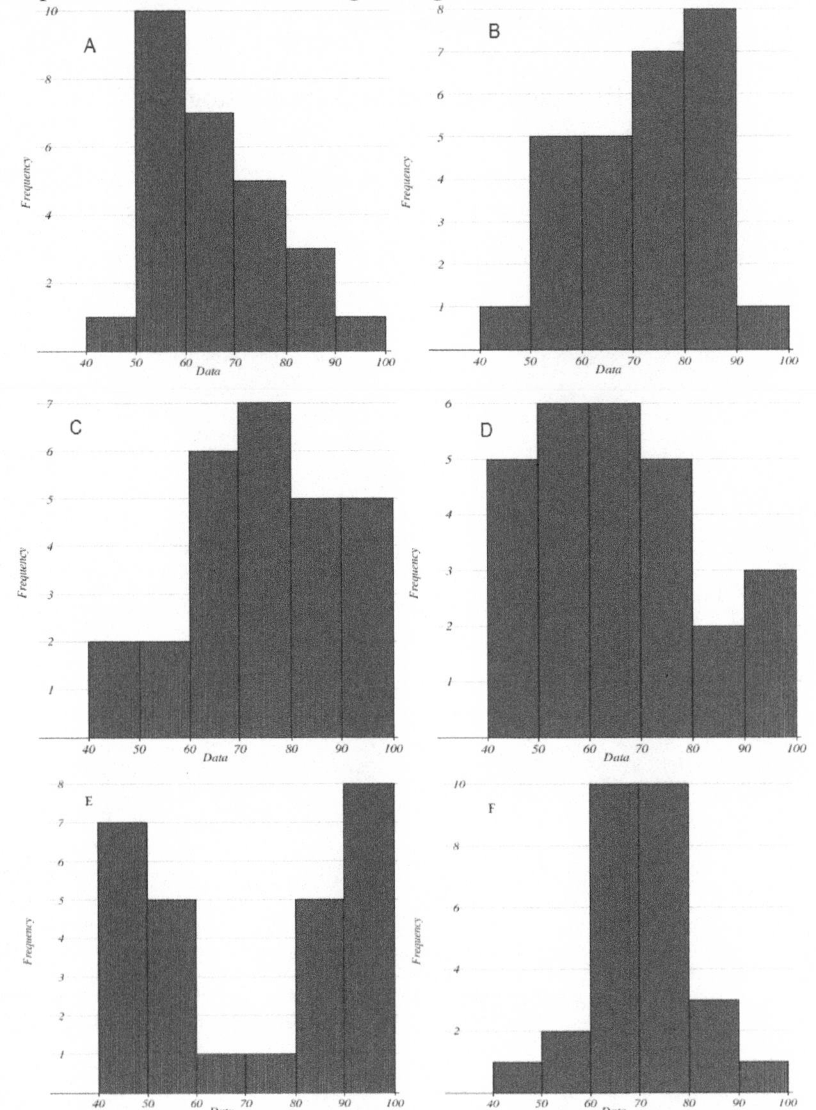

The mean $\overline{x}$ and the S.D. σ are given in the table:

	1	2	3	4	5	6
$\overline{x}$	74.6	65.7	70	72.0	65.7	70.6
σ	14.5	15.6	20.6	12.7	12.1	10.3

a. Find the number of students in the sample: ______

b. Which distribution will the highest SD: _____

c. Which distribution will the lowest SD: _____

d. Match between the histograms and the numerical results. Use the table:

$\overline{x}$ and σ	Class
1	
2	
3	
4	
5	
6	

4. In a certain math class the following grades were obtained:

68, 79, 75, 89, 54, 81, 88, 62, 67, 75, 64, 85, 97, 77, 79, 90, 75, 89, 76, 68

a. State the number of elements in the set: ___________

b. What kind of data is this? __________________

c. Fill the table:

Grade	Mid – Grade (Mi)	Frequency (fi)	fi x Mi	$(Mi - m)^2$	$fi(Mi - m)^2$
50 – 60					
61 – 70					
71 – 80					
81 – 90					
91 – 100					
Total					

d. Obtain the mean: $m =$ ____________

e. The numbers in the 6th column give us an idea about the _____________

of each _____________ to the spread of the data.

f. The sum of the numbers in the 6th column gives us an idea about the

______________ of the data. In case this number is 0 it means that

____ for example:

g. Find the Variance:_________Find the Standard Deviation S.D: _______

h. Write down the formula for the Variance of a population (s^2):

i. Write down the formula for the Standard Deviation of a population (s):

j. Find the answers to all the different parts using your GDC.

5. In a certain class the following heights (in m) of students were collected:

1.77, 1.60, 1.89, 1.54, 1.77, 1.65, 1.86, 1.51, 1.67, 1.94, 1.73, 1.70, 1.66

a. State the number of elements in the set: ___________

b. What kind of data is this? __________________

c. Fill the table:

Height	Mid – Height (Mi)	Frequency (fi)	Fi x Mi	$(Mi - m)^2$	$fi(Mi - m)^2$
[1.50 – 1.60)					
[1.60 – 1.70)					
[1.70– 1.80)					
[1.80 – 1.90)					
[1.90 – 2.00)					
Total					

d. Obtain the mean: m = _____________

e. The numbers in the 6th column give us an idea about the _____________ of each _____________ to the spread of the data.

f. The sum of the numbers in the 6th column gives us an idea about the __________________ of the data. In case this number is 0 it means that ____ for example:

g. Find the Variance (assuming population): ____________________

h. Find the Standard Deviation S.D. (assuming population): ____________

i. Find the answers to all the different parts using your GDC.

6. In a certain class students eye color was collected:

   Brown, Black, Brown, Blue, Brown, Blue, Green, Brown, Black, Green

   a. State the number of elements in the set: ___________

   b. What kind of data is this? __________________
   c. Fill the table:

Eye Color	Mid – Color (Mi)	Frequency (fi)	Fi x Mi
Brown			
Blue			
Green			
Black			
Total			

   d. What can you say about the measures of spread in this case?

7. The sum of the grades of a group of 3 students is 240. Given that the grades for an arithmetic sequence and that its standard deviation is $\sqrt{128}$:

   a. The mean grade.
   b. The grades of the students.

8. The time it takes a pool to be filled was measured by using a sample of 80 pools and the following results were obtained. Find

   a. The mean.
   b. The standard deviation.

Time (hours)	Number of pools
$3 \le t \le 4$	1
$4 < t \le 5$	2
$5 < t \le 6$	3
$6 < t \le 7$	9
$7 < t \le 8$	12
$8 < t \le 9$	13
$9 < t \le 10$	4
Total	

   c. Later it was discovered that one more pool was tested. If the standard deviation has not changed by adding it to the sample, find out how much time it took to fill this pool

9. A group of students obtained the following grades: 60, x, y, 50, 80. The mean of the sample is 68 and its variance is 136. Find x and y.

2.4. – CORRELATION

1. In many occasions variables may be related to each other, for example:
    - Age – Height
    - Level of education – Average income
    - Resistance to wind – gasoline consumption

   Give 3 other examples; discuss the kind of relation that exists between the variables:

2. The relation between variables is called: __________ and if it is ___________ it can be classified in the following way:

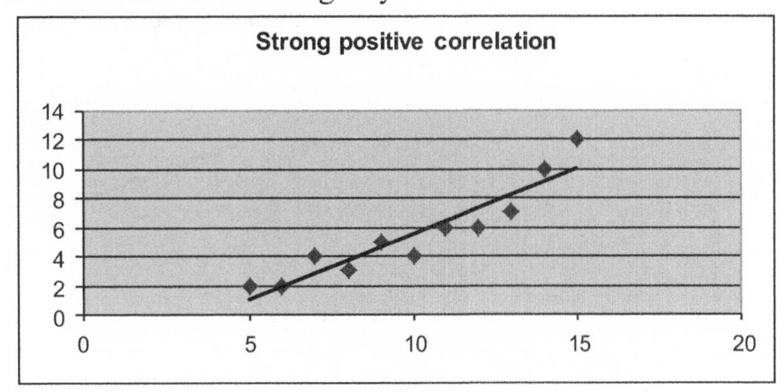

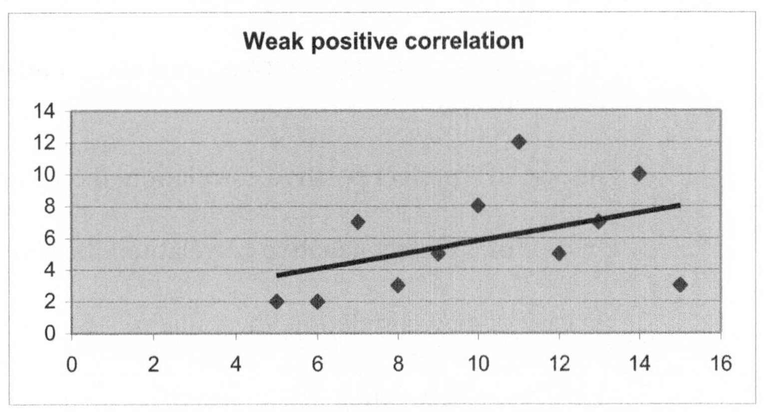

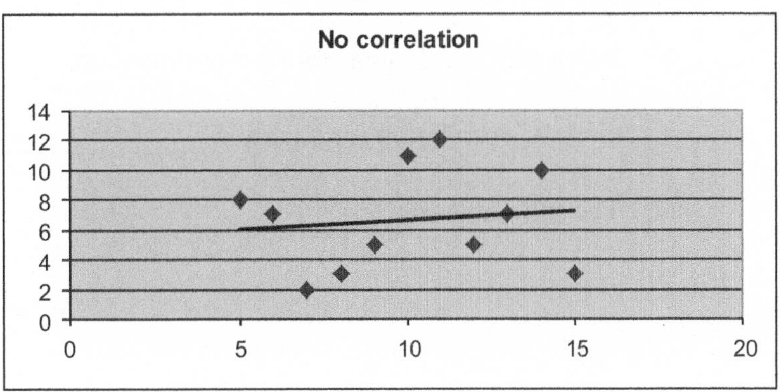

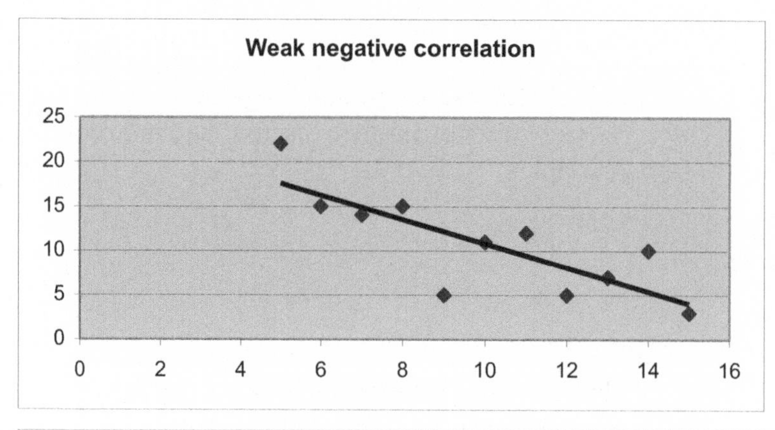

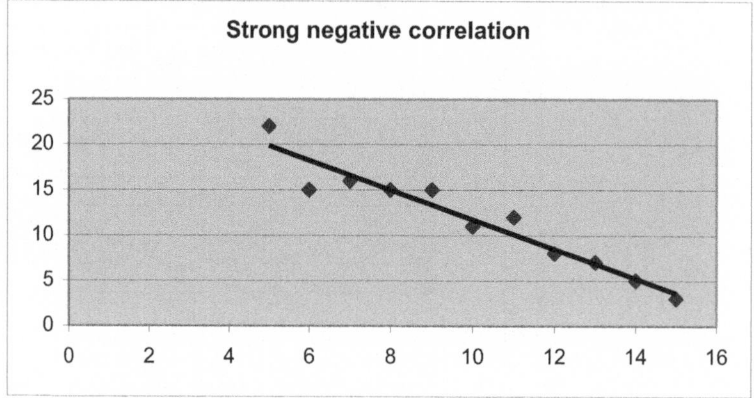

3. This correlation is characterized by a certain number called _____________ coefficient (r).

4. In case of a perfect positive correlation the value of r is ________

5. In case of a perfect negative correlation the value of r is ________

6. In case of a no correlation the value of r is ________

7. Finally r is between _______ and _______

8. All of the correlations above mentioned are ___________. There can be other kinds of correlation for example __________________

9. The full name of r is ____

10. If $r \in [0.75, 1)$ we say there is a ________________________ Correlation.

11. If $r \in [0.5, 0.75)$ we say there is a ________________________ Correlation.

12. If $r \in [0.25, 0.5)$ we say there is a ________________________ Correlation.

13. If $r \in (-0.25, 0.25)$ we say there is a ________________________ Correlation.

14. If $r \in (-0.5, -0.25]$ we say there is a ________________________ Correlation.

15. If $r \in (-0.75, -0.5]$ we say there is a ________________________ Correlation.

Name	John	Dean	Elisa	Marc	Heather	Alicia	Raquel	Kevin	Alex	Deena
HW Done (%)	58	90	75	50	40	95	100	85	75	82
Grade (%)	70	80	80	65	55	78	86	89	82	70

16. If $r \in (-1, -0.75]$ we say there is a ________________________ Correlation.

17. In a certain math class the following data about students was found:

a. Represent the data on a graph:

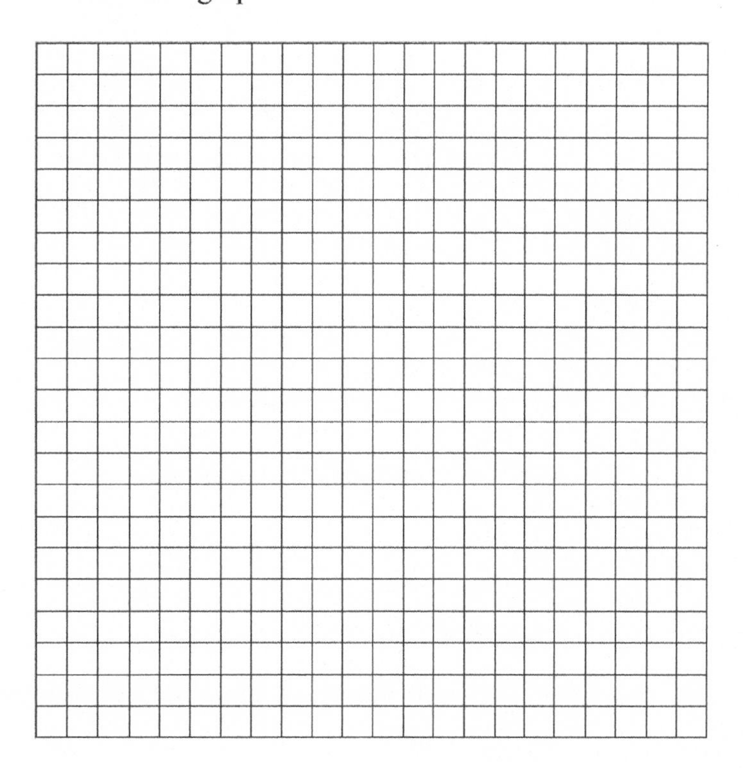

b. Is their correlation? _______________ what kind? ______________

c. Try to predict the value of r: ___________________

d. In order to calculate the value of r first find:

$\bar{x}$ = ____________ $\bar{y}$ = _____________

Complete the table:

Name	x_i	$(x_i - \bar{x})^2$	y_i	$(y_i - \bar{y})^2$	$x_i y_i$
John	58		70		
Dean	90		80		
Elisa	75		80		
Marc	50		65		
Heather	40		55		
Alicia	95		78		
Raquel	100		86		
Kevin	85		89		
Alex	75		82		
Deena	82		70		
Total					

Use the table to find Sx, Sy and Sxy using the following formulas taken from IB information booklet:

$$S_x = \sqrt{\frac{\sum_{i=1}^{i=n}(x_i - \bar{x})^2}{n}}, S_y = \sqrt{\frac{\sum_{i=1}^{i=n}(y_i - \bar{y})^2}{n}}, S_{xy} = \frac{\left(\sum_{i=1}^{i=n}(x_i y_i) - \frac{\sum_{i=1}^{i=n} x_i \sum_{i=1}^{i=n} y_i}{n}\right)}{n}$$

Sx = ____________ Sy = ____________, Sxy = ____________

Find r using $r = \frac{S_{xy}}{S_x S_y}$ r = ___________

e. Was your prediction accurate?

f. Find r using your GDC: _______ this is the value of r performing a regression of y on x.

g. By exchanging x with y, find r for regression of x on y: _________ Draw a conclusion.

LINE OF BEST FIT

18. The line of best fit is the straight line that most approximates to the scatter diagram obtained. The equation of the line is given by:

$$y-\overline{y}=\frac{S_{xy}}{(S_x)^2}(x-\overline{x})$$

19. Write this expression in the forma y = mx + b

Name	John	Dean	Elisa	Marc	Heather	Alicia	Raquel	Kevin	Alex	Deena
HW Done (%)	58	90	75	50	40	95	100	85	75	82
Grade (%)	70	80	80	65	55	78	86	89	82	70

20. By looking at the expression it can be seen that the slope of the line is m = ____

21. Given the data

Using your GDC to find:

a. r = ____________

b. $\overline{x}$ = ________ $\overline{y}$ = ________

c. The line of best fit for y on x is: ______________________________

d. By exchanging x with y find the line of best fit for x on y: ____________

e. Find the point of intersection of the 2 regression lines and draw a conclusion.

22. In a group of students height and weight correlation was studies. The results are given by the table below.

Height (cm)	Weight (kg)
165	58
170	62
172	80
169	65
188	88
163	52
191	95
177	72

a. $\bar{x} =$ _______ $\bar{y} =$ _________

b. Write the equation of the regression line in the form y = mx + c

c. Use your equation in part a to predict the weight of a student who is 174cm tall.

d. Write down the correlation coefficient and the kind of correlation that exists.

e. By exchanging x with y find the line of best fit for x on y: ______________

f. Find the point of intersection of the 2 regression lines and draw a conclusion.

23. In a group of students the reading speed was studied in relation to age of the student. The results are given by the table below.

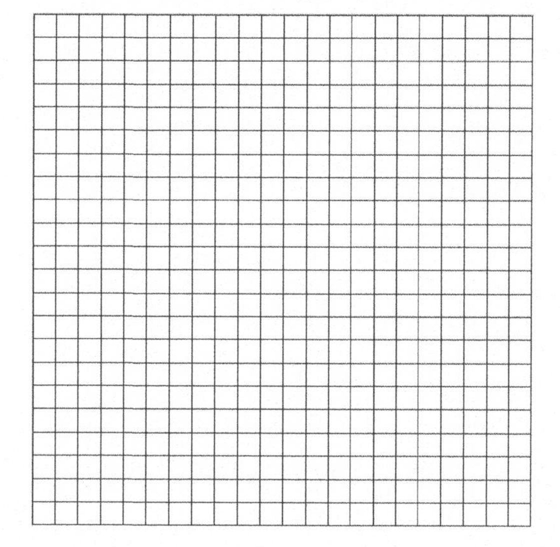

Age (years)	Reading speed (words per minute)
15	98
12	65
17	111
19	120
18	122
16	102
19	143
17	100
13	80
14	85
14	95
15	90

a. Write the equation of the regression line in the form y = mx + c

b. Use your equation in part a to predict the reading speed of a student who is 11 years old.

c. Write down the correlation coefficient and the kind of correlation that exists.

d. Draw a scatter diagram to show the data.

e. $\overline{x}$ = ___ = ____________________ $\overline{y}$ = ___ = ____________________

f. Plot the point ($\overline{x}$, $\overline{y}$) on your scatter diagram. Label this point as A.

g. Draw the regression line on the diagram.

2.5. – PROBABILITY

Probability is the science of chance or likelihood of an event happening

If a random experiment is repeated ____ times in such a way that each of the trials is identical and independent, where n(A) is the __________________ event A occurred, then:

$$\text{Relative frequency of event A} = P(A) = \frac{n(A)}{N} \qquad (N \to \infty)$$

Exercises

1. In an unbiased coin what is P(head) ?

   This probability is called ___________________________.

2. Explain the difference between theoretical probability and "regular" probability.

3. Throw a drawing pin and fill the table:

	Fell pointing upwards	Fell on its side	Total number of throws
Number of events			
Probability			

4. The definition of probability ("***Laplace law***")is:

$$P(A) = \frac{Number \_\_\_\_\_\_\_\_\_\_\_\_\_\_\_\_\_\_\_\_}{Total \_\_\_\_\_\_\_\_\_\_\_\_\_\_\_\_\_\_\_\_}$$

Properties of probability

1. $0 \leq P(A) \leq 1$

2. $P(U) = 1$

Venn diagrams

Event	Set Language	Venn diagram	Probability result
Complementary event (A')	Not A		P(A') =
The _________ of A and B (A ∩ B)	Set of elements that belongs to A _____ B		P(A ∪ B) =
The _________ of A and B (A ∪ B)	Set of elements that belongs to A _____ B ___ both		
If (A ∩ B) = ∅ A and B are said to be: ________	The sets A and B are __________________		P(A ∪ B) = P(A ∩ B) =

1. Given the Venn diagram. Shade A ∩ B

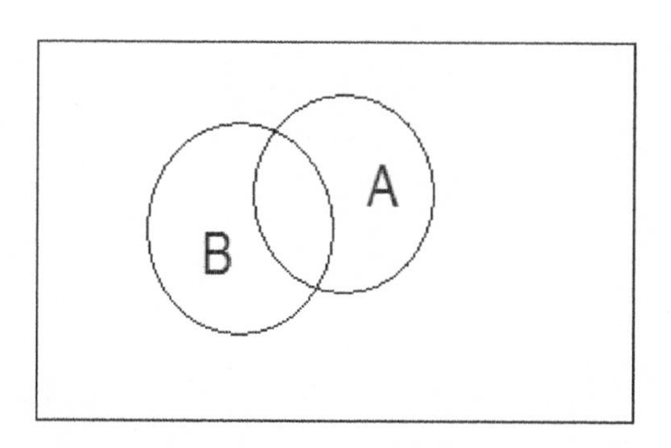

2. Given the Venn diagram. Shade A ∩ B'

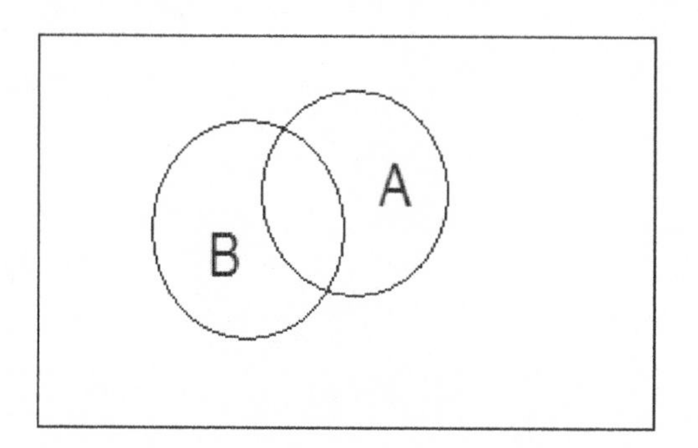

3. Given the Venn diagram. Shade B'

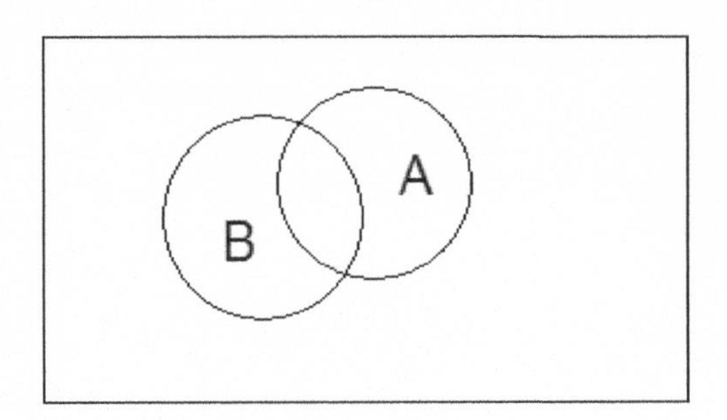

4. Given the Venn diagram. Shade $A' \cap B'$

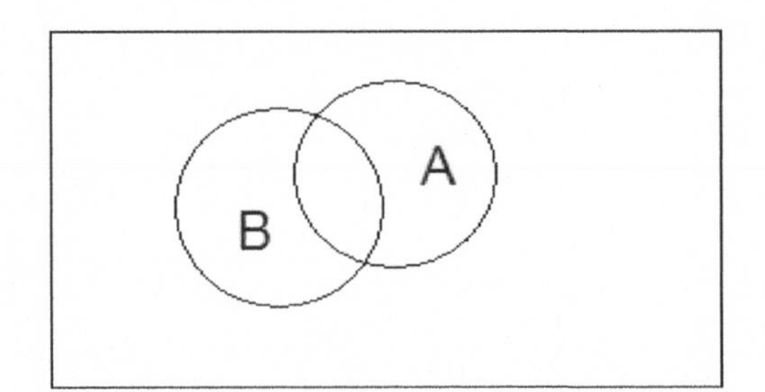

5. Given the Venn diagram. Shade $A \cup B$

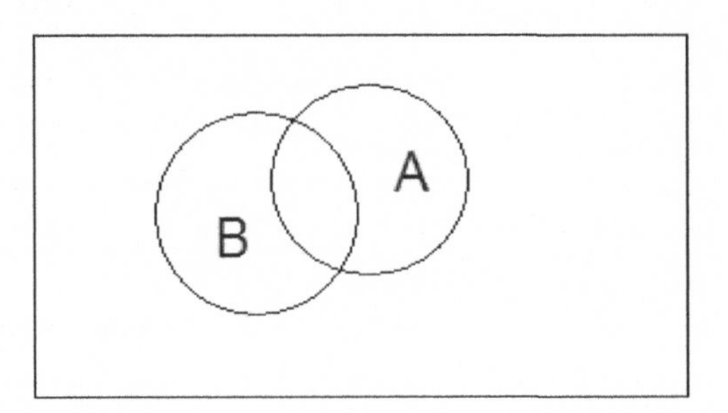

6. Given the Venn diagram. Shade $A' \cup B$

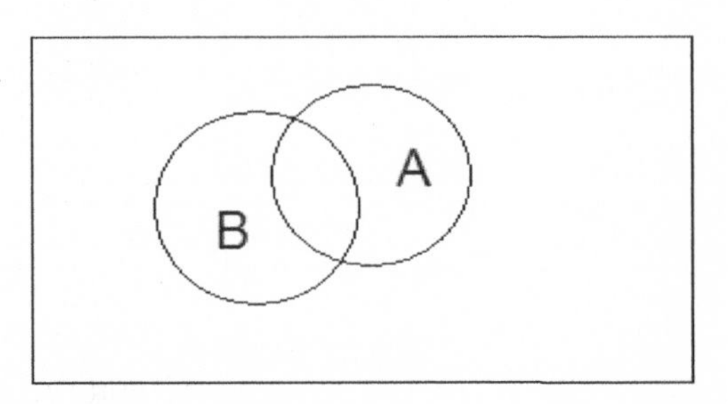

7. Given the Venn diagram. Shade $A' \cup B'$

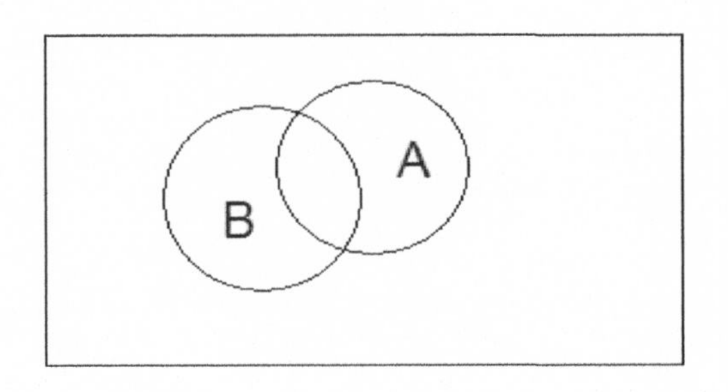

8. Given the Venn diagram. Shade $A \cup B$

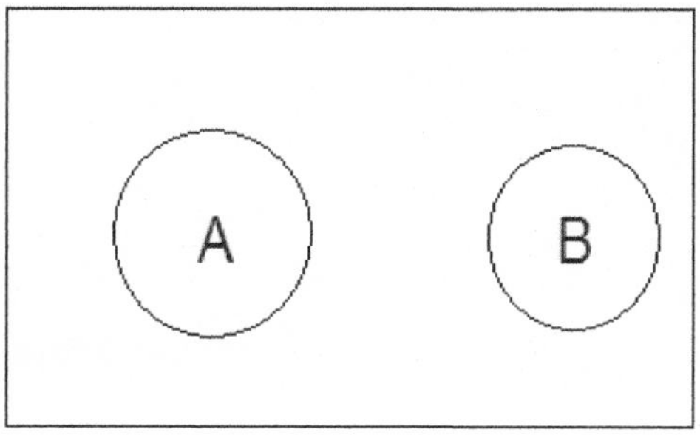

9. Given the Venn diagram. Shade $A \cup B'$

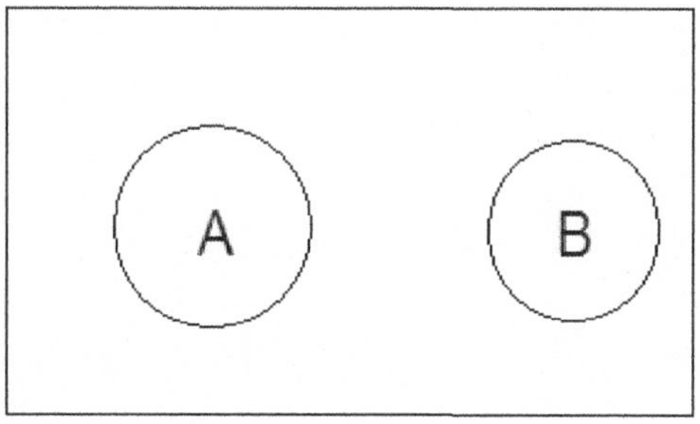

10. Given the Venn diagram. Shade $A \cap B'$

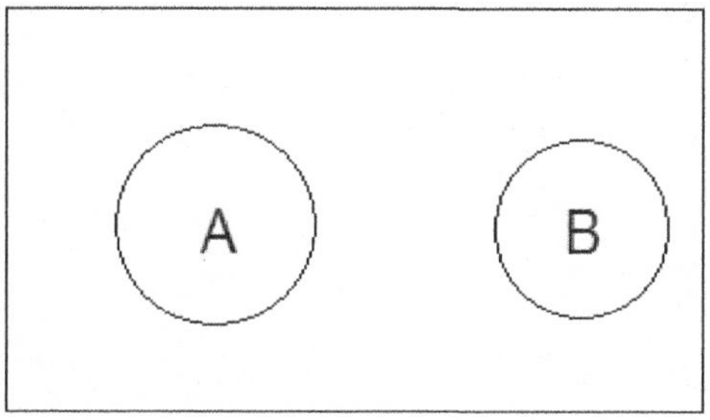

11. Given the Venn diagram. Shade $A \cap B$

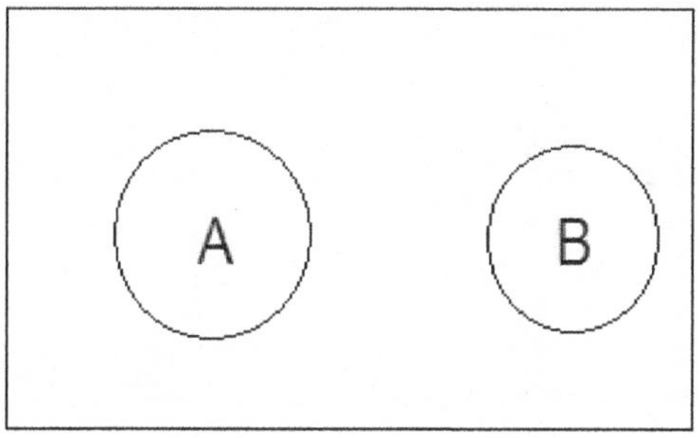

12. Given the Venn diagram. Shade $A \cap B \cap C$

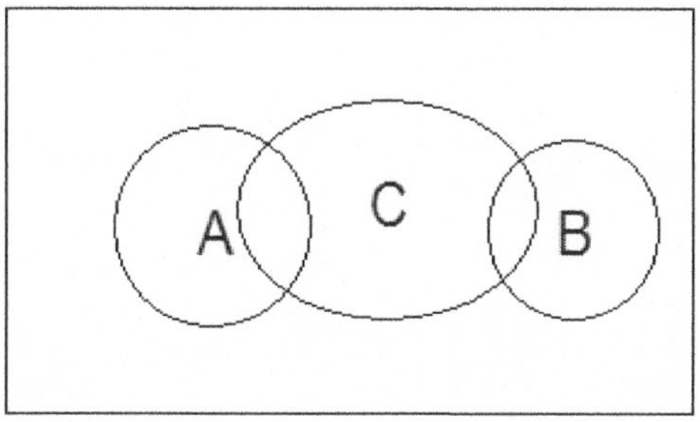

13. Given the Venn diagram. Shade $(A \cup B) \cap C$

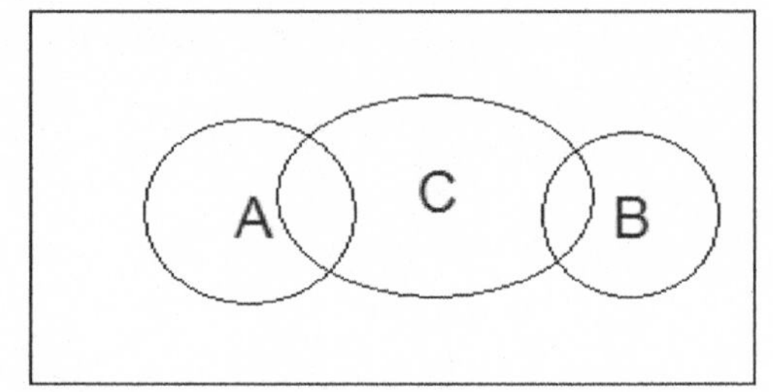

14. Given the Venn diagram. Shade $(A' \cup B) \cap C$

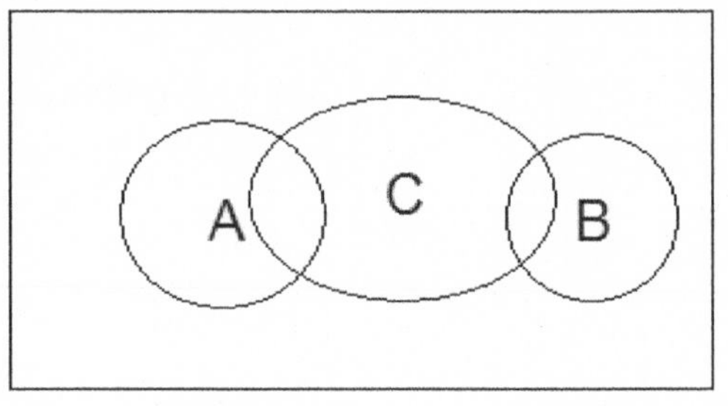

15. Given the Venn diagram. Shade $(A \cup B) \cap C'$

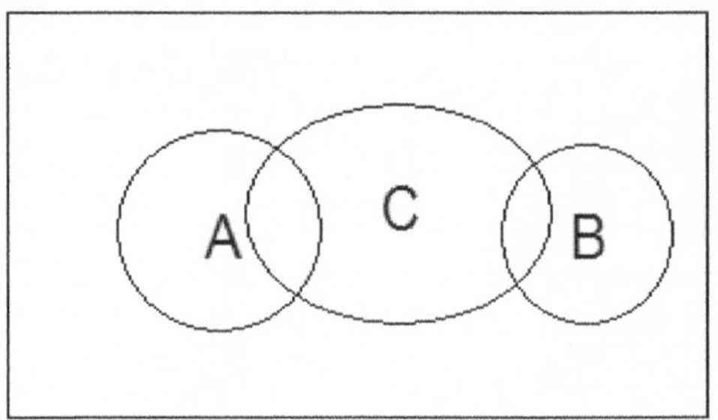

16. Given the Venn diagram. Shade $A \cap B \cap C$

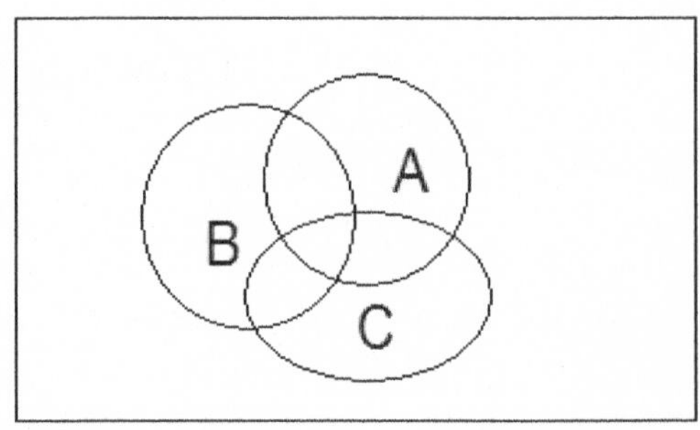

17. Given the Venn diagram. Shade $(A \cap B) \cap C'$

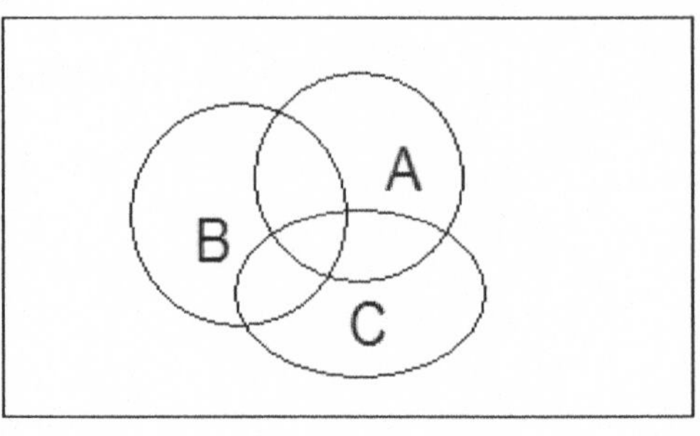

18. Given the Venn diagram. Shade $(A' \cap B) \cap C$

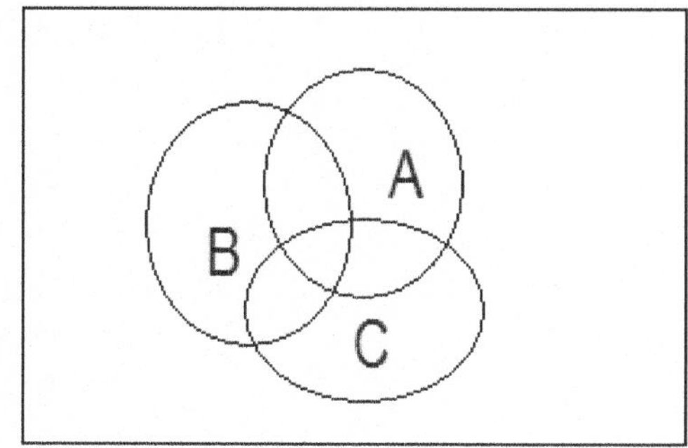

19. Given the Venn diagram. Shade $(A \cap B') \cap C$

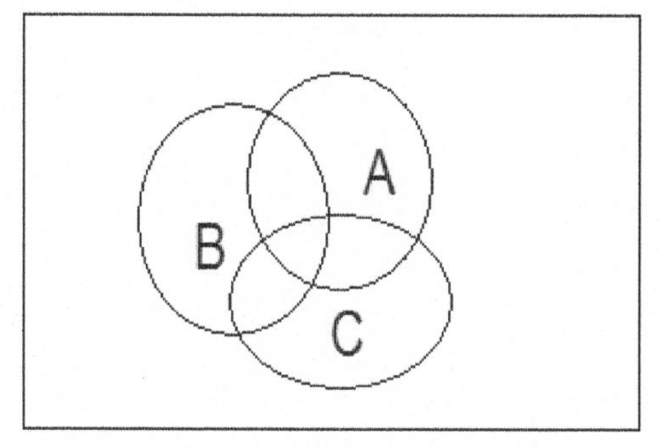

20. The events A and B are such $P(A) = 0.2$, $P(B) = 0.4$ and $P(A \cup B) = 0.5$. Find:

a. $P(A \cap B)$
b. $P(B')$
c. Sketch the corresponding Venn diagram.
d. $P(A' \cap B)$
e. $P(A' \cap B')$
f. Are the events A and B Independent? Explain.

21. The events A and B are such $P(A) = 0.15$, $P(B) = 0.3$ and $P(A \cup B) = 0.4$, Find:

a. $P(A \cap B)$
b. $P(B')$
c. Sketch the corresponding Venn diagram.
d. $P(A' \cap B)$
e. $P(A' \cap B')$
f. Are the events A and B Independent? Explain.

22. The events A and B are such $P(A) = 0.3$, $P(B) = 0.6$ and $P(A \cup B) = 0.9$, Find:

a. $P(A \cap B)$
b. $P(B')$
c. Sketch the corresponding Venn diagram.
d. $P(A' \cap B)$
e. $P(A' \cap B')$
f. Are the events A and B Independent? Explain.

23. The events A and B are such $P(A) = 0.2$, $P(B) = 0.9$ and $P(A \cap B) = 0.1$, Find:

a. $P(A \cup B)$
b. $P(B')$
c. Sketch the corresponding Venn diagram.
d. $P(A' \cap B)$
e. $P(A' \cap B')$
f. Are the events A and B Independent? Explain.

24. 20% of certain city census consume alcohol regularly, 40% do sport regularly and 10% do both.

a. Represent the information in a diagram.
b. Calculate the probability that someone chosen at random only drinks alcohol regularly.
c. Calculate the probability that someone chosen at random only drink alcohol regularly or only practices sport regularly (but not both).
d. Calculate the probability that someone picked at random does not drink alcohol nor practices sport regularly.

25. $P(A) = 0.46$, $P(B) = 0.33$, $P(A \cap B) = 0.15$.

a. Represent the information in a diagram.
b. Find the probability that an event is not A nor B.

INDEPENDENT EVENTS

Informal definition: P(B) is not influenced by P(A).

Formal definition : $P(A \cap B) = P(A)P(B)$

Exercises

1. What is the difference between independent events and mutually exclusive events?

2. Give an example of independent events.

3. In a certain town the probability of a rainy day is 0.58 and the probability of strong wind is 0.76. If these are independent events, find the probability of:

    a. A rainy windy day.
    b. A dry windy day.
    c. A dry and not windy day.
    d. 2 consecutive rainy days.
    e. 2 consecutive windy rainy days.

CONDITIONAL PROBABILITY

Informal definition: **Knowing** that B has happened, what is the probability that A will happen (Written as P(A|B))

Formal definition: The probability of and event A given event B is:

$$P(A|B) = \frac{P(A \cap B)}{P(B)}, \text{ P(B)} \neq 0$$

4. Two dice numbered one to six are rolled onto a table.

   a. Sketch a **lattice** diagram to show this information.
   b. Find the probability that the sum is 7.
   c. Find the probability that the sum is more than 7.
   d. Find the probability that the sum is less than 4.
   e. Find the probability that the sum is even.
   f. Find the probability of obtaining a sum of five given that the sum is seven or less.
   g. Find the probability of obtaining a sum of 4 given that the sum is even.

5. A regular and special dice rolled on a table. The special is a 4 sided pyramid numbered with the numbers 1,3,5,7.

    a. Sketch a corresponding diagram.
    b. Find the probability that the sum of the dice will be odd.
    c. Find the probability that the sum of the dice will be 8.
    d. Find the probability that the sum of the dice will be less than 9.
    e. Find the probability of obtaining a sum of 10 knowing that the sum was more or equal to 6.

Worked Example

It is known that:

i. 1% of women aged 40 have breast cancer
ii. A mammography test has 80% success rate.
iii. A mammography test has 10% false alarm rate

A woman receives a positive mammography test, what is the probability she really has cancer?

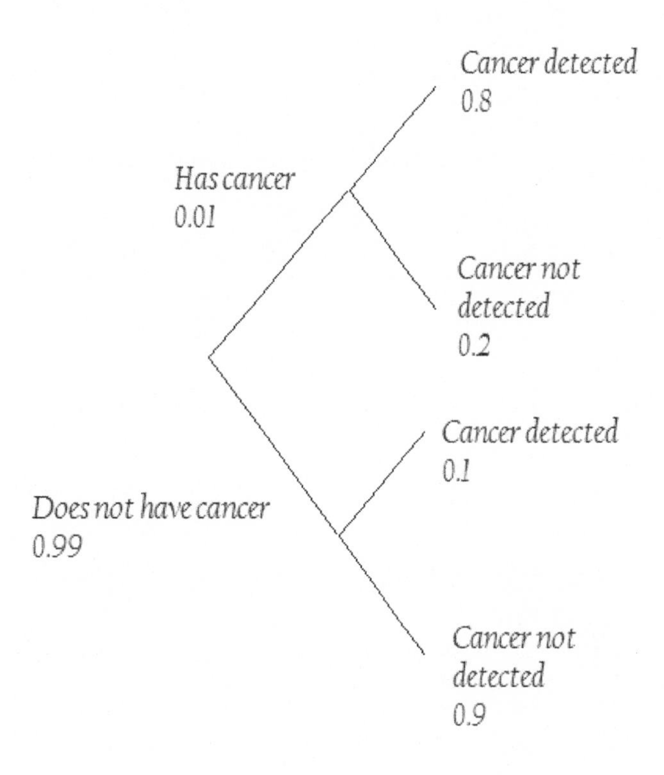

$$\text{P (True yes| (All Yeses)} = \frac{0.01 \cdot 0.8}{0.01 \cdot 0.8 + 0.99 \cdot 0.1} \approx 0.0748$$

The woman has 7.5% probability to have cancer.

2. Two special dice numbered one to seven are rolled onto a table.

   a. Sketch a corresponding diagram.
   b. Find the probability that the product is 6
   c. Find the probability that the quotient is more than 3.
   d. Find the probability that the sum is a prime number.
   e. Find the probability that the sum is a perfect square given it is not a prime number.
   f. Find the probability of obtaining an even sum given that the sum is six or less.

3. A die and coin are rolled on a table.

    a. Sketch a corresponding diagram.
    b. Find the probability of getting Tail and an even number.
    c. Find the probability of getting Tail and a 4.

TREE DIAGRAMS

6. If the probability of tail is 0.53, find the probability of at least one tail in 2 throws.

7. An urn contains 8 cubes of which 5 are black and the rest are white.

   a. What is the probability to draw a white cube?
   b. Draw a tree diagram in case a 1st cube is drawn, it is **NOT replaced** and then another cube is drawn. Indicate all the probabilities on the tree diagram.
   c. Calculate the probability to draw 2 consecutive black cubes.
   d. Calculate the probability to draw **at least** 1 black cube.
   e. Given that the first cube drawn was white, calculate the probability that the 2nd is black.

8. A bag contains 3 red balls, 4 blue balls and 5 green balls. A ball is chosen at random from the bag and is not replaced. A second ball is chosen. Find the probability of choosing one green ball and one blue ball in any order.

9. Given that events A and B are independent with $P(A \cap B) = 0.4$ and $P(A \cap B') = 0$. Find $P(A \cup B)$.

10. Given that P(A) = 0.4, P(B) = 0.7 and $P(A \cup B) = 0.8$. Find:

a. $P(A \cap B)$
b. $P(A \mid B)$
c. Determine if A and B are independent events.

11. Given that P(A) = 0.4, P(B) = 0.6 and $P(A \cup B) = 0.76$.

a. Find $P(A \cap B)$
b. Are events A and B mutually exclusive? Explain.
c. Are events A and B independent?

12. The events A and B are independent, where A is the event "it will rain today" and B is the event "We will go out for pizza". It is known that

$$P(B) = 0.3,\ P(A \mid B) = 0.6,\ P(A \mid B') = 0.5.$$

a. Complete the following tree diagram.

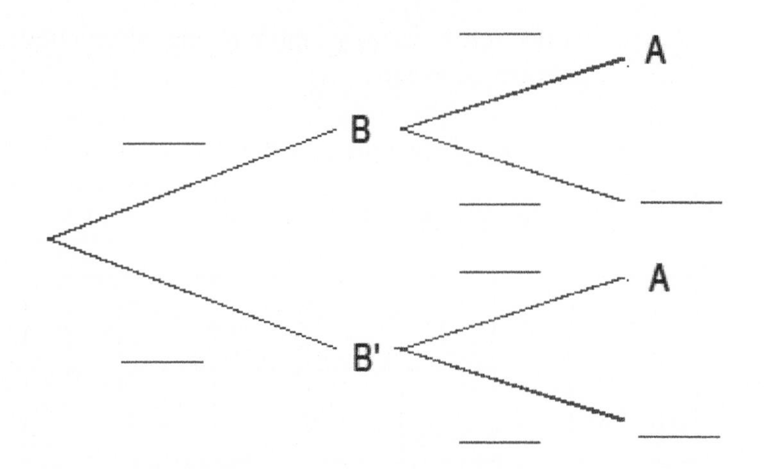

b. Calculate the probability that it rains knowing we went out for pizza.

2.6. – DISCRETE RANDOM VARIABLES

1. A ____________________ takes exactly n numerical values and each of these values corresponds to a single event in the sample space.

2. For example in rolling a die the possible values of X are: {______________}

3. A discrete random variable is one in which we can produce a ______________ number of events.

4. If we roll 2 dice the possible values of X are: {________________________}

   a. Fill the following table:

x											
P(X = x)											

   b. Represent the information in the table graphically:

   c. $\sum_{i=1}^{i=n} P(X = x_i) = P(X = x_1) + P(X = x_2) + \ldots + P(X = x_n) =$ ____

   d. Show that the last statement is satisfied in the problem mentioned:

Mean value or Expected of value

e. Find the mean value of the distribution E(X) = m.

f. Deduce the general expression for the mean E(X) discrete probability distribution:

g. This mean is usually called “the ______________________________of X”.

h. This number, E(X) can be interpreted in 2 ways:

A ____________________________________ Average.

A ____________________________________ Average.

5. The number of customers entering a shop during 1 hour follows the following table:

x	0	1	3	4	5
P(X = x)	$\frac{1}{6}$	$\frac{1}{12}$	$\frac{5}{12}$	$\frac{1}{6}$	

a. Fill the blank in the table.

b. Represent the information in the table graphically:

c. $\sum_{i=1}^{i=n} P(X = x_i) = P(X = x_1) + P(X = x_2) + \ldots + P(X = x_n) =$ ____

d. Show that the last statement is satisfied in the problem mentioned:

e. Find the mean value of the distribution E(X).

6. Fill the blanks:

   a. E(a) = __________ (a is a constant). Give an example:

   b. E(aX) = ____________.

   c. E(f(X)) = $\sum_{i=i}^{i=n} f(x_i) \times P(X = x_i)$. An example would be:

   E(aX + b) =______________________________.

7. Given the following probability distribution

x	2	3	5	6	10
P(X = x)	$\frac{1}{6}$	$\frac{1}{12}$	$\frac{5}{12}$	0	

a. Fill the blank.

b. E(X) = ____

c. E(2X) = ____

d. E(4X) = ____

e. 2E(X) = ____

f. 4E(X) = ____

g. $(E(X))^2$ = ____

h. $E(X^2)$ = ____

i. $E(X^3)$ = ____

j. E($\sqrt{X}$) = ____

k. Repeat the process using your GDC.

l. In general is $(E(X))^2 = E(X^2)$? _______ Is it possible in a specific case? _______

Variance and standard deviation

a. The Variance measures the ___________________.

b. Variance is defined as:

$$Var(X) = E((X-\mu)^2) = \sum_{i=i}^{i=n} (x-\mu)^2 P(X = x)$$

Or

$$Var(X) = E(X^2) - (E(X))^2 = E(X^2) - \mu^2$$

Use the data from exercise 7 to find:

Find Var(X) = ____

c. Standard deviation is defined as Sd(X) = ______________.

d. In this case Sd(X) = ________________. We use the Sd(X) and not the variance because Sd has __________________________ as the original distribution.

e. Calculate Var(2X) = _____________________________________. How is it related to Var(X)?

f. Var(aX) = __________________.

g. Var(a) = ___________ (a is a constant)

Given 2 distributions:

x	1	2	3	4
P(X = x)	$\frac{1}{6}$	$\frac{2}{6}$	$\frac{1}{6}$	$\frac{2}{6}$

x	7	8	9	10
P(X = x)	$\frac{1}{6}$	$\frac{2}{6}$	$\frac{1}{6}$	$\frac{2}{6}$

Find for both of them

h. Represent them both on the same graph:

i. The 2nd distribution is ________________ as the 1st one only ________________

j. E(X) = ____

k. E(X) = ____

l. $E(X^2)$ = ____

m. $E(X^2)$ = ____

n. Var(X) = ____

o. Var(X) = ____

Your conclusions:

p. Var(X + b) = ______________________

q. Var(a(X + b)) = ______________________

r. Var(aX + c) = ______________________

2.7. – THE BINOMIAL DISTRIBUTION

1. Dichotomous Experiment – An experiment with ______ possible results:

   heads or_______, male or_______, adult or child etc.

2. The probabilities of the results are P(A) and P(A') = _________________

3. The variable X is discrete. It is called a Binomial Distribution to B(n, p). n

   is ____________________ p is ______________ and q is ____________.

4. The probability <u>that X would have the value k</u> is given by:

$$P(X = k) = \binom{n}{k} p^k q^{n-k}, k = 0,1,2...n$$

$$E(x) = \mu = np$$
$$Var(X) = \sigma^2 = npq$$
$$Sd(X) = \sigma = \sqrt{npq}$$

The mode of X is the value of x with the largest probability.

5. If $B(1, \frac{1}{2})$ find:

   a. P(X = 0) = ______________________________________

   b. P(X = 1) = ______________________________________

   c. P(X = 2) = ______________________________________

   d. Mode of X is ____________________________________

   e. E(X) = ___________ Var(X) = ___________ Sd(X) = ________

   f. Write down the probability of the expected value: _________

6. If $B(3, \frac{1}{2})$ find:

   a. $P(X = 0) =$ ______________________________

   b. $P(X = 1) =$ ______________________________

   c. $P(X = 2) =$ ______________________________

   d. $P(X = 3) =$ ______________________________

   e. $P(X = 2) =$ ______ means that ____________________

   f. Mode of X is ______________________________

   g. $P(X < 2) =$ ______________________________

   h. $P(X \geq 2) =$ ______________________________

   i. $E(X) =$ ____________ $Var(X) =$ ____________ $Sd(X) =$ _________

   j. Write down the probability of the expected value: _________

7. If $B(3, \frac{1}{6})$ find:

   a. $P(X = 0) =$ ______________________________

   b. $P(X = 1) =$ ______________________________

   c. $P(X = 2) =$ ______________________________

   d. $P(X = 3) =$ ______________________________

   e. $P(X = 2) =$ ______ means that ____________________

   f. Mode of X is ______________________________

   g. $P(X < 2) =$ ______________________________

   h. $P(X \geq 2) =$ ______________________________

   i. $E(X) =$ ____________ $Var(X) =$ ____________ $Sd(X) =$ _________

   j. Write down the probability of the expected value: _________

8. If $B(20, \frac{1}{2})$ Using GDC binompdf(n,p,x), binompdf(n,p,(x_1,x_n)), binomcdf(n,p,x) for $P(X \leq x)$

   a. $P(X = 5) =$ ____________________

   b. $P(X = 10) =$ ____________________

   c. $P(X = 18) =$ ____________________

   d. $P(X < 8) =$ ____________________

   e. $P(X \leq 8) =$ ____________________

   f. $P(X \geq 13) =$ ____________________

   g. $P(X > 13) =$ ____________________

   h. $E(X) =$ __________ $Var(X) =$ __________ $Sd(X) =$ ________

   i. Write down the probability of the expected value: ________

9. If $B(70, 0.2)$ Using GDC binompdf(n,p,x), binompdf(n,p,(x_1,x_n)), binomcdf(n,p,x) for $P(X \leq x)$

   a. $P(X = 17) =$ ____________________

   b. $P(X = 36) =$ ____________________

   c. $P(X = 28) =$ ____________________

   d. $P(X < 50) =$ ____________________

   e. $P(X \leq 70) =$ ____________________

   f. $P(X \geq 38) =$ ____________________

   g. $P(X > 10) =$ ____________________

   h. $E(X) =$ __________ $Var(X) =$ __________ $Sd(X) =$ ________

   i. Write down the probability of the expected value: ________

10. A machine that makes products has a probability of 0.03 to build a defective product. The machine produces 500 products.

    a. Find the most probable number of defective products. Fin its probability.

    b. Find the probability that the machine produced 10 defective products.

    c. Find the probability that the machine produced less than 12 defective products

    d. Find the probability that the machine produced more than 18 defective products

11. A die it thrown 50 times.

    a. Find the probability that exactly 5 "ones" were obtained.

    b. Find the probability that exactly 20 results were even.

    c. Find the probability that less than 12 "ones" were obtained.

    d. Find the probability that more than 17 times a "six" or "five" were obtained.

2.08. – NORMAL DISTRIBUTION

Given the following information about a Group of people:

Weight	[40, 50)	[50, 60)	[60, 70)	[70, 80)	[80, 90)	[90, 100)	[100, 110)
Number of people	4	8	12	11	10	6	2

The histogram that represents this information is:

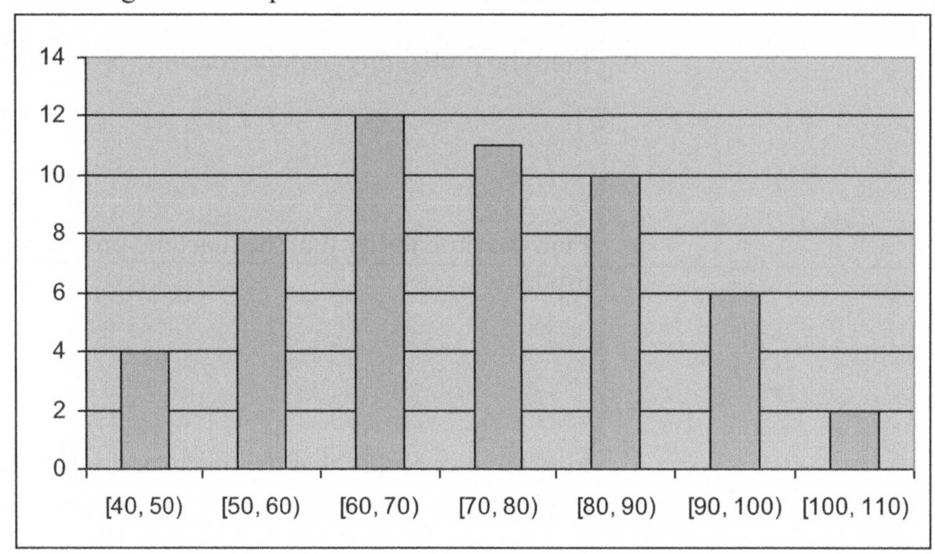

A bigger sample was taken to and the following information was obtained:

Weight	[40, 45)	[45, 50)	[50, 55)	[55, 60)	[60, 65)	[65, 70)	[70, 75)
Number of people	7	12	20	22	30	36	34

Weight	[75, 80)	[80, 85)	[85, 90)	[90, 95)	[95, 100)	[100, 105)	[105, 110)
Number of people	26	16	12	5	3	2	1

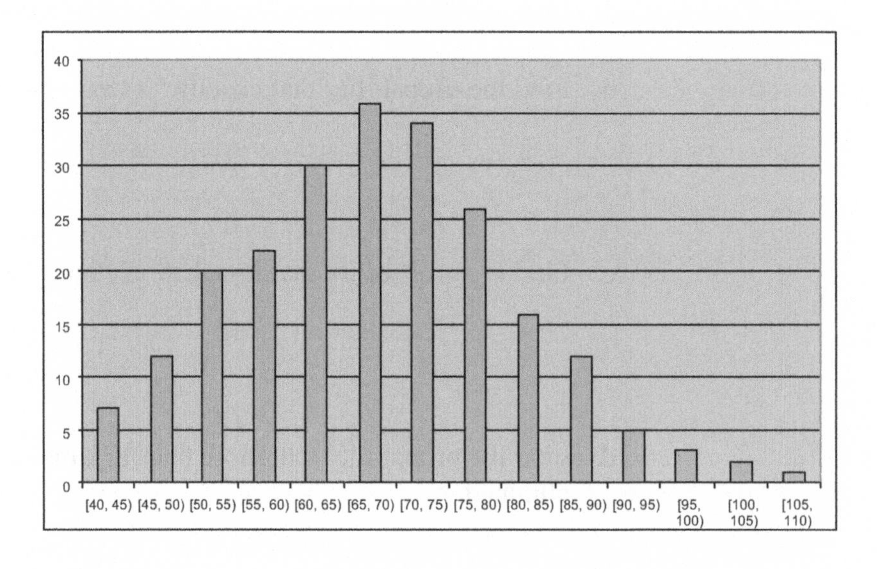

What do you observe? Can you guess how would a bigger sample look like?

As you can see in the second case, the histogram can be approximated by the drawn curve. That curve is called the **normal distribution**. The variables are distributed as for example: height, weight, shoe size and many other variables, specifically biological variables.

The function that describes the normal distribution is:

$$f(z)=\frac{1}{\sqrt{2\pi}}e^{\left(-\frac{z^2}{2}\right)}, -\infty < z < \infty$$

1. The normal distribution is characterized by two numbers: The ________ μ and the ____________________ σ

2. Fill the missing data for the following distributions:

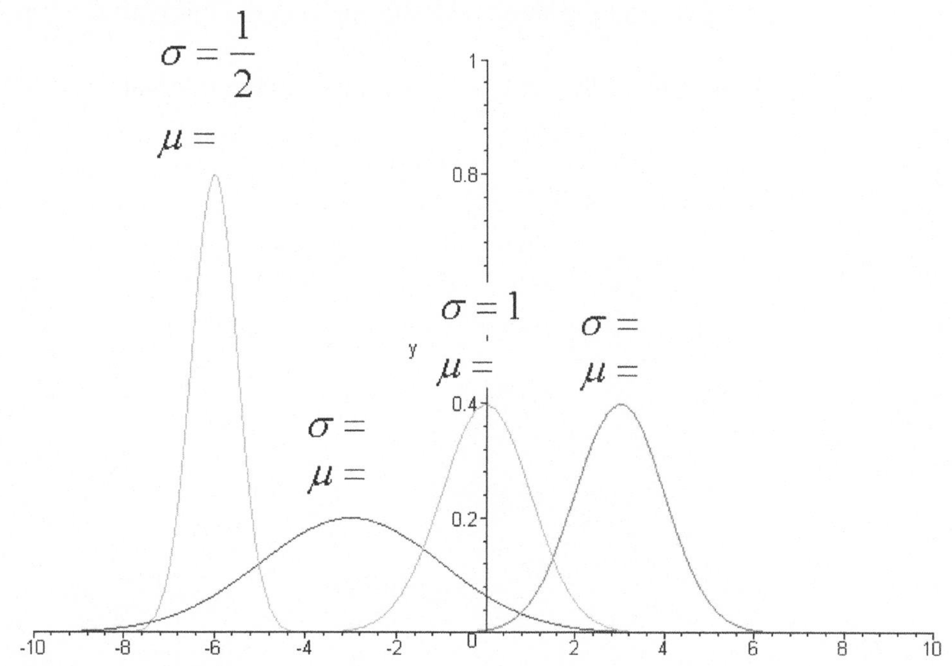

3. **The standard normal distribution** is the one with $\mu =$ __ y $\sigma =$ __ (Green)

4. The mean μ is located at the _____________ of the distribution.

5. The standard deviation σ represents the distance between the mean and the ________________

Properties of the normal distribution

6. The _______ under the curve or the probability from negative infinity to plus infinity is ____

7. The normal distribution is symmetrical that means that the area under the graph on each side of the mean is _____

8. The shape and position of a normal distribution depend on the parameters therefore there is an _______________ number of normal distributions. The distribution gets will narrower and taller as______________________

9. In general the area under the curve in the interval $\mu \pm 1\sigma$ is ________

10. In general the area under the curve in the interval $\mu \pm 2\sigma$ is ________

11. In general the area under the curve in the interval $\mu \pm 3\sigma$ is ________

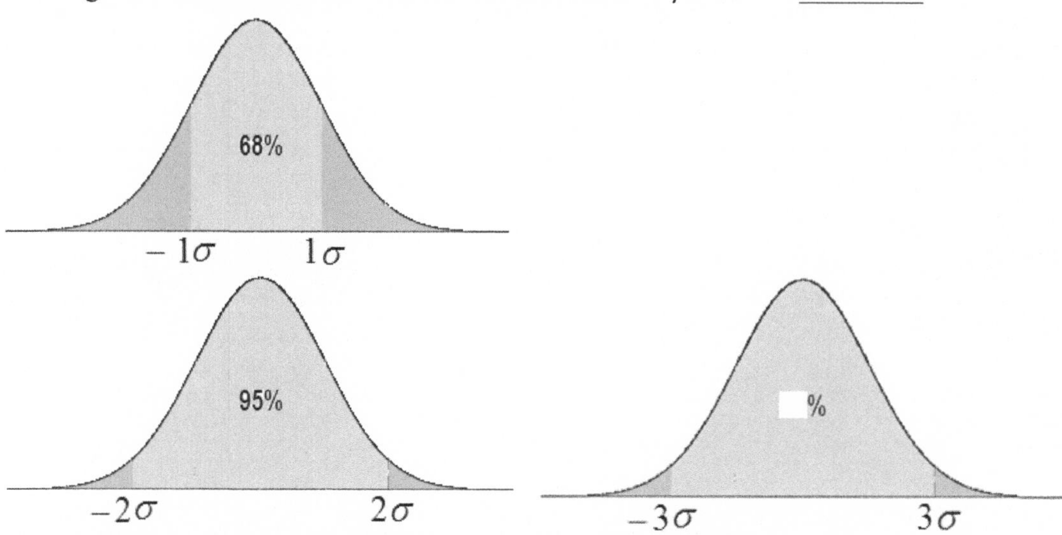

12. σ (the __________) gives us an idea about the _______________

13. μ (the ________) indicates the ______________________________

14. Normally the normal distribution is written as N(μ, σ^2), that means that a distribution N(28, 4) will have a mean of _______ and a SD of __________.

FINDING PROBABILIT OF $a < Z < b$

Shade and calculate use **GDC**: ShadeNorm(a, b) or ShadeNorm(a, b, μ, σ)

(Use large numbers for ∞ or $-\infty$)

15.

a. $P(Z \geq 0) =$ ____________________

b. $P(Z = 1) =$ ____________________

c. $P(Z < 1) =$ ____________________

d. $P(Z \geq 2) =$ ____________________

e. $P(Z \geq 2.23) =$ ____________________

f. $P(Z \geq 1.57) =$ ____________________

g. $P(Z \leq 1.86) =$ ____________________

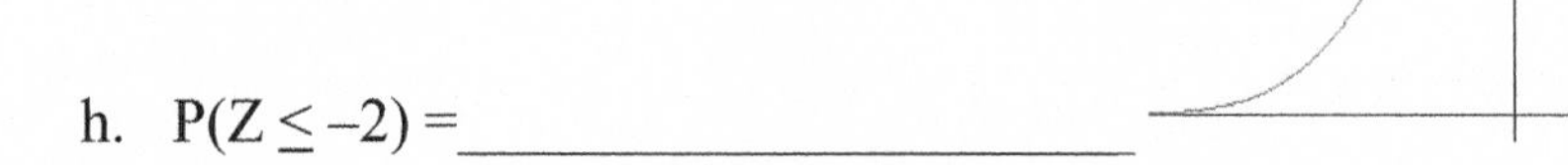

h. $P(Z \leq -2) =$ ____________________

i. $P(Z \leq -2.1) =$ ____________________

j. $P(Z \geq -3.11) =$ ____________________

k. $P(Z \geq -2) =$ ____________________

l. $P(Z \geq -0.58) =$ ____________________

m. $P(Z \leq -2.7) =$ ____________________

n. $P(-\infty \leq Z \leq -2.7) =$ ____________________

o. $P(3 \leq Z \leq -2.7) =$ ____________________

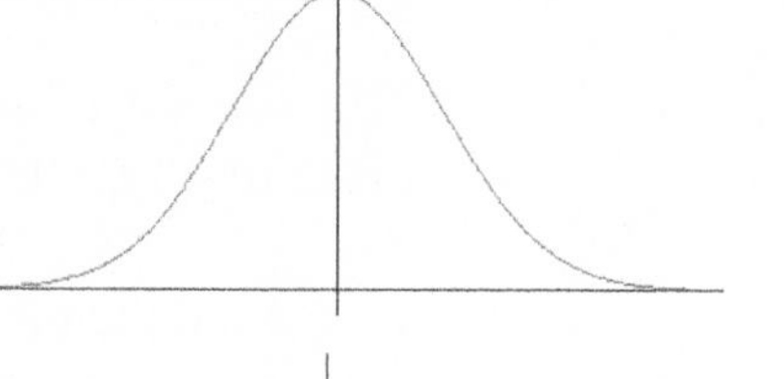

p. $P(1 \leq Z \leq 2) =$ ____________________

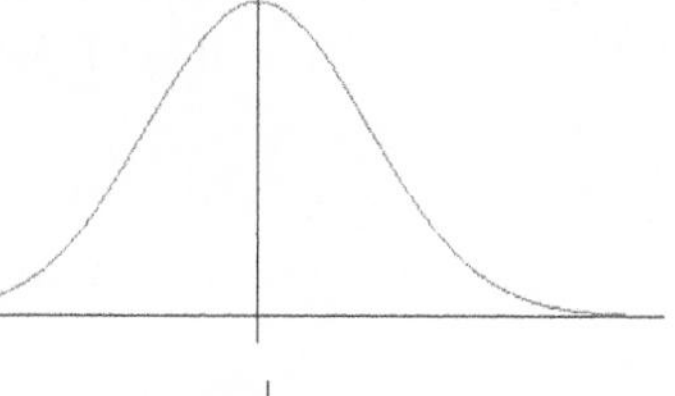

q. $P(-1.25 \leq Z \leq 0) =$ ________________

r. $P(-2.12 \leq Z \leq 1.65) =$ ______________

s. $P(-1.02 \leq Z \leq -0.25) =$ _____________

t. $P(0.97 \leq Z \leq 1.76) =$ _______________

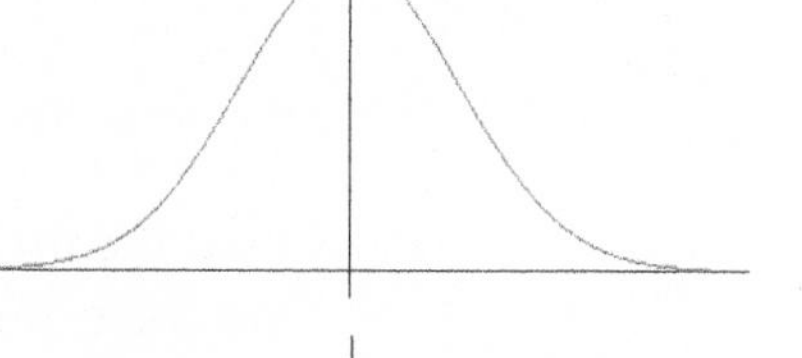

u. $P(1.54 \leq Z \leq \infty) =$ _________________

v. $P(1.31 \leq Z \leq 3.06) =$ _______________

FINDING PROBABILITY FOR $a < X < b$

The amount of time to produce a product follows a normal distribution with mean of 40 minutes and S. D. of 8 minutes.

16. Find the probability that the product is produced between 35 and 50 minutes. Shade the corresponding area on the following diagram.
    Use **GDC** to find your answer: normalcdf(35, 50, 40, 8)

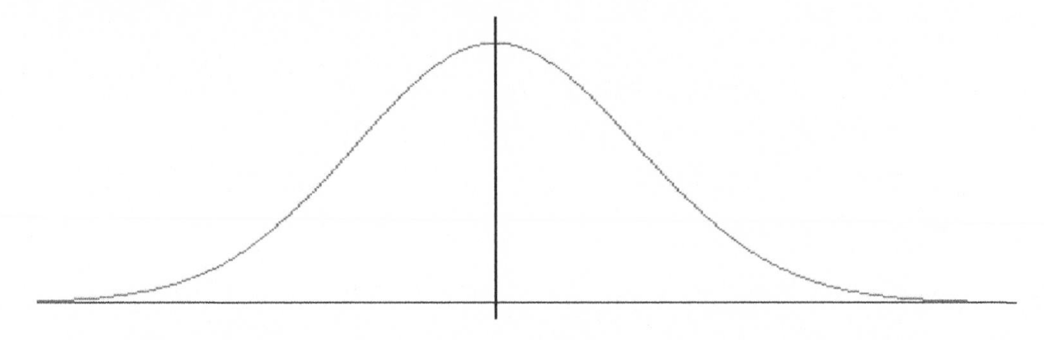

17. Find the probability that the product is produced in more than 38 minutes. Shade the corresponding area on the following diagram.
    Use GDC to find your answer: normalcdf(38, 1000, 40, 8)

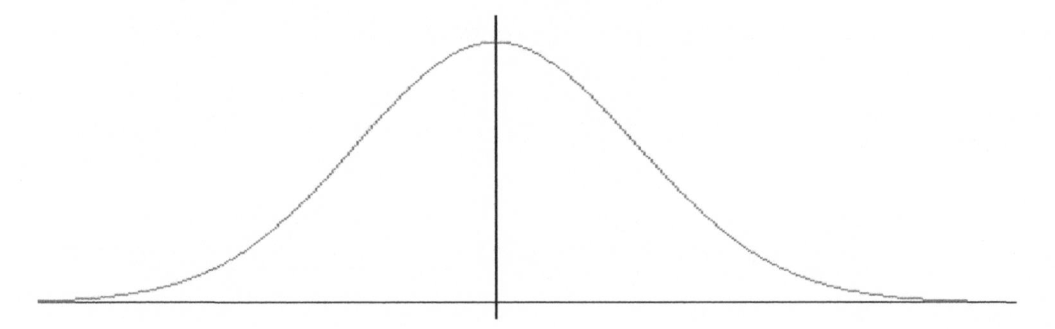

18. Find the probability that the product is produced in less than 34 minutes. Shade the corresponding area on the following diagram.
    Use GDC to find your answer: normalcdf(–1000,34, 40, 8)

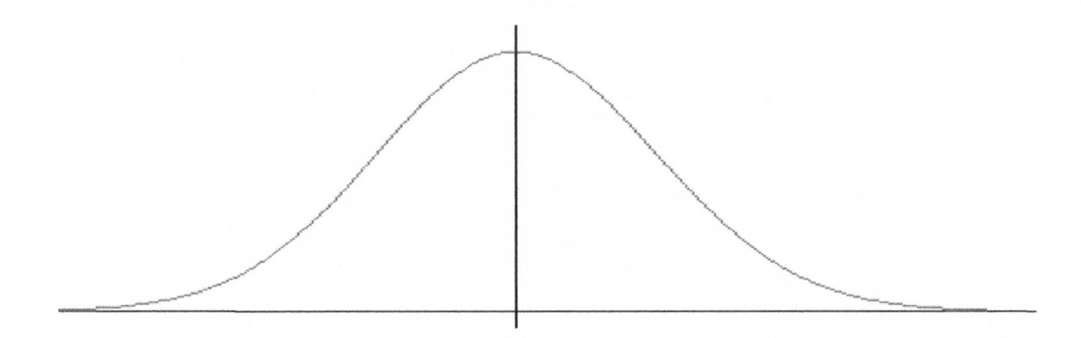

Exercises

19. In a normal distribution N(24, 6) Find and shade:

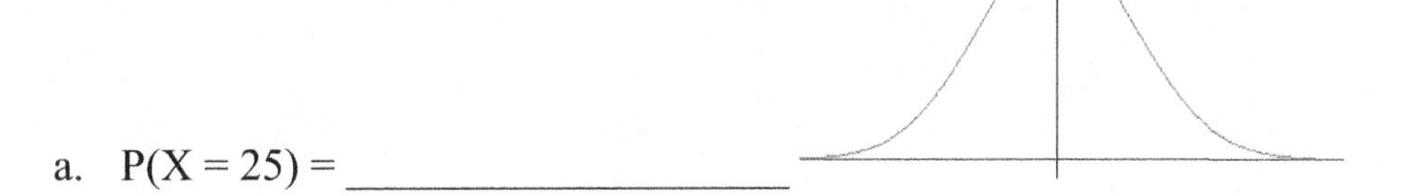

a. $P(X = 25) =$ ____________________

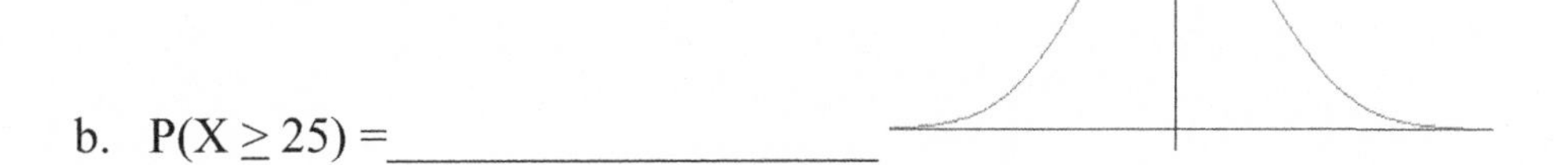

b. $P(X \geq 25) =$ ____________________

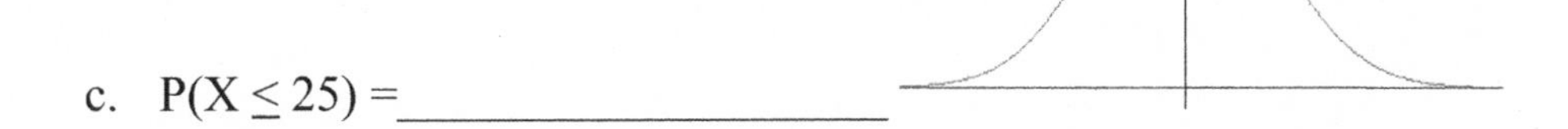

c. $P(X \leq 25) =$ ____________________

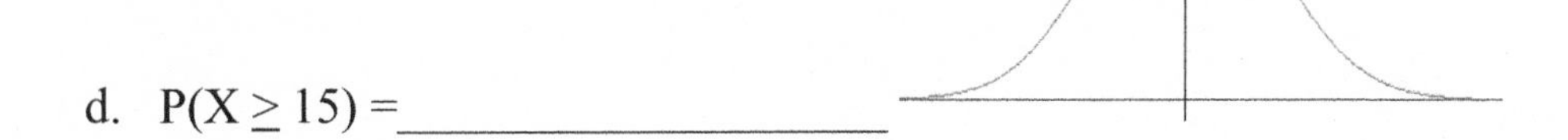

d. $P(X \geq 15) =$ ____________________

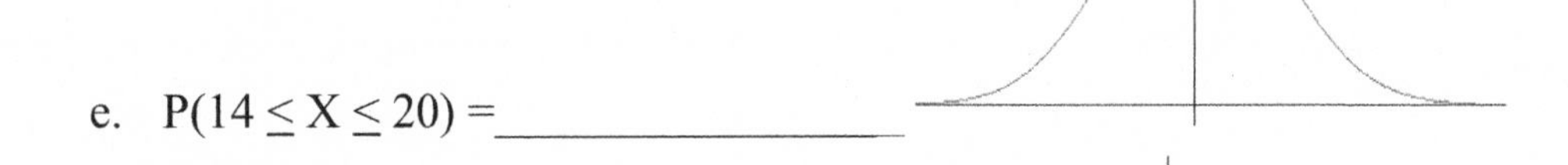

e. $P(14 \leq X \leq 20) =$ ____________________

f. $(19 \leq X \leq 31) =$ ____________________

20. In a lake there are 3000 fish distributed according to a normal distribution with a mean of 26cm and a standard deviation of 7cm.

a. Find and shade on the graph the interval in which 68% of the fish lengths are. How many fish in this case?

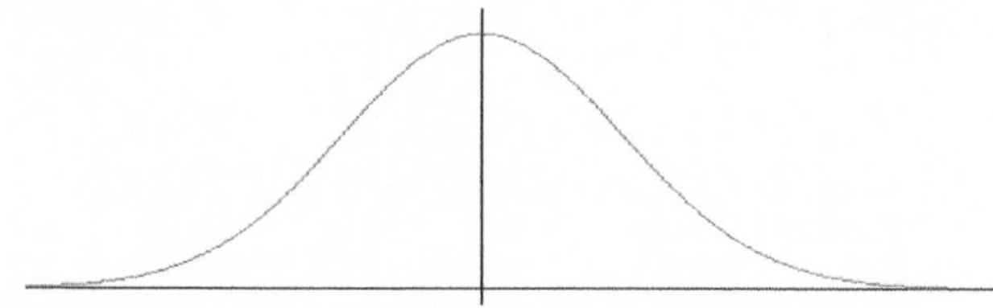

b. Find and shade on the graph the interval in which 95% of the fish lengths are. How many fish in this case?

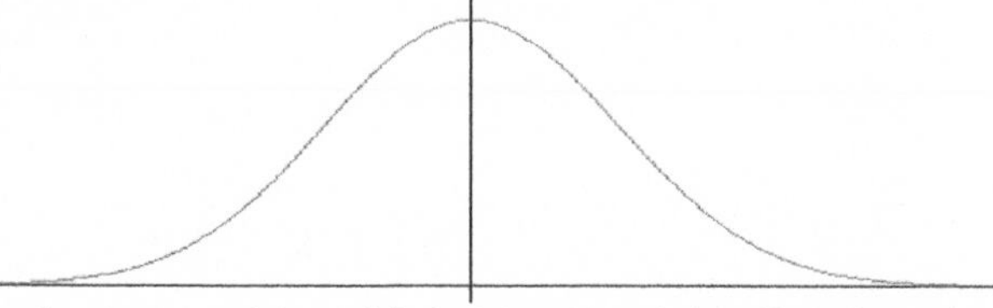

c. Find and shade on the graph the interval in which 99.7% of the fish lengths are. How many fish in this case?

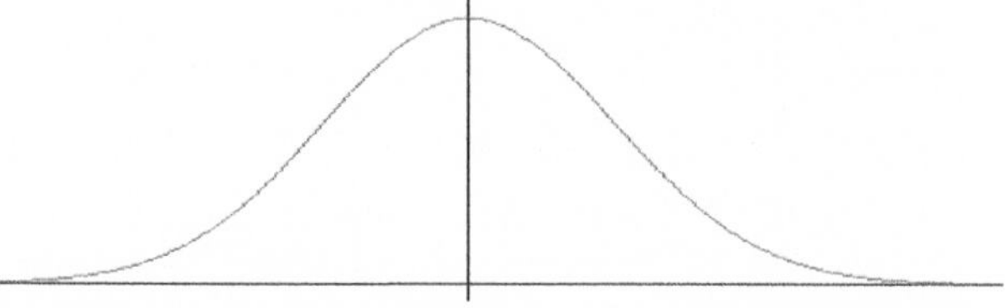

d. Find and the probability for a fish to measure between 23 and 28 cm. Shade on graph. How many fish in this would you expect in this case to be in this interval?

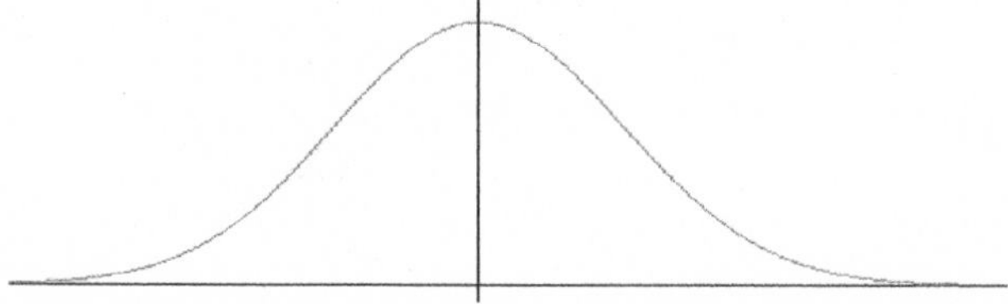

e. Find and the probability for a fish to measure between 12 and 24 cm. Shade on graph. How many fish in this would you expect in this case to be in this interval?

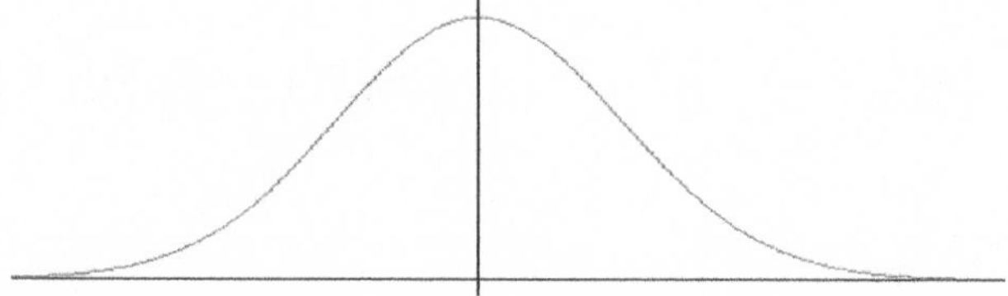

f. Find and the probability for a fish to measure between 27 and 28 cm. Shade on graph. How many fish in this would you expect in this case to be in this interval?

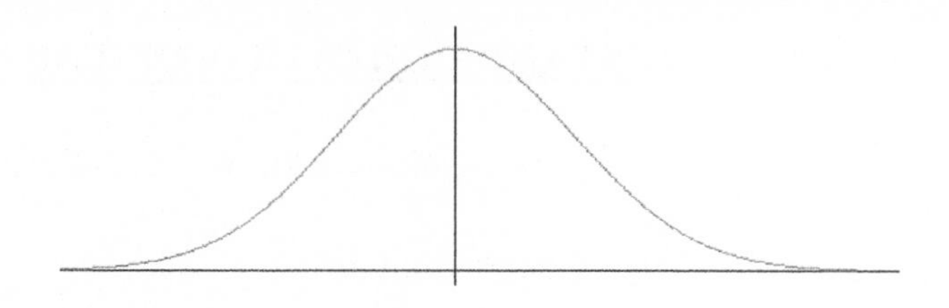

g. Find and shade on graph the probability for a fish to measure more than 26 cm. How many fish in this case?

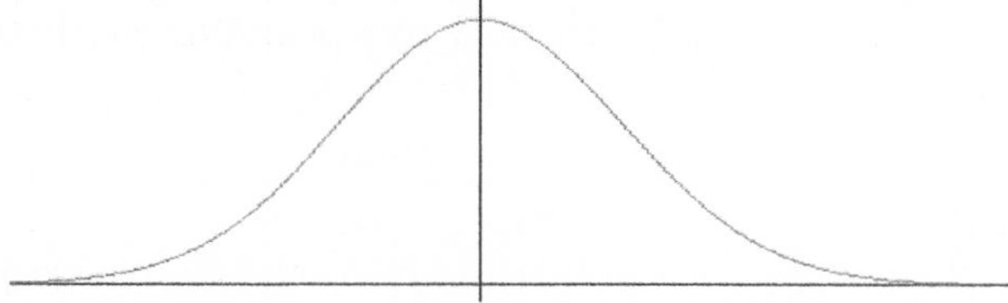

h. Find and shade on graph the probability for a fish to measure exactly 27 cm.

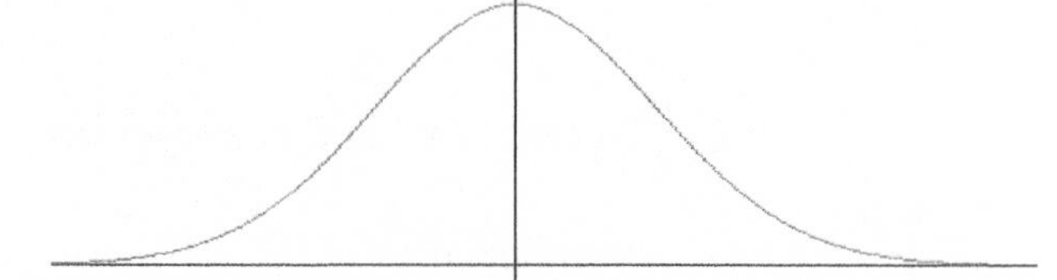

i. Find and shade on graph the probability for a fish to measure exactly 20 cm.

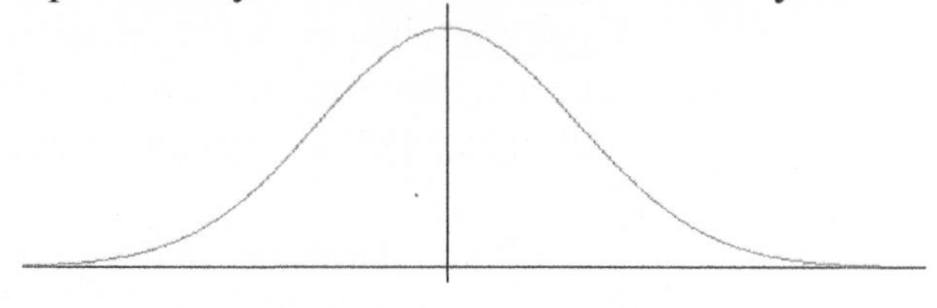

STANDARDIZATION OF THE NORMAL DISTRIBUTION

21. As we already know there is an __________ number of normal distributions, depending on _____ and ______. The standard distribution is one of them, the distribution in which the _________ is _____ and the SD is _______

22. Usually in a problem the distribution is not the standard therefore _____ is not _______ and ___________ is not ____. The way to transform any normal distribution to the standard one is the following: $Z = \dfrac{X - \mu}{\sigma}$

23. In reality what this expression means is rescaling the variable. And Z is the number of __________________ away from the mean.

Example The personnel manager of a large company requires applicants for a post take a certain test and achieve a score of 515. If test scores are normally distributed with mean 485 and standard deviation 30 what percentage of applicants pass the test?

Calculating the value of Z we get:

$$Z = \frac{X - \mu}{\sigma} = \frac{515 - 485}{30} = 1$$

$P(X \geq 500) = P(Z \geq 1) = 0.1587$, 15.87% of participants would pass the test. This result also means 515 is 1 standard deviation away from the mean.

24. Given a distribution N(22, 5) , find the standard variable Z, shade and calculate:

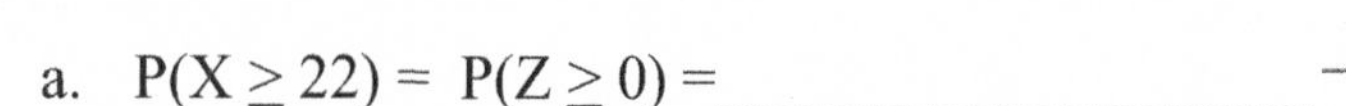

a. $P(X \geq 22) = P(Z \geq 0) =$ ____________________

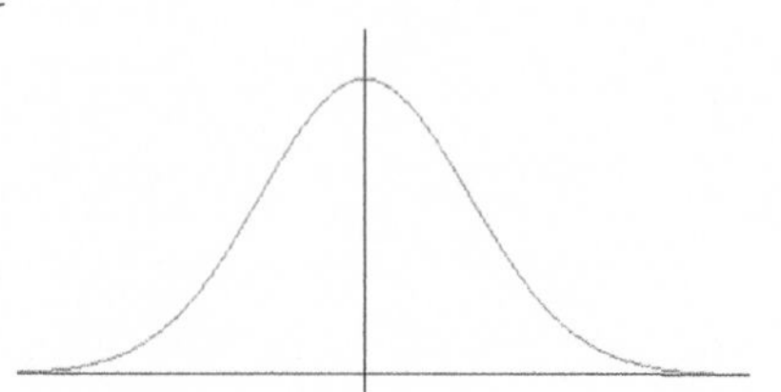

b. $P(X = 27) = P(Z = 1) =$ ____________________

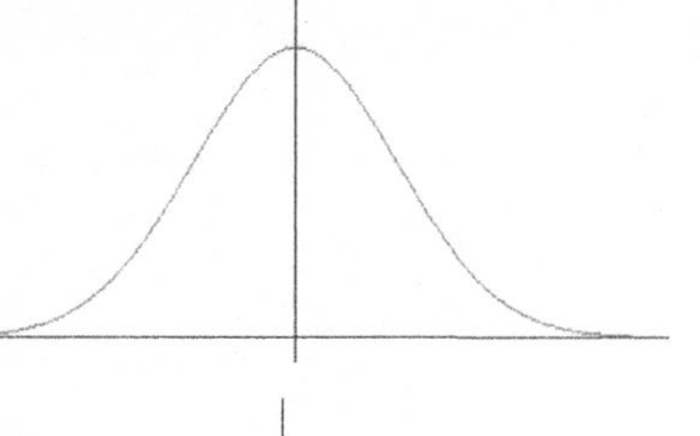

c. $P(X < 20) = P(Z < \_\_) =$ ____________________

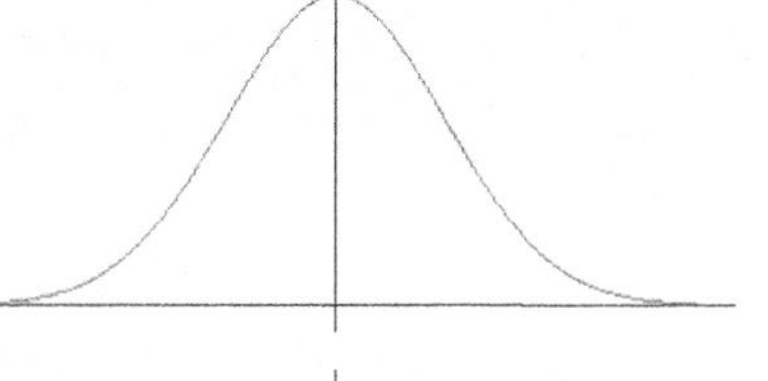

d. $P(X \geq 25) =$ ________________________________

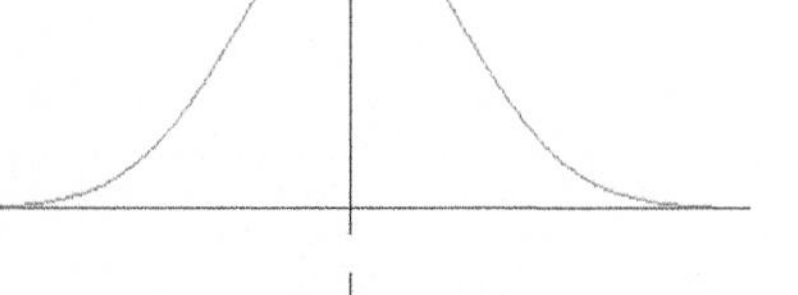

e. $P(X \geq 15) =$ ________________________________

f. $P(X \geq 0) =$ _________________________________

g. $P(X \leq 18) =$ ________________________________

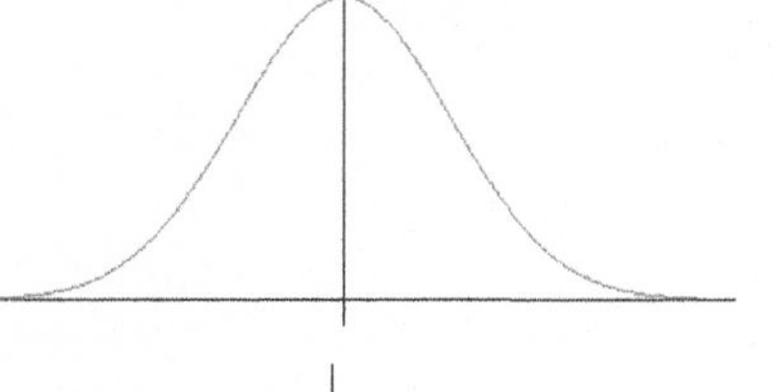

h. $P(-\infty \leq X \leq 27) =$ ___________________________

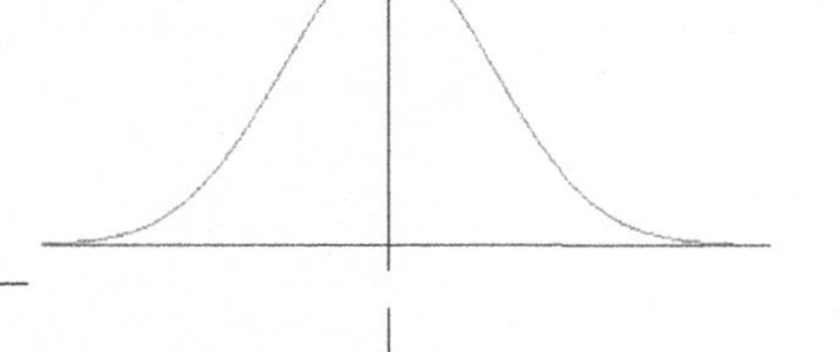

i. $P(20 \leq X \leq 25) =$ ___________________________

j. $P(12 \leq X \leq 18) =$ ___________________________

FINDING INVERSE NORMAL PROBABILITIES

25. The amount of time (X) to produce a product follows a normal distribution with mean of 40 minutes and S. D. of 8 minutes.

   a. Find the value of a, if 6% of the products are produced in less than a min. Shade the corresponding area on the following diagram. Use GDC to find your answer: invNorm(0.06, 40, 8)

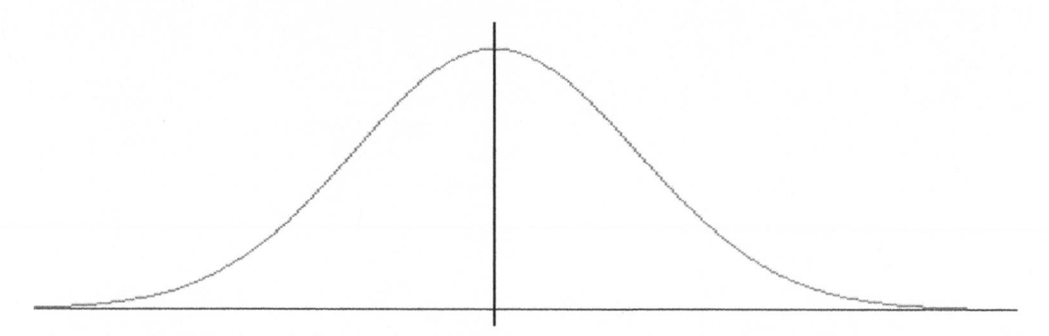

   b. Find the value of a, if 13% of the products are produced in more than a min. Shade the corresponding area on the following diagram. Use GDC to find your answer: invNorm(0.87, 40, 8)

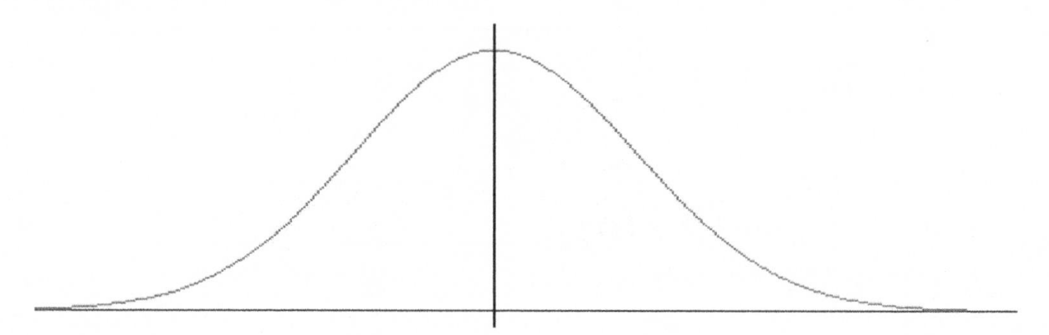

Find the value of a and b if the middle 50% of the products are produced in between a and b min. Shade the corresponding area on the following diagram. Use GDC to find your answer: , invNorm(0.25, 40, 8), invNorm(0.75, 40, 8)

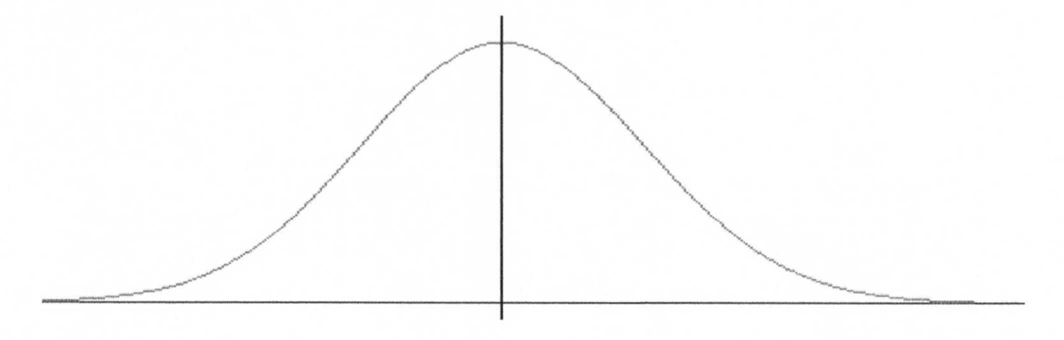

26. In a lake there are 2000 fish distributed according to a normal distribution with a mean of 26cm and a standard deviation of 7cm.

a. Find and shade the length interval for 80% of the fish. How many fish are expected to be in the interval in this case?

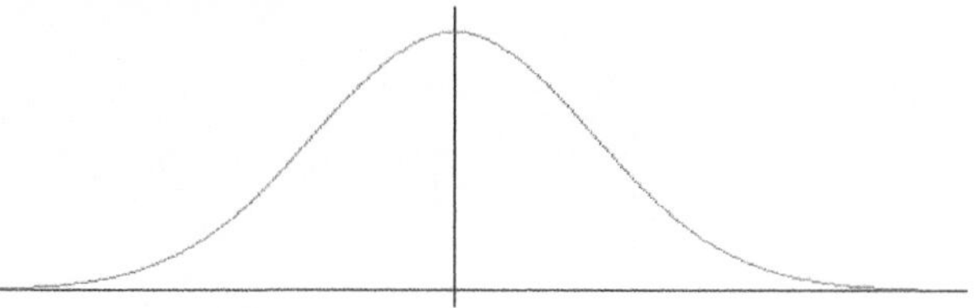

b. Find and shade the length interval for 90% of the fish. How many fish are expected to be in the interval in this case?

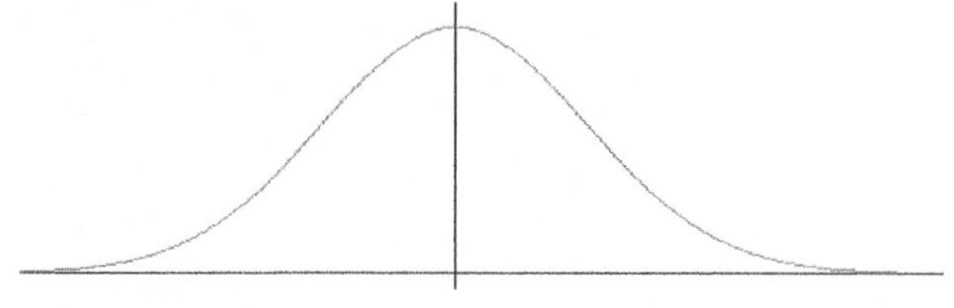

c. Find and shade the length interval for 75% of the fish. How many fish are expected to be in the interval in this case?

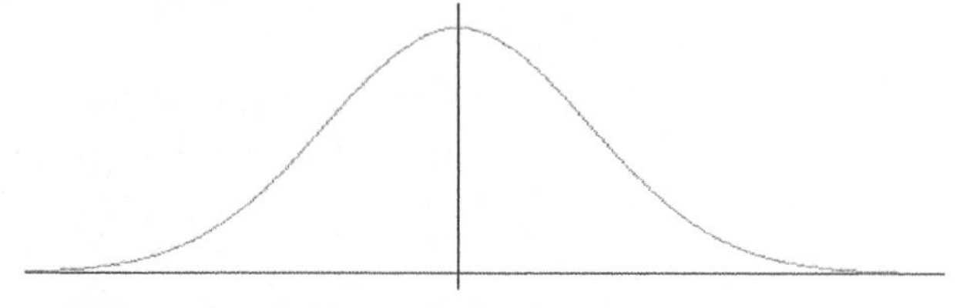

d. There is a probability of 0.2 that a fish's length is more than q, find q. How many fish are expected to be in the interval in this case?

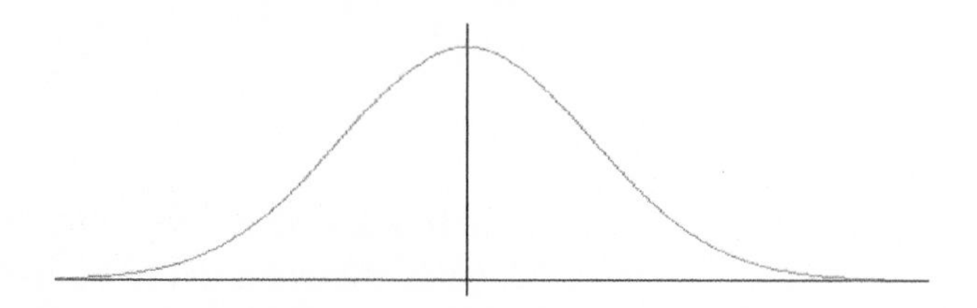

e. There is a probability of 0.32 that a fish's length is less than w, find w. How many fish are expected to be in the interval in this case?

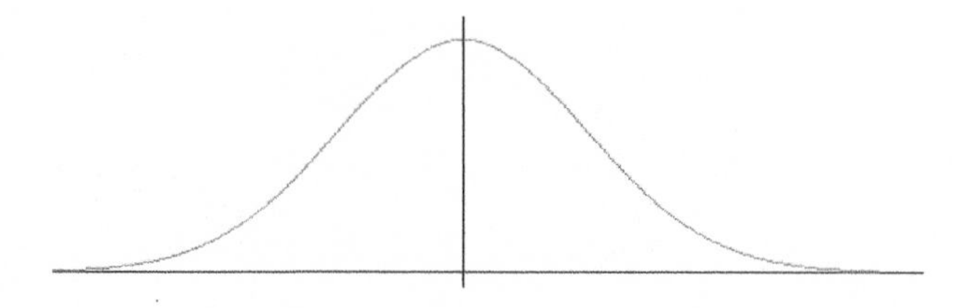

f. There is a probability of 0.4 that a fish's length is between a and b, find a and b. How many fish are expected to be in the interval in this case?

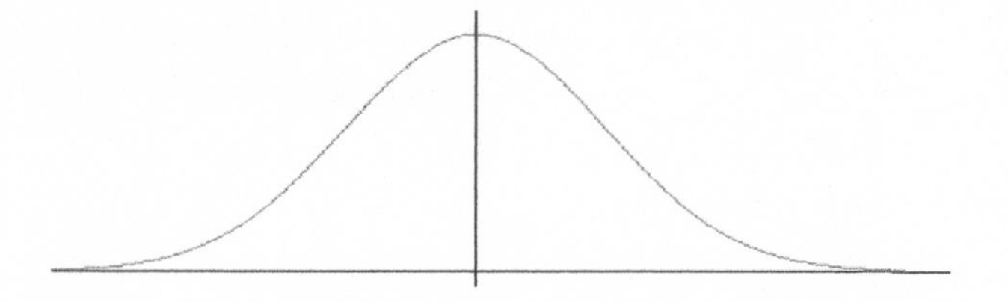

g. There is a probability of 0.6 that a fish's length is between a and b, find a and b. How many fish are expected to be in the interval in this case?

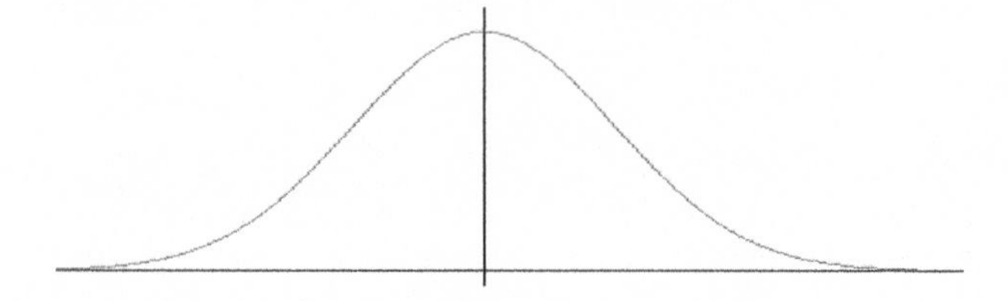

h. There is a probability of 0.1 that a fish's length is less than t, find t. How many fish are expected to be in the interval in this case?

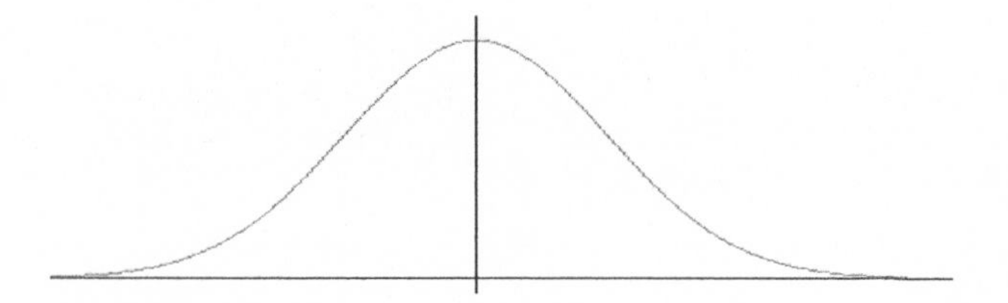

i. Find and shade the interval in which 65% of the fish measure. How many fish are expected to be in the interval in this case?

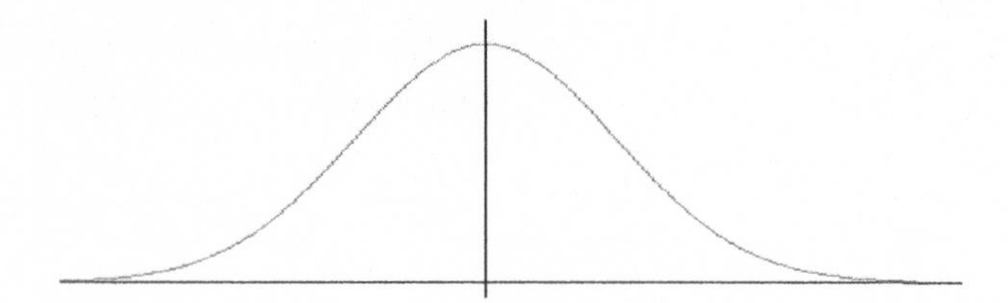

25. Calculate k if $P(X \le k) = 0.6103$ and X is a normal distribution N(15, 4)

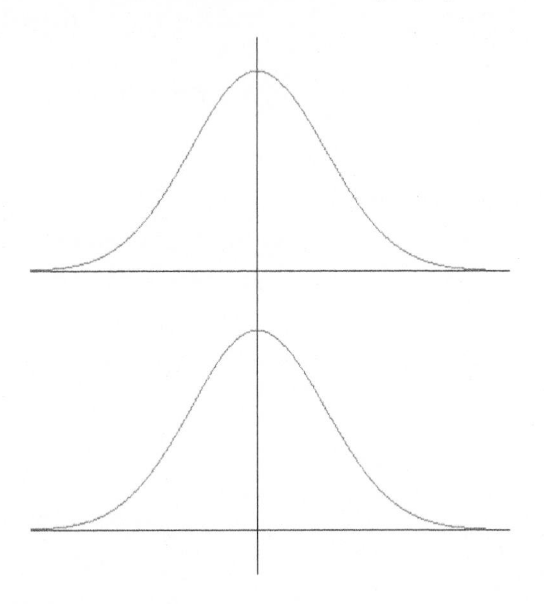

26. It is known that $P(X \le 7) = 0.9147$ and $P(X \le 6.5) = 0.7517$. Calculate

a. μ and σ
b. k so that $P(X \ge k) = 0.3$

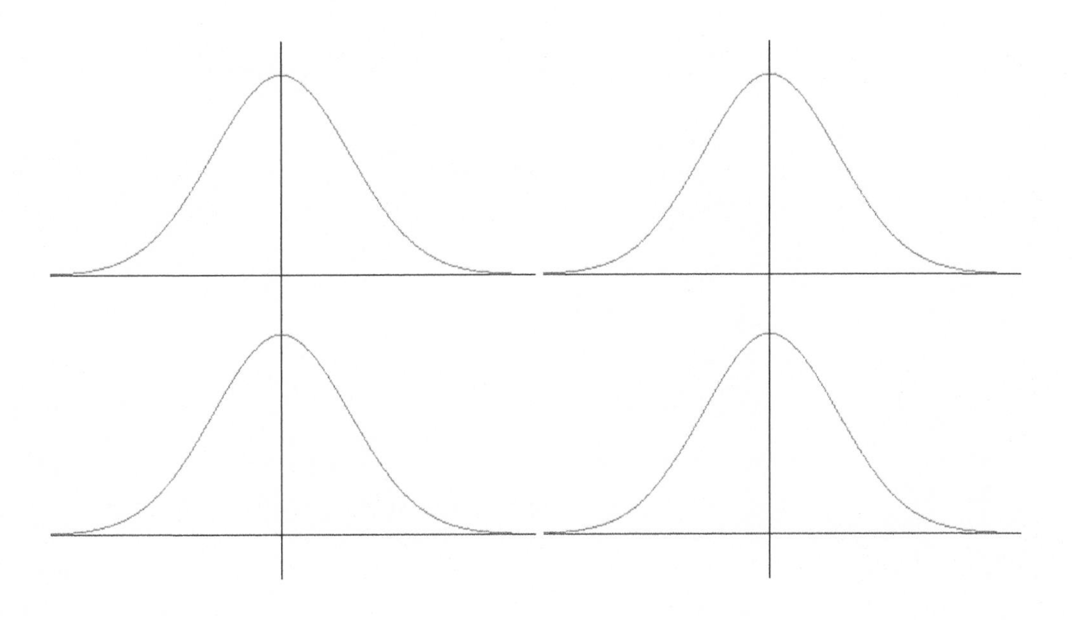

27. 500 high school students' grades are distributed normally with a mean of 72 and a standard deviation of 6.

a. Find the interval mean plus/minus 2 standard deviations.

b. What percentage of scores are between scores 60 and 70? How many students in this group?

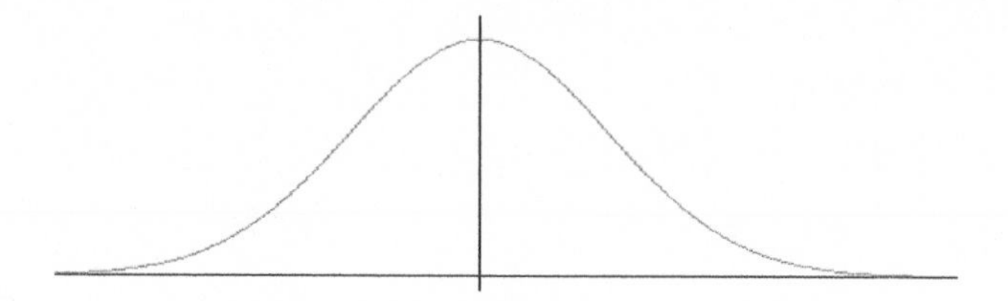

c. What percentage of scores are more than 88? How many students in this group?

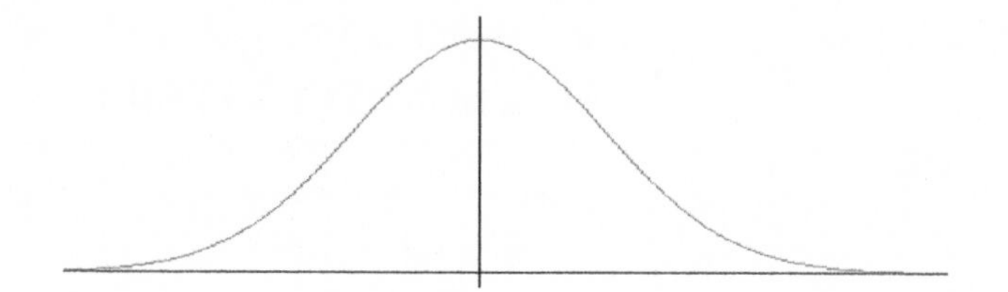

d. What percentage of scores are less than 60? How many students in this group?

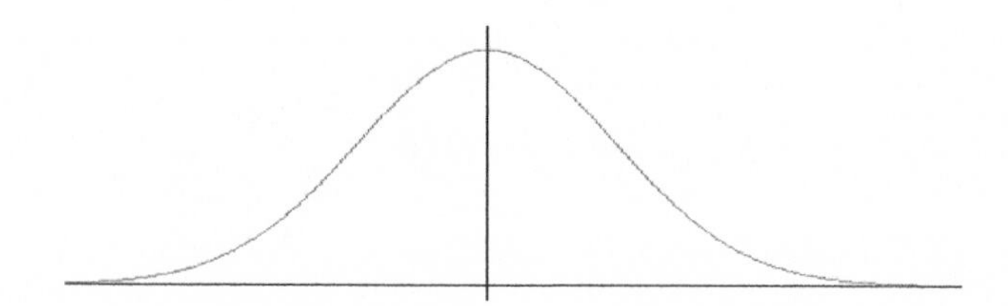

e. Can students' grades distribute normally? Explain.

28. The time it takes to complete a certain journey is normally distributed with a mean of 50 days and a standard deviation of 4 days.

   a. The probability that the length of the journey lies between 53 and 60 days is represented by the shaded area in the following diagram.

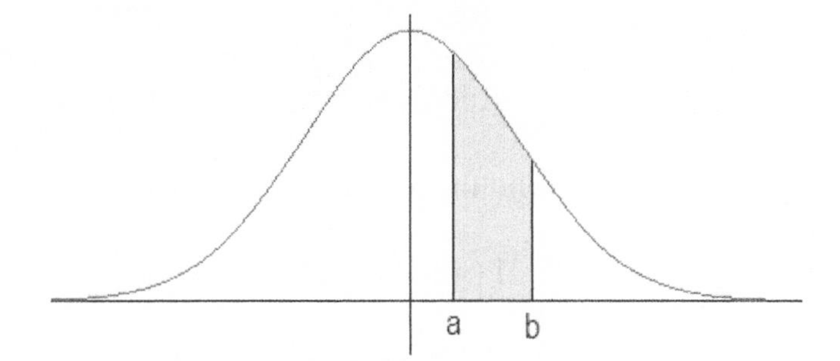

   Write down the values of *a* and *b*.

   b. Find the probability that the length of the journey is more than 57 days.

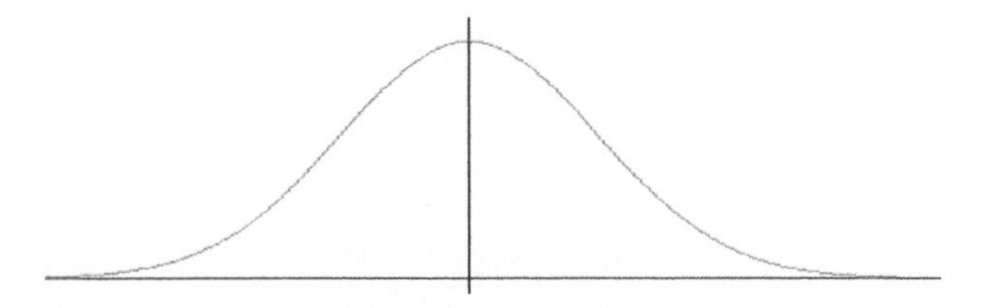

   c. Find the probability that the length of the journey is between 56 and 61 days.

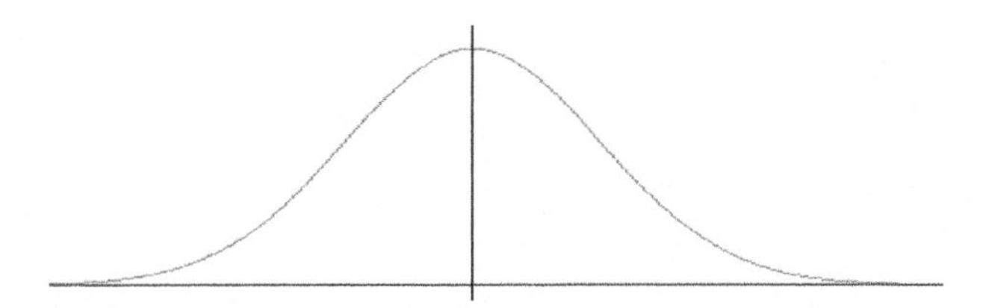

   d. 80% of the travellers complete the journey after x days. Find x.

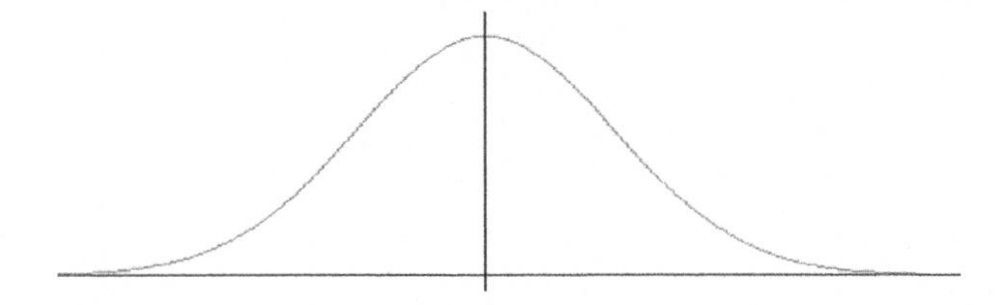

29. The weight of a certain animal is normally distributed with mean of 150 kg and standard deviation of 12 kg. We classify the animals in the following way:

Small	weight < 130
Medium	$130 \le$ weight < 170
Big	$170 \le$ weight

Add these boundaries to your diagram.

a. Find the probability for each one the cases described.

P(weight < 130) = ______________

P($130 <$ weight < 170) = ______________

P(weight > 170) = ______________

b. There is a probability of 0.2 for an animal to have a weight bigger than q. Find q.

P(weight $>$ q) = 0.2   q = _________

c. In a jungle with 3000 animals how many are expected to have a weight bigger than q?

ANSWER KEY

1.1. – RATE OF CHANGE

Example 1: Oil prices, represented as a function of time P(t):

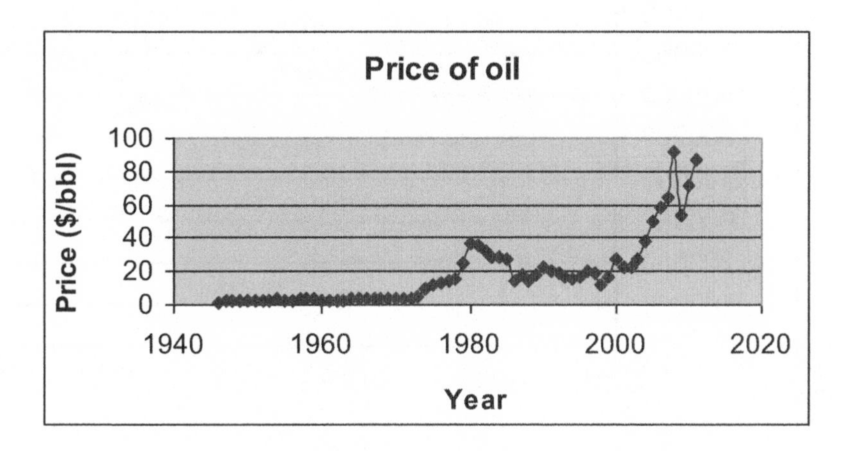

1. As you can see there have been periods of time in history in which the prices have changed slowly, Identify one of them: $t \in (1950, 1970)$
2. In other periods the prices have been changing very quickly, identify one

   positive change: $t \in (2003, 2005)$ and one negative change: $t \in (2008, 2009)$
3. In this graph what are the units of the change of price: $\left[\dfrac{\$}{bbl \cdot year}\right]$

4. Find the average rate of change in oil prices between 1970 and 1985. Is this average similar to the real change in prices? Explain your answer.

   $Av_{1970-1985} = \dfrac{24}{15} = 1.6 \ \frac{\$}{bbl \cdot year}$ It is not similar to real change as the prices went up and down during that period of time.

5. Find the average rate of change between 1945 and 2005, how can this change be represented graphically?

   $Av_{1945-2005} = \dfrac{48}{60} = 0.8 \ \frac{\$}{bbl \cdot year}$ The average rate of change is the slope of the line the connects the two points.

Example 2: Population of 20 – 29 year olds in southern Europe for example, represented as a function of time P(t):

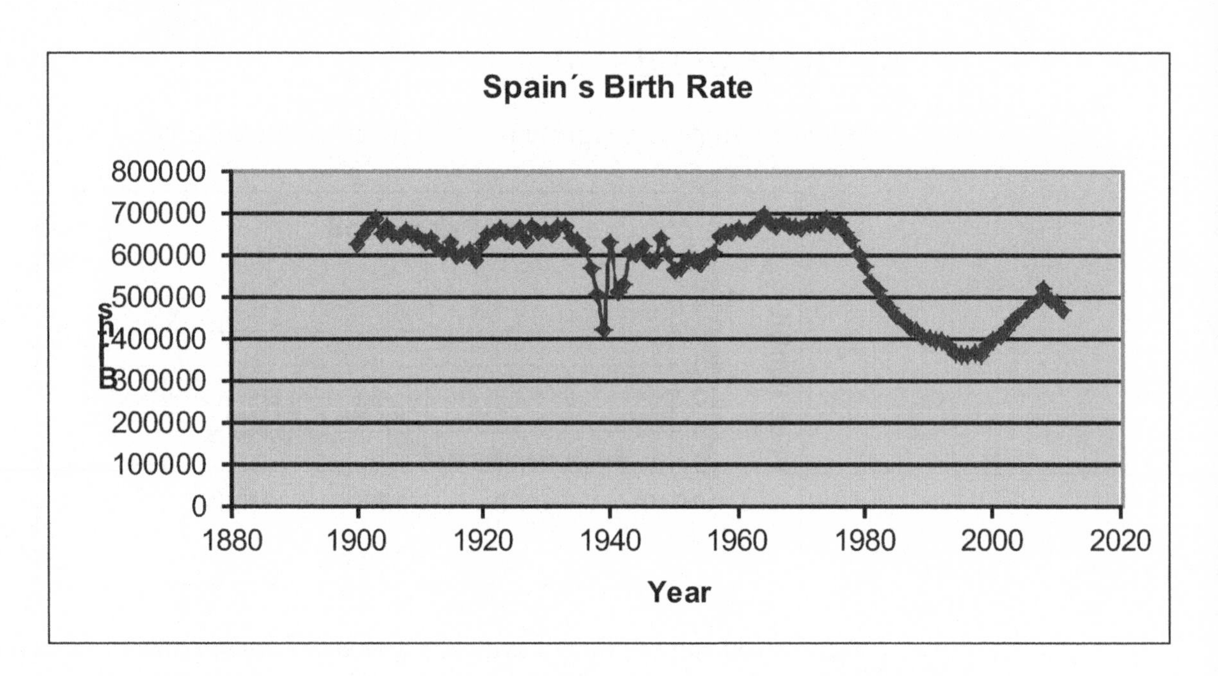

6. During what period of time the fastest change occurs? $t \in (1939,1940)$

7. In this graph what are the units of the change of birth: $\left[\frac{Births}{year}\right]$

8. Find the average rate of change between 1960 and 2000. Is this average similar to the real change in births? Explain your answer.

$Av_{1960-2000} = -\frac{260000}{40} = -6500_{\frac{Births}{year}}$ It shows some similarity to the real tendency.

9. Find the average rate of change between 2000 and 2010, how can this change be represented graphically?

$Av_{2000-2010} = \frac{100000}{10} = 10000_{\frac{Births}{year}}$ The average rate of change is the slope of the line the connects the two points.

1.2. – INTRODUCTION TO LIMITS

1. $x \to \infty$ means that x approaches infinity
2. $x \to -\infty$ means that x approaches negative infinity
3. $x \to 3$ means that x approaches 3, either slightly less or slightly more than 3
4. $x \to 3^+$ means that x approaches 3 from the right x is slightly more than 3
5. $x \to 3^-$ means that x approaches 3 from the left x is slightly less than 3
6. $x \to 0^-$ means that x approaches 0 from the right x is slightly more than 0
7. $x \to 0^+$ means that x approaches 0 from the left x is slightly less than 0

GRAPHICAL INTERPRETATION OF LIMITS

1. Given the graph of the function:

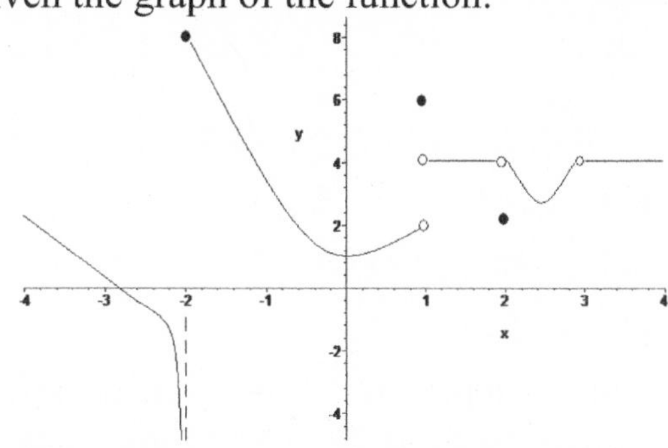

a. $\lim_{x\to 0^-}(f(x))=1$ $\lim_{x\to 0^+}(f(x))=$ 1 f(0) = 1 $\lim_{x\to 0}(f(x))=1$

b. $\lim_{x\to -3^+}(f(x))=0.4$ $\lim_{x\to -3^-}(f(x))=0.4$ $f(-3)=0.4$ $\lim_{x\to -3}(f(x))=0.4$

c. $\lim_{x\to -2^+}(f(x))=8$ $\lim_{x\to -2^-}(f(x))=-\infty$ $f(-2)=8$ $\lim_{x\to -2}(f(x))=$D.E.

d. $\lim_{x\to 1^-}(f(x))=2$ $\lim_{x\to 1^+}(f(x))=4$ $f(1)=6$ $\lim_{x\to 1}(f(x))=$D.E.

e. $\lim_{x\to 2^+}(f(x))=4$ $\lim_{x\to 2^-}(f(x))=4$ $f(2)=2$ $\lim_{x\to 2}(f(x))=4$

f. Using the graph find all the values of a for which f(a) does not exist: a = 3

2. Given the graph of the function:

a. $\lim_{x\to 0^-}(f(x))=2.4$

b. $\lim_{x\to 0^+}(f(x))=2.4$

c. $\lim_{x\to 0}(f(x))=2.4$

d. $\lim_{x\to -3^+}(f(x))=-\infty$

e. $\lim_{x\to -3^-}(f(x))=-\infty$

f. $\lim_{x\to -3}(f(x))=-\infty$

g. $f(-3)=$ D.E.

h. $Lim_{x\to 3^+}(f(x))=4$

i. $Lim_{x\to 3^-}(f(x))=-\infty$

j. $Lim_{x\to 3}(f(x))=$ D.E

k. $f(3)=4$

l. $\lim_{x\to -1^-}(f(x))=\infty$

m. $\lim_{x\to -1^+}(f(x))=\infty$

n. $\lim_{x\to -1}(f(x))=\infty$

o. $f(-1)=$ D.E.

g. State the equations of all the asymptotes: $x=-3, x=-1, x=3$

3. Find the following limits: $\lim_{x\to\infty}(f(x)) = 2$ $\lim_{x\to\infty}(f(x))$=D.E. $\lim_{x\to\infty}(f(x)) = 3$

4. Find the limits: $\lim_{x\to-\infty}(f(x)) =$ D.E. $\lim_{x\to\infty}(f(x)) = 0$

   $\lim_{x\to-\infty}(f(x)) = \infty$ $\lim_{x\to-\infty}(f(x)) = -3$

5. Given the following data for a certain function $f(x)$:

x	-17	-13	k	0	p	8	12	22	55
$f(x)$	0	1	1	8	2	11	N	-3	-7

   a. The limits: $Lim_{x\to-17}(f(x)) = 0$ $Lim_{x\to-13}(f(x)) = 1$ $Lim_{x\to p}(f(x)) = 2$
   b. $Lim_{x\to-1}(f(x)) = 1,\ k = -1$
   c. $Lim_{x\to p}(f(x)) + Lim_{x\to 55}(f(x)) = 2 - 7 = -5$
   d. $f^{-1}(-2) = 12,\ N = -2$

6. Horizontal asymptotes appear at the ends of the graph (left or right). In case we look for them we need to check the limit of the function when x tends to Infinity or negative infinity.
7. Vertical asymptotes appear when x tends to a value and f(x) tends to infinity or negative infinity. We check lateral limits to see the behaviour of the function next to it.
8. Given the following data for a certain function $f(x)$:

x	-7	-1	0	2	p	7	11	23	35
$f(x)$	4	0	4	8	2	11	N	5	5

   e. Find the value of the following limits:
   $Lim_{x\to 0}(f(x)) = 4$ $Lim_{x\to 2}(f(x)) = 8$ $Lim_{x\to 11}(f(x)) = N$
   f. $Lim_{x\to 11}(f(x)) = Lim_{x\to p}(f(x))$, N = 2.
   g. Find $Lim_{x\to-1}(f(x)) - Lim_{x\to 7}(f(x)) = 0 - 11 = -11$

1.3. – DEFINITION OF DERIVATIVE

1. The derivative is the slope of the tangent to the function at a certain point.
2. Given the function, sketch the tangent in each one of the points:

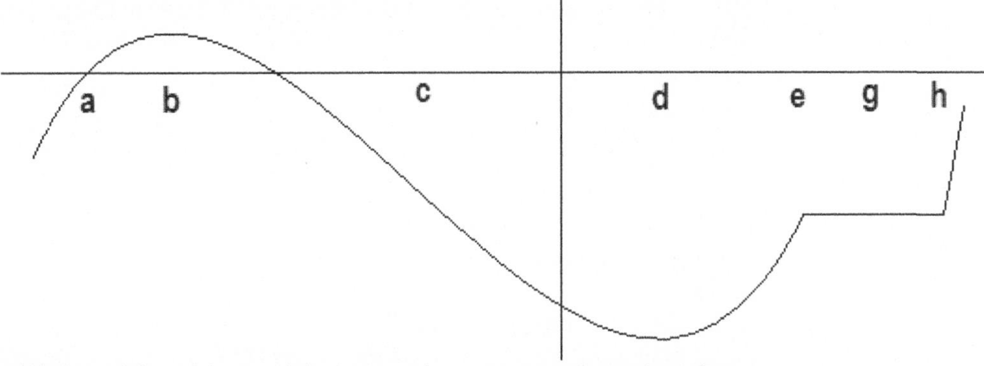

Fill the table with: Positive, negative, zero or doesn't exist.

	x = a	x = b	x = c	x = d	x = e	x = g	x = h
f(x)	Zero	Positive	Negative	Negative	Negative	Negative	Negative
f'(x)	Positive	Zero	Negative	Zero	D.E.	Zero	D.E

3. Given the function, sketch the tangent in each one of the points:

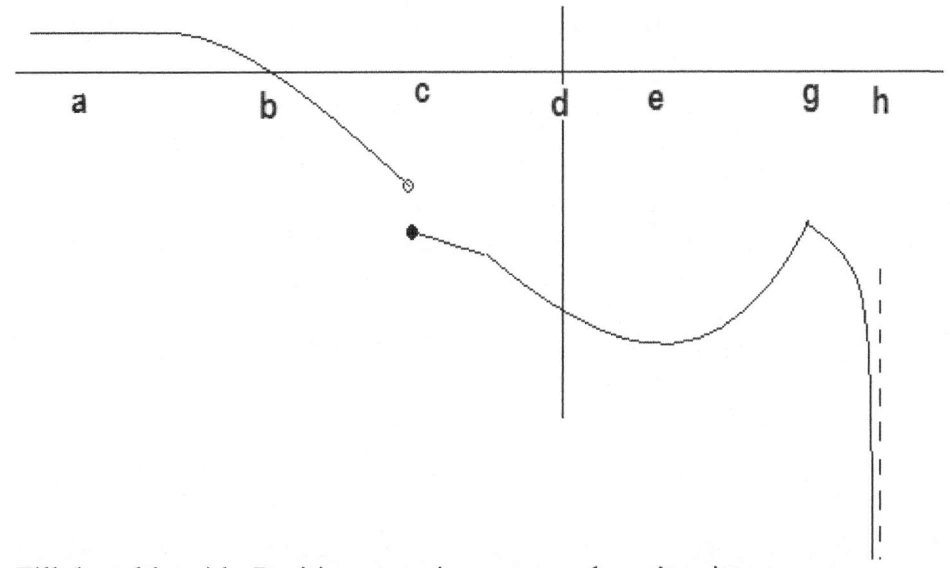

Fill the table with: Positive, negative, zero or doesn't exist.

	x = a	x = b	x = c	x = d	x = e	x = g	x = h
f(x)	Positive	Zero	Negative	Negative	Negative	Negative	D.E.
f'(x)	Zero	Negative	D.E.	Negative	Zero	D.E.	D.E.

4. Given the function f(x) = –x^2. f represents the temperature as the function of height x given in km:

5. Fill the blanks and indicate the corresponding points on the graph:
   f(1) = –1 f(1.4) = –1.96
   Draw the line that connects the points and find its slope
   $$m = \frac{-1.96-(-1)}{1.4-1} = -2.4$$ 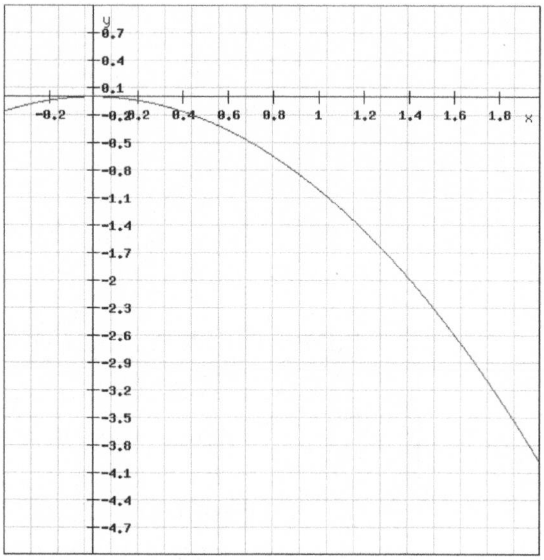
6. Fill the blanks and indicate the corresponding points on the graph:
   f(1) = –1 f(1.2) = –1.44
   Draw the line that connects the points and find its slope
   $$m = \frac{-1.21-(-1)}{1.2-1} = -2.2$$
7. Fill the blanks and indicate the corresponding points on the graph:
   f(1) = –1 f(1.1) =–1.21
   Draw the line that connects the points and find its slope
   $$m = \frac{-1.21-(-1)}{1.1-1} = -2.1$$
8. What do you think the slope of the tangent at the point where x = 1 is? 2
9. Looking at the process to find the slope at the point where x = 1, can you think how to find the slope of the tangent in general? Choose a point very (!, in reality infinitely close) close to it on its left or right and find the slope between those points.
10. What does the slope **between 2 points** represent? Make reference to height and temperature and give units. It represents the **mean** rate of change of temperature with height, its units are degrees/km
11. What does the slope of the tangent to the function **at a certain point** (the derivative) represent? Make reference to height and temperature and give units. It represents the **instantaneous** rate of change of temperature with height, its units are degrees/km
12. The slope between 2 points is the **mean** rate of change
13. The slope at a certain point is the **instantaneous** rate of change

FORMAL DEFINITION OF DERIVATIVE

Differentiate the following functions, use the definition ONLY:

1. $f(x) = mx + b$

$$\frac{df}{dx} = f'(x) = \lim_{h\to 0}\frac{f(x+h)-f(x)}{h} = \lim_{h\to 0}\frac{m(x+h)+b-mx+b}{h} = m$$

2. $f(x) = x^2 + k$

$$\frac{df}{dx} = f'(x) = \lim_{h\to 0} \frac{f(x+h)-f(x)}{h} = \lim_{h\to 0} \frac{(x+h)^2+k-(x^2+k)}{h} =$$

$$\lim_{h\to 0} \frac{2xh+h^2}{h} = \lim_{h\to 0} \frac{h(2x+h)}{h} = \lim_{h\to 0} \left(2x+h\right) = 2x$$

3. $f(x) = x^3 + k$

$$\frac{df}{dx} = f'(x) = \lim_{h\to 0} \frac{f(x+h)-f(x)}{h} = \lim_{h\to 0} \frac{(x+h)^3+k-(x^3+k)}{h} =$$

$$\lim_{h\to 0} \frac{3x^2h+3xh^2+h^3}{h} = \lim_{h\to 0} \frac{h(3x^2+3xh+h^2)}{h} = \lim_{h\to 0} \left(3x^2+3xh+h^2\right) = 3x^2$$

4. $f(x) = 4x - 3x^2$

$$\frac{df}{dx} = f'(x) = \lim_{h\to 0} \frac{f(x+h)-f(x)}{h} = \lim_{h\to 0} \frac{4(x+h)-3(x+h)^2-(4x-3x^2)}{h} = 4-6x$$

5. $f(x) = \sqrt{x+1}$

$$\frac{df}{dx} = f'(x) = \lim_{h\to 0} \frac{f(x+h)-f(x)}{h} = \lim_{h\to 0} \frac{\sqrt{x+h+1}-\sqrt{x+1}}{h} =$$

$$\lim_{h\to 0} \frac{\sqrt{x+h+1}-\sqrt{x+1}}{h} \cdot \frac{(\sqrt{x+h+1}+\sqrt{x+1})}{(\sqrt{x+h+1}+\sqrt{x+1})} = \lim_{h\to 0} \frac{(x+h+1)-(x+1)}{h} \cdot \frac{1}{(\sqrt{x+h+1}+\sqrt{x+1})}$$

$$\lim_{h\to 0} \frac{h}{h} \cdot \frac{1}{(\sqrt{x+h+1}+\sqrt{x+1})} = \frac{1}{2\sqrt{x+1}}$$

6. $f(x) = \dfrac{1}{2x+1}$

$$\frac{df}{dx} = f'(x) = \lim_{h\to 0} \frac{f(x+h)-f(x)}{h} = \lim_{h\to 0} \frac{\frac{1}{2(x+h)+1} - \frac{1}{2x+1}}{h} =$$

$$\lim_{h\to 0} \frac{(2x+1)-(2(x+h)+1)}{h(2(x+h)+1)(2x+1)} = \lim_{h\to 0} \frac{-2h}{h(2(x+h)+1)(2x+1)} = \frac{-2}{(2x+1)^2}$$

7. $f(x) = \dfrac{-3}{-x+2}$

$$\frac{df}{dx} = f'(x) = \lim_{h\to 0} \frac{f(x+h)-f(x)}{h} = \lim_{h\to 0} \frac{\frac{-3}{(-(x+h))+2} - \frac{-3}{-x+2}}{h} =$$

$$\lim_{h\to 0} \frac{(3x-6)+3(-(x+h)+2)}{h(-(x+h)+2)(-x+2)} = \lim_{h\to 0} \frac{-3h}{h(-(x+h)+2)(-x+2)} = \frac{-3}{(-x+2)^2}$$

8. $f(x) = \sqrt{2x} + 1$

$$\frac{df}{dx} = f'(x) = \lim_{h\to 0} \frac{f(x+h)-f(x)}{h} = \lim_{h\to 0} \frac{\_\_\_\_\_\_ - \_\_\_\_\_\_}{h} =$$

9. $f(x)=\sqrt{3x-5}+1$

$$\frac{df}{dx}=f'(x)=\lim_{h\to 0}\frac{f(x+h)-f(x)}{h}=\lim_{h\to 0}\frac{\sqrt{3(x+h)-5}+1-(\sqrt{3x-5}+1)}{h}=$$

$$\lim_{h\to 0}\frac{\sqrt{3(x+h)-5}-\sqrt{3x-5}}{h}\cdot\frac{(\sqrt{3(x+h)-5}+\sqrt{3x-5})}{(\sqrt{3(x+h)-5}+\sqrt{3x-5})}=$$

$$\lim_{h\to 0}\cdot\frac{3(x+h)-5-(3x-5)}{h(\sqrt{3(x+h)-5}+\sqrt{3x-5})}=\frac{3}{2\sqrt{3x-5}}$$

10. $f(x)=\frac{4}{5x+1}+2$

$$\frac{df}{dx}=f'(x)=\lim_{h\to 0}\frac{f(x+h)-f(x)}{h}=\lim_{h\to 0}\frac{\frac{4}{5(x+h)+1}-\frac{4}{5x+1}}{h}=$$

$$\lim_{h\to 0}\frac{(20x+4)-4(5(x+h)+1)}{h(5(x+h)+1)(5x+1)}=\lim_{h\to 0}\frac{-20h}{h(5(x+h)+1)(5x+1)}=\frac{-20}{(5x+1)^2}$$

11. $f(x)=\sqrt{2x-3}$

$$\frac{df}{dx}=f'(x)=\lim_{h\to 0}\frac{f(x+h)-f(x)}{h}=...=\frac{2}{2\sqrt{2x+3}}=\frac{1}{\sqrt{2x+3}}$$

12. $f(x)=\frac{1}{3x-4}$

$$\frac{df}{dx}=f'(x)=\lim_{h\to 0}\frac{f(x+h)-f(x)}{h}=...=\frac{-3}{(3x-4)^2}$$

13. Given the following function, find:

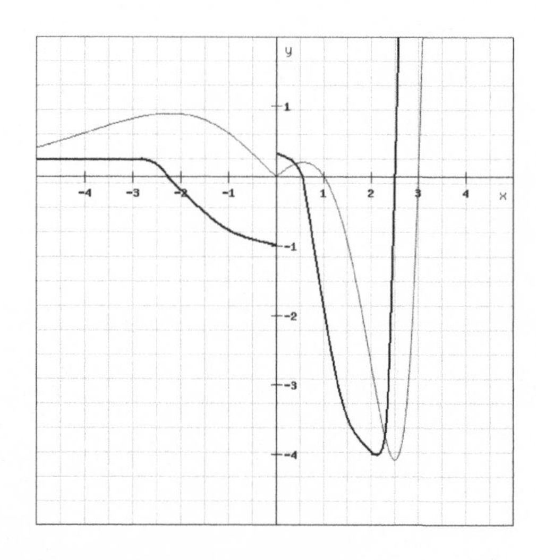

a. $f(-4)\approx 0.6 \quad f'(-4)\approx\frac{1}{3}$

b. $f(-3)\approx 0.8 \quad f'(-3)\approx\frac{1}{3}$

c. $f(-2.3)\approx 0.9 \quad f'(-2.3)=0$

d. $f(-1)\approx 0.6 \quad f'(-1)\approx -1$

e. $f(0)=0 \quad f'(0)=D.E$

f. $f(0.2)\approx 0.2 \quad f'(0.2)\approx 0.3$

g. $f(0.6)\approx 0.2 \quad f'(0.6)\approx 0$

h. $f(2)\approx -2.5 \quad f'(2)\approx -4.5$

i. $f(2.5)=-4 \quad f'(2.5)=0$

j. $f(3)=0 \quad f'(3)\approx 10$

Use the information obtained to sketch the derivative on the same graph.

14. When the derivative is positive it means that the function is <u>increasing</u>

15. When the derivative is <u>negative</u> it means that the function is <u>decreasing</u>

16. When the derivative is zero it means that the function has <u>a stationary point (the tangent is horizontal)</u>

1.4. – GRAPHING THE DERIVATIVE (GRADIENT FUNCTION)

Draw the graph of the derivative of the following functions on the graph below:

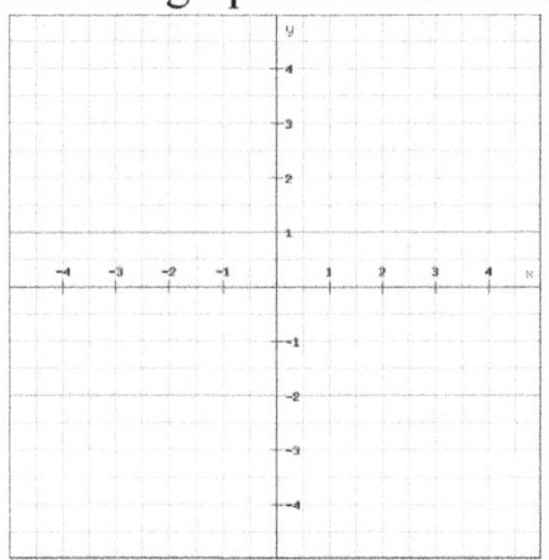

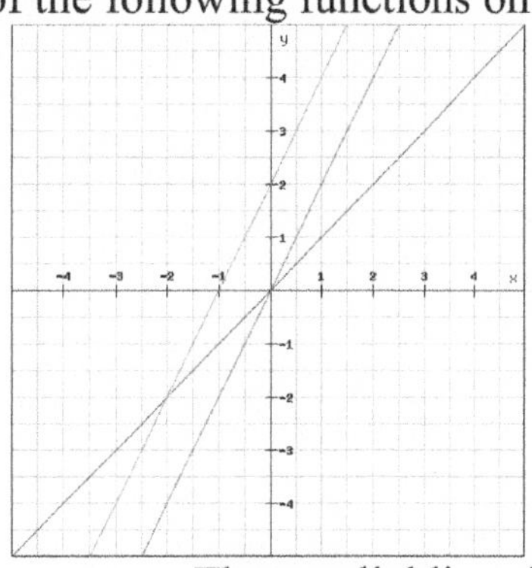

Both same derivative $f'(x) = 0$

The parallel lines have the same derivative $f'(x) = 2$, the other $f'(x) = 1$

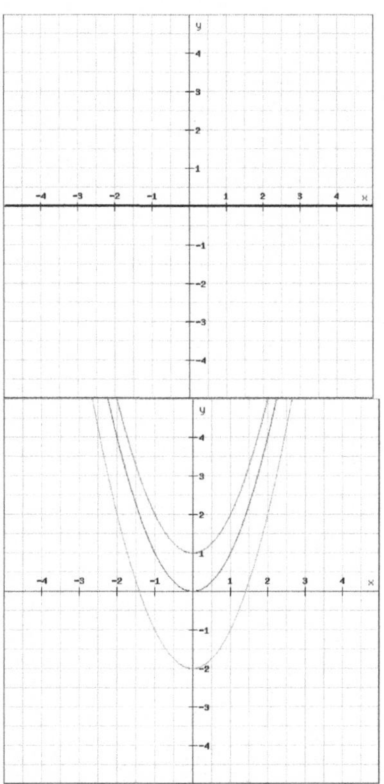

The parabolas only differ in vertical translation, therefore have the same derivative.

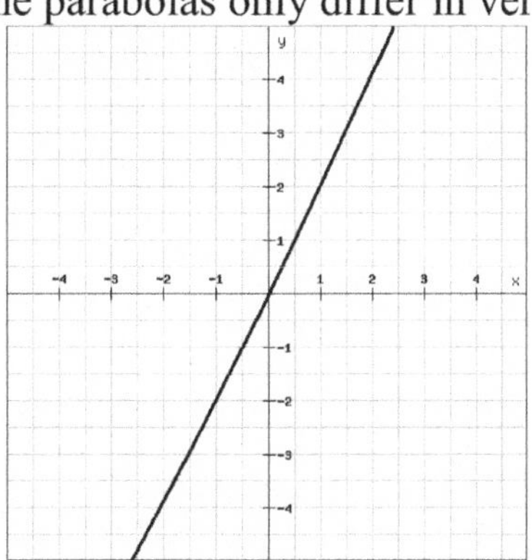

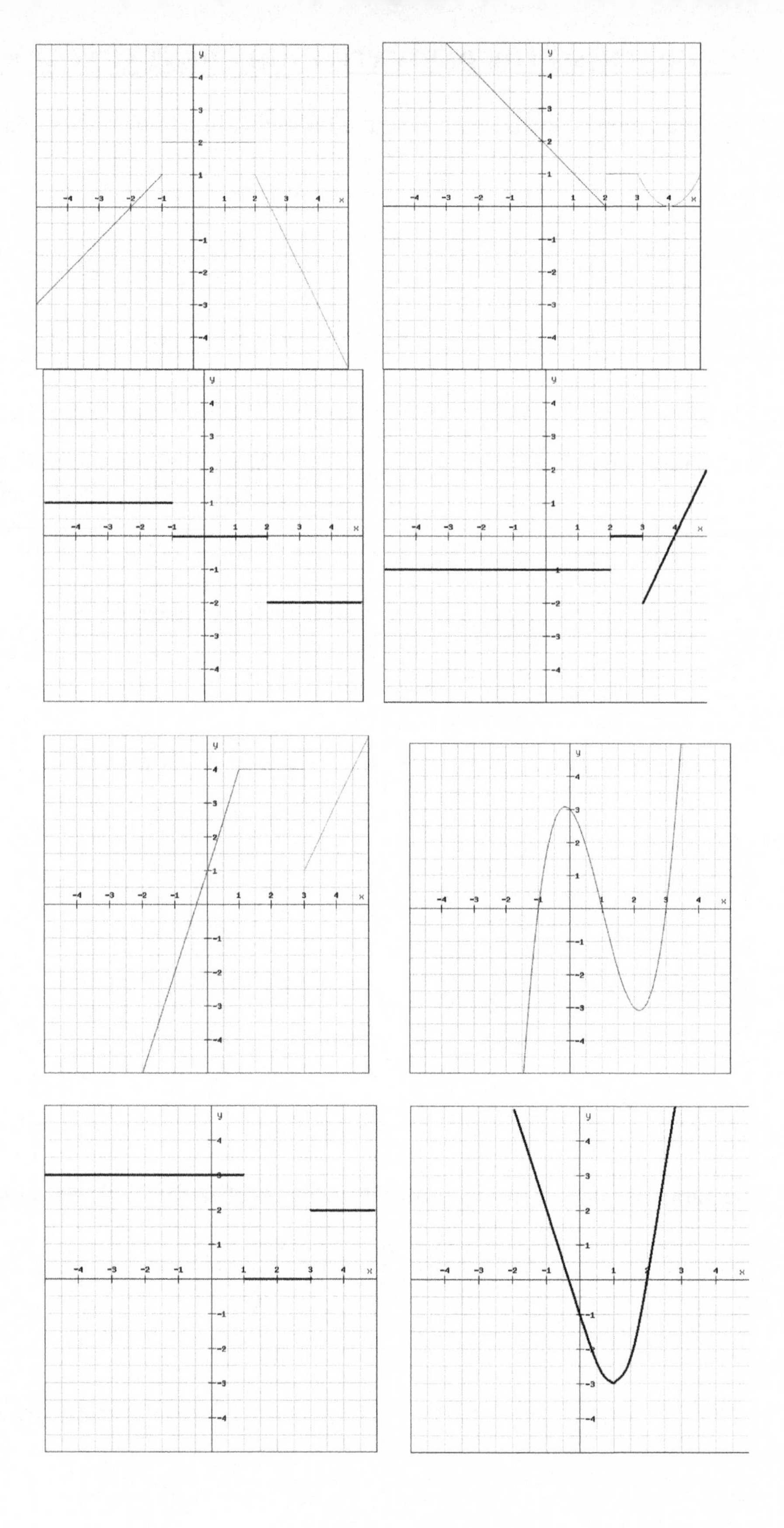

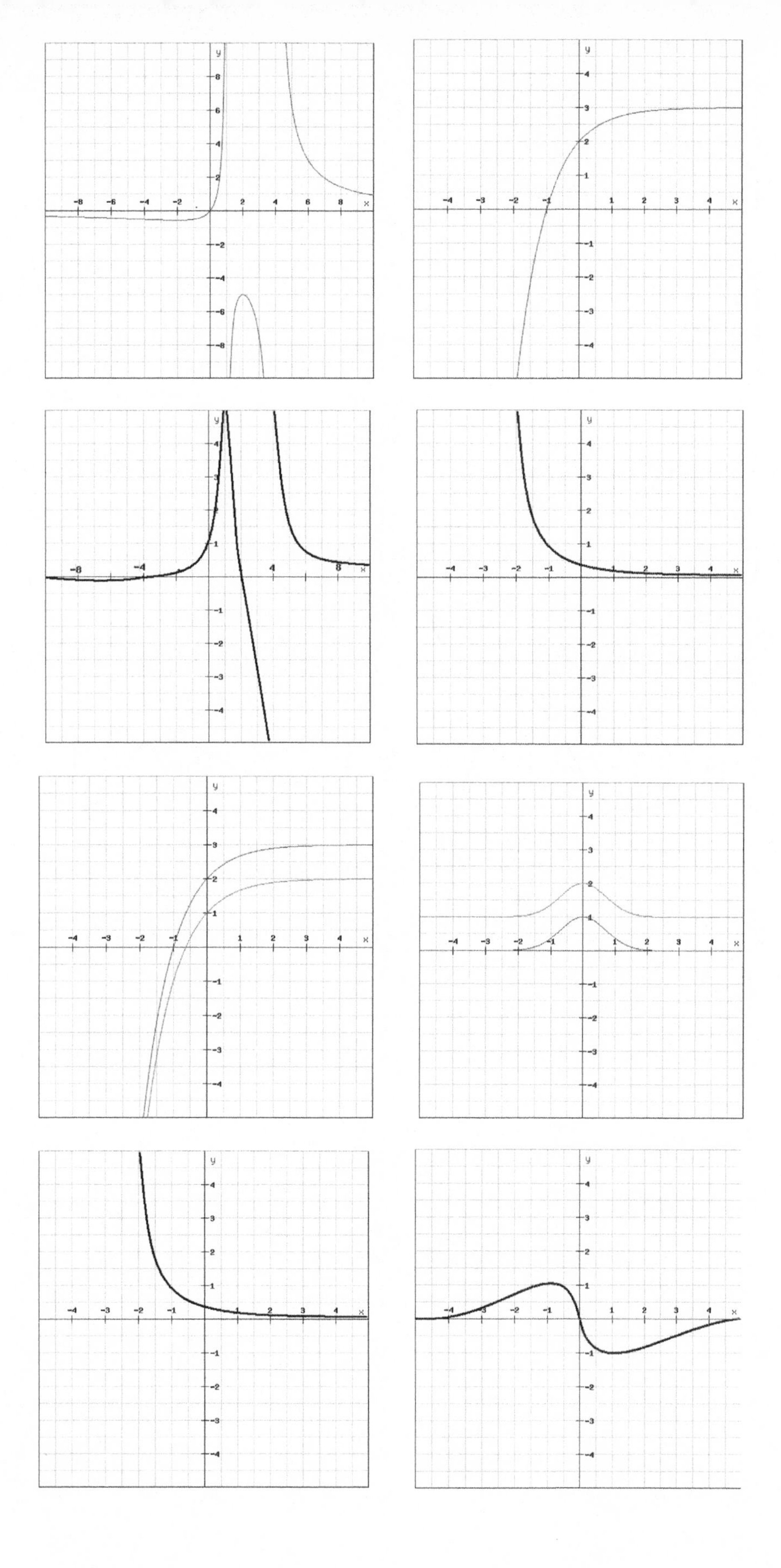

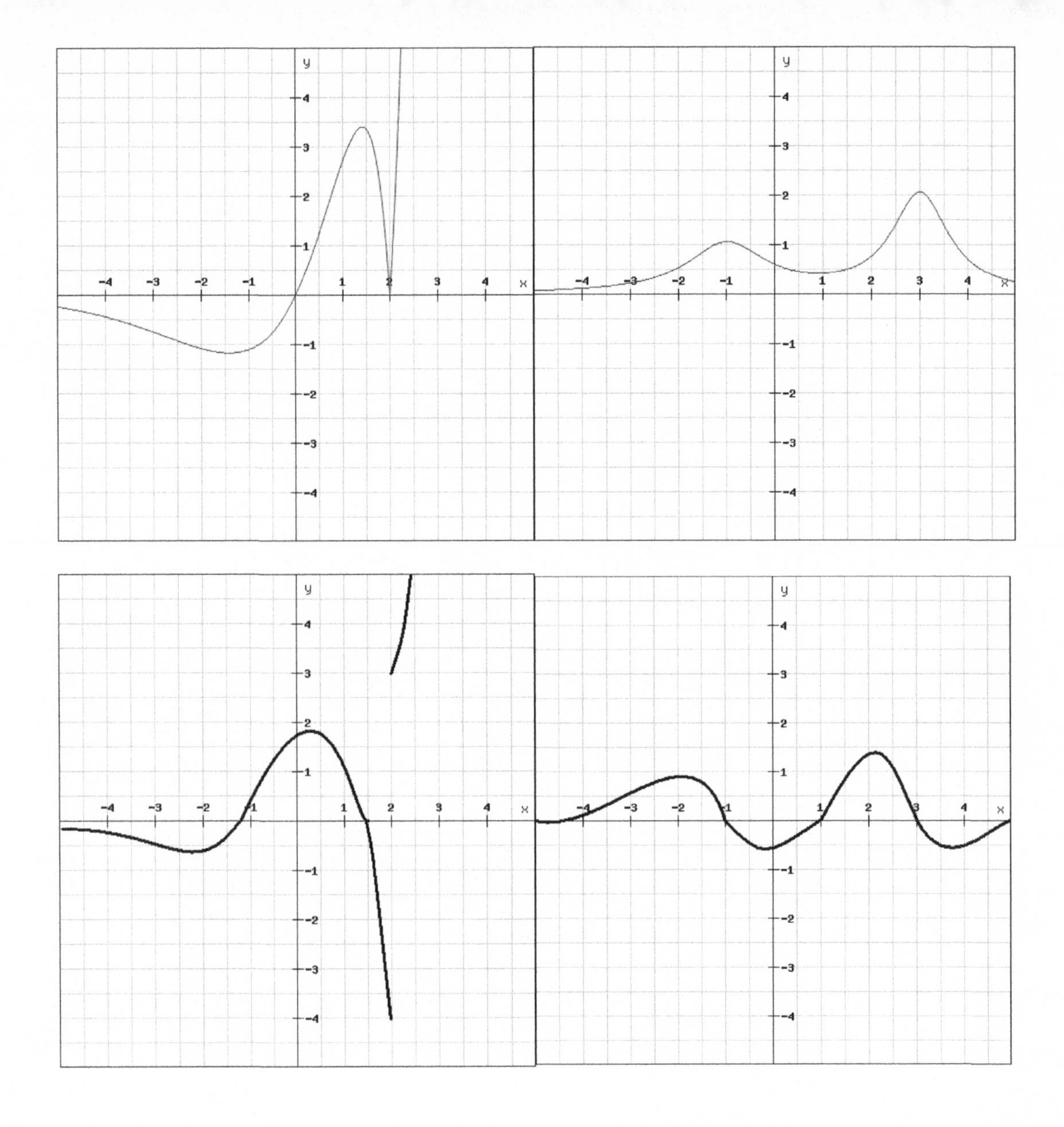

y
x
-4
-3
-2
-1
1
2
3
4

1.5. – GRAPHING THE ANTIDERIVATIVE

Draw the graph of the derivative of the following functions on the graph below:

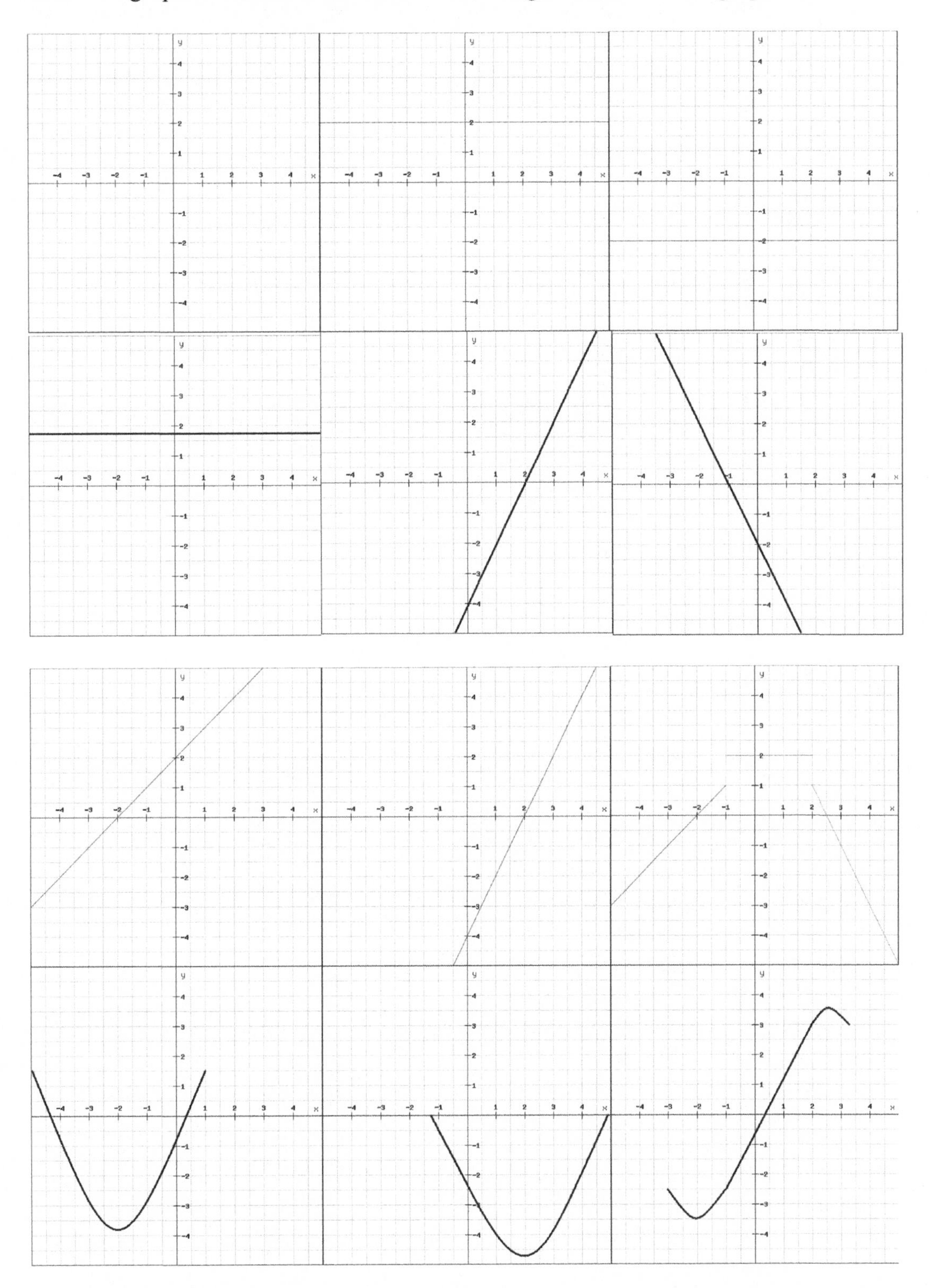

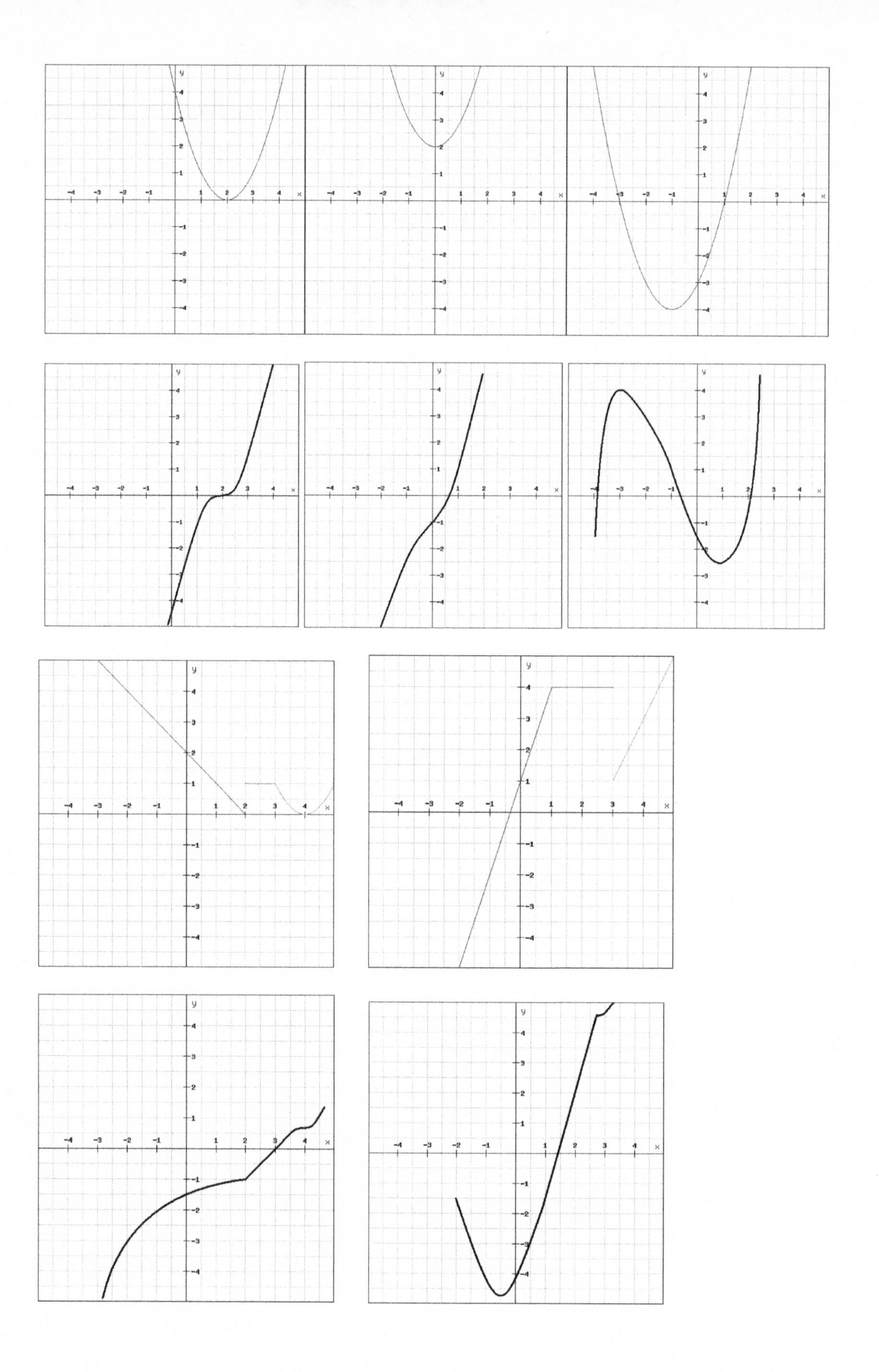

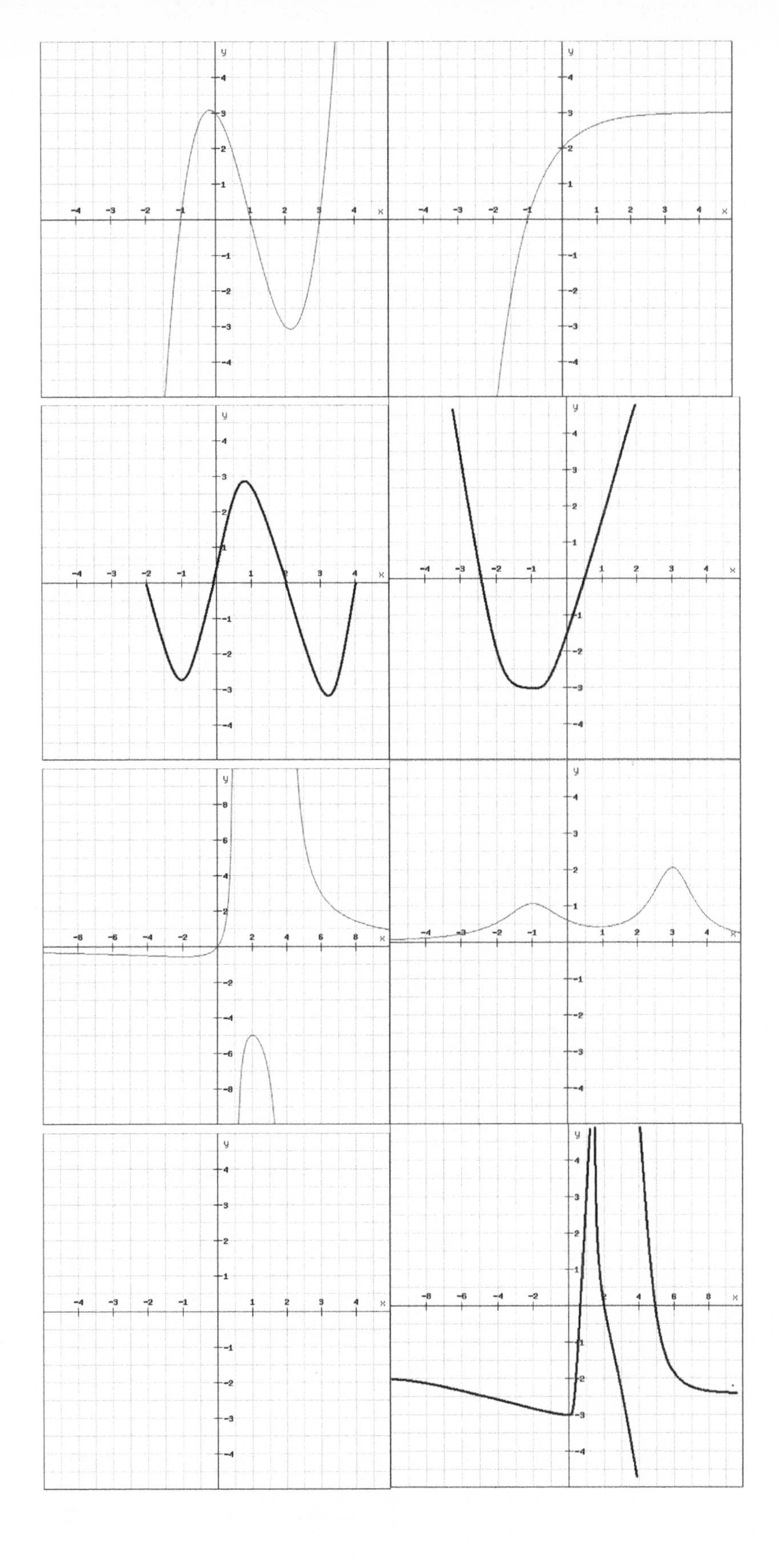

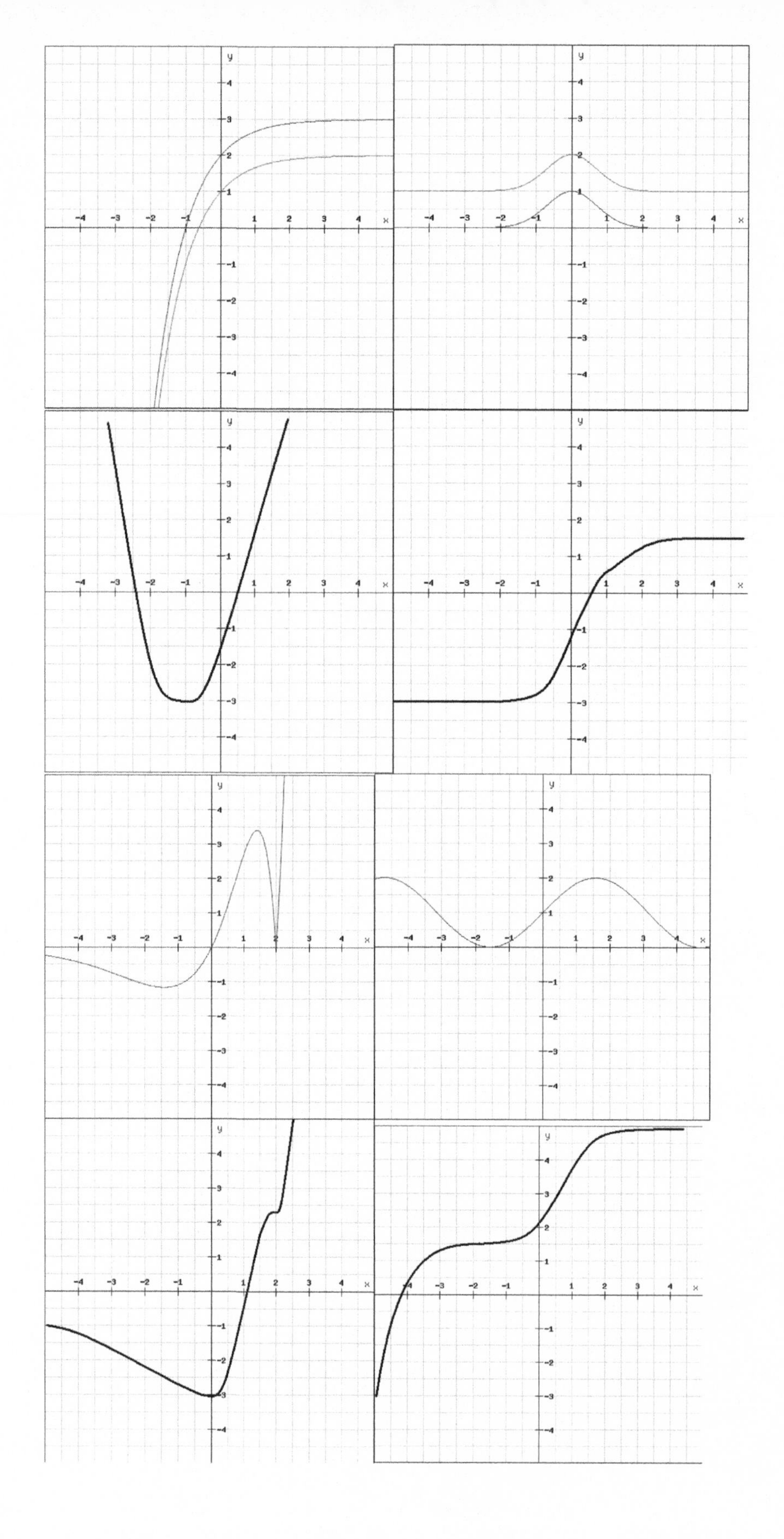

1.6. – TANGENTS AND NORMALS TO FUNCTIONS

1. Given the function f(x) = 2x². Sketch it.

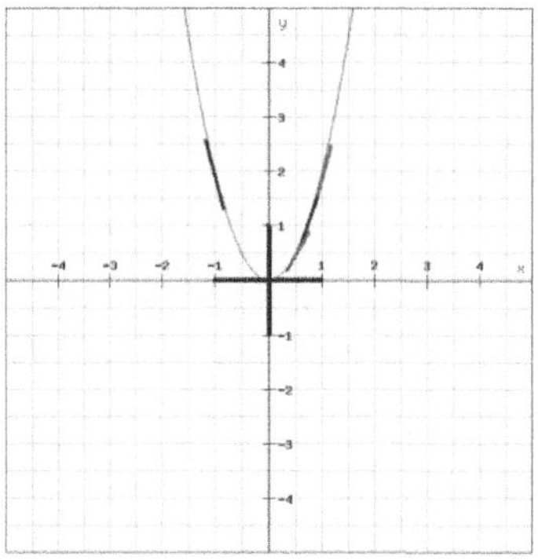

   a. $f'(x)=\lim_{h\to 0}\dfrac{f(x+h)-f(x)}{h}=\lim_{h\to 0}\dfrac{2(x+h)^2-2x^2}{h}=...=4x$

   b. $f'(1)=4$

   c. $f'(0)=0$

   d. $f'(x)=4x=3; x=\dfrac{3}{4}; \left(\dfrac{3}{4},\dfrac{9}{8}\right)$

   e. $f'(x)=4x=-4; x=-1; (-1,2)$

   f. $f'(x)=4x=2; x=\dfrac{1}{2}; \left(\dfrac{1}{2},\dfrac{1}{2}\right)$

   g. $f'(x)=4x=-5; x=-\dfrac{5}{4}; \left(-\dfrac{5}{4},\dfrac{25}{8}\right)$

   h. $m=f'(1)=4; point=(1,2); y=4x+b; y=4x-2$

   i. $Tangent: m=f'(0)=0; point=(0,0); y=b; y=0$
      $Normal: x=0$

   j. $Tangent: m=f'(-2)=-8; point=(-2,8); y=-8x+b; y=-8x-8$
      $Normal: m=\dfrac{1}{8}; point=(-2,8); y=\dfrac{1}{8}x+b; y=\dfrac{1}{8}x+\dfrac{33}{4}$

2. Given the function $f(x)=-\dfrac{2}{x}+1$. Sketch it.

   a. $f'(x)=\lim_{h\to 0}\dfrac{f(x+h)-f(x)}{h}=\lim_{h\to 0}\dfrac{\left(-\dfrac{2}{x+h}+1\right)-\left(-\dfrac{2}{x}+1\right)}{h}=...=\dfrac{2}{x^2}$

   b. $f'(1)=2$

   c. Out of domain, not possible.

   d. $f'\left(\dfrac{1}{2}\right)=8.$

   e. $f'(x)=\dfrac{2}{x^2}=-3$ No such point exists.

   f. $f'(x)=\dfrac{2}{x^2}=\dfrac{1}{2}: x=\pm 2; (2,0),(-2,2)$

   g. $f'(x)=\dfrac{2}{x^2}=-\dfrac{5}{3}$ no such point exists.

   h. $f'(x)=\dfrac{2}{x^2}=6: x=\pm\dfrac{1}{\sqrt{3}}; \left(\dfrac{1}{\sqrt{3}},1-\dfrac{2\sqrt{3}}{3}\right),\left(\dfrac{1}{\sqrt{3}},1+\dfrac{2\sqrt{3}}{3}\right).$

   i. $m=f'(1)=2; point=(1,-1); y=2x+b; y=2x-3$

   j. Out of domain, not possible.

k.

$$Tangent: m = f'\left(\frac{1}{2}\right) = 8; point = \left(\frac{1}{2}, -3\right); y = 8x + b; y = 8x - 7$$

$$Normal: m = -\frac{1}{8}; point = \left(\frac{1}{2}, -3\right); y = -\frac{1}{8}x + b; y = -\frac{1}{8}x - \frac{47}{16}$$

3. Given the function $f(x) = -x^2 - x$. Sketch it.

a. $f'(x) = \lim_{h\to 0} \dfrac{f(x+h) - f(x)}{h} = \lim_{h\to 0} \dfrac{\left(-(x+h)^2 - (x+h)\right) - \left(-x^2 - x\right)}{h} = ... = -2x - 1$

b. $f'(-1) = 1$

c. $f'(2) = -5$

d. $f'(-4) = 7$

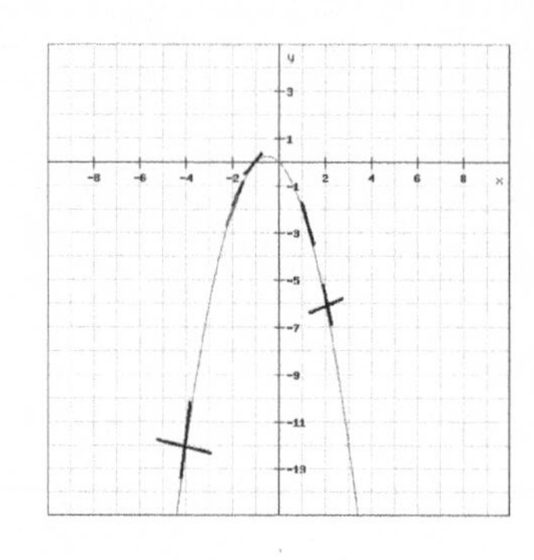

e. $f'(x) = -2x - 1 = 2; x = -\frac{3}{2}; \left(-\frac{3}{2}, -\frac{3}{4}\right)$

f. $f'(x) = -2x - 1 = -2.3; x = 0.65; (0.65, -1.0725)$

g. $f'(x) = -2x - 1 = 3; x = -2; (-2, -2)$

h. $f'(x) = -2x - 1 = -5; x = 2; (2, -6)$

i. $m = f'(-1) = 1; point = (-1, 0); y = x + b; y = x + 1$

j.

$$Tangent: m = f'(2) = -5; point = (2, -6); y = -5x + b; y = -5x + 4$$

$$Normal: m = \frac{1}{5}; point = (2, -6); y = \frac{1}{5}x + b; y = \frac{1}{5}x - \frac{32}{5}$$

k.

$$Tangent: m = f'(-4) = 7; point = (-4, -12); y = 7x + b; y = 7x + 16$$

$$Normal: m = -\frac{1}{7}; point = (-4, -12); y = -\frac{1}{7}x + b; y = -\frac{1}{7}x - \frac{88}{7}$$

4. Given the function $f(x) = -3x^2 + 1$. Sketch it.

a. $f'(x) = \lim_{h\to 0} \dfrac{f(x+h) - f(x)}{h} = \lim_{h\to 0} \dfrac{\left(-3(x+h)^2 + 1\right) - \left(-3x^2 + 1\right)}{h} = ... = -6x$

b. $f'(1) = 6$

c. $f'(0) = 0$

d. $f'(2) = -12$

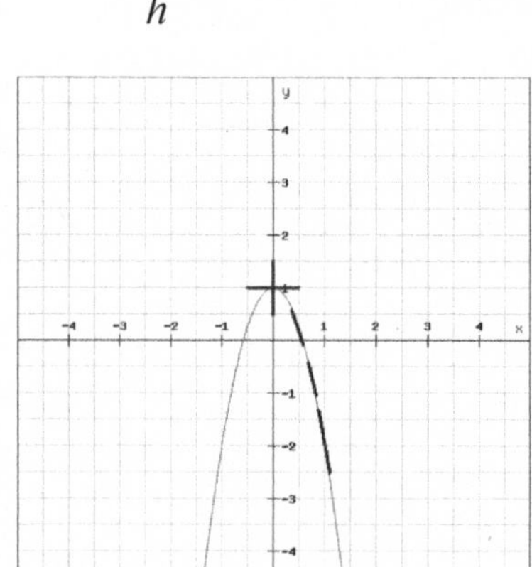

e. $f'(x) = -6x = 3; x = \frac{1}{2}; \left(\frac{1}{2}, \frac{1}{4}\right)$

f. $f'(x) = -6x = -4; x = \frac{2}{3}; \left(\frac{2}{3}, -\frac{1}{3}\right)$

g. $f'(x) = -6x = -5; x = \frac{5}{6}; \left(\frac{5}{6}, -\frac{13}{12}\right)$

h. $Tangent: m = f'(0) = 0; point = (0,1); y = 1$

$Normal: x = 0$

5. Given the function f(x) = $\dfrac{3}{x-2}$. Sketch it.

a. $f'(x) = \lim_{h\to 0}\dfrac{f(x+h)-f(x)}{h} = \lim_{h\to 0}\dfrac{\frac{3}{x+h-2}-\frac{3}{x-2}}{h} = \ldots = \dfrac{-3}{(x-2)^2}$

b. $f'(1) = -3$

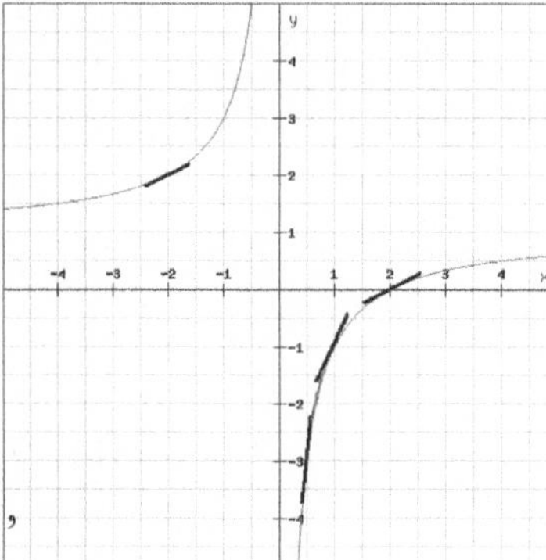

c. $f'(2) =$ Does not exist.

d. $f'(\frac{1}{2}) = -\frac{4}{3}$

e. $f'(x) = \dfrac{-3}{(x-2)^2} = -3; x_1 = 1, x_2 = 3; (1,3), (3,1),$

f. $f'(x) = \dfrac{-3}{(x-2)^2} = \dfrac{1}{2}$ No solution, no such point.

g. $f'(x) = \dfrac{-3}{(x-2)^2} = -\dfrac{5}{3}; (x-2)^2 = \dfrac{9}{5}; x = 2 \pm \dfrac{3}{\sqrt{5}}; \left(2+\dfrac{3}{\sqrt{5}}, \sqrt{5}\right), \left(2-\dfrac{3}{\sqrt{5}}, -\sqrt{5}\right)$

h. $f'(1) = -3; point = (1,-3); y = -3x + b; y = -3x$

i. Does not exist, out of domain

j.

$Tangent: m = f'(\frac{1}{2}) = -\frac{4}{3}; point = \left(\frac{1}{2}, -2\right); y = -\frac{4}{3}x + b; y = -\frac{4}{3}x - \frac{4}{3}$

$Normal: m = \frac{3}{4}; point = \left(\frac{1}{2}, -2\right); y = \frac{3}{4}x + b; y = \frac{3}{4}x - \frac{19}{8}$

1.7. – DERIVATIVES

Polynomial Functions Differentiate the following functions:

1. $f'(x)=0$
2. $f'(x)=0$
3. $f'(x)=1$
4. $f'(x)=5$
5. $f'(x)=5k$
6. $f'(x)=-2$
7. $f'(x)=-2$
8. $f'(x)=-2$
9. $f'(x)=2x+3$
10. $f'(x)=2x+7$
11. $f'(x)=6bx+2$
12. $f'(x)=22x^{21}+1$
13. $f'(x)=4x^3+2$
14. f $f'(x)=5x^4+1$
15. $f'(x)=22x^{21}+x^{-2}$
16. $f'(x)=2x-2-2x^{-3}$
17. $f'(x)=5ax^4-8x^3+20x^{-3}-3x^{-4}$
18. $f'(x)=10x-10-\frac{2}{3}x^{-\frac{5}{3}}+2x$
19. $f'(x)=-100x^{19}-2x$
20. $f'(x)=3x^2+12x-\frac{1}{2}x^{-\frac{1}{2}}-\frac{1}{3}x^{-\frac{2}{3}}$
21. $f'(x)=-5x^4-12x+2+\frac{1}{6}x^{-\frac{5}{6}}-\frac{3}{4}x^{-\frac{1}{4}}$
22. $f'(x)=-7x^6+2x-5-\frac{3}{2}x^{\frac{1}{2}}-\frac{4}{3}x^{\frac{1}{3}}+\frac{2}{3}x^{-\frac{5}{3}}$
23. $f'(x)=-4bx^3-8x$
24. $f'(x)=2x^{-3}+3$
25. $f'(x)=30x^{-3}+3$
26. $f'(x)=-\frac{15}{2}x^{-4}-6b$

27. $f(x) = \frac{1}{6}x^3 - 3 + \frac{\sqrt{x}+3}{3} - \frac{1+x\sqrt{2}}{7}$ $\quad f'(x)=\frac{1}{2}x^2+\frac{1}{6}x^{-\frac{1}{2}}-\frac{\sqrt{2}}{7}$

28. $f(x) = \frac{2}{3}x^{\frac{2}{3}} - 3x^{\frac{1}{2}} + 2e^2 - x\log(3)$ $\quad f'(x)=\frac{4}{9}x^{-\frac{1}{3}}-\frac{3}{2}x^{-\frac{1}{2}}-\log(3)$

29. $f(x) = 3x^2+\frac{2}{3}x^{\frac{4}{9}}-5x^{\frac{2}{5}}$ $\quad f'(x)=6x+\frac{8}{27}x^{-\frac{5}{9}}-2x^{-\frac{3}{5}}$

30. $f(x) = x^2 + 3x + 4 + 3x^2 + b\frac{7}{6}x^{-\frac{4}{9}} - 5x^{\frac{3}{2}}$ $\quad f'(x)=8x+3-\frac{28b}{54}x^{-\frac{13}{9}}-\frac{15}{2}x^{\frac{1}{2}}$

31. $f(x) = -12x - 13 + 3bx + 4 + 3x^{-3} + \frac{7}{6}x^{-\frac{1}{9}} - 5x^{\frac{-7}{2}}$ $\quad f'(x)=-12+3b-9x^{-4}-\frac{7}{54}x^{-\frac{10}{9}}+\frac{35}{2}x^{-\frac{9}{2}}$

32. $f(x) = -x^3 + 6x^2 - 8 - x\sqrt{x} - \sqrt[3]{x} + \cos(4)x^{-1}$ $\quad f'(x)=-3x^2+12x-\frac{3}{2}x^{\frac{1}{2}}-\frac{1}{3}x^{-\frac{2}{3}}-\cos(4)x^{-2}$

33. $f(x) = 4x^2 + 9x - 4 + 3x^2 + \frac{7}{6}x^{-\frac{4}{9}} - 5x^{\frac{3}{2}} + \ln(2)x^2$ $\quad f'(x)=8x+9-\frac{28}{54}x^{-\frac{13}{9}}-\frac{15}{2}x^{-\frac{1}{2}}+2\ln(2)x$

34. $f(x) = 8x - x\sqrt{x} - \sqrt[3]{2x}$ $\quad f'(x)=8-\frac{3}{2}x^{\frac{1}{2}}-\frac{\sqrt[3]{2}}{3}x^{-\frac{2}{3}}$

35. $f(x) = -x^3 + 6x^{22} - 8 - x\sqrt{x} - \sqrt[3]{x}x^2$ $\quad f'(x)=-3x^2+132x^{21}-\frac{3}{2}x^{\frac{1}{2}}-\frac{7}{3}x^{\frac{4}{3}}$

Exponential functions

36. $f(x) = 8x - e^x$ $\qquad f'(x) = 8 - e^x$

37. $f(x) = 2e^x - x$ $\qquad f'(x) = 2e^x - 1$

38. $f(x) = 5e^x - \sqrt{x} - \sqrt[3]{2x}$ $\qquad f'(x) = 5e^x - \frac{1}{2}x^{-\frac{1}{2}} - \frac{\sqrt[3]{2}}{3}x^{-\frac{2}{3}}$

39. $f(x) = -3e^x - x\sqrt{x} - \sqrt[5]{x^2}$ $\qquad f'(x) = -3e^x - \frac{3}{2}x^{\frac{1}{2}} - \frac{2}{5}x^{-\frac{3}{5}}$

Logarithmic functions

40. $f(x) = 2\ln(x) - \sqrt{x\sqrt{x}}$ $\qquad f'(x) = \frac{2}{x} - \frac{3}{4}x^{-\frac{1}{4}}$

41. $f(x) = \frac{1}{\sqrt[5]{x}} - \frac{\sqrt{x}}{2x} - \frac{\sqrt[5]{x^2}}{\sqrt{x}} - \ln(x)$ $\qquad f'(x) = -\frac{1}{5}x^{-\frac{6}{5}} + \frac{1}{4}x^{-\frac{3}{2}} + \frac{1}{10}x^{-\frac{11}{10}} - \frac{1}{x}$

42. $f(x) = \frac{\sqrt{x}+3}{3} - \frac{1+x\sqrt{2}}{7} - \frac{2}{3x} + \log(x)$ $\qquad f'(x) = \frac{1}{6}x^{\frac{1}{2}} - \frac{\sqrt{2}}{7} + \frac{2}{3}x^{-2} + \frac{1}{\ln(10)x}$

43. $f(x) = 2e^x - \frac{\ln(5)}{\sqrt{2}x} - \log_2(x)$ $\qquad f'(x) = 2e^x + \frac{\ln(5)}{\sqrt{2}}x^{-2} - \frac{1}{\ln(2)x}$

44. $f(x) = \ln(7) - \frac{\cos(1)+\sqrt{2}}{7}e^x - x\sqrt{\frac{1}{2x}} - 2\log_e(x)$ $\qquad f'(x) = -\frac{\cos(1)+\sqrt{2}}{7}e^x - \frac{1}{2\sqrt{2}}x^{-\frac{1}{2}} - \frac{1}{x}$

Trigonometric functions

45. $f(x) = \ln(8) - 2e^x + \cos(x)$ $\qquad f'(x) = -2e^x - \sin(x)$

46. $f(x) = \cos(2)x^2 - 23.7e^x - \sin(x)$ $\qquad f'(x) = 2\cos(2)x - 23.7e^x - \cos(x)$

47. $f(x) = x^{-\frac{13}{9}} - 33^{\sqrt{2}} - 2\cos(x)$ $\qquad f'(x) = -\frac{13}{9}x^{-\frac{22}{9}} + 2\sin(x)$

48. $f(x) = (1+2^{\sqrt{2}})x - e^x + 5\cos(x)$ $\qquad f'(x) = (1+2^{\sqrt{2}}) - e^x - 5\sin(x)$

49. $f(x) = 2\sin(x) + \sin(8)\ln(6)x - e^x$ $\qquad f'(x) = 2\cos(x) + \sin(8)\ln(6) - e^x$

50. $f(x) = \cos(x) + \frac{5\sqrt{x}}{3x} - e^x$ $\qquad f'(x) = -\sin(x) - \frac{5}{6}x^{-\frac{3}{2}} - e^x$

51. $f(x) = 2\cos(x) - \ln(7) - \frac{x\ln(11)+\sqrt{2}}{\cos(7)} - \frac{\sin(1)}{3+\sqrt{2}}x + \log_9(x)$

$$f'(x) = -2\sin(x) - \frac{\ln(11)}{\cos(7)} - \frac{\sin(1)}{3+\sqrt{2}} + \frac{1}{\ln(9)x}$$

PRODUCT RULE $(fg)' = f'g + fg'$

52. f(x) = (x + 2)(x + 3) $f'(x) = 1\cdot(x+2)+(x+3)\cdot 1 = 2x+5$

53. $f(x) = (x^2 - 2)(x^2 + 3)$ $f'(x) = 2x\cdot(x^2+3)+(x^2-2)\cdot 2x$

54. $f(x) = (2x + 2)(5x^2 - 3 + e^x)$ $f'(x) = 2\cdot(5x^2-3+e^x)+(2x+2)\cdot(10x+e^x)$

55. $f(x) = (-x + 2 - \cos(x))(5x^8 - 3x)$

$$f'(x) = (-1+\sin(x))\cdot(5x^8-3x)+(-x+2-\cos(x))\cdot(40x-3)$$

56. $f(x) = (-x^9 + 2 + \sin(x))(x + 3x^2)$

$$f'(x) = (-9x^8+\cos(x))\cdot(x+3x^2)+(-x^9+2+\sin(x))\cdot(1+6x)$$

57. $f(x) = (2\ln(x)+3x^2+\frac{7}{6}x^{-\frac{4}{9}} - 5x^{\frac{3}{2}})(x^2-1 - \cos(x))$

$$f'(x) = (\frac{2}{x}+6x-\frac{28}{54}x^{-\frac{13}{9}}-\frac{15}{2}x^{\frac{1}{2}})\cdot(x^2-1-\cos(x))+(2\ln(x)+3x^2+\frac{7}{6}x^{-\frac{4}{9}}-5x^{\frac{3}{2}})\cdot(2x+\sin(x))$$

58. $f(x) = (2\log(x) - \frac{7}{6}\frac{2}{x^{\frac{2}{3}}} - 5\frac{2}{x})(x^2-1) + \sin(x)$

$$f'(x) = (\frac{2}{\ln(10)x}+6x+\frac{28}{18}x^{-\frac{5}{3}}+10x^{-2})\cdot(x^2-1)+(2\log(x)-\frac{14}{6}x^{-\frac{2}{3}}-\frac{10}{x})\cdot(2x)+\cos(x)$$

59. $f(x) = (\log_3(x) + \frac{7}{6}\frac{2}{x^{\frac{2}{3}}} - 5\frac{2}{x})(x^2-1 + e^x - \sin(x)) - e^x + \log_2(x)$

$$f'(x) = (\frac{1}{\ln(3)x}+\frac{28}{18}x^{-\frac{5}{3}}+10x^{-2})\cdot(x^2-1+e^x-\sin(x))+(\log_3(x)-\frac{14}{6}x^{-\frac{2}{3}}-\frac{10}{x})\cdot(2x+e^x-\cos(x))-e^x+\frac{1}{\ln(2)x}$$

60. $f(x) = (\frac{1}{6}\frac{}{x^{-\frac{2}{3}}} - \frac{2}{x^5})(x^2-\sqrt{x}) + \cos(x)$

$$f'(x) = (\frac{1}{9}x^{-\frac{1}{3}}+10x^{-6})\cdot(x^2-\sqrt{x})+(\frac{1}{6}x^{\frac{2}{3}}-\frac{2}{x^5})\cdot(2x-\frac{1}{2}x^{-\frac{1}{2}})-\sin(x)$$

61. $f(x) = (\frac{1}{6}x - \frac{2}{x^{\frac{1}{2}}})(x^2 - \frac{1}{\sqrt[3]{x}} - \sin(x) + \cos(x) + e^x) + e^x + \cos(x)$

$$f'(x) = (\frac{1}{6}+x^{-\frac{3}{2}})\cdot(x^2-x^{-\frac{1}{3}}-\sin(x)+\cos(x)+e^x)+(\frac{1}{6}x-2x^{-\frac{1}{2}})\cdot(2x+\frac{1}{3}x^{-\frac{4}{3}}-\cos(x)-\sin(x)+e^x)+e^x-\sin(x)$$

QUOTIENT RULE $\left(\dfrac{f}{g}\right) = \dfrac{f'g - fg'}{g^2}$

62. $f(x) = \dfrac{x+1}{2x^2}$ $\qquad f'(x) = \dfrac{1\cdot 2x^2 - (x+1)\cdot 4x}{(2x^2)^2}$

63. $f(x) = \dfrac{2x^2+x}{x^2}$ $\qquad f'(x) = \dfrac{(4x+1)\cdot x^2 - (2x^2+x)\cdot 2x}{(x^2)^2}$

64. $f(x) = \dfrac{x^2+\sqrt{x}+1}{-x^4}$ $\qquad f'(x) = \dfrac{(2x+\frac{1}{2}x^{-\frac{1}{2}})\cdot(-x^4) - (x^2+\sqrt{x}+1)\cdot(-4x^3)}{(-x^4)^2}$

65. $f(x) = \dfrac{x^{\frac{2}{3}} - x}{2x^2+x}$ $\qquad f'(x) = \dfrac{(\frac{2}{3}x^{-\frac{1}{3}} - 1)\cdot(2x^2+x) - (x^{\frac{2}{3}} - x)\cdot(4x+1)}{(2x^2+x)^2}$

66. $f(x) = -4\dfrac{\sin(x)+x}{3x}$ $\qquad f'(x) = -4\cdot\dfrac{(\cos(x)+1)\cdot(3x) - (\sin(x)+x)\cdot(3)}{(3x)^2}$

67. $f(x) = \dfrac{x-\log(x)}{\log(x)+1}$ $\qquad f'(x) = \cdot\dfrac{(1-\frac{1}{\ln(10)x})\cdot(\log(x)+1) - (x-\log(x))\cdot(\frac{1}{\ln(10)x})}{(\log(x)+1)^2}$

68. $f(x) = \tan(x)$ $\qquad f'(x) = \dfrac{\cos(x)\cdot\cos(x)+\sin(x)\cdot\sin(x)}{(\cos(x))^2} = \dfrac{1}{(\cos(x))^2}$

69. $f(x) = 2\dfrac{x+e^x}{\cos(x)}$ $\qquad f'(x) = 2\cdot\dfrac{(1+e^x)\cdot\cos(x)+(x+e^x)\cdot\sin(x)}{(\cos(x))^2}$

70. $f(x) = \dfrac{\sin(x)+\ln(x)}{x^4}$ $\qquad f'(x) = \dfrac{(\cos(x)+\frac{1}{x})\cdot x^4 - (\sin(x)+\ln(x))\cdot 4x^3}{(x^4)^2}$

71. $f(x) = \dfrac{x^{-\frac{2}{5}} + \sin(x) + \ln(x)}{2x^{3.2}+1}$ $\qquad f'(x) = \dfrac{(-\frac{2}{5}x^{-\frac{7}{5}} + \cos(x) + \frac{1}{x})\cdot(2x^{3.2}+1) - (x^{-\frac{2}{5}} + \cos(x) + \frac{1}{x})\cdot 4.6x^{2.2}}{(2x^{3.2}+1)^2}$

72. $f(x) = \dfrac{\sin(x)(x+1)}{2x^2}$

$$f'(x) = \frac{\left(\cos(x)\cdot(x+1)+\sin(x)\cdot 1\right)\cdot 2x^2 - (\sin(x)\cdot(x+1))\cdot 4x}{(2x^2)^2}$$

73. $f(x) = \dfrac{(3x+1)(2x+2)}{e^x}$

$$f'(x) = \frac{\left(3\cdot(2x+2)+(3x+1)\cdot 2\right)\cdot e^x - ((3x+1)\cdot(2x+2))\cdot e^x}{(e^x)^2}$$

74. $f(x) = \dfrac{e^x}{2x}$ $\qquad f'(x) = \dfrac{e^x\cdot 2x - e^x\cdot 2}{(2x)^2}$

CHAIN RULE

$$(f(g))' = f'(g)g'$$

75. $f(x) = \sin(3x)$ — $f'(x) = \cos(3x)\cdot 3$

76. $f(x) = -3\tan(-2x)$ — $f'(x) = \dfrac{-3\cdot(-2)}{(\cos(-2x))^2}$

77. $f(x) = 2\cos(6x^2)$ — $f'(x) = -2\sin(6x^2)\cdot 12x$

78. $f(x) = -(4x+5)^2$ — $f'(x) = -2(4x+5)\cdot 4$

79. $f(x) = -3(6x-1)^{-10}$ — $f'(x) = 30(6x-1)^{-11}\cdot 6$

80. $f(x) = 2(3x^2+3)^{80}$ — $f'(x) = 160(3x^2+3)^{79}\cdot 6$

81. $f(x) = e^{4x} + 2^{2x}$ — $f'(x) = e^{4x}\cdot 4 + 2^{2x}\cdot\ln(2)\cdot 2$

82. $f(x) = 5e^{4x} - 3^{4x}$ — $f'(x) = 5e^{4x}\cdot 4 - 3^{4x}\cdot\ln(3)\cdot 4$

83. $f(x) = e^{\sin(x)}$ — $f'(x) = e^{\sin(x)}\cdot\cos(x)$

84. $f(x) = (5-3x^{2.3})^{-6}$ — $f'(x) = -6(5-3x^{2.3})^{-7}\cdot(-6.9)$

85. $f(x) = 5^x$ — $f'(x) = 5^x\cdot\ln(5)$

86. $f(x) = 5^{\sin(x)}$ — $f'(x) = 5^{\sin(x)}\cdot\ln(5)\cdot\cos(x)$

87. $f(x) = 5^{\cos(2x)}$ — $f'(x) = 5^{\cos(2x)}\cdot\ln(5)\cdot(-\sin(2x))\cdot 2$

88. $f(x) = (7-x)^{-2}$ — $f'(x) = -2(7-x)^{-3}(-1)$

89. $f(x) = x\sin(2x)$ — $f'(x) = \sin(2x) + x\cos(2x)\cdot 2$

90. $f(x) = 4xe^{3x}$ — $f'(x) = 4e^{3x} + 4x\cdot e^{3x}\cdot 3$

91. $f(x) = 3x^2\cos(5x^2)$ — $f'(x) = 6x\cdot\cos(5x^2) + 6x\cdot\sin(5x^2)\cdot 10x$

92. $f(x) = e^x - 4^x$ — $f'(x) = e^x\cdot -4^x\cdot\ln(4)$

93. $f(x) = -2^x + x$ — $f'(x) = -2^x\cdot\ln(2) + 1$

94. $f(x) = 7^x - x^{10}$ — $f'(x) = 7^x\cdot\ln(7) - 10x^9$

95. $f(x) = 5e^x + 3^x$ — $f'(x) = 5e^x + 3^x\cdot\ln(3)$

96. $f(x) = \left(\dfrac{2}{3}\right)^x$ — $f'(x) = \left(\dfrac{2}{3}\right)^x\cdot\ln(\dfrac{2}{3})$

97. $f(x) = \left(\dfrac{1}{4}\right)^{x+1}$ — $f'(x) = \left(\dfrac{1}{4}\right)^{x+1}\cdot\ln(\dfrac{1}{4})$

98. $f(x) = -3x\log_2(3x+2)$ — $f'(x) = -3\cdot\log_2(3x+2) - 3x\cdot\dfrac{3}{(3x+2)\ln(2)}$

99. $f(x) = 4x^5\log_4(5x^2+x)$ — $f'(x) = 20x^4\cdot\log_4(5x^2+x) + 4x^5\cdot\dfrac{10x}{(5x^2+x)\ln(4)}$

100. $f(x) = (2-3x)(4+5x)^{-3}$ — $f'(x) = (-3)(4+5x)^{-3} + (2-3x)\cdot(-3)(4+5x)^{-4}\cdot 5$

101. $f(x) = (5-\ln(x))e^{\sin(x)}$ — $f'(x) = -\dfrac{1}{x}\cdot e^{\sin(x)} + (5-\ln(x))\cdot e^{\sin(x)}\cdot\cos(x)$

102. $f(x) = (\sin(3x))^3$ $\qquad f'(x) = 3(\sin(3x))^2 \cdot \cos(3x) \cdot 3$

103. $f(x) = (4x^2 + 3x + 2 - e^x)^{\frac{5}{4}}$ $\qquad f'(x) = \frac{5}{4}(4x^2 + 3x + 2 - e^x)^{\frac{1}{4}} \cdot (8x + 3 - e^x)$

104. $f(x) = \sqrt{(\sin(3x) + 2x)}$ $\qquad f'(x) = \frac{1}{2}(\sin(3x) + 2x)^{-\frac{1}{2}} \cdot (\cos(3x) \cdot 3 + 2)$

105. $f(x) = \frac{3}{\sqrt{(\ln(x))}}$ $\qquad f'(x) = -\frac{3}{2}(\ln(x))^{-\frac{3}{2}} \cdot \frac{1}{x}$

106. $f(x) = x^2(\sin(3x^2 - 5x + 3) + 2x)$

$$f'(x) = 2x \cdot (\sin(3x^2 - 5x + 3) + 2x) + x^2 \cdot (\sin(3x^2 - 5x + 3) \cdot (6x - 5) + 2)$$

107. $f(x) = \sqrt{\frac{2x+1}{2^x}}$ $\qquad f'(x) = \frac{1}{2}\left(\frac{2x+1}{2^x}\right)^{-\frac{1}{2}} \cdot \frac{2 \cdot 2^x - (2x+1) \cdot 2^x \ln(2)}{(2^x)^2}$

108. $f(x) = 3^{\sqrt{x}}$ $\qquad f'(x) = 3^{\sqrt{x}} \cdot \ln(3) \cdot \frac{1}{2} x^{-\frac{1}{2}}$

109. $f(x) = 3^{\sqrt[3]{x}} + x$ $\qquad f'(x) = 3^{\sqrt[3]{x}} \cdot \ln(3) \cdot \frac{1}{3} x^{-\frac{2}{3}} + 1$

110. $f(x) = (\ln(3x^2 + x))^{-2}$ $\qquad f'(x) = -2(\ln(3x^2 + x))^{-3} \cdot \frac{6x+1}{3x^2 + x}$

111. $f(x) = \sin(\ln(x^2))$ $\qquad f'(x) = \cos(\ln(x^2)) \cdot \frac{2x}{x^2} = \frac{2\cos(\ln(x^2))}{x}$

112. $f(x) = 2^{\cos(x^2)}$ $\qquad f'(x) = 2^{\cos(x^2)} \cdot \ln(2) \cdot (-\sin(x^2)) \cdot 2x$

113. $f(x) = \ln(x + \cos(\sqrt{x}))$ $\qquad f'(x) = \frac{1 - \sin(\sqrt{x}) \cdot \frac{1}{2} x^{-\frac{1}{2}}}{x + \cos(\sqrt{x})}$

114. $f(x) = \frac{\sin(3x^2) - \ln(2x - 1)}{e^{2x} + 4x}$

$$f'(x) = \frac{\left(\cos(3x^2) \cdot 6x - \frac{2}{2x-1}\right) \cdot \left(e^{2x} + 4x\right) - \left(\sin(3x^2) - \ln(2x - 1)\right) \cdot \left(2e^{2x} + 4\right)}{\left(e^{2x} + 4x\right)^2}$$

115. $f(x) = \frac{Ln(\sin(3x+1)^{-2})}{\left(\frac{1}{\cos(2x)}\right)} = Ln(\sin(3x+1)^{-2}) \cdot \cos(2x)$

$$f'(x) = \frac{\cos((3x+1)^{-2}) \cdot (-2(3x+1)^{-3} \cdot 3)}{\sin((3x+1)^{-2})} \cdot \cos(2x) + Ln(\sin((3x+1)^{-2}) \cdot (-\sin(2x) \cdot 2)$$

HIGHER DERIVATIVES

1. $f(x) = x^2$

$$\frac{df}{dx} = f'(x) = 2x$$

$$\frac{d^2 f}{dx^2} = f''(x) = 2$$

2. $f(x) = \ln(x)$

$$\frac{df}{dx} = f'(x) = x^{-1}$$

$$\frac{d^2 f}{dx^2} = f''(x) = -x^{-2}$$

3. $f(x) = \sin(x)$

$$\frac{df}{dx} = f'(x) = \cos(x)$$

$$\frac{d^2 f}{dx^2} = f''(x) = -\sin(x)$$

4. $f(x) = e^{2x}$

$$\frac{df}{dx} = f'(x) = 2e^{2x}$$

$$\frac{d^2 f}{dx^2} = f''(x) = 4e^{2x}$$

$$\frac{d^3 f}{dx^3} = f'''(x) = 8e^{2x}$$

$$\frac{d^n f}{dx^n} = f^{(n)}(x) = 2^n e^{2x}$$

5. $f(x) = xe^x$

$$\frac{df}{dx} = f'(x) = e^x(x+1)$$

$$\frac{d^2 f}{dx^2} = f''(x) = e^x(x+2)$$

$$\frac{d^3 f}{dx^3} = f'''(x) = e^x(x+3)$$

$$\frac{d^n f}{dx^n} = f^{(n)}(x) = e^x(x+n)$$

6. $f(x) = \sin(e^x)$

$$\frac{df}{dx} = f'(x) = \cos(e^x)\cdot e^x$$

$$\frac{d^2 f}{dx^2} = f''(x) = e^x(\cos(e^x) - e^x \sin(x))$$

$$\frac{d^3 f}{dx^3} = f'''(x) = e^x(\cos(e^x) - 3e^x \sin(x) - e^{2x}\cos(e^x))$$

$$\frac{d^4 f}{dx^4} = f^{(4)}(x) = e^x(\cos(e^x) - 7e^x \sin(x) - 6e^{2x}\cos(e^x) + e^{3x}\sin(x))$$

7. $f(x) = \ln(2x)$

$$\frac{df}{dx} = f'(x) = \frac{1}{x}$$

$$\frac{d^2 f}{dx^2} = f''(x) = -\frac{1}{x^2}$$

$$\frac{d^3 f}{dx^3} = f'''(x) = \frac{2}{x^3}$$

$$\frac{d^n f}{dx^n} = f^{(n)}(x) = \frac{(n-1)!}{x^n}$$

<u>1.8. – STATIONARY (OR CRITICAL) POINTS</u>

1. In a maximum or minimum point of a "smooth" function the slope of the tangent to the function is **<u>zero</u>**. Sketch an example:

2. There is one more situation in which the slope of the tangent to the function is <u>zero</u>, such point is called: <u>horizontal inflection point</u>. An example:

3. In order to find a stationary points′ <u>x coordinate</u> we equal the **<u>derivative</u>** to **<u>zero</u>**. For example the function $f(x) = 2x^2 + 2x$, $f'(x) = 4x+2=0$, $x = -0.5$

4. To find the stationary points′ y coordinate we **<u>plug the x found into the function</u>**. In the last example $f(-2) = 4$

5. Once we found the stationary point we have to decide if it's a **<u>maximum</u>**, **<u>minimum</u>** or **<u>horizontal inflection point</u>**.

6. We will discuss 3 methods to check if a function has minimum, maximum or horizontal inflection point at a <u>certain point</u>.

<u>The 3 methods are:</u>

1. Check the **<u>value of the function</u>** on both "sides" of the point and close to it. If both sides′ values are higher the point is **<u>a minimum</u>** if both sides are lower the point is **<u>a maximum</u>** and if one side is higher and the other lower we have a **<u>horizontal inflection point</u>** Example: $f(x) = 2x^2 + 2x$

   $f'(x) = 4x + 2 = 0; x = -\frac{1}{2}$

   $f(-0.51) = -0.4998; f(-0.5) = -0.5; f(-0.49) = -0.4998$

   As both adjacent points are higher the point is a minimum.

2. Build a diagram including all the zeros in the first derivative and all the places it is not defined, indicating **the sign of the derivative**. Example: $f(x) = 2x^4 + x^2$

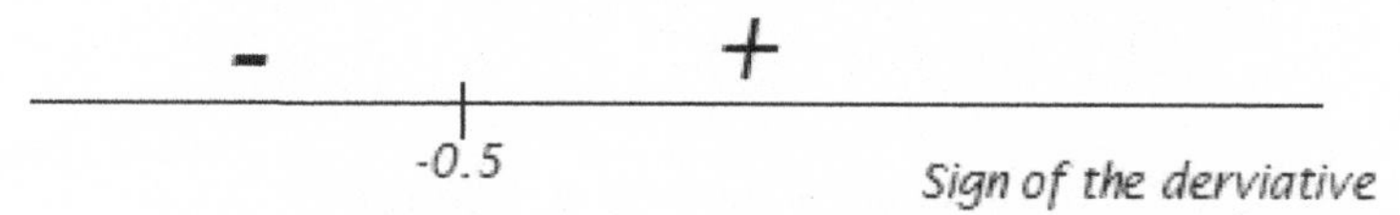

As can be seen the function decreases and then increases around the stationary point and therefore it is a minimum.

3. Use the 2nd derivative. As you could see if the 2nd derivative, at the point in which the 1st derivative is 0, is positive the function is **concave up** and the point would be a **minimum**. if the 2nd derivative, at the point in which the 1st derivative is 0, is negative the function is **concave down** and the point would be a **maximum.** if the 2nd derivative is also 0 this test is **inconclusive**.

Example: $f(x) = 2x^3 + x^2$

$$f'(x) = 6x^2 + 2x = 0; x = 0, -\frac{1}{3}; (0,0), (-\frac{1}{3}, \frac{1}{27})$$

$$f''(x) = 12x + 2; f''(0) = 2; f''(-\frac{1}{3}) = -2$$

As can be seen the function is concave up at x = 0 so (0, 0) is a minimum and concave down at x = – 1/3 so (– 1/3, 1/27) is a maximum.

Example: $f(x) = x^4$

$$f'(x) = 4x^3 = 0; x = 0; (0,0)$$

$$f''(x) = 12x^2; f''(0) = 0$$

As can be seen the function is not concave up nor down at x = 0 (2nd derivative is 0) so we cannot determine in this case what kind of stationary point is (0, 0) using this test. If we sketch the function using the GDC we can see that (0, 0) is a minimum.

SECOND DERIVATIVE

1. The 1st derivative of a function gives **the slope of the tangent to the function at a point.**

2. In case $f(x) = x^2$, the first derivative is **2x** and the 2nd derivative is **2**. As you can see the second derivative is always **positive**. and that means that the function is always **concave up**.

3. In case $f(x) = x^3 - 3x^2$:
   The first derivative is **$3x^2 - 6x$** and the 2nd derivative is **$6x - 6$**. As you can see the second derivative is positive for **$x > 1$**, negative for **$x < 1$** and exactly 0 for **$x = 1$** That means that when the 2nd derivative is positive the function is **concave up** when the 2nd derivative is negative the function is **concave down** and when the 2nd derivative is 0 the function might have an **inflection point**.

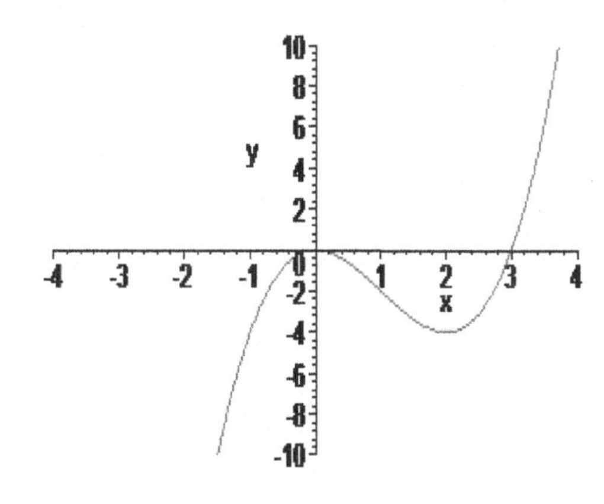

4. In case $f(x) = x^4$
   The first derivative is **$4x^3$** and the 2nd derivative is **$12x^2$**. As you can see the second derivative is positive for **$x > 0$**, negative for **$x < 0$** and exactly 0 for **$x = 0$** That means that when the 2nd derivative is positive the function is **concave up** when the 2nd derivative is negative the function is **concave down** and when the 2nd derivative is 0 the function might have an **inflection point** but in this case it has a **minimum.**

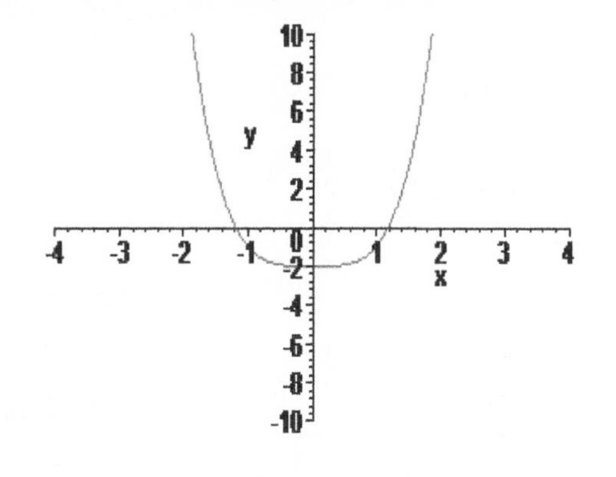

5. If $f'(a) = 0$ it means the function has a **stationary point** at *a*.

6. If f'(*a*) < 0 it means the function is **decreaseing** at *a*.

7. If $f'(a) \neq$ and $f''(a) = 0$ it means the function **may have an inflection point** at *a*.

8. If possible, fill the following table with a sketch of the function around the point where $x = a$.

	$f''(a) = 0$	$f''(a) > 0$	$f''(a) < 0$
$f'(a)=0$			
$f'(a) > 0$			
$f'(a) < 0$			

4. A certain function satisfies: $f(a) = 2, f'(a) = 1, f''(a) < 0$

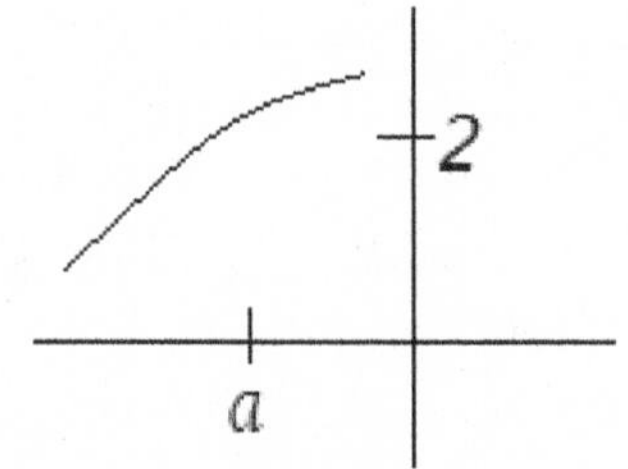

5. A certain function satisfies: $f(a) = -2, f'(a) = -2, f''(a) < 0$

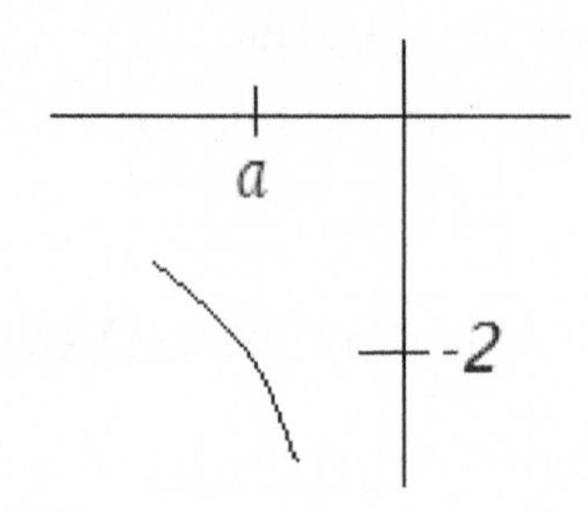

6. A certain function satisfies: $f(a) = 0$ $f'(a) = -2, f''(a) = 0$

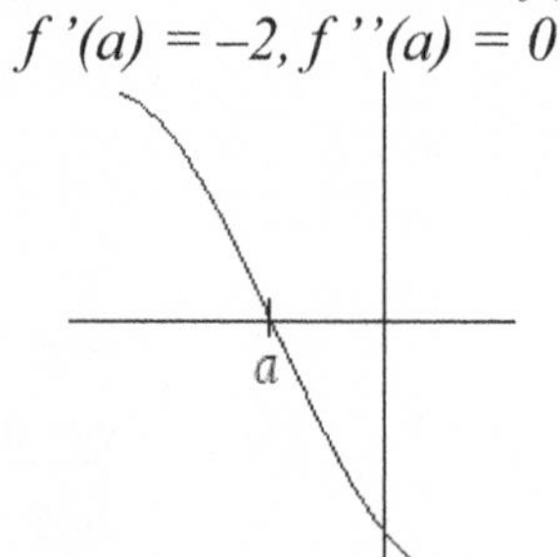

7. A certain function satisfies: $f(a) = 3$ $f'(a) = 3, \quad f''(a) = 0$

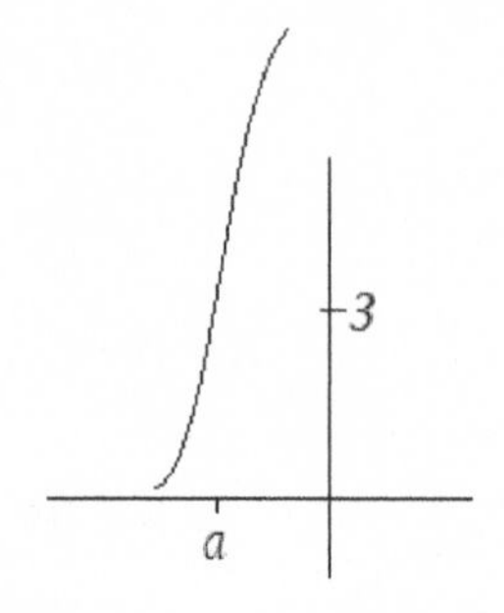

8. Sketch the graph of a function which has all the following properties:

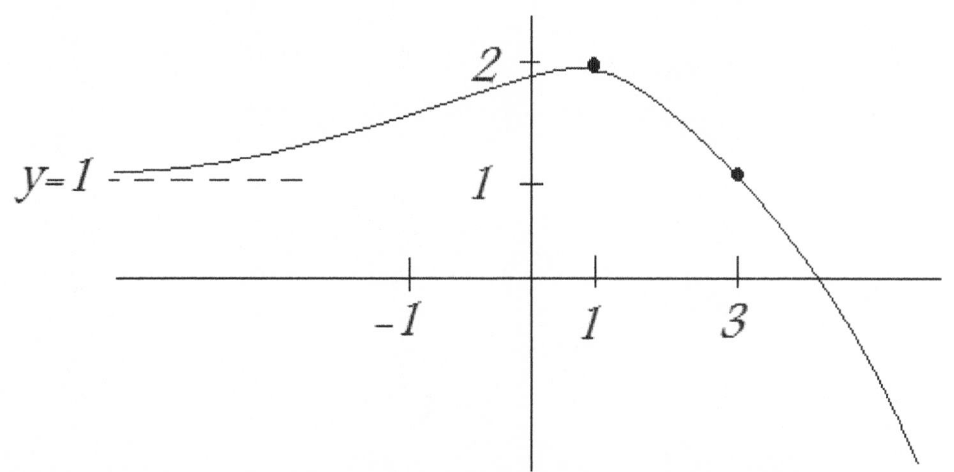

9. Sketch the graph of a function which has all the following properties:

a. $\lim_{x \to 2^-} f(x) = -\infty$

b. $\lim_{x \to 2^+} f(x) = \infty$

c. $\lim_{x \to -\infty} f(x) = 0$

d. $f(-2) = 2, f(5) = 1, f(0) = 0$

e. $f'(x) > 0$ if $x < -2$ or $x > 5$

f. $f'(x) > 0$ if $-2 < x < 2, 2 < x < 5$

g. $f'(5) = 0, f'(-2) = 0$

h. $f''(x) > 0$ if $x < -3$ or $x > 2$

i. $f''(x) < 0$ if $-3 < x < 2$

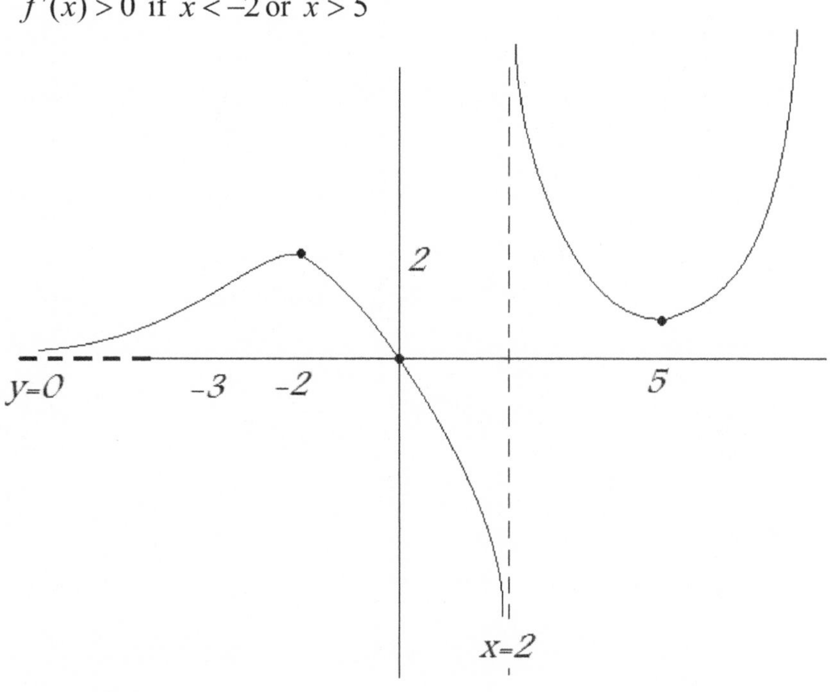

10. Sketch the graph of a function which has all the following properties:

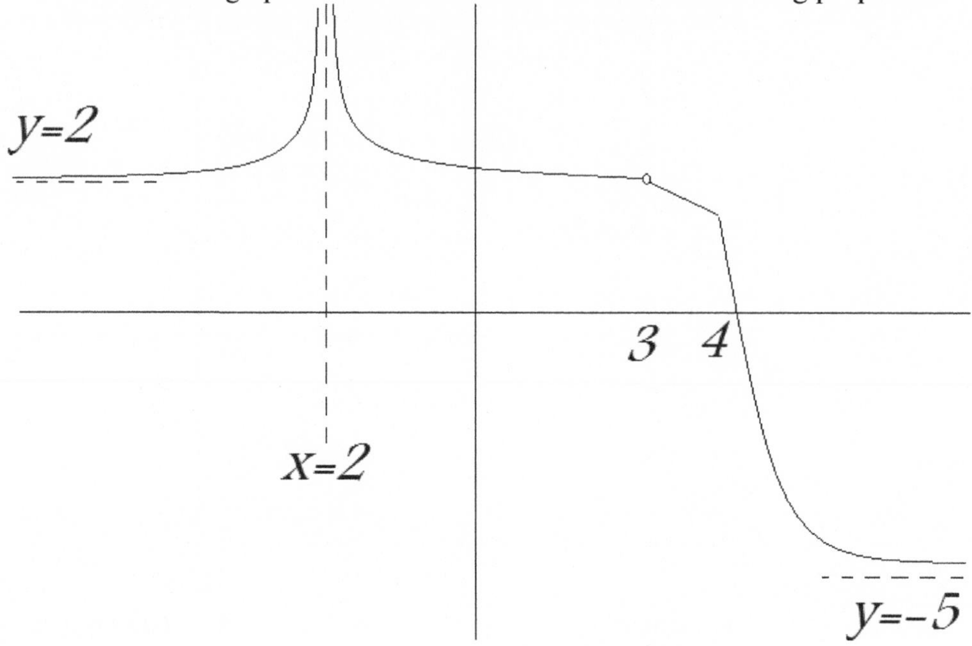

11.

$f(1)=1 \Rightarrow a+b+c=1$

$f'(1)=0; \Rightarrow 2a+b=0$

$f'(2)=-2; \Rightarrow 4a+b=-2$

$a=-1$

$b=2$

$c=0$

12.

$f(0)=-1 \Rightarrow c=-1$

$f'(1)=0; \Rightarrow 3+2a+b=0$

$f''(\frac{2}{3})=0; \Rightarrow 4+2a=0$

$a=-2$

$b=1$

$c=0$

13.

$f(0)=0 \Rightarrow 0=0$

$f'(0)=0 \Rightarrow c=0$

$f(2)=16; \Rightarrow 8a+4b=16$

$f''(2)=0; \Rightarrow 12a+2b=0$

$a=-1$

$b=6$

$c=0$

14.

$f(1)=3 \Rightarrow a+b=3$

$f'(1)=0 \Rightarrow -a+2b=0$

$a=2$

$b=1$

1.9. – FUNCTION ANALYSIS

A. POLYNOMIALS WITH NATURAL POWER

1. Graph the following functions. Obtain and indicate all x and y intercepts maximum, minimum and inflection points on the graph (include their coordinates)

$y=x$ $\quad$ $y=x^2$ $\quad$ $y=x^3$

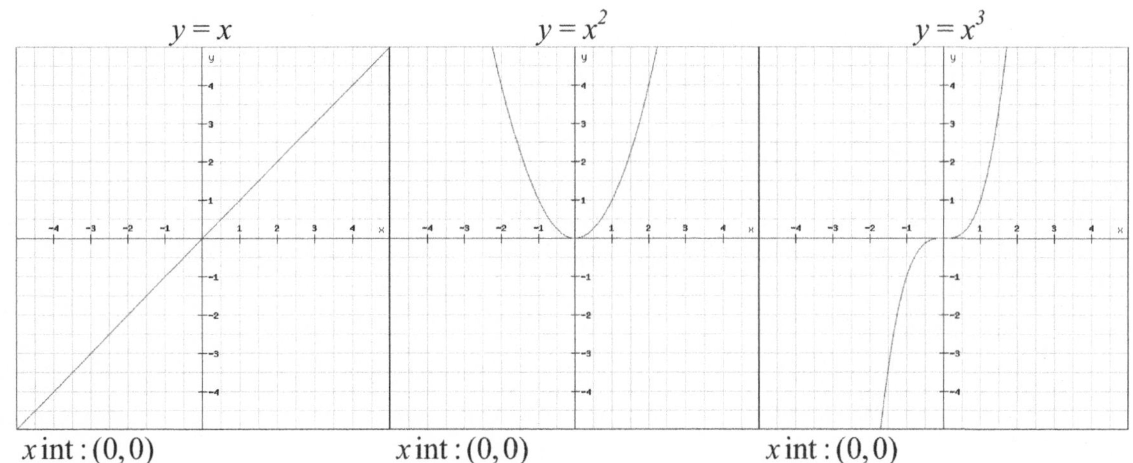

$y=x$	$y=x^2$	$y=x^3$
$x\,\text{int}:(0,0)$	$x\,\text{int}:(0,0)$	$x\,\text{int}:(0,0)$
$y\,\text{int}:(0,0)$	$y\,\text{int}:(0,0)$	$y\,\text{int}:(0,0)$
$Max: None$	$Max: None$	$Max: None$
$Min: None$	$Min:(0,0)$	$Min: None$
$Inflection\quad po\text{int}s: None$	$Inflection\quad po\text{int}s: None$	$Inflection\quad po\text{int}s:(0,0)$

$y=x^4$ $\quad$ $y=x^5$ $\quad$ $y=x^6$

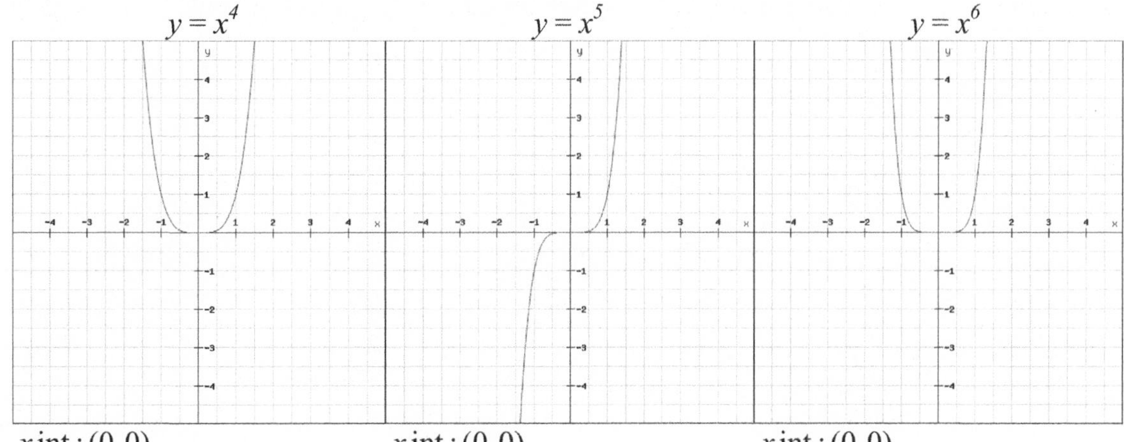

$y=x^4$	$y=x^5$	$y=x^6$
$x\,\text{int}:(0,0)$	$x\,\text{int}:(0,0)$	$x\,\text{int}:(0,0)$
$y\,\text{int}:(0,0)$	$y\,\text{int}:(0,0)$	$y\,\text{int}:(0,0)$
$Max: None$	$Max: None$	$Max: None$
$Min:(0,0)$	$Min: None$	$Min:(0,0)$
$Inflection\quad po\text{int}s: None$	$Inflection\quad po\text{int}s:(0,0)$	$Inflection\quad po\text{int}s: None$

Conclusion: Even Powers have similar end behaviour (up – up or down – down). Odd powers have similar end behaviour (up – down or down – up)

2. Graph the following functions. Obtain and indicate all x and y intercepts maximum, minimum and inflection points on the graph (include their coordinates)

$y = (x+2)^2 + 1$	$y = (x-2)^3 - 3$	$y = (x+3)^4 - 6$

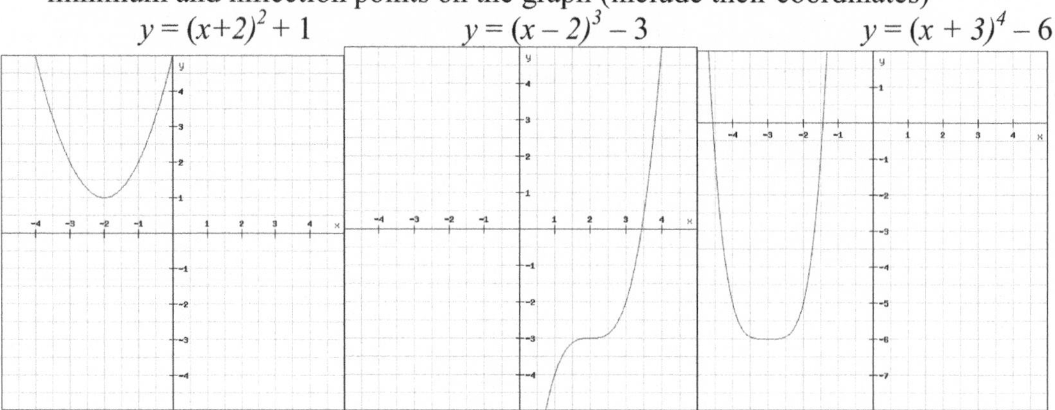

$x\text{int}: None$	$x\text{int}: (\sqrt[3]{3}+2, 0)$	$x\text{int}: (\pm\sqrt[4]{6}-3, 0)$
$y\text{int}: (0,5)$	$y\text{int}: (0,-11)$	$y\text{int}: (0,75)$
$Max: None$	$Max: None$	$Max: None$
$Min: (-2,1)$	$Min: None$	$Min: (-3,-6)$
$Inflection \quad points: None$	$Inflection \quad points: (2,-3)$	$Inflection \quad points: None$

Conclusion: These are the same functions as in the previous part after an application of horizontal and vertical translations.

3. Graph the following functions. Obtain and indicate all x and y intercepts maximum, minimum and inflection points on the graph (include their coordinates)

$y = -(x+2)^2 + 1$	$y = -(x-2)^3 - 3$	$y = -(x+3)^4 - 6$

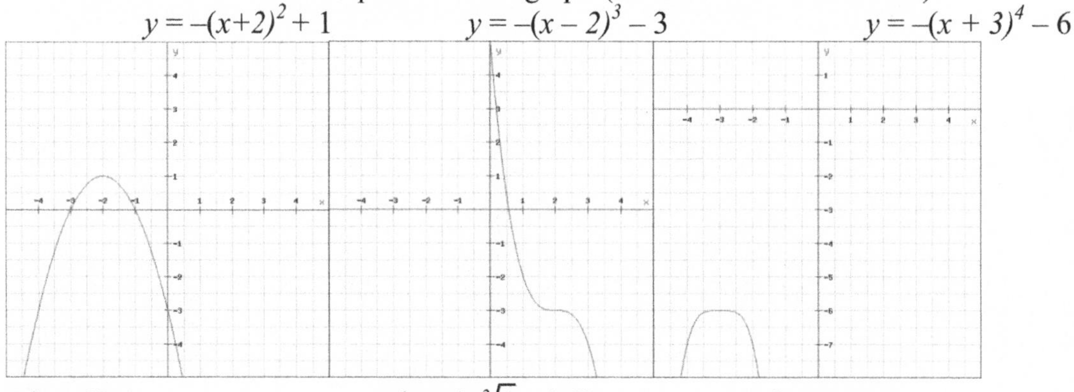

$x\text{int}: None$	$x\text{int}: (-\sqrt[3]{3}+2, 0)$	$x\text{int}: None$
$y\text{int}: (0,-3)$	$y\text{int}: (0,5)$	$y\text{int}: (0,-87)$
$Max: (-2,1)$	$Max: None$	$Max: (-3,-6)$
$Min: None$	$Min: None$	$Min: None$
$Inflection \quad points: None$	$Inflection \quad points: (2,-3)$	$Inflection \quad points: None$

Conclusion: These are the same functions as in the previous part after an application of horizontal and vertical translations and a reflection in the x axis.

4. Graph the following functions. Obtain and indicate all x and y intercepts:

$y = x(x^2+1) =$ $\qquad$ $y = x(x+1)(x+1)$ $\qquad$ $y = x(x+1)(x-1)$

$y = -x(x+2)(x-3)$ $\qquad$ $y = x(x^3+1)$ $\qquad$ $y = x(x^3-1)$

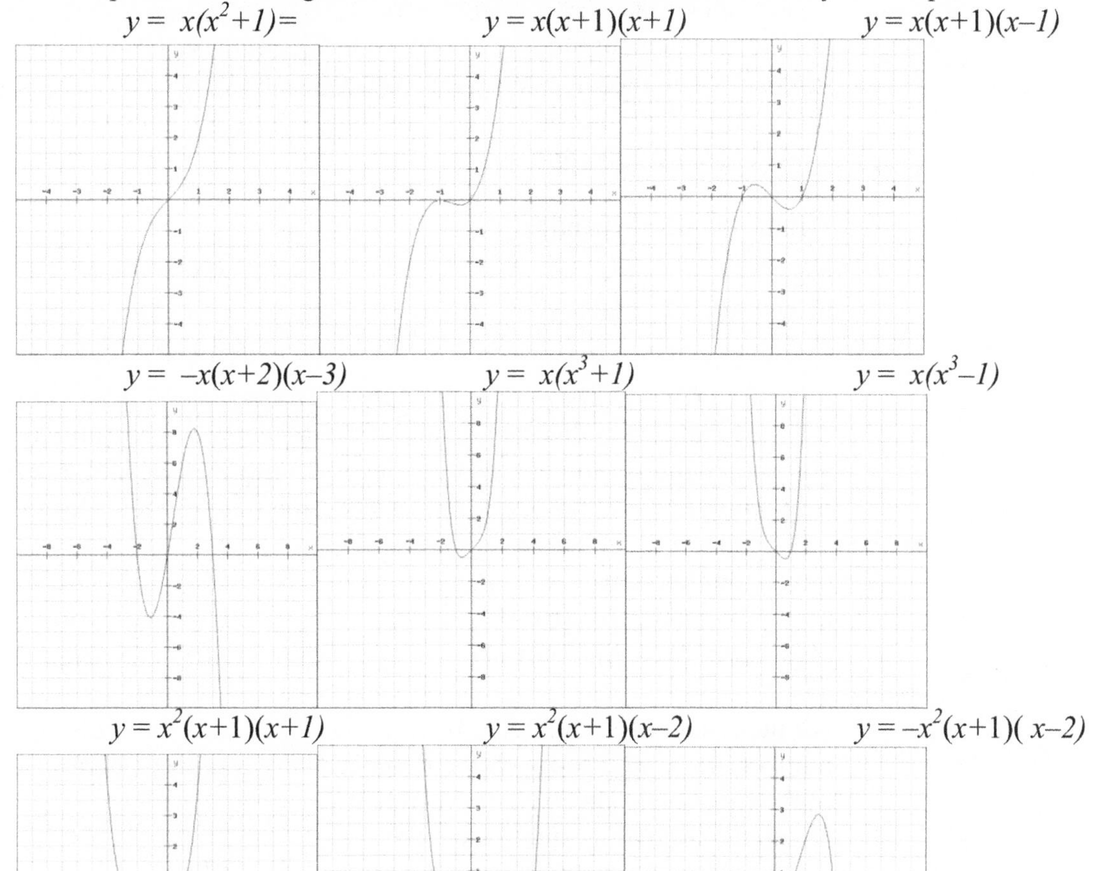

$y = x^2(x+1)(x+1)$ $\qquad$ $y = x^2(x+1)(x-2)$ $\qquad$ $y = -x^2(x+1)(x-2)$

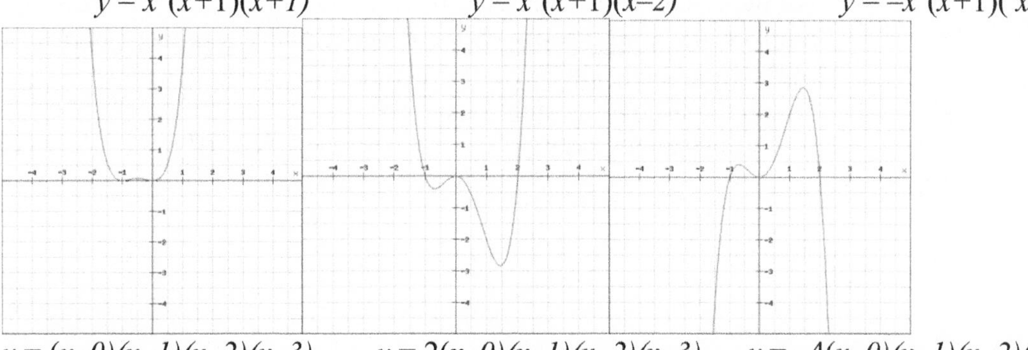

$y = (x-0)(x-1)(x-2)(x-3)$ $\qquad$ $y = 2(x-0)(x-1)(x-2)(x-3)$ $\qquad$ $y = -4(x-0)(x-1)(x-2)(x-3)$

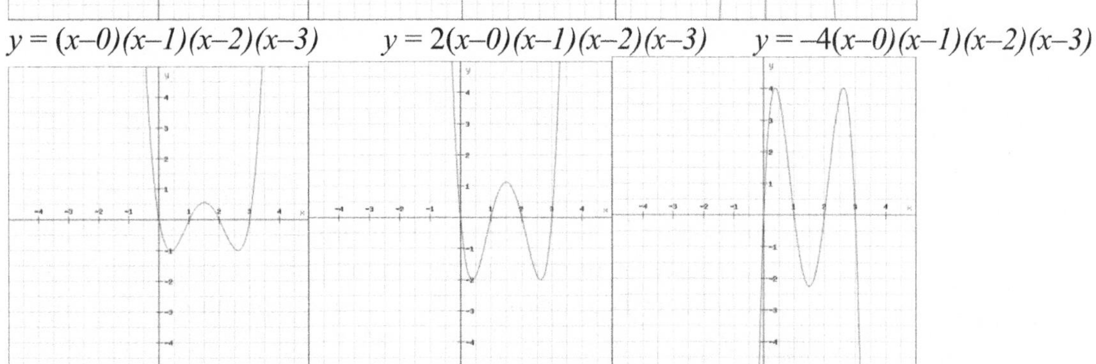

5. Fill the blanks (expand)

   a) $y = x^3$
   b) $y = x(x^2+1) = x^3 + x$
   c) $y = x(x+1)(x+1) = x^3 + 2x^2 + x$
   d) $y = x(x+1)(x-1) = x^3 - x$
   e) $y = -x(x+2)(x-3) = -x^3 - x^2 - 6x$
   f) $y = -(x-1)^3 = -x^3 + 3x^2 - 3x + 1$

   All the functions in this section are of the **3rd** degree. They all have an **inflection point** They all have at least 1 **x intercept.** Sometimes they have **2 or 3 x intercepts.** If at one end the function tends to **infinity** then on the other end it will tend to **negative infinity**.

6. Fill the blanks (expand)

   a) $y = x^4$
   b) $y = x(x^3+1) = x^4 + x$
   c) $y = x(x^3-1) = x^4 - x$
   d) $y = x^2(x+1)(x+1) = x^4 + 2x^3 + x^2$
   e) $y = x^2(x+1)(x-1) = x^4 - x^2$
   f) $y = x^2(x+1)(x-2) = x^4 - x^3 - 2x^2$
   g) $y = -x^2(x+1)(x-2) = -x^4 + x^3 + 2x^2$
   h) $y = -(x-2)^4 = -x^4 + 8x^3 - 24x^2 + 32x - 16$

   All the functions in this section are of the **4th** degree. They all have at least one **stationary point**. Sometimes they have two **minimums** and one **maximum** or two **maximum** and one **minimum**. If one end the function tends to **infinity** then on the other end it will tend to **infinity** as well.

7. Given the functions:

   a) $y = (x-1)(x-2)(x-3)(x-4)$
   b) $y = 2(x-1)(x-2)(x-3)(x-4)$
   c) $y = 3(x-1)(x-2)(x-3)(x-4)$
   d) $y = -4(x-1)(x-2)(x-3)(x-4)$

   All the functions in this section are of the **4th** degree. On multiplying a function by a number, the **x intercepts stay** the same. The **y intercept changes**. The general aspect of the function is **similar**/very different

8. Graph the following functions

   $y = -(x-1)(x-2)^2(x-4)^3$ $\quad$ $y = -(x-2)^3(x-4)^4$ $\quad$ $y = (x-2)(x^2-1)(x^2+1)$

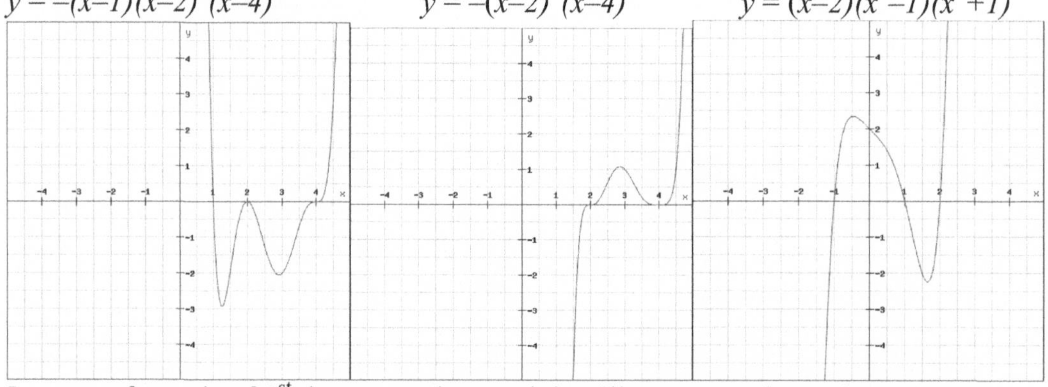

In case a factor is of 1st degree on the graph it will correspond an **x intercept**
In case a factor is of even degree on the graph it will correspond a **max** or **min**
In case a factor is of odd (> 1) degree on the graph it will correspond an **inflection point**

9. Graph the following functions. Obtain and indicate all x and y intercepts on the graph (include their coordinates). Sketch a dashed line (use a pen or pencil) to indicate horizontal and/or vertical asymptotes.

a. $y = \dfrac{2x}{x-1}$

Vertical asymptote(s): x = 1

Horizontal asymptote(s): y = 2

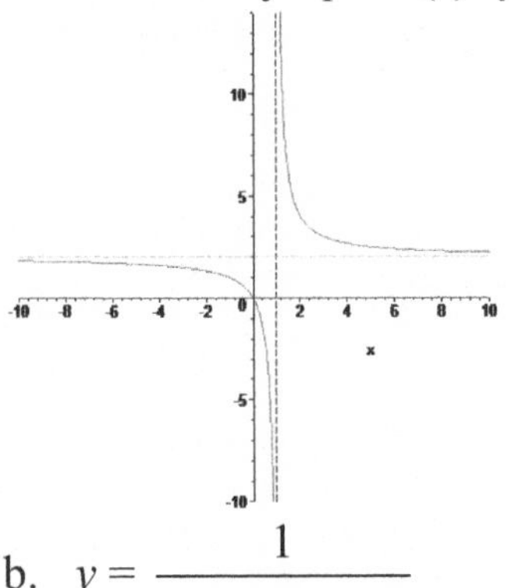

c. $y = \dfrac{3x^2}{(x+1)(x-4)}$

Vertical asymptote(s): x = –1, 4

Horizontal asymptote(s): y = 3

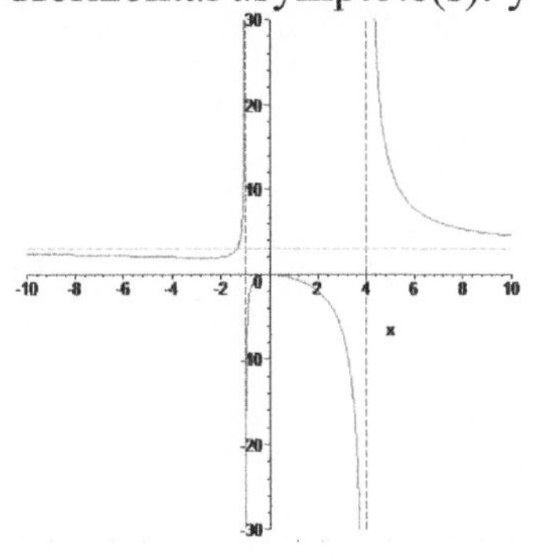

b. $y = \dfrac{1}{(x+1)(x-2)}$

Vertical asymptote(s): x = –1, 2

Horizontal asymptote(s): y = 0

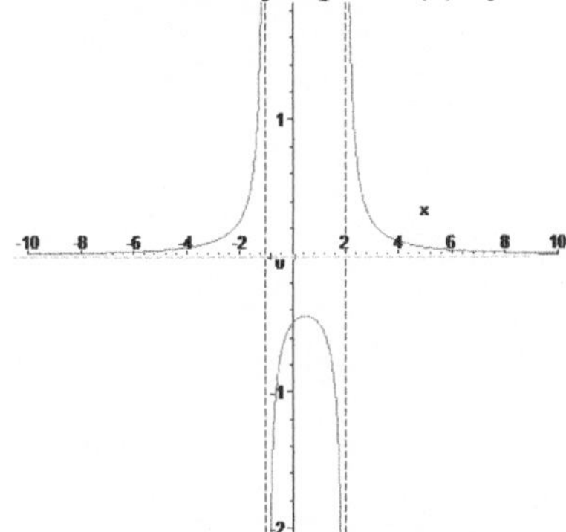

d. $y = xe^x$

Vertical asymptote(s): None

Horizontal asymptote(s): y = 0

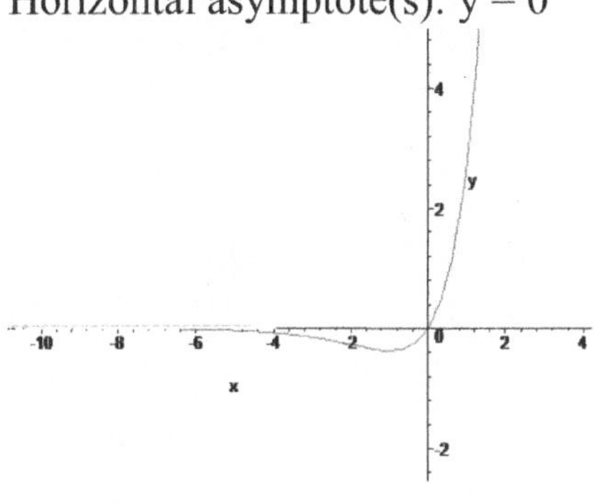

10. Given the following function, fill the table:

x = a	x = –3	x = –2	x = – 1	x =–0.6	x = 0	x =1	x = 1.5	x = 2
f(x)	21	0	≈–1.5	≈–1.7	0	13	24	0
f'(x)	≈–10	0	≈–0.5	0	0	≈8	0	D.E.
f''(x)	≈1	0	≈2	≈2	0	0	≈–4	D.E.

Conclusions:

a. In a "smooth" maximum or minimum the **derivative is 0**

b. In a horizontal inflection point both **first and second derivatives are zero.**

c. In a non–horizontal inflection point **first derivative is different than 0 and second derivatives iszero.**.

11. Use GDC to sketch the functions $f(x) = x^3$ and $g(x) = 4^x + 2^{-x} - 8$

f(x) > g(x) for $x \in (-1.8, 2)$

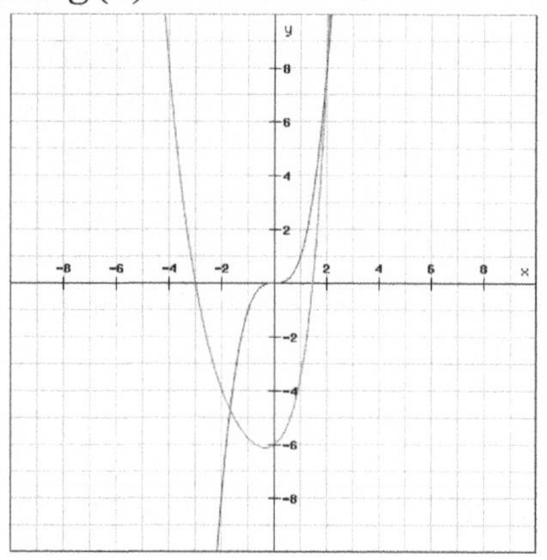

12. Use GDC to sketch the functions $f(x) = x^2$ and $g(x) = \ln(x)$

f(x) > g(x) for $x \in \Re$

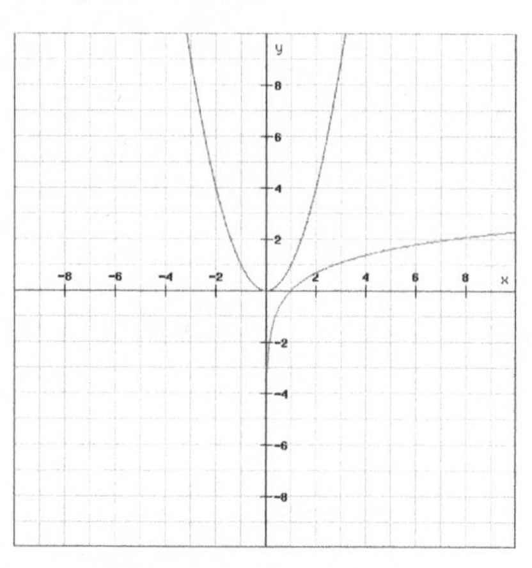

13. $f(x) = x^4, x \in [-1, 2]$

$Domain: x \in [-1, 2]$

$Vertical \quad Asymptotes: None$

$Horizontal \quad Asymptotes: None$

$Slant \quad Asymptotes: None$

$y - \text{int}: (0, 0)$

$x - \text{int}: (0, 0)$

$Inflection \quad po\text{int}s: None$

$Extrema: (0, 0), \text{min}, Absolute \quad \text{max}: (2, 16)$

$Range: f(x) \in [0, 16]$

$Increase: x \in (0, 2)$

$Decrease: x \in (-1, 0)$

$Concave - up: x \in (-1, 2)$

$Concave - down: Never$

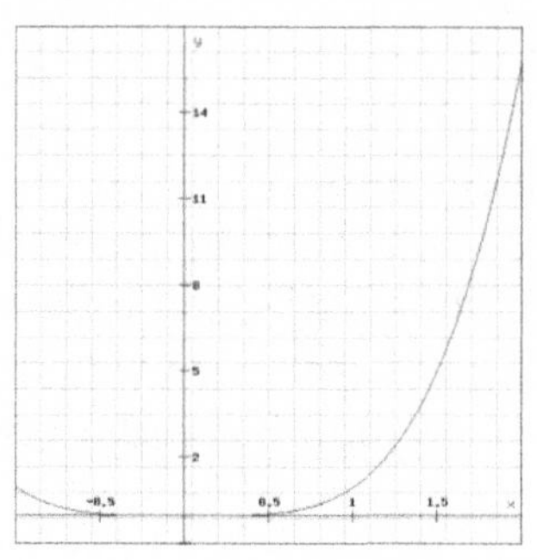

14. $f(x) = -x^6 + 6, x \in$ □

$Domain: x \in \Re$

$Vertical \quad Asymptotes: None$

$Horizontal \quad Asymptotes: None$

$Slant \quad Asymptotes: None$

$y - \text{int}: (0,6)$

$x - \text{int}: (\pm\sqrt[6]{6}, 0)$

$Inflection \quad points: None$

$Extrema: (0,6), \max$

$Range: f(x) \in [-\infty, 6]$

$Increase: x \in (-\infty, 0)$

$Decrease: x \in (0, \infty)$

$Concave - up: Never$

$Concave - down: x \in \Re$

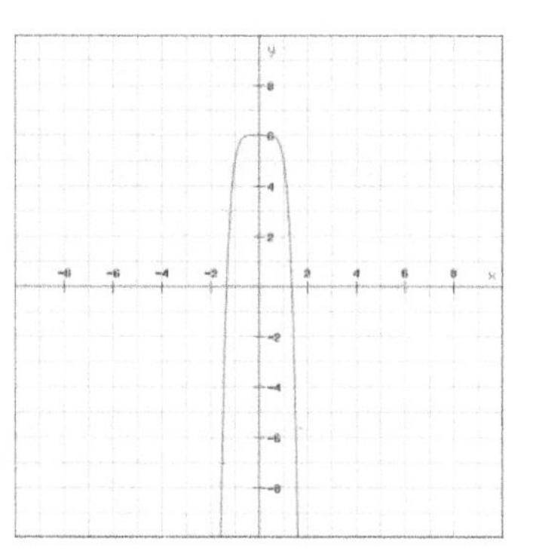

15. $f(x) = x^2(x+2), x \in [-\frac{3}{2}, \frac{1}{2}]$

$Domain: x \in [-\frac{3}{2}, \frac{1}{2}]$

$Vertical \quad Asymptotes: None$

$Horizontal \quad Asymptotes: None$

$Slant \quad Asymptotes: None$

$y - \text{int}: (0,0)$

$x - \text{int}: None$

$Inflection \quad points: (-\frac{2}{3}, \frac{16}{27})$

$Extrema: (0,0), \min; (-\frac{4}{3}, \frac{32}{27}), \max$

$Range: f(x) \in [0, \frac{32}{27}]$

$Increase: x \in (-\frac{3}{2}, -\frac{4}{3}) \cup (0, \frac{1}{2})$

$Decrease: x \in (-\frac{4}{3}, 0)$

$Concave - up: x \in (-\frac{2}{3}, \frac{1}{2})$

$Concave - down: x \in (-\frac{3}{2}, -\frac{2}{3})$

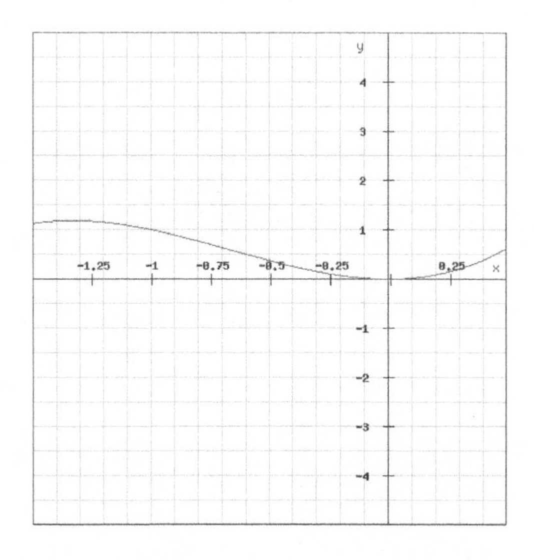

16. $f(x) = x(x+2)(x-1), x \in \square$

$Domain: x \in \Re$

$Extrema: (\frac{-1+\sqrt{7}}{3}, \approx -0.631), \min, (\frac{-1-\sqrt{7}}{3}, \approx 2.11), \max$

$Vertical\quad Asymptotes: None$

$Range: f(x) \in \Re$

$Horizontal\quad Asymptotes: None$

$Increase: x \in (-\infty, \frac{-1-\sqrt{7}}{3}) \cup (\frac{-1+\sqrt{7}}{3}, \infty)$

$Slant\quad Asymptotes: None$

$Decrease: x \in (\frac{-1-\sqrt{7}}{3}, \frac{-1+\sqrt{7}}{3})$

$y-\text{int}: (0,0)$

$Concave-up: x \in (-\frac{1}{3}, \infty)$

$x-\text{int}: (0,0), (-2,0), (1,0)$

$Concave-down: x \in (-\infty, -\frac{1}{3})$

$Inflection\quad points: (-\frac{1}{3}, \frac{20}{27})$

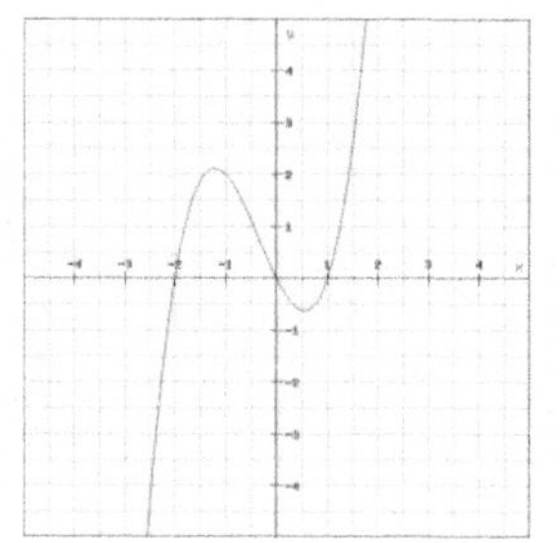

17. $f(x) = 2x^3 + 11x^2 + 10x - 8, x \in \square$

$Domain: x \in \Re$

$Extrema: (\frac{-11+\sqrt{61}}{6}, \approx -10.5), \min, (\frac{-11-\sqrt{61}}{6}, \approx 7.14), \max$

$Vertical\quad Asymptotes: None$

$Range: f(x) \in \Re$

$Horizontal\quad Asymptotes: None$

$Increase: x \in (-\infty, \frac{-11-\sqrt{61}}{6}) \cup (\frac{-11+\sqrt{61}}{6}, \infty)$

$Slant\quad Asymptotes: None$

$Decrease: x \in (\frac{-11-\sqrt{61}}{6}, \frac{-11+\sqrt{61}}{6})$

$y-\text{int}: (0,-8)$

$Concave-up: x \in (-\frac{11}{6}, \infty)$

$x-\text{int}: (\frac{1}{2}, 0), (-2,0), (-4,0)$

$Concave-down: x \in (-\infty, -\frac{11}{6})$

$Inflection\quad points: (-\frac{11}{6}, -\frac{91}{54})$

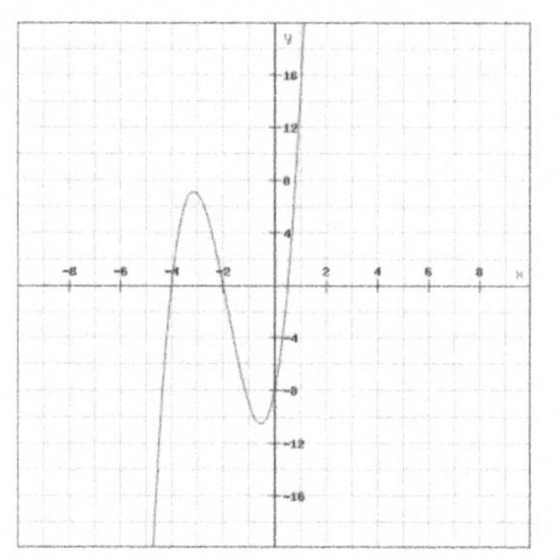

18. $f(x) = x^3 - x^2, x \in [0,2]$

Domain : $x \in [0,2]$

Extrema : $(0,0)$, max; $(\frac{2}{3}, -\frac{4}{27})$, *Absolute Max* : $(2,4)$

Vertical Asymptotes : *None*

Range : $f(x) \in [-\frac{4}{27}, 4]$

Horizontal Asymptotes : *None*

Increase : $x \in (-\frac{2}{3}, 4)$

Slant Asymptotes : *None*

Decrease : $x \in (0, \frac{2}{3})$

$y - \text{int} : (0,0)$

Concave – up : $x \in (\frac{1}{3}, 2)$

$x - \text{int} : (0,0), (1,0)$

Concave – down : $x \in (0, \frac{1}{3})$

Inflection points : $(\frac{1}{3}, -\frac{2}{27})$

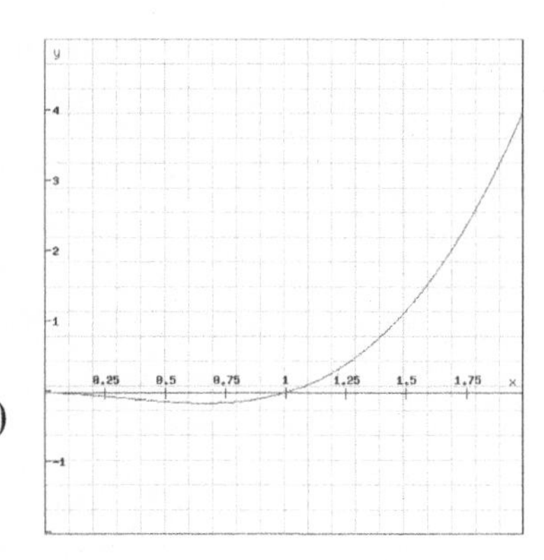

19. $f(x) = 2x^4 - 4x^2, x \in \mathbb{R}$

Domain : $x \in \mathbb{R}$

Extrema : $(0,0)$, max; $(-1,-2)(1,-2)$, min

Vertical Asymptotes : *None*

Range : $f(x) \in [-2, \infty)$

Horizontal Asymptotes : *None*

Increase : $x \in (-1,0) \cup (1,\infty)$

Slant Asymptotes : *None*

Decrease : $x \in (-\infty,-1) \cup (0,1)$

$y - \text{int} : (0,0)$

Concave – up : $x \in (-\infty, -\frac{1}{\sqrt{3}}) \cup (\frac{1}{\sqrt{3}}, \infty)$

$x - \text{int} : (0,0), (\pm 1, 0)$

Concave – down : $x \in (-\frac{1}{\sqrt{3}}, \frac{1}{\sqrt{3}})$

Inflection points : $(-\frac{1}{\sqrt{3}}, -\frac{10}{9}), (\frac{1}{\sqrt{3}}, -\frac{10}{9})$

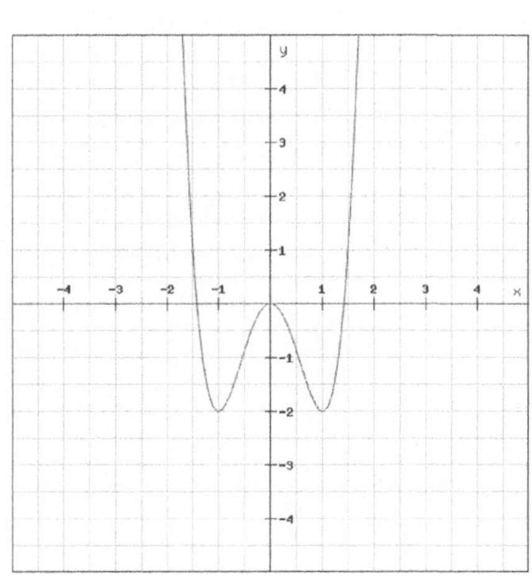

20. $f(x) = x^4 - 2x^3, x \in \mathbb{R}$

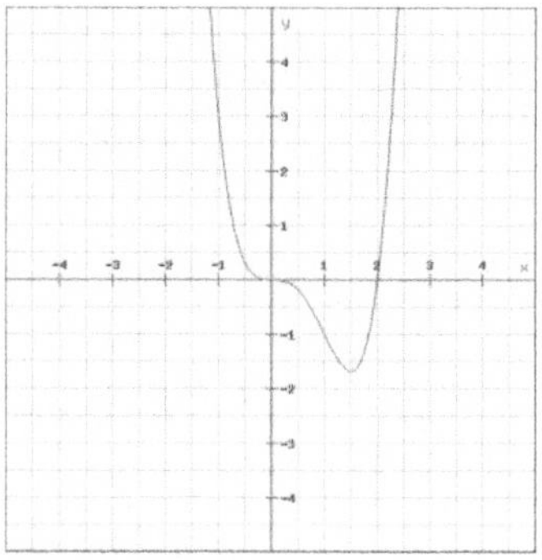

$Domain: x \in \mathbb{R}$ $Extrema(\frac{3}{2}, -\frac{27}{16})$, min

$Vertical \quad Asymptotes: None$ $Range: f(x) \in [-\frac{27}{16}, \infty)$

$Horizontal \quad Asymptotes: None$ $Increase: x \in (\frac{3}{2}, \infty)$

$Slant \quad Asymptotes: None$ $Decrease: x \in (-\infty, \frac{3}{2})$

$y-\text{int}: (0,0)$ $Concave-up: x \in (-\infty, 0) \cup (1, \infty)$

$x-\text{int}: (0,0), (2,0)$ $Concave-down: x \in (0,1)$

$Inflection \quad po\text{int}s: (0,0) Horizontal, (1,-1)$

21. A function of the 3rd degree that intercepts the x axis at (2, 0), (–3, 0) and (–0.5, 0). Is it possible to make this function have a y intercept (0, 10)? Yes:

$$f(x) = a(x-2)(x+3)(x+\frac{1}{2}); f(0) = 10; a = -\frac{10}{3}; f(x) = -\frac{10}{3}(x-2)(x+3)(x+\frac{1}{2})$$

22. A function of the 4th degree that intercepts the x axis at (1, 0), (2, 0), (5, 0) and (–1, 0). Is it possible to make this function have a y intercept (0, 5)? Yes:

$$f(x) = a(x-1)(x-2)(x-5)(x+1); f(0) = 5; a = -\frac{1}{2}; f(x) = -\frac{1}{2}(x-1)(x-2)(x-5)(x+1)$$

23. The expression of $f(x) = x^3$ shifted 2 positions to the right and 3 positions down.
    $f(x) = (x-2)^3 - 3$
24. The expression of $f(x) = x^4$ shifted 4 positions to the left and 6 positions up.
    $f(x) = (x+4)^4 + 6$
25. In case the first derivative of a function is 0 at a certain point, this point can be a **maximum** or a **minimum** or a **horizontal inflection point**
26. In case the 1st derivative is 0 and the 2nd derivative is positive at a certain point, the point must be a **minimum**
27. In case the 1st derivative is 0 and the 2nd derivative is negative at a certain point, the point must be a **maximum**
28. In case the 1st derivative is 0 and the 2nd derivative is also 0 at a certain point, the point can be a **maximum** or a **minimum** or a **horizontal inflection point**
29. In the parts where $f'(x) > 0$ the function is **increasing**
30. In the parts where $f''(x) > 0$ the function is **decreasing**

B. POLYNOMIALS WITH RATIONAL POWER

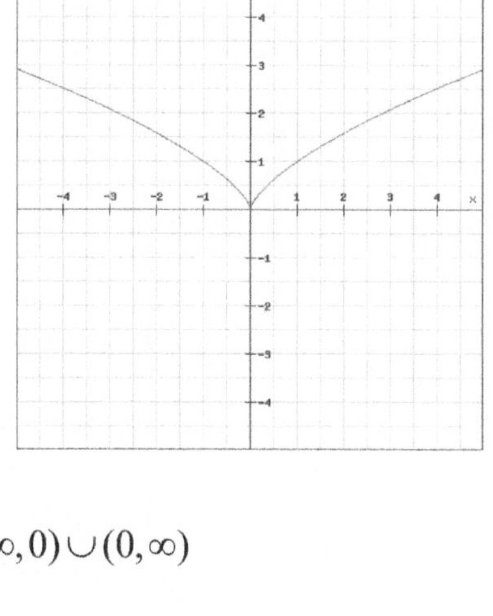

31. $f(x) = x^{\frac{2}{3}}, x \in \mathbb{R}$

$Domain : x \in \mathbb{R}$ $\quad$ $Extrema : (0,0), \min$

$Vertical \quad Asymptotes : None$ $\quad$ $Range : f(x) \in [0, \infty)$

$Horizontal \quad Asymptotes : None$ $\quad$ $Increase : x \in (0, \infty)$

$Lim_{x \to -\infty}(f(x)) = \infty \quad Lim_{x \to \infty}(f(x)) = \infty$

$Slant \quad Asymptotes : None$ $\quad$ $Decrease : x \in (-\infty, 0)$

$y - \text{int} : (0,0)$ $\quad$ $Concave - up : Never$

$x - \text{int} : (0,0)$ $\quad$ $Concave - down : x \in (-\infty, 0) \cup (0, \infty)$

$Inflection \quad po\text{int}s : None$

$*Attention : Derivative \quad is \quad undefined \quad at \quad x = 0$

32. $f(x) = x^{\frac{4}{3}}, x \in \mathbb{R}$

$Domain : x \in \mathbb{R}$ $\quad$ $Extrema : (0,0), \min$

$Vertical \quad Asymptotes : None$ $\quad$ $Range : f(x) \in [0, \infty)$

$Horizontal \quad Asymptotes : None$ $\quad$ $Increase : x \in (0, \infty)$

$Lim_{x \to -\infty}(f(x)) = \infty \quad Lim_{x \to \infty}(f(x)) = \infty$

$Slant \quad Asymptotes : None$ $\quad$ $Decrease : x \in (-\infty, 0)$

$y - \text{int} : (0,0)$ $\quad$ $Concave - up : x \in (-\infty, 0) \cup (0, \infty)$

$x - \text{int} : (0,0)$ $\quad$ $Concave - down : Never$

$Inflection \quad po\text{int}s : None$

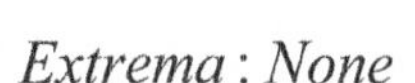

33. $f(x) = 2x^{-\frac{4}{3}}, x \in \mathbb{R}$

$Domain : x \in (-\infty, 0) \cup (0, \infty)$ $\quad$ $Extrema : None$

$Vertical \quad Asymptotes : x = 0$ $\quad$ $Range : f(x) \in (0, \infty)$

$Lim_{x \to 0^-}(f(x)) = \infty \quad Lim_{x \to 0^+}(f(x)) = \infty$ $\quad$ $Increase : x \in (-\infty, 0)$

$Horizontal \quad Asymptotes : y = 0$ $\quad$ $Decrease : x \in (0, \infty)$

$Lim_{x \to \infty}(f(x)) = 0 \quad Lim_{x \to \infty}(f(x)) = 0$ $\quad$ $Concave - up : x \in (-\infty, 0) \cup (0, \infty)$

$Slant \quad Asymptotes : None$ $\quad$ $Concave - down : Never$

$y - \text{int} : None$

$x - \text{int} : None$

$Inflection \quad po\text{int}s : None$

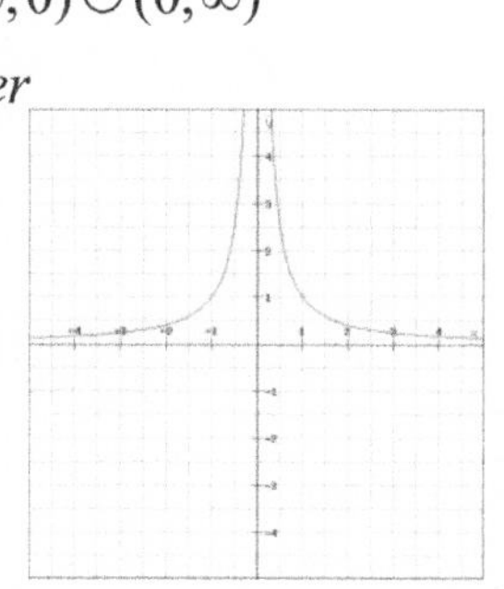

34. $f(x) = x - x^{\frac{2}{3}}, x \in \mathbb{R}$

$Domain: x \in \mathbb{R}$

$Extrema: (0,0), \min, (\frac{8}{27}, \approx -0.148)$

$Vertical \quad Asymptotes: None$

$Range: f(x) \in (-\infty, \infty)$

$Horizontal \quad Asymptotes: None$

$Increase: x \in (-\infty, 0) \cup (\frac{8}{27}, \infty)$

$Lim_{x \to -\infty}(f(x)) = -\infty \quad Lim_{x \to \infty}(f(x)) = \infty$

$Slant \quad Asymptotes: None$

$Decrease: x \in (0, \frac{8}{27})$

$y - \text{int}: (0,0)$

$Concave - up: x \in (-\infty, 0) \cup (0, \infty)$

$x - \text{int}: (0,0), (1,0)$

$Concave - down: Never$

$Inflection \quad points: None$

$* Attention: Derivative \quad is \quad undefined \quad at \quad x = 0$

35. $f(x) = x + x^{-\frac{2}{3}}, x \in \mathbb{R}$

$Domain: x \in (-\infty, 0) \cup (0, \infty)$

$Extrema: (\frac{\sqrt[5]{72}}{3}, \approx 1.96)$

$Vertical \quad Asymptotes: x = 0$

$Range: f(x) \in (-\infty, \infty)$

$Lim_{x \to 0^-}(f(x)) = \infty \quad Lim_{x \to 0^+}(f(x)) = \infty$

$Increase: x \in (-\infty, 0) \cup (\frac{\sqrt[5]{72}}{3}, \infty)$

$Horizontal \quad Asymptotes: None$

$Decrease: x \in (0, \frac{\sqrt[5]{72}}{3})$

$Lim_{x \to -\infty}(f(x)) = -\infty \quad Lim_{x \to \infty}(f(x)) = \infty$

$Concave - up: x \in (-\infty, 0) \cup (0, \infty)$

$Slant \quad Asymptotes: y = x$

$Concave - down: Never$

$y - \text{int}: None$

$x - \text{int}: (-1, 0)$

$Inflection \quad points: None$

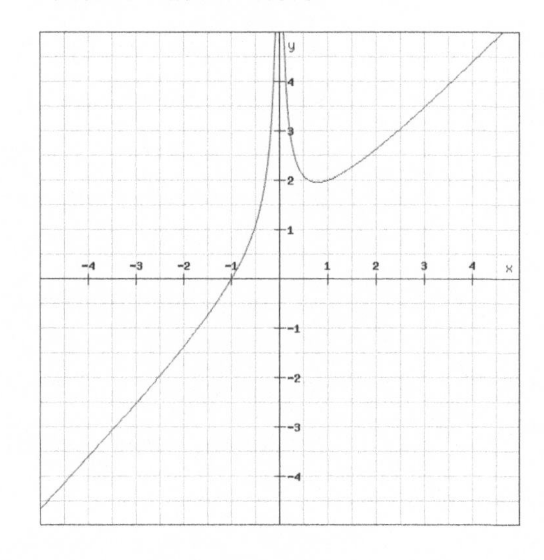

C. RATIONAL FUNCTIONS

36. $f(x)=\dfrac{3(x+2)}{(x-5)(x+2)}+4, x\in\mathbb{R}$

$Domain: x\in(-\infty,-2)\cup(-2,5)\cup(5,\infty)$

$Vertical \quad Asymptotes: x=5$

$Lim_{x\to 2^-}(f(x))=\dfrac{7}{2} \quad Lim_{x\to -2^+}(f(x))=\dfrac{7}{2}$

$Lim_{x\to 5^-}(f(x))=-\infty \quad Lim_{x\to 5^+}(f(x))=\infty$

$Horizontal \quad Asymptotes: y=4$

$Lim_{x\to-\infty}(f(x))=4 \quad Lim_{x\to\infty}(f(x))=4$

$Slant \quad Asymptotes: None$

$y-\text{int}:(0,\dfrac{17}{5})$

$x-\text{int}:(\dfrac{17}{4},0)$

$Inflection \quad po\text{int}s: None$

$Extrema: None$

$Range: f(x)\in(-\infty,\dfrac{7}{2})\cup(\dfrac{7}{2},4)\cup(4,\infty)$

$Increase: x\in Never$

$Decrease: x\in(-\infty,-2)\cup(-2,5)\cup(5,\infty)$

$Concave-up: x\in(-\infty,-2)\cup(-2,5)$

$Concave-down: x\in(5,\infty)$

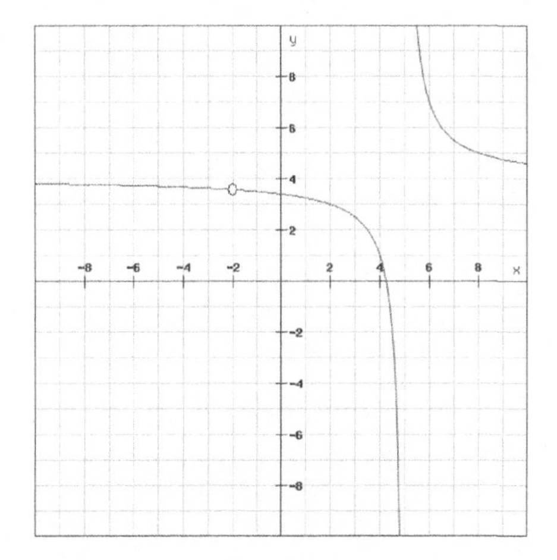

37. $f(x)=\dfrac{2x}{x+1}, x\in\mathbb{R}$

$Domain: x\in(-\infty,-1)\cup(-1,\infty)$

$Vertical \quad Asymptotes: x=-1$

$Lim_{x\to-1^-}(f(x))=\infty \quad Lim_{x\to-1^+}(f(x))=-\infty$

$Horizontal \quad Asymptotes: y=2$

$Lim_{x\to-\infty}(f(x))=2 \quad Lim_{x\to\infty}(f(x))=2$

$Slant \quad Asymptotes: None$

$y-\text{int}:(0,0)$

$x-\text{int}:(0,0)$

$Inflection \quad po\text{int}s: None$

$Extrema: None$

$Range: f(x)\in(-\infty,2)\cup(2,\infty)$

$Increase: x\in(-\infty,-1)\cup(-1,\infty)$

$Decrease: Never$

$Concave-up: x\in(-\infty,-1)$

$Concave-down: x\in(-1,\infty)$

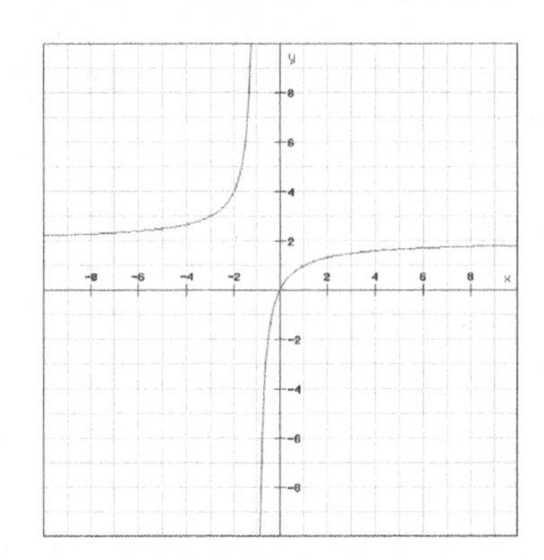

38. $f(x)=\dfrac{1}{x^2}, x\in\mathbb{R}$

$Domain: x \in (-\infty, 0) \cup (0, \infty)$

$Vertical \quad Asymptotes: x = 0$

$Lim_{x \to 0^-}(f(x)) = \infty \quad Lim_{x \to 0^+}(f(x)) = \infty$

$Horizontal \quad Asymptotes: y = 0$

$Lim_{x \to -\infty}(f(x)) = 0 \quad Lim_{x \to \infty}(f(x)) = 0$

$Slant \quad Asymptotes: None$

$y - \text{int}: None$

$x - \text{int}: None$

$Inflection \quad points: None$

$Extrema: None$

$Range: f(x) \in (0, \infty)$

$Increase: x \in (-\infty, 0)$

$Decrease: x \in (0, \infty)$

$Concave - up: x \in (-\infty, 0) \cup (0, \infty)$

$Concave - down: Never$

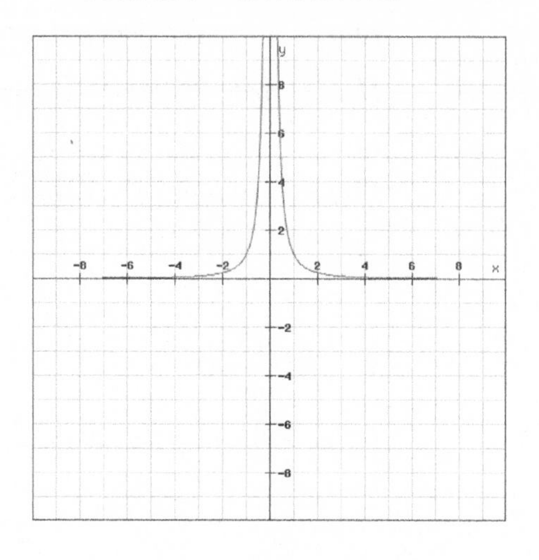

39. $f(x) = \dfrac{2}{(x-3)^2} - 4, x \in$ □

$Domain: x \in (-\infty, 3) \cup (3, \infty)$

$Vertical \quad Asymptotes: x = 3$

$Lim_{x \to 3^-}(f(x)) = \infty \quad Lim_{x \to 3^+}(f(x)) = \infty$

$Horizontal \quad Asymptotes: y = -4$

$Lim_{x \to -\infty}(f(x)) = -4 \quad Lim_{x \to \infty}(f(x)) = -4$

$Slant \quad Asymptotes: None$

$y - \text{int}: (0, -\dfrac{34}{9})$

$x - \text{int}: (\pm \dfrac{1}{\sqrt{2}} + 3, 0)$

$Inflection \quad points: None$

$Extrema: None$

$Range: f(x) \in (-4, \infty)$

$Increase: x \in (-\infty, 3)$

$Decrease: x \in (3, \infty)$

$Concave - up: x \in (-\infty, 3) \cup (3, \infty)$

$Concave - down: Never$

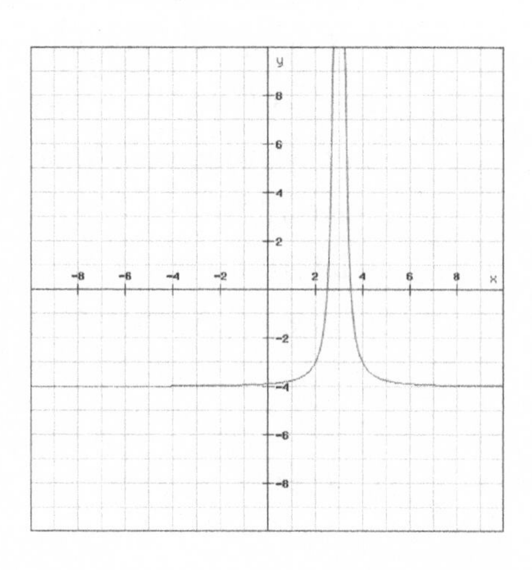

40. $f(x) = \dfrac{1}{x^2+1}, x \in \mathbb{R}$

$Domain: x \in \mathbb{R}$

$Vertical \quad Asymptotes: None$

$Horizontal \quad Asymptotes: y = 0$

$Lim_{x \to -\infty}(f(x)) = 0 \quad Lim_{x \to \infty}(f(x)) = 0$

$Slant \quad Asymptotes: None$

$y - \text{int}: (0,1)$

$x - \text{int}: None$

$Inflection \quad po\,\text{int}\,s: (\pm\dfrac{1}{\sqrt{3}}, \dfrac{3}{4})$

$Extrema: (0,1), \text{max}$

$Range: f(x) \in (0,1]$

$Increase: x \in (-\infty, 0)$

$Decrease: x \in (0, \infty)$

$Concave - up: x \in (-\infty, -\dfrac{1}{\sqrt{3}}) \cup (\dfrac{1}{\sqrt{3}}, \infty)$

$Concave - down: x \in (-\dfrac{1}{\sqrt{3}}, \dfrac{1}{\sqrt{3}})$

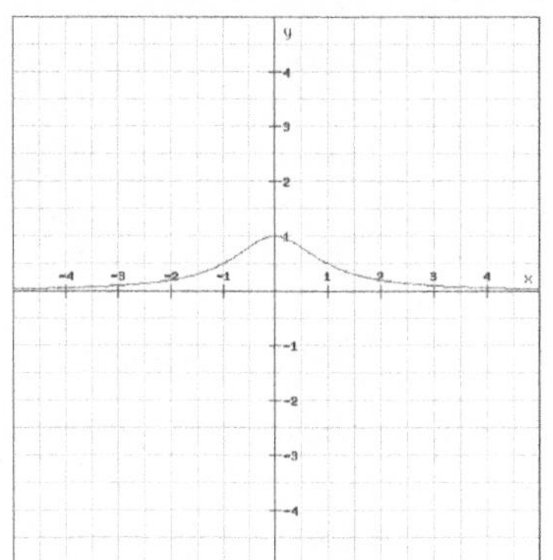

41. $f(x) = \dfrac{x}{x^2+2}, x \in \mathbb{R}$

$Domain: x \in \mathbb{R}$

$Vertical \quad Asymptotes: None$

$Horizontal \quad Asymptotes: y = 0$

$Lim_{x \to -\infty}(f(x)) = 0 \quad Lim_{x \to \infty}(f(x)) = 0$

$Slant \quad Asymptotes: None$

$y - \text{int}: (0,0)$

$x - \text{int}: (0,0)$

$Inflection \quad po\,\text{int}\,s: (\pm\sqrt{6}, \dfrac{\pm\sqrt{6}}{8})$

$Extrema: (-\sqrt{2}, -\dfrac{\sqrt{2}}{4}), \text{min}, (\sqrt{2}, \dfrac{\sqrt{2}}{4}), \text{max}$

$Range: f(x) \in [-\dfrac{\sqrt{2}}{4}, \dfrac{\sqrt{2}}{4}]$

$Increase: x \in (-\sqrt{2}, \sqrt{2})$

$Decrease: x \in (-\infty, -\sqrt{2}) \cup (\sqrt{2}, \infty)$

$Concave - up: x \in (-\sqrt{6}, 0) \cup (\sqrt{6}, \infty)$

$Concave - down: x \in (-\infty, -\sqrt{6}) \cup (0, \sqrt{6})$

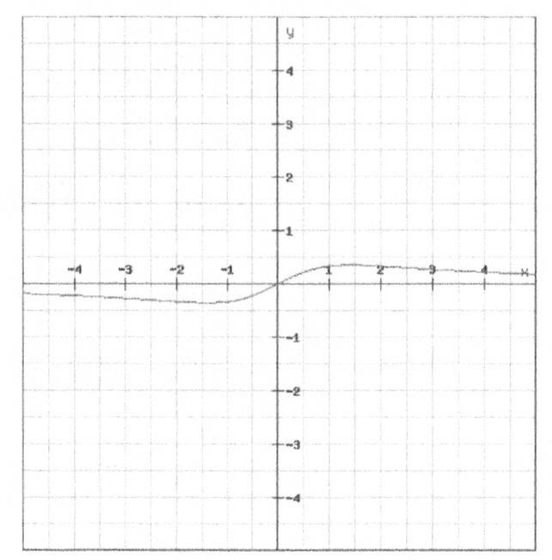

42. $f(x)=\dfrac{2}{(x-2)(x+3)}, x\in □$

$Domain: x\in(-\infty,-3)\cup(-3,2)\cup(2,\infty)$

$Extrema: (-\frac{1}{2},-\frac{8}{25})$

$Vertical \quad Asymptotes: x=3, x=2$

$Range: f(x)\in(-\infty,-\frac{8}{25}]\cup(0,\infty)$

$Lim_{x\to-3^-}(f(x))=\infty \quad Lim_{x\to-3^+}(f(x))=-\infty$

$Increase: x\in(-\infty,-3)\cup(-3,-\frac{1}{2})$

$Lim_{x\to2^-}(f(x))=-\infty \quad Lim_{x\to2^+}(f(x))=\infty$

$Decrease: x\in(-\frac{1}{2},2)\cup(2,\infty)$

$Horizontal \quad Asymptotes: y=0$

$Lim_{x\to-\infty}(f(x))=0 \quad Lim_{x\to\infty}(f(x))=0$

$Concave-up: x\in(-\infty,-3)\cup(2,\infty)$

$Slant \quad Asymptotes: None$

$Concave-down: x\in(-3,2)$

$y-\text{int}: (0,-\frac{1}{3})$

$x-\text{int}: None$

$Inflection \quad points: None$

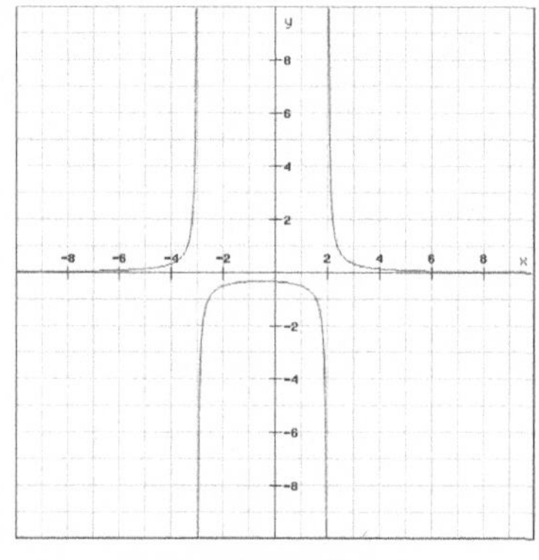

43. $f(x)=\dfrac{-3}{x^2-5x-6}, x\in □$

$Domain: x\in(-\infty,-1)\cup(-1,6)\cup(6,\infty)$

$Extrema: (\frac{5}{2},-\frac{8}{49})$

$Vertical \quad Asymptotes: x=-1, x=6$

$Range: f(x)\in(-\infty,-\frac{8}{49}]\cup(0,\infty)$

$Lim_{x\to-1^-}(f(x))=\infty \quad Lim_{x\to-1^+}(f(x))=-\infty$

$Increase: x\in(-\infty,-1)\cup(-1,\frac{5}{2})$

$Lim_{x\to6^-}(f(x))=-\infty \quad Lim_{x\to6^+}(f(x))=\infty$

$Decrease: x\in(\frac{5}{2},6)\cup(6,\infty)$

$Horizontal \quad Asymptotes: y=0$

$Lim_{x\to-\infty}(f(x))=0 \quad Lim_{x\to\infty}(f(x))=0$

$Concave-up: x\in(-\infty,-1)\cup(6,\infty)$

$Slant \quad Asymptotes: None$

$Concave-down: x\in(-1,6)$

$y-\text{int}: (0,-\frac{1}{3})$

$x-\text{int}: None$

$Inflection \quad points: None$

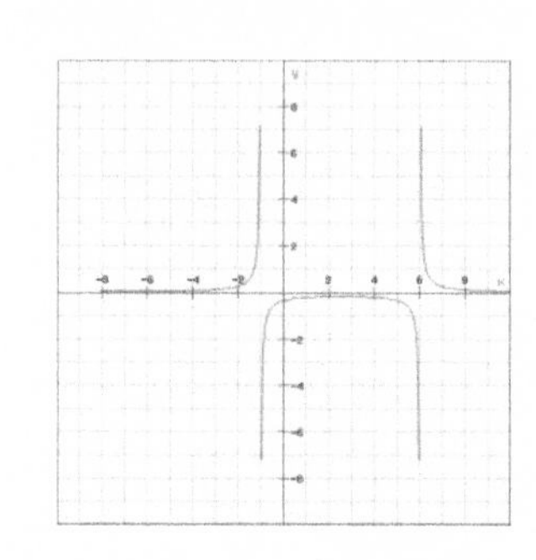

44. $f(x)=\dfrac{x^2}{x-1}, x\in \square$

$Domain: x\in(-\infty,1)\cup(1,\infty)$

$Vertical\quad Asymptotes: x=1$

$Lim_{x\to -1^-}(f(x))=\infty \quad Lim_{x\to -1^+}(f(x))=-\infty$

$Horizontal\quad Asymptotes: None$

$Lim_{x\to -\infty}(f(x))=-\infty \quad Lim_{x\to\infty}(f(x))=\infty$

$Slant\quad Asymptotes: y=x+1$

$y-\text{int}:(0,0)$

$x-\text{int}:(0,0)$

$Inflection\quad po\text{int}\,s: None$

$Extrema:(0,0),\text{max},(2,4),\text{min}$

$Range: f(x)\in(-\infty,0]\cup[4,\infty)$

$Increase: x\in(-\infty,0)\cup(2,\infty)$

$Decrease: x\in(0,1)\cup(1,2)$

$Concave-up: x\in(1,\infty)$

$Concave-down: x\in(-\infty,1)$

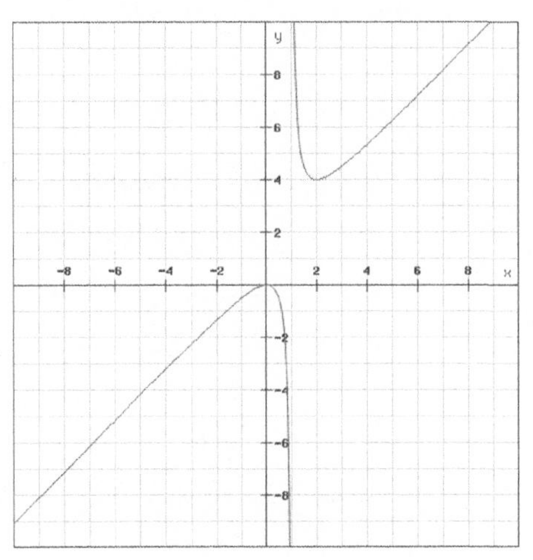

45. $f(x)=\dfrac{2x^2}{(x+3)(x-1)}, x\in \square$

$Domain: x\in(-\infty,-3)\cup(-3,1)\cup(1,\infty)$

$Vertical\quad Asymptotes: x=-3, x=1$

$Lim_{x\to -3^-}(f(x))=\infty \quad Lim_{x\to -3^+}(f(x))=-\infty$

$Lim_{x\to 1^-}(f(x))=-\infty \quad Lim_{x\to 1^+}(f(x))=\infty$

$Horizontal\quad Asymptotes: y=2$

$Lim_{x\to -\infty}(f(x))=2 \quad Lim_{x\to\infty}(f(x))=2$

$Slant\quad Asymptotes: None$

$y-\text{int}:(0,0)$

$x-\text{int}:(0,0)$

$Inflection\quad po\text{int}\,s:(\approx 4.70,\approx 1.55)$

$Extrema:(0,0),\text{max},(3,\frac{3}{2}),\text{min}$

$Range: f(x)\in(-\infty,0]\cup[\frac{3}{2},\infty)$

$Increase: x\in(-\infty,-3)\cup(-3,0)\cup(3,\infty)$

$Decrease: x\in(0,1)\cup(1,3)$

$Concave-up: x\in(-\infty,-3)\cup(1,\approx 4.70)$

$Concave-down: x\in(-3,1)\cup(\approx 4.70,\infty)$

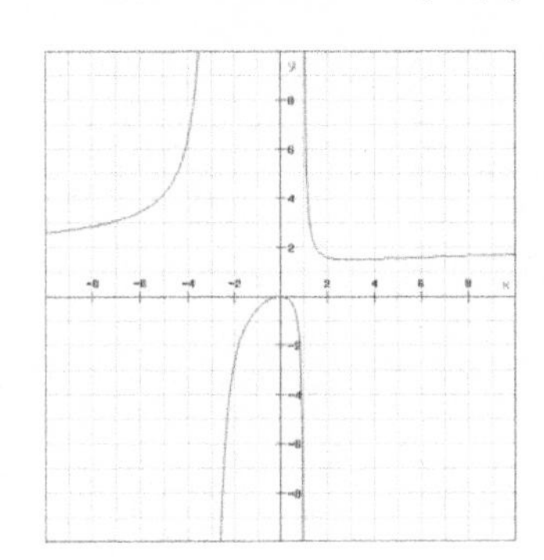

46. $f(x)=\dfrac{x^2+3}{x-1}, x\in \square$

47. $f(x) = \dfrac{-1}{x^2 - x}, x \in \mathbb{R}$

48. $f(x) = \dfrac{3x+1}{x^2 - x}, x \in \mathbb{R}$

$Domain: x \in (-\infty, 0) \cup (0,1) \cup (1, \infty)$

$Vertical \quad Asymptotes: x = 0, x = 1$

$Lim_{x \to 0^-}(f(x)) = \infty \quad Lim_{x \to 0^+}(f(x)) = -\infty$

$Lim_{x \to 1^-}(f(x)) = -\infty \quad Lim_{x \to 1^+}(f(x)) = \infty$

$Horizontal \quad Asymptotes: y = 0$

$Lim_{x \to -\infty}(f(x)) = 0 \quad Lim_{x \to \infty}(f(x)) = 0$

$Slant \quad Asymptotes: None$

$y - \text{int}: None$

$x - \text{int}: (-\frac{1}{3}, 0)$

$Inflection \quad points: (\approx -1.70, \approx -0.893)$

$Extrema: (-1, -1), \text{max}, (\frac{1}{3}, -9), \text{min}$

$Range: f(x) \in (-\infty, -9] \cup [-1, \infty)$

$Increase: x \in (-1, 0) \cup (0, \frac{1}{3})$

$Decrease: x \in (-\infty, -1) \cup (\frac{1}{3}, 1) \cup (1, \infty)$

$Concave - up: x \in (-0.893, 0) \cup (1, \infty)$

$Concave - down: x \in (-\infty, -0.893) \cup (0, 1)$

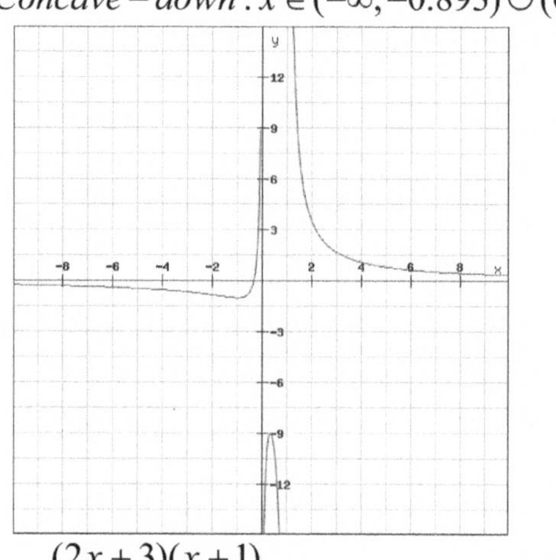

49. The function $f(x) = 2x + 3$, 2nd graph, $f(x) = \dfrac{(2x+3)(x+1)}{(x+1)}$

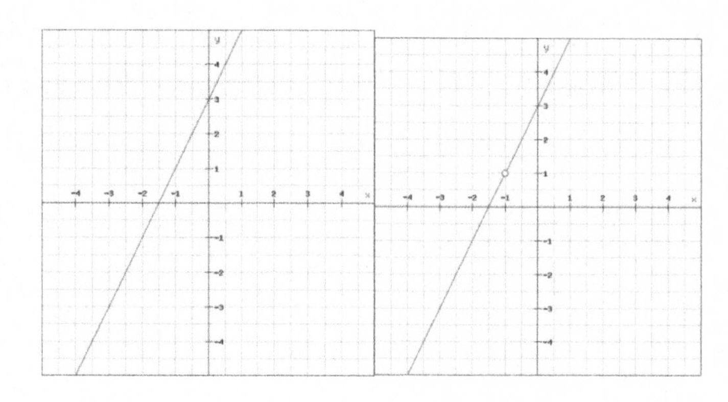

50. Determine the equations of all the asymptotes of the following functions and discuss their continuity:

a. $f(x)=\dfrac{2x^3+3x+1}{x^3-x}$, in consequence f(x) is continuous $x\in\square, x\notin\{-1,0,1\}$, infinite discontinuity at $x=-1,0,1$

$Domain: x\notin\{-1,0,1\}$

$Lim_{x\to-1^-}(f(x))=\infty \quad Lim_{x\to-1^+}(f(x))=-\infty$

$Lim_{x\to0^-}(f(x))=\infty \quad Lim_{x\to0^+}(f(x))=-\infty$

$Lim_{x\to1^-}(f(x))=-\infty \quad Lim_{x\to1^+}(f(x))=\infty$

$Vertical \quad Asymptotes: x=0, x=1, x=-1$

$Lim_{x\to-\infty}(f(x))=2 \quad Lim_{x\to\infty}(f(x))=2$

$Horizontal \quad Asymptotes: y=2$

$Slant \quad Asymptotes: None$

b. $f(x)=\dfrac{x^3-x^2}{x^2-3x+2}=\dfrac{x^2(x-1)}{(x-1)(x-2)}$, in consequence f(x) is continuous $x\in\square, x\notin\{-1,0,1\}$, infinite discontinuity at $x=2$, removable discontinuity at $x=1$

$Domain: x\notin\{1,2\}$

$Lim_{x\to1^-}(f(x))=-1 \quad Lim_{x\to1^+}(f(x))=-1$

$Lim_{x\to2^-}(f(x))=-\infty \quad Lim_{x\to2^+}(f(x))=\infty$

$Vertical \quad Asymptotes: x=2$

$Lim_{x\to-\infty}(f(x))=-\infty \quad Lim_{x\to\infty}(f(x))=\infty$

$Horizontal \quad Asymptotes: None$

$Slant \quad Asymptotes: y=x+2$

c. $f(x)=\dfrac{5x^3+3x^2+1}{x^2-2}$, in consequence f(x) is continuous $x\in\square, x\notin\{-\sqrt{2},\sqrt{2}\}$, infinite discontinuity at $x=\sqrt{2},\sqrt{2}$

$Domain: x\notin\{1,2\}$

$Lim_{x\to-\sqrt{2}^-}(f(x))=-\infty \quad Lim_{x\to-\sqrt{2}^+}(f(x))=\infty$

$Lim_{x\to2^-}(f(x))=-\infty \quad Lim_{x\to2^+}(f(x))=\infty$

$Vertical \quad Asymptotes: x=\sqrt{2}, x=-\sqrt{2}$

$Lim_{x\to-\infty}(f(x))=-\infty \quad Lim_{x\to\infty}(f(x))=\infty$

$Horizontal \quad Asymptotes: None$

$Slant \quad Asymptotes: y=5x+3$

d. $f(x)=\dfrac{x-2x^2}{3x^2-9x+6}=\dfrac{x(1-2x)}{3(x-2)(x-1)}$, in consequence f(x) is continuous

$x\in \square, x\notin\{1,2\}$, infinite discontinuity at $x=1,2$

$Domain: x\notin\{1,2\}$

$Lim_{x\to 1^-}(f(x))=-\infty \quad Lim_{x\to 1^+}(f(x))=\infty$

$Lim_{x\to 2^-}(f(x))=\infty \quad Lim_{x\to 2^+}(f(x))=-\infty$

$Vertical \quad Asymptotes: x=1, x=2$

$Lim_{x\to -\infty}(f(x))=-\dfrac{2}{3} \quad Lim_{x\to \infty}(f(x))=-\dfrac{2}{3}$

$Horizontal \quad Asymptotes: y=2-\dfrac{2}{3}$

$Slant \quad Asymptotes: None$

51. Vertical asymptotes are of the form **x = a** Their origin is a function in which a certain value of **x** makes the denominator of the function **0** and numerator **different than 0**
52. Horizontal asymptotes are of the form Their meaning is significant for **large negative** and **large positive values** of x. Sometimes a function can have a certain horizontal asymptote for **large negative values** and a different horizontal asymptote for **large positive values**. In a rational function which is of the form $f(x)=\dfrac{a_1x^n+a_2x^{n-1}+\ldots}{b_1x^m+b_2x^{m-1}+\ldots}$ when **n = m** the function will have a horizontal asymptote of the form $y=\dfrac{a_1}{b_1}$
53. Slant (or oblique) asymptotes are of the form **y = mx + b** Their meaning is significant for **large negative** and **large positive values** of x. Sometimes a function can have a certain horizontal asymptote for **large negative values** and a different horizontal asymptote for **large positive values**. In a rational function which is of the form $f(x)=\dfrac{a_1x^n+a_2x^{n-1}+\ldots}{b_1x^m+b_2x^{m-1}+\ldots}$, when **n = m + 1** the function will have a slant asymptote.
54. (T/**F**) All functions must have at least one vertical asymptote.
55. (T/**F**) All functions must have at least one horizontal asymptote.
56. (T/**F**) All functions must have at least one slant asymptote.
57. (T/**F**) A function that has two vertical asymptotes cannot have a slant asymptote.
58. (**T**/F) A function that has two slant asymptotes cannot have a horizontal asymptote.

D. GENERAL FUNCTIONS

59. $f(x) = e^x - x, x \in \mathbb{R}$

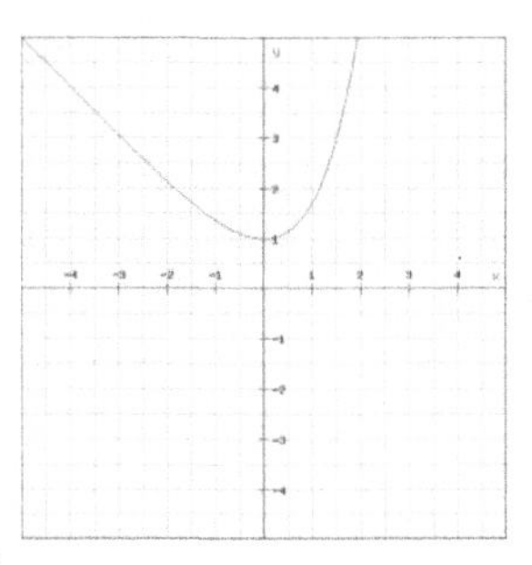

$Domain: x \in (-\infty, \infty)$

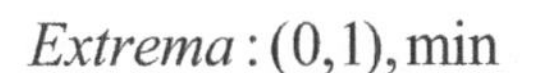

$Extrema: (0,1), \min$

$Vertical \quad Asymptotes: None$

$Range: f(x) \in [1, \infty)$

$Horizontal \quad Asymptotes: None$

$Increase: x \in (0, \infty)$

$Lim_{x \to -\infty}(f(x)) = \infty \quad Lim_{x \to \infty}(f(x)) = \infty$

$Decrease: x \in (-\infty, 0)$

$Slant \quad Asymptotes: y = -x(Left)$

$Concave - down: Never$

$y - \text{int}: (0,1)$

$Concave - up: \in (-\infty, \infty)$

$x - \text{int}: None$

$Inflection \quad po\text{int}s: None$

60. $f(x) = e^x + x, x \in \mathbb{R}$

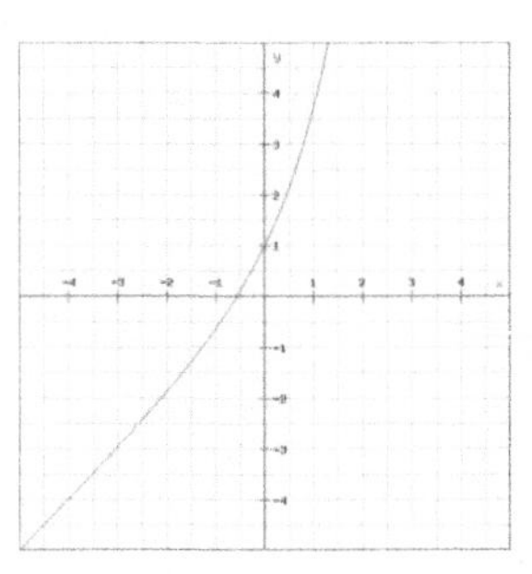

$Domain: x \in (-\infty, \infty)$

$Extrema: None$

$Vertical \quad Asymptotes: None$

$Range: f(x) \in (-\infty, \infty)$

$Horizontal \quad Asymptotes: None$

$Increase: x \in (-\infty, \infty)$

$Lim_{x \to -\infty}(f(x)) = -\infty \quad Lim_{x \to \infty}(f(x)) = \infty$

$Decrease: Never$

$Slant \quad Asymptotes: y = x(Left)$

$Concave - down: Never$

$y - \text{int}: (0,1)$

$Concave - up: \in (-\infty, \infty)$

$x - \text{int}: (-0.567, 0)$

$Inflection \quad po\text{int}s: None$

61. $f(x) = \dfrac{2}{1 + e^x}$

$Domain: x \in (-\infty, \infty)$

$Extrema: None$

$Vertical \quad Asymptotes: None$

$Range: f(x) \in (0, 2)$

$Horizontal \quad Asymptotes: y = 2(Left), y = 0(Right)$

$Increase: Never$

$Lim_{x \to -\infty}(f(x)) = 2 \quad Lim_{x \to \infty}(f(x)) = 0$

$Decrease: x \in (-\infty, \infty)$

$Slant \quad Asymptotes: None$

$Concave - down: x \in (-\infty, 0)$

$y - \text{int}: (0,1)$

$Concave - up: x \in (0, \infty)$

$x - \text{int}: None$

$Inflection \quad po\text{int}s: (0,1)$

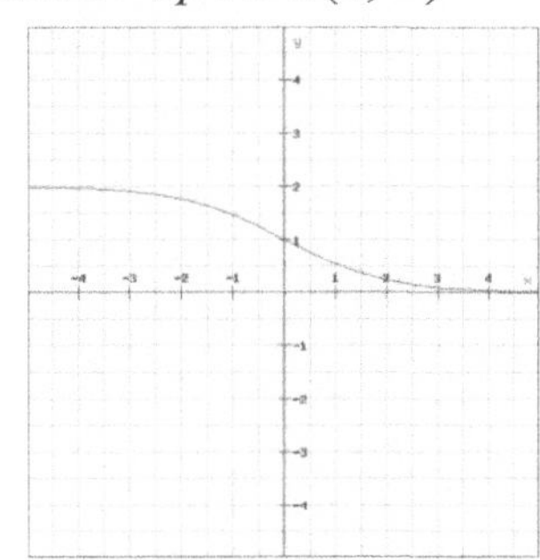

62. $f(x)=\dfrac{2}{2-e^{x}}$

$Domain: x \in (-\infty, \ln(2)) \cup (\ln(2), -\infty)$

$Vertical \quad Asymptotes: x = \ln(2)$

$Lim_{x\to \ln(2)^-}(f(x)) = \infty \; Lim_{x\to \ln(2)^+}(f(x)) = -\infty$

$Horizontal \quad Asymptotes: y = 1(Left), y = 0(Right)$

$Lim_{x\to -\infty}(f(x)) = 1 \quad Lim_{x\to \infty}(f(x)) = 0$

$Slant \quad Asymptotes: None$

$y-\text{int}: (0,2)$

$x-\text{int}: None$

$Inflection \quad po\text{int}s: None$

$Extrema: None$

$Range: f(x) \in (-\infty, 0) \cup (1, \infty)$

$Increase: x \in (-\infty, \ln(2)) \cup (\ln(2), -\infty)$

$Decrease: Never$

$Concave-down: x \in (\ln(2), \infty)$

$Concave-up: x \in (-\infty, \ln(2))$

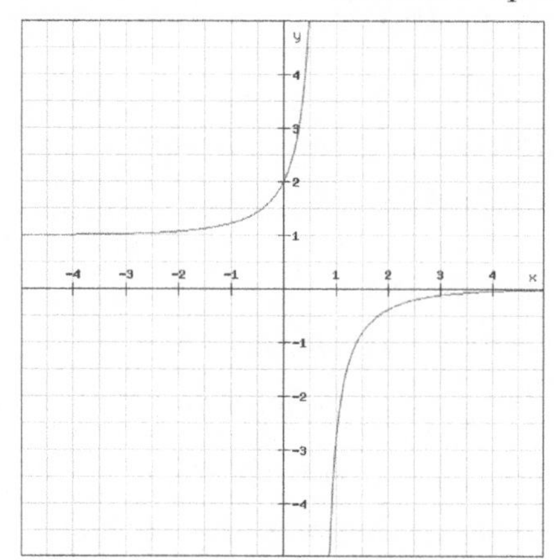

63. $f(x) = x\ln(x), x \in \square$

$Domain: x \in (0, \infty)$

$Vertical \quad Asymptotes: None$

$Lim_{x\to 0^+}(f(x)) = 0$

$Horizontal \quad Asymptotes: None$

$Lim_{x\to \infty}(f(x)) = \infty$

$Slant \quad Asymptotes: None$

$y-\text{int}: None$

$x-\text{int}: (1,0)$

$Inflection \quad po\text{int}s: None$

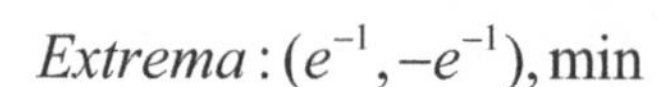

$Extrema: (e^{-1}, -e^{-1}), \min$

$Range: f(x) \in [-e^{-1}, \infty)$

$Increase: x \in (e^{-1}, \infty)$

$Decrease: x \in (0, e^{-1})$

$Concave-down: Never$

$Concave-up: x \in (0, \infty)$

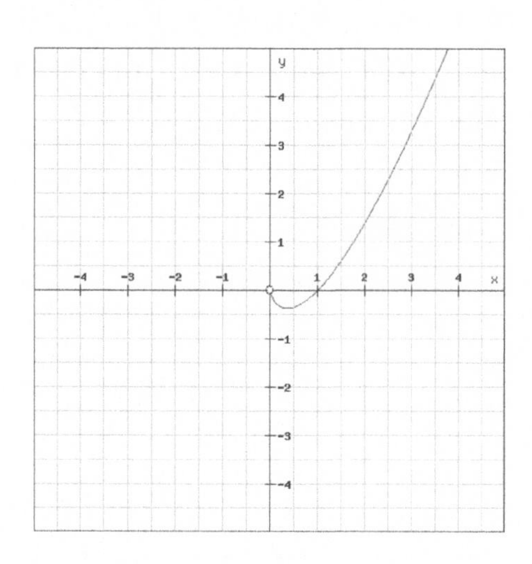

64. $f(x) = x\ln(x^2), x \in$ □

$Domain: x \in (-\infty, 0) \cup (0, \infty)$

$Vertical \quad Asymptotes: None$

$Lim_{x \to 0^-}(f(x)) = 0 \quad Lim_{x \to 0^+}(f(x)) = 0$

$Horizontal \quad Asymptotes: None$

$Lim_{x \to -\infty}(f(x)) = -\infty \quad Lim_{x \to \infty}(f(x)) = \infty$

$Slant \quad Asymptotes: None$

$y - \text{int}: None$

$x - \text{int}: (1,0), (-1,0)$

$Inflection \quad po\text{int}s: None$

$Extrema: (e^{-1}, -2e^{-1}), \min, (-e^{-1}, 2e^{-1}), \max$

$Range: f(x) \in (-\infty, \infty)$

$Increase: x \in (-\infty, -e^{-1}) \cup (e^{-1}, \infty)$

$Decrease: x \in (-e^{-1}, e^{-1})$

$Concave-down: x \in (-\infty, 0)$

$Concave-up: x \in (0, \infty)$

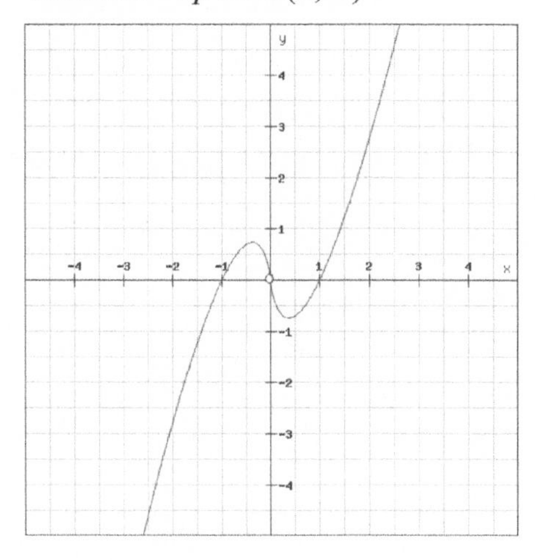

65. $f(x) = x^2\ln(x), x \in$ □

$Domain: x \in (0, \infty)$

$Vertical \quad Asymptotes: None$

$Lim_{x \to 0^+}(f(x)) = 0$

$Horizontal \quad Asymptotes: None$

$Lim_{x \to \infty}(f(x)) = \infty$

$Slant \quad Asymptotes: None$

$y - \text{int}: None$

$x - \text{int}: (1,0)$

$Inflection \quad po\text{int}s: None$

$Extrema: (e^{-\frac{1}{2}}, -\frac{1}{2}e^{-1}), \min$

$Range: f(x) \in [-\frac{1}{2}e^{-1}, \infty)$

$Increase: x \in (e^{-\frac{1}{2}}, \infty)$

$Decrease: x \in (0, e^{-\frac{1}{2}})$

$Concave-down: Never$

$Concave-up: x \in (0, \infty)$

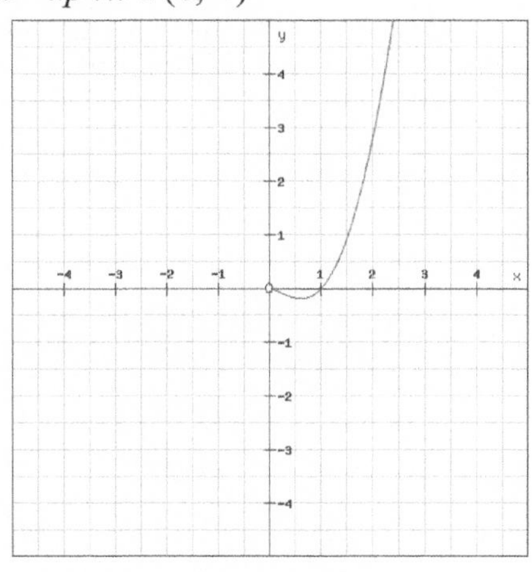

66. $f(x) = x(\ln(x))^2, x \in \mathbb{R}$

$Domain: x \in (0,\infty)$

$Vertical \quad Asymptotes: None$

$Lim_{x\to 0^+}(f(x)) = 0$

$Horizontal \quad Asymptotes: None$

$Lim_{x\to\infty}(f(x)) = \infty$

$Slant \quad Asymptotes: None$

$y-\text{int}: None$

$x-\text{int}: (1,0)$

$Inflection \quad points: (e^{-1}, e^{-1})$

$Extrema: (e^{-2}, 4e^{-2}), \max, (1,0), \min$

$Range: f(x) \in [0,\infty)$

$Increase: x \in (0, e^{-2}) \cup (1,\infty)$

$Decrease: x \in (e^{-2}, 1)$

$Concave-down: x \in (0, e^{-1})$

$Concave-up: x \in (e^{-1}, \infty)$

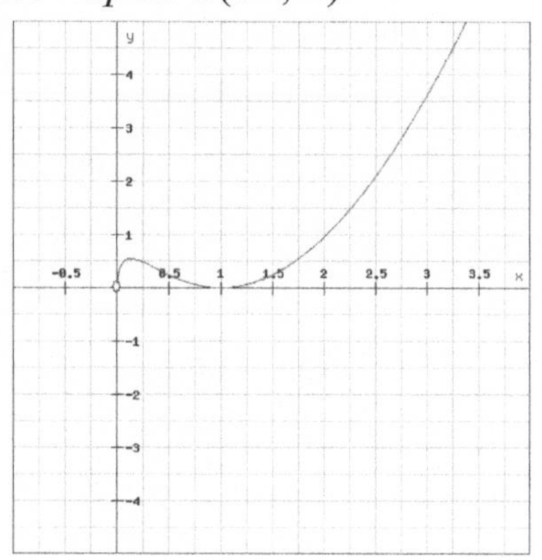

67. $f(x) = \dfrac{\ln(x)}{x}, x \in \mathbb{R}$

$Domain: x \in (0,\infty)$

$Vertical \quad Asymptotes: x = 0$

$Lim_{x\to 0^+}(f(x)) = -\infty$

$Horizontal \quad Asymptotes: y = 0$

$Lim_{x\to\infty}(f(x)) = 0$

$Slant \quad Asymptotes: None$

$y-\text{int}: None$

$x-\text{int}: (1,0)$

$Inflection \quad points: (e^{\frac{3}{2}}, \frac{3}{2}e^{-\frac{3}{2}})$

$Extrema: (e, e^{-1}), \max$

$Range: f(x) \in (-\infty, e^{-1}]$

$Increase: x \in (0, e)$

$Decrease: x \in (e, \infty)$

$Concave-down: x \in (0, e^{\frac{3}{2}})$

$Concave-up: x \in (e^{\frac{3}{2}}, \infty)$

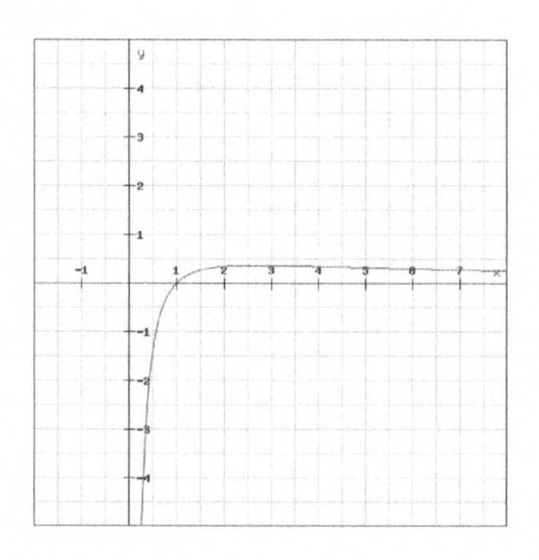

68. $f(x)=\sqrt{x}-x, x \in \square$

$Domain: x \in [0,\infty)$

$Vertical \quad Asymptotes: None$

$Lim_{x \to 0^+}(f(x))=0$

$Horizontal \quad Asymptotes: None$

$Lim_{x \to \infty}(f(x))=-\infty$

$Slant \quad Asymptotes: None$

$y-\text{int}:(0,0)$

$x-\text{int}:(0,0),(1,0)$

$Inflection \quad points: None$

$Extrema: (\frac{1}{4},\frac{1}{4}), \max$

$Range: f(x) \in (-\infty,\frac{1}{4}]$

$Increase: x \in (0,\frac{1}{4})$

$Decrease: x \in (\frac{1}{4},\infty)$

$Concave-down: x \in (0,\infty)$

$Concave-up: Never$

69. $f(x)=x^2-\frac{1}{x}, x \in \square$

$Domain: x \in (-\infty,0) \cup (0,\infty)$

$Vertical \quad Asymptotes: x=0$

$Lim_{x \to 0^-}(f(x))=\infty \quad Lim_{x \to 0^+}(f(x))=-\infty$

$Horizontal \quad Asymptotes: None$

$Lim_{x \to -\infty}(f(x))=\infty \quad Lim_{x \to \infty}(f(x))=\infty$

$Slant \quad Asymptotes: None$

$y-\text{int}: None$

$x-\text{int}:(1,0)$

$Inflection \quad points:(1,0)$

$Extrema: (-2^{-\frac{1}{3}},\frac{3}{2}2^{\frac{1}{3}}), \min$

$Range: f(x) \in (-\infty,\infty)$

$Increase: x \in (-2^{-\frac{1}{3}},0) \cup (0,\infty)$

$Decrease: x \in (-\infty,-2^{-\frac{1}{3}})$

$Concave-down: x \in (0,1)$

$Concave-up: x \in (-\infty,0) \cup (1,\infty)$

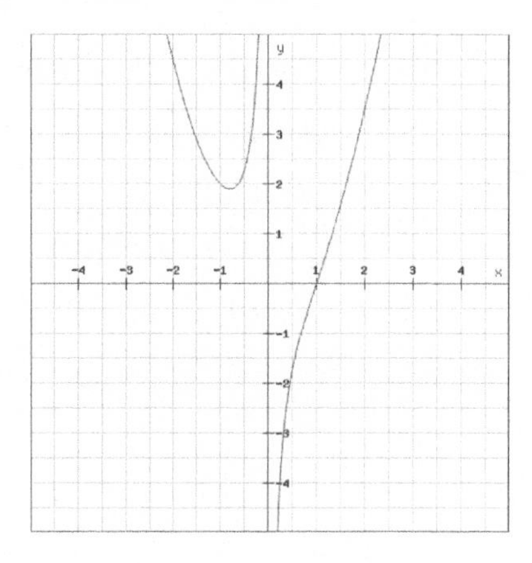

70. $f(x)=x^2+\dfrac{2}{x}, x\in\square$

$Domain: x\in(-\infty,0)\cup(0,\infty)$

$Vertical \quad Asymptotes: x=0$

$Lim_{x\to0^-}(f(x))=-\infty \quad Lim_{x\to0^+}(f(x))=\infty$

$Horizontal \quad Asymptotes: None$

$Lim_{x\to-\infty}(f(x))=\infty \quad Lim_{x\to\infty}(f(x))=\infty$

$Slant \quad Asymptotes: None$

$y-\text{int}: None$

$x-\text{int}: (-2^{\frac{1}{3}},0)$

$Inflection \quad points: (-2^{\frac{1}{3}},0)$

$Extrema: (1,3), \min$

$Range: f(x)\in(-\infty,\infty)$

$Increase: x\in(1,\infty)$

$Decrease: x\in(-\infty,0)\cup(0,1)$

$Concave-down: x\in(-2^{\frac{1}{3}},0)$

$Concave-up: x\in(-\infty,-2^{\frac{1}{3}})\cup(0,\infty)$

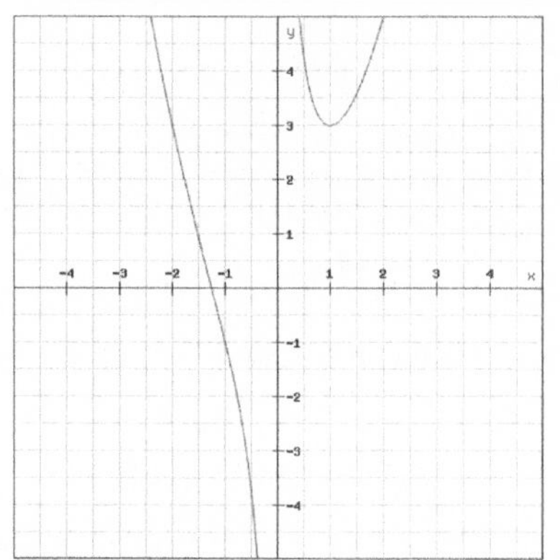

71. $f(x)=\sin(x^2), x\in\square$

$Domain: x\in(-\infty,\infty) \quad Extrema: \min: (0,0), (\dfrac{\pm\sqrt{6\pi+8\pi k}}{2},-1), k\in\square \ \max: (\dfrac{\pm\sqrt{2\pi+8\pi k}}{2},1), k\in\square)$

$Vertical \quad Asymptotes: None \qquad Range: f(x)\in[-1,1]$

$Horizontal \quad Asymptotes: None$

$Lim_{x\to-\infty}(f(x))=D.E. \quad Lim_{x\to\infty}(f(x))=D.E.$

$Decrease: x\in(\dfrac{-\sqrt{2\pi+8\pi k}}{2},\dfrac{-\sqrt{6\pi+8\pi k}}{2})\cup(\dfrac{-\sqrt{2\pi+8\pi k}}{2},0)\cup(\dfrac{\sqrt{2\pi+8\pi k}}{2},\dfrac{\sqrt{6\pi+8\pi k}}{2}), k\in\square$

$Increase: x\in(\dfrac{-\sqrt{6\pi+8\pi k}}{2},\dfrac{-\sqrt{2\pi+8\pi k}}{2})\cup(0,\dfrac{\sqrt{2\pi+8\pi k}}{2},0)\cup(\dfrac{\sqrt{6\pi+8\pi k}}{2},\dfrac{\sqrt{2\pi+8\pi k}}{2}), k\in\square$

$Concave-down: Beyond \quad Level \qquad Concave-up: Beyond \quad Level$

$Slant \quad Asymptotes: None$

$y-\text{int}: (0,0)$

$x-\text{int}: (\pm\sqrt{\pi k},0), k\in\square$

$Inflection \quad points: Beyond \quad Level$

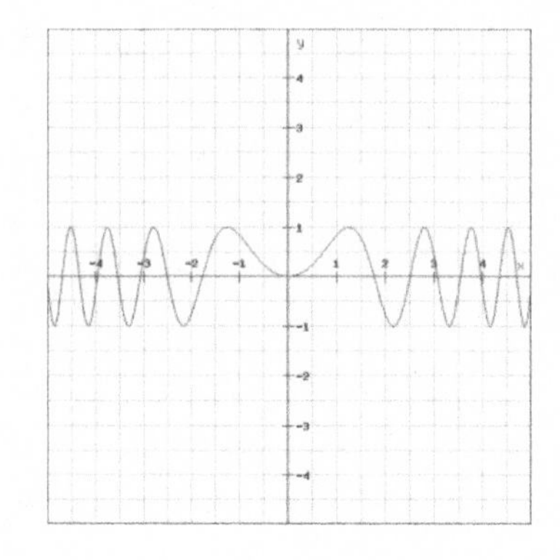

72. $f(x)=\sin(x)+x, x\in\square$

$Domain: x\in(-\infty,\infty)$

$Vertical \quad Asymptotes: None$

$Horizontal \quad Asymptotes: None$

$Lim_{x\to-\infty}(f(x))=\infty \quad Lim_{x\to\infty}(f(x))=-\infty$

$Slant \quad Asymptotes: None$

$y-\text{int}:(0,0)$

$x-\text{int}:(0,0)$

$Extrema:(\pi+2\pi k,\pi+2\pi k), k\in\square, Inflection \quad poi$

$Range: f(x)\in(-\infty,\infty)$

$Increase: x\in(-\infty,\infty)$

$Decrease: Never$

$Concave-down: x\in(2\pi k,\pi+2\pi k), k\in\square$

$Concave-up: x\in(\pi+2\pi k,2\pi+2\pi k), k\in\square$

$Inflection \quad points:(\pi+2\pi k,\pi+2\pi k), k\in\square, Horizontal \quad Inflection \quad points$

$(2\pi k,2\pi k), k\in\square, Non-Horizontal \quad Inflection \quad points$

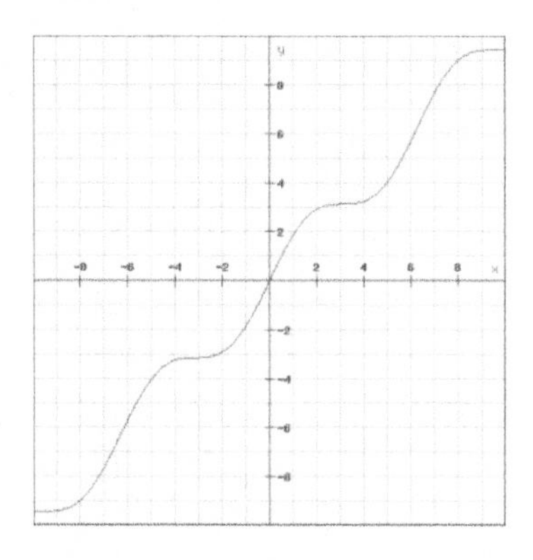

73. $f(x)=x(1-\ln(x^2)), x\in\square$

$Domain: x\in(-\infty,0)\cup(0,\infty)$

$Vertical \quad Asymptotes: None$

$Lim_{x\to0^-}(f(x))=0 \quad Lim_{x\to0^+}(f(x))=0$

$Horizontal \quad Asymptotes: None$

$Lim_{x\to-\infty}(f(x))=\infty \quad Lim_{x\to\infty}(f(x))=-\infty$

$Slant \quad Asymptotes: None$

$y-\text{int}: None$

$x-\text{int}:(e^{\frac{1}{2}},0),(-e^{\frac{1}{2}},0)$

$Inflection \quad points: None$

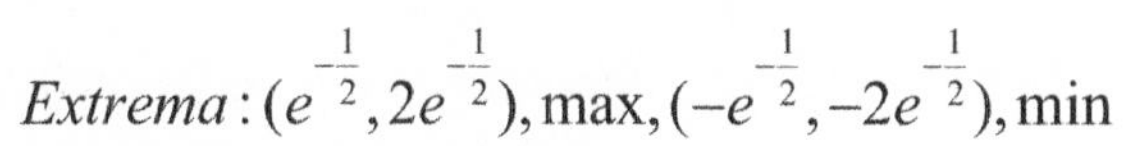

$Extrema:(e^{-\frac{1}{2}},2e^{-\frac{1}{2}}),\max,(-e^{-\frac{1}{2}},-2e^{-\frac{1}{2}}),\min$

$Range: f(x)\in(-\infty,\infty)$

$Increase: x\in(-e^{-\frac{1}{2}},e^{-\frac{1}{2}})$

$Decrease: x\in(-\infty,-e^{-\frac{1}{2}})\cup(e^{-\frac{1}{2}},\infty)$

$Concave-down: x\in(0,\infty)$

$Concave-up: x\in(-\infty,0)$

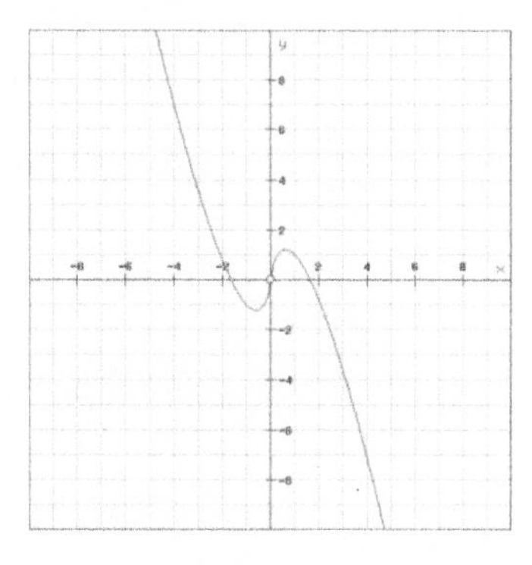

74. $f(x)=e^{x-x^2}, x\in□$

$Domain: x\in(-\infty,\infty)$

$Extrema: (\frac{1}{2}, e^{\frac{1}{4}}), \max$

$Vertical\quad Asymptotes: None$

$Range: f(x)\in(0, e^{\frac{1}{4}}]$

$Horizontal\quad Asymptotes: y=0$

$Increase: x\in(-\infty,\frac{1}{2})$

$Lim_{x\to-\infty}(f(x))=0\quad Lim_{x\to\infty}(f(x))=0$

$Decrease: x\in(\frac{1}{2},\infty)$

$Slant\quad Asymptotes: None$

$y-\text{int}: (0,1)$

$x-\text{int}: None$

$Inflection\quad points: (\frac{1-\sqrt{2}}{2},0),(\frac{1+\sqrt{2}}{2},0)$

$Concave-up: x\in(-\infty,\frac{1-\sqrt{2}}{2})\cup(\frac{1+\sqrt{2}}{2},\infty)$

$Concave-down: x\in(\frac{1-\sqrt{2}}{2},\frac{1+\sqrt{2}}{2})$

75. $f(x)=x^3(1-\ln(x^2)), x\in□$

$Domain: x\in(-\infty,0)\cup(0,\infty)$

$Extrema: (e^{\frac{1}{6}},\frac{2}{3}e^{\frac{1}{2}}), \max, (-e^{\frac{1}{6}},-\frac{2}{3}e^{\frac{1}{2}}), \min$

$Vertical\quad Asymptotes: None$

$Range: f(x)\in(-\infty,\infty)$

$Lim_{x\to0^-}(f(x))=0\quad Lim_{x\to0^+}(f(x))=0$

$Increase: x\in(-e^{\frac{1}{6}},e^{\frac{1}{6}})$

$Horizontal\quad Asymptotes: None$

$Decrease: x\in(-\infty,-e^{\frac{1}{6}})\cup(e^{\frac{1}{6}},\infty)$

$Lim_{x\to-\infty}(f(x))=\infty\quad Lim_{x\to\infty}(f(x))=-\infty$

$Concave-down: x\in(-\frac{5}{3}e^{-1},0)\cup(\frac{5}{3}e^{-1},\infty)$

$Slant\quad Asymptotes: None$

$Concave-up: x\in(-\infty,-\frac{5}{3}e^{-1})\cup(0,\frac{5}{3}e^{-1})$

$y-\text{int}: None$

$x-\text{int}: (e^{\frac{1}{2}},0),(-e^{\frac{1}{2}},0)$

$Inflection\quad points: (e^{-\frac{1}{3}},\frac{5}{3}e^{-1},),(-e^{-\frac{1}{3}},-\frac{5}{3}e^{-1})$

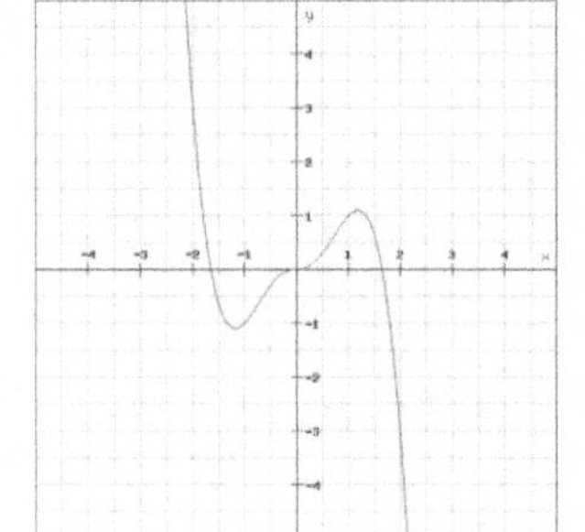

76. $f(x) = e^{x^3 - x^2}, x \in \mathbb{R}$

Domain: $x \in (-\infty, \infty)$

Vertical Asymptotes: *None*

Horizontal Asymptotes: $y = 0$

$Lim_{x \to -\infty}(f(x)) = 0$ $Lim_{x \to \infty}(f(x)) = \infty$

Slant Asymptotes: *None*

$y-\text{int}: (0,1)$

$x-\text{int}$: *None*

Inflection points: $(\approx 0.315, \approx 0.934), (\approx -0.620, \approx 0.536)$

Extrema: $(0,1), \max, (\frac{2}{3}, e^{-\frac{4}{27}}), \max$

Range: $f(x) \in (0, \infty)$

Increase: $x \in (-\infty, 0) \cup (\frac{2}{3}, \infty)$

Decrease: $x \in (0, \frac{2}{3})$

Concave-up: $x \in (-\infty, \approx -0.620) \cup (\approx 0.315, \infty)$

Concave-down: $x \in (\approx -0.620, \approx 0.315)$

77. $f(x) = \ln(x^2 - 1), x \in \mathbb{R}$

Domain: $x \in (-\infty, -1) \cup (1, \infty)$

Vertical Asymptotes: $x = -1, x = 1$

$Lim_{x \to -1^-}(f(x)) = -\infty$ $Lim_{x \to 1^+}(f(x)) = -\infty$

Horizontal Asymptotes: *None*

$Lim_{x \to -\infty}(f(x)) = \infty$ $Lim_{x \to \infty}(f(x)) = \infty$

Slant Asymptotes: *None*

$y-\text{int}$: *None*

$x-\text{int}: (\sqrt{2}, 0), (-\sqrt{2}, 0)$

Inflection points: *None*

Extrema: *None*

Range: $f(x) \in (-\infty, \infty)$

Increase: $x \in (1, \infty)$

Decrease: $x \in (-\infty, -1)$

Concave-down: $x \in (-\infty, -1) \cup (1, \infty)$

Concave-up: *Never*

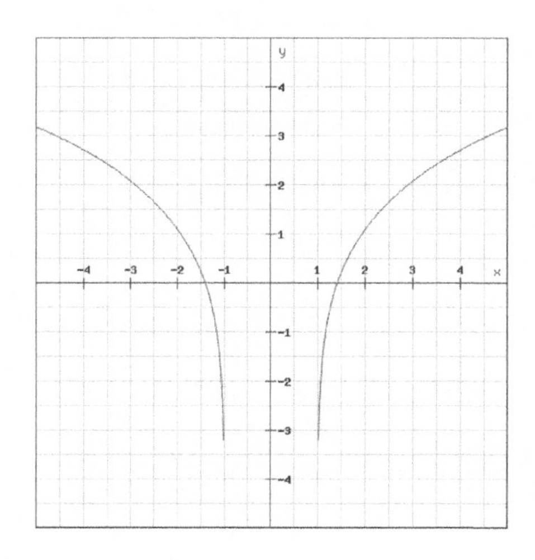

78. $f(x) = \ln(4 - x^2), x \in □$

$Domain: x \in (-2,2)$

$Vertical \quad Asymptotes: x = -2, x = 2$

$Lim_{x \to -2^+}(f(x)) = -\infty \quad Lim_{x \to 2^-}(f(x)) = -\infty$

$Horizontal \quad Asymptotes: None$

$Lim_{x \to -\infty}(f(x)) = D.E. \quad Lim_{x \to \infty}(f(x)) = D.E.$

$Slant \quad Asymptotes: None$

$y - \text{int}: (0, \ln(4))$

$x - \text{int}: (\sqrt{3}, 0), (-\sqrt{3}, 0)$

$Inflection \quad points: None$

$Extrema: (0, \ln(4)), \max$

$Range: f(x) \in (-\infty, \infty)$

$Increase: x \in (-2,0)$

$Decrease: x \in (0,2)$

$Concave - down: x \in (-2,2)$

$Concave - up: Never$

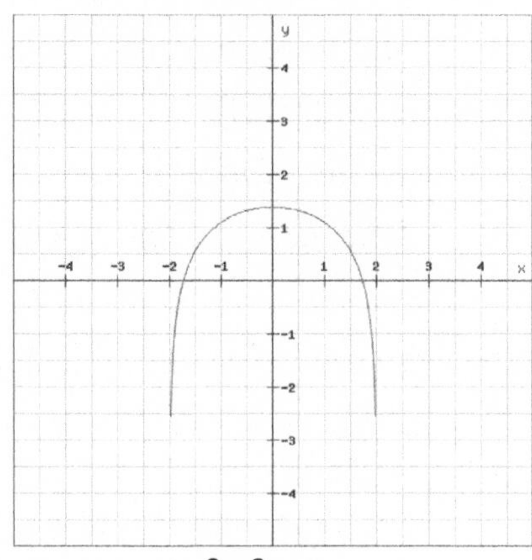

79. $f(x) = \sqrt{3x - x^2}$

$Domain: x \in [0,3]$

$Vertical \quad Asymptotes: None$

$Lim_{x \to 0^+}(f(x)) = 0 \quad Lim_{x \to 3^-}(f(x)) = 0$

$Horizontal \quad Asymptotes: None$

$Lim_{x \to -\infty}(f(x)) = D.E. \quad Lim_{x \to \infty}(f(x)) = D.E.$

$Slant \quad Asymptotes: None$

$y - \text{int}: (0,0)$

$x - \text{int}: (0,0), (3,0)$

$Inflection \quad points: None$

$Extrema: (\frac{3}{2}, \frac{3}{2}), \max$

$Range: f(x) \in (0, \frac{3}{2})$

$Increase: x \in (0, \frac{3}{2})$

$Decrease: x \in (\frac{3}{2}, 3)$

$Concave - down: x \in (0,3)$

$Concave - up: Never$

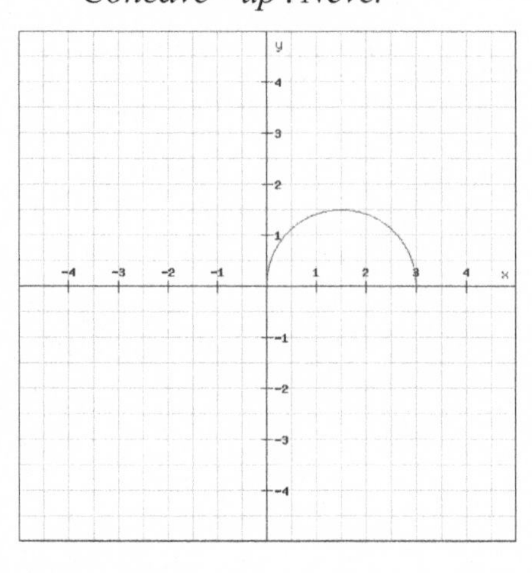

80. $f(x)=\dfrac{1}{\sqrt{3x-x^2}}$

$Domain: x \in (0,3)$

$Vertical \quad Asymptotes: x=0, x=3$

$Lim_{x\to 0^+}(f(x))=\infty \quad Lim_{x\to 3^-}(f(x))=\infty$

$Horizontal \quad Asymptotes: None$

$Lim_{x\to -\infty}(f(x))=D.E. \quad Lim_{x\to\infty}(f(x))=D.E.$

$Slant \quad Asymptotes: None$

$y-\text{int}: None$

$x-\text{int}: None$

$Inflection \quad points: None$

$Extrema: (\frac{3}{2},\frac{2}{3}), \text{min}$

$Range: f(x)\in[\frac{2}{3},\infty)$

$Increase: x\in(\frac{3}{2},3)$

$Decrease: x\in(0,\frac{3}{2})$

$Concave-down: Never$

$Concave-up: x\in(0,3)$

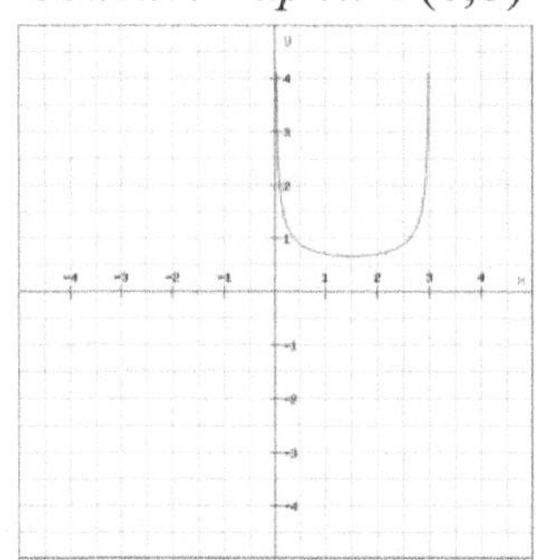

81. $f(x)=\dfrac{1}{\sin(x)+1}$

$Domain: x\in\square, x\neq \frac{3\pi}{2}+2\pi k, k\in\square$

$Vertical \quad Asymptotes: x=\frac{3\pi}{2}+2\pi k, k\in\square$

$Lim_{x\to \frac{3\pi}{2}+2\pi k^+}(f(x))=\infty \quad Lim_{x\to \frac{3\pi}{2}+2\pi k^-}(f(x))=\infty$

$Horizontal \quad Asymptotes: None$

$Lim_{x\to -\infty}(f(x))=D.E. \quad Lim_{x\to\infty}(f(x))=D.E.$

$Slant \quad Asymptotes: None$

$y-\text{int}: (0,1)$

$x-\text{int}: None$

$Inflection \quad points: None$

$Extrema: (\frac{\pi}{2}+2\pi k,\frac{1}{2}), k\in\square, \text{min}$

$Range: f(x)\in[\frac{1}{2},\infty)$

$Increase: x\in(\frac{\pi}{2}+2\pi k,\frac{3\pi}{2}+2\pi k), k\in\square$

$Decrease: x\in(\frac{3\pi}{2}+2\pi k,\frac{5\pi}{2}+2\pi k), k\in\square$

$Concave-down: Never$

$Concave-up: x\neq\frac{3\pi}{2}+2\pi k, k\in\square$

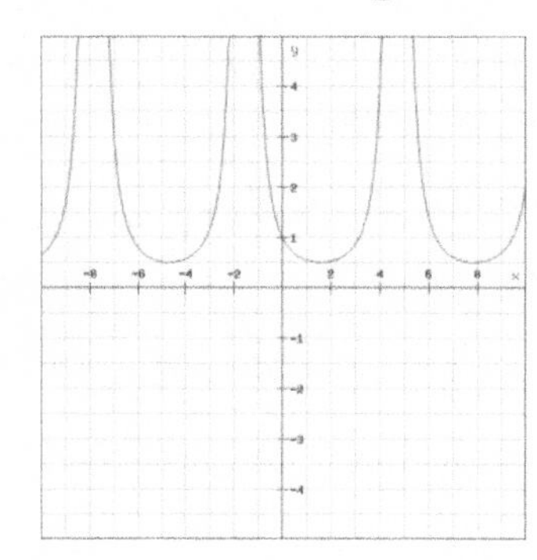

1.10. – INDEFINITE INTEGRATION

1. $\int x^{75} - 12x + 2dx = \frac{x^{76}}{76} - \frac{12x^2}{2} + 2x + C$

2. $\int \frac{1}{x^3} - 3x^{\frac{2}{3}} + 31xdx = \frac{x^{-2}}{-2} - \frac{9x^{\frac{5}{3}}}{5} + 31\frac{x^2}{2} + C$

3. $\int \sqrt[4]{\frac{1}{x^3}} - x + 1 + \pi + \cos(1) + edx = 4x^{\frac{1}{4}} - \frac{x^2}{2} + x + \pi x + \cos(1)x + ex + C$

4. $\int \frac{1}{x^3} - 3x + 3dx = \frac{x^{-2}}{-2} - \frac{3x^2}{2} + 3x + C$

5. $\int \frac{1}{x^2} - \frac{3}{\sqrt{2x^3}} dx = \frac{x^{-1}}{-1} + \frac{6x^{-\frac{1}{2}}}{\sqrt{2}} + C$

6. $\int \frac{4}{x^5} - \frac{3}{2x^2} dx = \frac{4x^{-4}}{-4} - \frac{3x^{-1}}{-2} + C$

7. $\int \frac{-5}{x^{55}} - \frac{5}{7x^{211}} dx = \frac{5x^{-54}}{54} + \frac{5x^{-210}}{7 \cdot 210} + C$

8. $\int \frac{2}{x} - \frac{5}{x} dx = -3Ln(x) + C$

9. $\int \frac{2}{x^3} + \frac{5}{3x^{10}} - \frac{2}{x} dx = \frac{2x^{-2}}{-2} + \frac{5x^{-9}}{-27} - 2Ln(x) + C$

10. $\int \frac{15}{x} - x^{12} dx = 15Ln(x) - \frac{x^{13}}{13} + C$

11. $\int \frac{2}{x^3} + \frac{5}{3x^{10}} - \frac{2}{x} dx = \frac{2x^{-2}}{-2} + 5\frac{x^{-9}}{-27} - 2Ln(x) + C$

12. $\int \sqrt{\frac{a}{x}} + \frac{a}{x} + \frac{x}{a} - ae^x + \frac{1}{a} + x^a dx = 2\sqrt{a}x^{\frac{1}{2}} + aLn(x) + \frac{x^2}{2a} - ae^x + \frac{x}{a} + \frac{x^{a+1}}{a+1} + C$

13. $\int 0.1x - 0.2e^x dx = \frac{x^2}{20} - \frac{1}{5}e^x + C$

14. $\int \frac{1}{x} - 15e^x + 0.2dx = Ln(x) - 15e^x + 0.2x + C$

15. $\int \sqrt{\frac{2}{x}} + \frac{2}{3} - e^x dx = 2\sqrt{2}x^{\frac{1}{2}} + \frac{2}{3}x - e^x + C$

16. $\int \frac{2}{x^{40}} + \frac{2}{7x^{12}} - 5e^x dx = -\frac{2x^{-39}}{41 \cdot 39} - \frac{2x^{-11}}{7 \cdot 11} - 5e^x + C$

17. $\int 7\cos(x) + 12x dx = 7\sin(x) + 6x^2 + C$

18. $\int -\cos(x) - \sin(x) - \frac{2}{x} + \frac{2}{x^2} - e^x dx = -\sin(x) + \cos(x) - 2Ln(x) - 2x^{-1} - e^x + C$

19. $\int \cos(4) + 7e^x + \frac{3}{x^{12}} dx = \cos(4) \cdot x + 7e^x + \frac{3x^{-11}}{-11} + C$

20. $\int \cos(x) + \sin(x) + \frac{3}{x} dx = \sin(x) - \cos(x) + 3\ln(x) + C$

21. $\int \cos(4) + \sin(x) + \frac{3}{\sqrt{x^7}} dx = \cos(4) \cdot x - \cos(x) + \frac{3x^{\frac{9}{2}}}{\left(\frac{9}{2}\right)} + C$

22. $\int 7 - \frac{a}{x} + \frac{b}{2x^5} + 4dx = 3x - a\ln(x) + \frac{bx^{-4}}{-8} + C$

23. $\int \frac{1}{3}\cos(x) + \frac{1}{2} - \sqrt{3}e^x + \sqrt{3} + \sqrt{2}x - \frac{2}{x} + \frac{1}{2x} + 1 + x dx =$

$$\frac{1}{3}\sin(x) + \frac{1}{2}x - \sqrt{3}e^x + \sqrt{3} \cdot x + \sqrt{2}\frac{x^2}{2} - \frac{3}{2}\ln(x) + x + \frac{x^2}{2} + C$$

24. $\int \frac{1}{3}\sin(x) + \frac{5}{2} - \sqrt{3}e^x + \sqrt{7} + \sqrt{2}x - \frac{a}{x} + \frac{1}{bx} + 1 + x dx =$

$$-\frac{1}{3}\cos(x) + \frac{5}{2}x - \sqrt{3}e^x + \sqrt{7} \cdot x + \sqrt{2}\frac{x^2}{2} - a\ln(x) + \frac{1}{b}\ln(x) + x + \frac{x^2}{2} + C$$

Exercises:

25. $\int 2x\cos(x^2)dx = \sin(x^2) + C$

26. $\int -2\sin(-x^3)x^2 dx = \frac{-2\cos(-x^3)}{3} + C$

27. $\int xe^{x^2+3} dx = \frac{e^{x^2+3}}{2} + C$

28. $\int \cos(x^3 + 1)x^2 dx = \frac{\sin(x^3+1)}{3} + C$

29. $\int \frac{4x}{x^2+2} dx = 2Ln(x^2 + 2) + C$

30. $\int x^3 \sin(x^4 + 5)dx = -\frac{\cos(x^4 + 5)}{4} + C$

31. $\int \frac{4}{(3x+5)^7}dx = \frac{4(3x+5)^{-6}}{-6\cdot 3} + C$

32. $\int e^{\frac{x}{2}}dx = 2e^{\frac{x}{2}} + C$

33. $\int 2x\sin(3x^2+52)dx = -\frac{\cos(3x^2+52)}{3} + C$

34. $\int 5\cos(3x+5)dx = \frac{5\sin(3x+5)}{3} + C$

35. $\int \frac{20x+2}{5x^2+x}dx = 2Ln(5x^2+x) + C$

36. $\int \frac{2}{5}\cos(\frac{x}{2}+5)dx = \frac{4}{5}\sin(\frac{x}{2}+5) + C$

37. $\int \frac{x^2}{x^3+3}dx = \frac{Ln(x^3+3)}{3} + C$

38. $\int (3x^2-4)e^{x^3-4x}dx = e^{x^3-4x} + C$

39. $\int 5x(x^2-4)^{-6}dx = \frac{-(x^2-4)^{-5}}{2} + C$

40. $\int 15(e^x-4)^{11}e^x dx = \frac{15(e^x-4)^{12}}{12} + C$

41. $\int x^2 e^{4x^3+17}dx = \frac{e^{4x^3+17}}{12} + C$

42. $\int e^{-5x+7}dx = \frac{e^{-5x+7}}{-5} + C$

43. $\int \frac{2x+3}{x^2+3x}dx = Ln(x^2+3x) + C$

44. $\int \frac{4x+2}{2x^2+2x+7}dx = Ln(2x^2+2x+7) + C$

45. $\int \frac{4}{7}\cos(-7x+11)dx = \frac{4}{-49}\sin(-7x+11) + C$

46. $\int \frac{4x}{3}\cos(3x^2+15)dx = \frac{4}{18}\sin(3x^2+15) + C$

47. $\int \frac{4}{7}\sin(3x+5)dx = -\frac{4}{21}\cos(3x+5) + C$

48. $\int \frac{4x}{3(x^2-5)^4}dx = -\frac{4}{18}(x^2-5)^{-3} + C$

49. $\int \frac{2x-5}{(x^2-5x)^5}dx = \frac{(x^2-5x)^{-4}}{-8} + C$

50. $\int -\frac{2x^3}{(x^4-3)^5}dx = \frac{(x^4-3)^{-4}}{8} + C$

51. $\int -\frac{2x}{3(x^2-3)}dx = -\frac{1}{3}Ln(x^2-3) + C$

58. $\int \frac{3x^2+5x}{x}dx = \int 3x+5dx = \frac{3x^2}{2} + 5x + C$

59. $\int \frac{x^3+x^2-2\sqrt{x}+1}{\sqrt[3]{x}}dx = \int x^{\frac{8}{3}} + x^{\frac{5}{3}} - 2x^{\frac{1}{6}} + x^{-\frac{1}{3}}dx = \frac{3x^{\frac{11}{3}}}{11} + \frac{3x^{\frac{8}{3}}}{8} - 3x^{\frac{4}{6}} + \frac{3x^{\frac{2}{3}}}{2} + C$

60. $\int \frac{\sqrt{x}}{x^4}dx = \int x^{-\frac{7}{2}}dx = -\frac{2x^{-\frac{5}{2}}}{5} + C$

61. $\int (\sqrt{x}+\sqrt{\frac{1}{x}})dx = \frac{2x^{\frac{3}{2}}}{3} + 2x^{\frac{1}{2}} + C$

62. $\int \frac{\sqrt{x}+\sqrt[3]{x^2}}{\sqrt[6]{x^5}} dx = \int x^{-\frac{1}{3}} + x^{-\frac{1}{6}} dx = \frac{3x^{\frac{2}{3}}}{2} + \frac{6x^{\frac{5}{6}}}{5} + C$

63. $\int \frac{x^2+\sqrt[3]{x^2}}{\sqrt{x}} dx = \int x^{\frac{3}{2}} + x^{\frac{1}{6}} dx = \frac{2x^{\frac{5}{2}}}{5} + \frac{6x^{\frac{7}{6}}}{7} + C$

64. $\int \frac{dx}{x^2 \sqrt[5]{x^2}} = \int x^{-\frac{12}{5}} dx = \frac{-5x^{-\frac{7}{5}}}{7} + C$

65. $\int (3x+5)dx = \frac{3x^2}{2} + 5x + C$

66. $\int (5x-7)^{-3} dx = \frac{(5x-7)^{-2}}{-10} + C$

67. $\int (15x-7)^{-\frac{1}{2}} dx = \frac{2(15x-7)^{\frac{1}{2}}}{15} + C$

68. $\int (12x+3)^{\frac{4}{7}} dx = \frac{7(12x+3)^{\frac{11}{7}}}{12 \cdot 11} + C$

69. $\int (12x+3)^{-\frac{1}{12}} dx = \frac{(12x+3)^{\frac{11}{12}}}{11} + C$

70. $\int 6x(3x^2+5)^2 dx = \frac{(3x^2+5)^3}{3} + C$

71. $\int 18x(6x^3+5)^{-1} dx = Ln(6x^3+5) + C$

72. $\int (60x^3-7)(15x^4-7x)^{-3} dx = \frac{(15x^4-7x)^{-2}}{-2} + C$

73. $\int (\frac{1}{x}+1)(\ln(x)+x)^{-\frac{1}{2}} dx = 2(\ln(x)+x)^{\frac{1}{2}} + C$

74. $\int 3x^4(2x^5+3)^{\frac{4}{7}} dx = \frac{21(2x^5+3)^{\frac{11}{7}}}{110} + C$

75. $\int\left(\frac{1}{\sqrt{x}}+2\right)(\sqrt{x}+x)^{\frac{2}{5}}\,dx=\frac{10(\sqrt{x}+x)^{\frac{7}{5}}}{7}+C$

76. $\int x^{-1}\,dx=Ln(x)+C$

77. $\int x^{-2}\,dx=-x^{-1}+C$

78. $\int e^{2x}(e^{2x}+2)^{-\frac{21}{4}}\,dx=\frac{-4(e^{2x}+2)^{-\frac{17}{4}}}{34}+C$

79. $\int\frac{2}{x+1}\,dx=2Ln(x+1)+C$

80. $\int\frac{1}{5x+1}\,dx=\frac{Ln(5x+1)}{5}+C$

81. $\int\frac{x}{3x^2+5}\,dx=\frac{Ln(3x^2+5)}{6}+C$

82. $\int\frac{2x}{x^2+1}\,dx=Ln(x^2+1)+C$

83. $\int\frac{x^2}{x^3-5}\,dx=\frac{Ln(x^3-5)}{3}+C$

84. $\int\frac{2x^3}{3x^4-5}\,dx=\frac{Ln(3x^4-5)}{6}+C$

85. $\int\frac{x^{-\frac{1}{2}}-2}{x^{\frac{1}{2}}-x}\,dx=2Ln(x^{\frac{1}{2}}-x)+C$

86. $\int\frac{3x^2+1}{x^3+x}\,dx=Ln(x^3+x)+C$

87. $\int\frac{3x^7}{2x^8+1}\,dx=\frac{3Ln(2x^8+1)}{16}+C$

88. $\int\frac{5x^{\frac{3}{2}}-4x}{x^{\frac{5}{2}}-x^2}\,dx=2Ln(x^{\frac{5}{2}}-x^2)+C$

89. $\int\frac{-5e^x}{e^x-4}\,dx=-5Ln(e^x-4)+C$

90. $\int\frac{2e^{3x+1}}{e^{3x+1}-3}\,dx=\frac{2Ln(e^{3x+1}-3)}{3}+C$

91. $\int\frac{14e^{7x+2}-2}{e^{7x+2}-x}\,dx=2Ln(e^{7x+2}-x)+C$

92. $\int\frac{4x+1}{8x^2+4x+4}\,dx=\frac{Ln(8x^2+4x+4)}{4}+C$

93. $\int\frac{(\tan(x)+3)^{-2}}{(\cos(x))^2}\,dx=-(\tan(x)+3)^{-1}+C$

94. $\int\frac{\sin(x)}{\cos(x)}\,dx=\int\tan(x)dx=-Ln(\cos(x))+C$

95. $\int\frac{1-\sin(x)}{x+\cos(x)}\,dx=\int\frac{1-\sin(x)}{x+\cos(x)}\,dx=Ln(x+\cos(x))+C$

96. $\int \frac{1}{x\ln(x)} dx = Ln(Ln(x)) + C$

97. $\int \frac{1}{x\ln(2x)} dx = Ln(Ln(2x)) + C$

98. $\int \frac{1}{(3x+1)\ln(3x+1)} dx = \frac{Ln(Ln(3x+1))}{3} + C$

99. $\int \frac{3x^2 + 5x - 1}{x} dx = \int 3x + 5 - \frac{1}{x} dx = \frac{3x^2}{2} + 5x - Ln(x) + C$

100. $\int \frac{x^3 + x^2 - 2\sqrt{x} + 1}{\sqrt[3]{x}} dx = \int x^{\frac{8}{3}} + x^{\frac{5}{3}} - 2x^{\frac{1}{6}} + x^{-\frac{1}{3}} dx = \frac{3x^{\frac{11}{3}}}{11} + \frac{3x^{\frac{5}{3}}}{5} - \frac{12x^{\frac{7}{6}}}{7} + \frac{3x^{\frac{2}{3}}}{2} + C =$

101. $\int \frac{\sqrt{\sqrt{x}}}{x^4} dx = \int x^{-\frac{15}{4}} dx = -\frac{4x^{-\frac{11}{4}}}{11} + C$

102. $\int (x\sqrt{x} + \sqrt[5]{\frac{1}{x}}) dx = \int (x^{\frac{3}{2}} + x^{-\frac{1}{5}}) dx = \frac{2x^{\frac{5}{2}}}{5} + \frac{5x^{\frac{4}{5}}}{4} + C$

103. $\int \frac{\sqrt{\sqrt{x}} + \sqrt[3]{x^2}}{\sqrt[6]{x^2}} dx = \int x^{-\frac{1}{12}} + x^{\frac{1}{3}} dx = \frac{12x^{\frac{11}{12}}}{11} + \frac{3x^{\frac{4}{3}}}{4} + C$

104. $\int \frac{2x^3 + 2\sqrt[3]{x^4}}{\sqrt{x}} dx = \int 2x^{\frac{5}{2}} + 2x^{\frac{5}{6}} dx = \frac{4x^{\frac{7}{2}}}{7} + \frac{12x^{\frac{11}{6}}}{11} + C$

105. $\int \frac{\sqrt[3]{x^4}}{x \cdot \sqrt{x}} dx = \int x^{-\frac{3}{4}} dx = 4x^{\frac{1}{4}} + C$

106. $\int (\frac{1}{x^2} - \frac{1}{x+1}) dx = -x^{-1} - Ln(x+1) + C$

107. $\int \left(\sqrt{x} + \frac{1}{\sqrt{x}}\right)^2 dx = \int x + 2 + \frac{1}{x} dx = \frac{x^2}{2} + 2x + Ln(x) + C =$

108. $\int \left(x^2 + \frac{1}{x}\right)^3 dx = \int x^6 + 3x^3 + 3 + x^{-3} dx = \frac{x^7}{7} + \frac{3x^4}{4} + 3x + \frac{x^{-2}}{-2} + C =$

109. $\int \left(\frac{1}{x^2} + \frac{1}{1+x^2}\right) dx = -x^{-1} + \arctan(x) + C$

110. $\int\left(\sqrt{x}+\frac{1}{x}\right)^2 dx = \int x + 2x^{\frac{3}{2}} + x^{-2} dx = \frac{x^2}{2} + \frac{4x^{\frac{5}{2}}}{5} - x^{-1} + C =$

111. $\int (nx)^{\frac{1-n}{n}} dx = \int n^{\frac{1-n}{n}} x^{\frac{1-n}{n}} dx = \frac{n^{\frac{1-n}{n}} x^{\frac{1-n}{n}+1}}{\frac{1-n}{n}+1} = n^{\frac{1}{n}} x^{\frac{1}{n}} + C$

112. $\int (a^{2/3} - x^{2/3})^3 dx = \int a^2 - 3a^{\frac{4}{3}} x^{\frac{2}{3}} + 3a^{\frac{2}{3}} x^{\frac{4}{3}} - x^2 dx = a^2 x - \frac{9a^{\frac{4}{3}} x^{\frac{5}{3}}}{5} + \frac{9a^{\frac{2}{3}} x^{\frac{7}{3}}}{7} - \frac{x^3}{3} + C$

113. $\int (\sqrt{x}+1)(x-\sqrt{x}+1) dx = \int x^{\frac{3}{2}} + 1 dx = \frac{2x^{\frac{5}{2}}}{5} + x + C$

114. $\int \frac{(x^2+1)(x^2-2)}{\sqrt[3]{x^2}} dx = \int x^{\frac{10}{3}} - x^{\frac{4}{3}} - 2x^{-\frac{2}{3}} dx = \frac{3x^{\frac{13}{3}}}{13} - \frac{3x^{\frac{7}{3}}}{7} - 6x^{\frac{1}{3}} + C$

115. $\int \sqrt{\frac{5}{x^3}} dx = \int \sqrt{5} \cdot x^{-\frac{3}{2}} dx = -2\sqrt{5} \cdot x^{-\frac{1}{2}} + C$

116. $\int (x+\sqrt{x})^2 dx = \int x^2 + 2x^{\frac{3}{2}} + x dx = \frac{x^3}{3} + \frac{4x^{\frac{5}{2}}}{5} + \frac{x^2}{2} + C$

117. $\int \frac{5}{x+4} dx = 5Ln(x+4) + C =$

118. $\int (x+\frac{1}{x^2})^3 dx = \int x^3 - 3 + 3x^{-3} - x^{-6} dx = \frac{x^4}{4} - 3x + \frac{3x^{-2}}{-2} - \frac{x^{-5}}{-5} + C$

119. $\int \frac{2}{2x+3} dx = Ln(2x+3) + C$

120. $\int \frac{e^x}{e^x+4} dx = Ln(e^x+4) + C$

121. $\int \frac{x^2}{x^3+8} dx = \frac{Ln(x^3+8)}{3} + C$

122. $\int \frac{a\,dx}{a-x} = -aLn(a-x) + C$

123. $\int \frac{e^{2x}}{e^{2x}+2} dx = \frac{Ln(e^{2x}+2)}{2} + C$

124. $\int \frac{sin(x)}{2+\cos(x)}dx = -Ln(2+\cos(x))+C$

125. $\int \frac{sin(Ln(x))}{x}dx = \cos(Ln(x))+C$

126. $\int \frac{dx}{tg\left(\frac{x}{5}\right)} = \int \frac{\cos(\frac{x}{5})}{\sin\left(\frac{x}{5}\right)}dx = 5Ln(\sin(\frac{x}{5}))+C$

127. $\int \frac{tg\left(\sqrt{x}\right)}{\sqrt{x}}dx = \int \frac{\sin\left(\sqrt{x}\right)}{\sqrt{x}\cdot\cos\left(\sqrt{x}\right)}dx = -2Ln(\cos(\sqrt{x}))+C$

128. $\int x\cot g(x^2+1)\,dx = \int \frac{x\cos(x^2+1)}{\sin(x^2+1)}dx = \frac{Ln(\sin(x^2+1))}{2}+C$

129. $\int \frac{Ln^3(x)}{x}dx = \frac{Ln^4(x)}{4}+C$

130. $\int \frac{e^x}{e^x-1}dx = Ln(e^x-1)+C=$

131. $\int \frac{\sqrt{x}+Ln^2(x)}{x}dx = \int x^{-\frac{1}{2}}+\frac{Ln^2(x)}{x}dx = 2x^{\frac{1}{2}}+\frac{Ln^3(x)}{3}+C=$

132. $\int \frac{x}{\sqrt{x^2+1}}dx = (x^2+1)^{\frac{1}{2}}+C$

133. $\int \sqrt{2-5x}\,dx = -\frac{2(2-5x)^{\frac{3}{2}}}{15}+C$

134. $\int \sqrt{5x^2-4x+3}\,(10x-4)dx = \frac{2(5x^2-4x+3)^{\frac{3}{2}}}{3}+C$

135. $\int \frac{x^2}{\sqrt{x^3+2}}dx = \frac{2(x^3+2)^{\frac{1}{2}}}{6}+C$

136. $\int \frac{3x^2}{\sqrt{1-2x^3}}dx = \frac{2(1-2x^3)^{\frac{1}{2}}}{-6}+C$

137. $\int 3x\sqrt{1-2x^2}\,dx = \frac{2(1-2x^2)^{\frac{3}{2}}}{-4}+C$

138. $\int \frac{x+3}{\sqrt{x^2+6x+4}}dx = (x^2+6x+4)^{\frac{1}{2}} + C$

139. $\int \frac{dx}{\sqrt{x+3}-\sqrt{x+2}} \cdot \frac{\sqrt{x+3}+\sqrt{x+2}}{\sqrt{x+3}+\sqrt{x+2}} = \int \frac{\sqrt{x+3}+\sqrt{x+2}}{1}dx = \frac{2(x+3)^{\frac{3}{2}}}{3} + \frac{2(x+2)^{\frac{3}{2}}}{3} +$

140. $\int \frac{\sqrt{x^2+4}+x}{\sqrt{x^2+4}}dx = \int 1 + \frac{x}{\sqrt{x^2+4}}dx = x + (x^2+4)^{\frac{1}{2}} + C =$

141. $\int \frac{dx}{\sqrt{x}\sqrt{1+\sqrt{x}}} = 4(1+\sqrt{x})^{\frac{1}{2}} + C$

142. $\int \frac{e^x}{\sqrt{1+e^x}}dx = 2(1+e^x)^{\frac{1}{2}} + C$

143. $\int (\cos(x) - sin(x))dx = \sin(x) + \cos(x) + C =$

144. $\int \frac{2-2sin^2(x)+3\cos(x)}{\cos(x)}\,dx = \int \frac{2\cos^2(x)+3\cos(x)}{\cos(x)}\,dx = \int 2\cos(x)+3\,dx = 2\sin(x)+3x+C$

145. $\int sin(x)\cdot\cos(x)\,dx = \frac{sin^2(x)}{2} + C$

146. $\int \frac{sin^2(x)-1+5sin^3(x)}{2sin^2(x)}\,dx = \int \frac{1}{2} - \frac{1}{2sin^2(x)} + \frac{5}{2}\sin(x)\,dx = \frac{x}{2} + \frac{\cot(x)}{2} - \frac{5}{2}\cos(x) +$

147. $\int 4^x dx = \frac{4^x}{Ln(4)} + C$

148. $\int 7^x dx = \frac{7^x}{Ln(7)} + C$

149. $\int 5^{2x} dx = \frac{5^{2x}}{2Ln(5)} + C$

150. $\int x\cdot 6^{x^2}\,dx = \frac{6^{x^2}}{2Ln(6)} + C =$

151. $\int (\cos 3x)2^{\sin 3x}dx = \frac{2^{\sin 3x}}{3Ln(2)} + C$

152. $\int e^{x} \cdot 9^{e^{x}} dx = \frac{9^{e^{x}}}{Ln(9)} + C$

153. $\int x^{2} \cdot 6^{4x^{3}+1} dx = \frac{6^{4x^{3}+1}}{12Ln(6)} + C$

154. $\int \frac{4^{\sqrt{x}}}{\sqrt{x}} dx = \frac{2 \cdot 4^{\sqrt{x}}}{Ln(4)} + C$

155. $\int e^{3x} dx = \frac{e^{3x}}{3} + C$

156. $\int x e^{3x^{2}} dx = \frac{e^{3x^{2}}}{6} + C$

157. $\int \frac{e^{x} + e^{-x}}{\left(e^{x} - e^{-x}\right)^{2}} dx = -(e^{x} - e^{-x})^{-1} + C$

158. $\int \frac{e^{3x} + e^{x} + 2}{e^{x}} dx = \int e^{2x} + 1 + 2 \cdot e^{-x} dx = \frac{e^{2x}}{2} + x - 2 \cdot e^{-x} + C$

159. $\int e^{x}\left(e^{x} + 2\right)^{2} dx = \frac{\left(e^{x} + 2\right)^{3}}{3} + C$

160. $\int \cos(x) \cdot e^{\sin(x)} dx = e^{\sin(x)} + C$

161. $\int \frac{e^{\frac{1}{x}}}{x^{2}} dx = -e^{\frac{1}{x}} + C$

162. $\int e^{x}\sqrt{1 - e^{x}} dx = \frac{-2(1 - e^{x})^{\frac{3}{2}}}{3} + C$

163. $\int \left(x^{2} - 2\right) e^{x^{3} - 6x + 5} dx = \frac{e^{x^{3} - 6x + 5}}{3} + C$

164. $\int \left(e^{x} - e^{-x}\right)\left(e^{x} + e^{-x}\right)^{4} dx = \frac{\left(e^{x} + e^{-x}\right)^{5}}{5} + C$

165. $\int \frac{1}{2x + 3} dx = \frac{Ln(2x + 3)}{2} + C$

166. $\int \frac{1}{2-3x}dx = \frac{Ln(2-3x)}{-3} + C$

167. $\int \frac{x^2+2x+3}{x}dx = \int x+2+\frac{3}{x}dx = \frac{x^2}{2}+2x+3Ln(x)+C$

168. $\int \frac{e^x}{1+e^x}dx = Ln(1+e^x)+C$

169. $\int \frac{(\ln(x))^3}{x}dx = \frac{(Ln(x))^4}{4}+C$

170. $\int \frac{x+2}{x-1}dx = Dividing \quad polynomials... = \int 1+\frac{3}{x-1}dx = x+3Ln(x-1)+C$

171. $\int \frac{x^2+2x+3}{x+1}dx = Dividing \quad polynomials... = \int x+1+\frac{2}{x+1}dx = \frac{x^2}{2}+x+2Ln(x+1)+C$

172. $\int (e^x-e^{-x})^2dx = \int e^{2x}-2+e^{-2x}dx = \frac{e^{2x}}{2}-2x+\frac{e^{-2x}}{-2}+C$

173. $\int \frac{\cos(x)}{\sin(x)}dx = Ln(\sin(x))+C$

174. $\int \frac{\ln(x)}{x}dx = \frac{(\ln(x))^2}{2}+C$

175. $\int \frac{xdx}{x+1} = \int 1-\frac{1}{x+1}dx = x-Ln(x+1)+C$

176. $\int x^2e^{x^3}dx = \frac{e^{x^3}}{3}+C$

177. $\int \frac{x-2}{x+1}dx = \int 1-\frac{3}{x+1}dx = x-3Ln(x+1)+C$

178. $\int \frac{2x-3}{x+1}dx = \int 2-\frac{5}{x+1}dx = 2x-5Ln(x+1)+C$

1.11. – DEFINITE INTEGRTION

The result of indefinite integration is a: function $= F(x) = \int f(x)dx$

The result of definite integration is a number $= \int_a^b f(x)dx = F(b) - F(a)$

Definite integration represents the "**area under the graph**".

1. Above the x axis definite integrals have a positive sign.
2. Below the x axis definite integrals have a negative sign.
3. $\int_2^3 \frac{1}{x} + 2xdx = \left[Ln(x) + x^2\right]_2^3 = \left[Ln(3) + 9\right] - \left[Ln(2) + 4\right] = Ln(\frac{3}{2}) + 5$
4. $\int_{\pi}^{\frac{3\pi}{2}} \cos(x) + xdx = \left[\sin(\frac{3\pi}{2}) + \frac{1}{2}\left(\frac{3\pi}{2}\right)^2\right] - \left[\sin(\pi) + \frac{1}{2}\pi^2\right] = -1 + \frac{5}{8}\pi^2$
5. $\int_1^e (\ln(x))dx = 1$
6. $\int_2^6 x^2 + 1dx = \left[\frac{x^3}{3} + x\right]_2^6 = \left[\frac{216}{3} + 6\right] - \left[\frac{8}{3} + 2\right] = \frac{220}{3}$
7. $\int_0^2 3^x dx = \left[\frac{3^x}{Ln(3)}\right]_0^2 = \left[\frac{9}{Ln(3)}\right] - \left[\frac{1}{Ln(3)}\right] = \frac{8}{Ln(3)}$
8. $\int_1^{\sqrt{2}} x \cdot 2^{-x^2} dx = \left[\frac{2^{-x^2}}{-2Ln(2)}\right]_1^{\sqrt{2}} = \left[\frac{2^{-2}}{-2Ln(2)}\right] - \left[\frac{2^{-1}}{-2Ln(2)}\right] = \frac{1}{8Ln(2)}$
9. $\int_0^{\frac{\pi}{6}} (\cos(\theta))4^{-\sin(\theta)} d\theta = \left[\frac{-4^{-\sin(\theta)}}{Ln(4)}\right]_0^{\frac{\pi}{6}} = \left[\frac{-4^{-\sin(\frac{\pi}{6})}}{Ln(4)}\right] - \left[\frac{-4^{-\sin(0)}}{Ln(4)}\right] = \left[\frac{1}{2Ln(4)}\right]$
10. $\int_{-3}^{-1} 10^{-x} dx = \left[\frac{-10^{-x}}{Ln(10)}\right]_{-3}^{-1} = \left[\frac{-10}{Ln(10)}\right] - \left[\frac{-10^3}{Ln(10)}\right] = \frac{990}{Ln(10)}$
11. $\int_0^{\frac{1}{2}} \frac{1}{\sqrt{1-x^2}} dx \approx 0.524$
12. $\int_{\sqrt{2}}^2 \frac{1}{x\sqrt{x^2-1}} dx \approx 0.268$
13. $\int_{-1}^1 \frac{1}{1+x^2} dx \approx 1.57$

14. $\int_0^3 e^{3-x}dx = \left[e^{3-x}\right]_0^3 = \left[e^0\right]-\left[e^3\right] = 1-e^3$

15. $\int_0^1 \frac{x^3}{x^4+1}dx = \left[\frac{Ln(x^4+1)}{4}\right]_0^1 = \left[\frac{Ln(2)}{4}\right]-\left[\frac{Ln(1)}{4}\right] = \frac{Ln(2)}{4}$

16. $\int_{\frac{\pi}{6}}^{\frac{\pi}{2}} \frac{\cos(x)}{\sin(x)}dx = \left[Ln(sin(x))\right]_{\frac{\pi}{6}}^{\frac{\pi}{2}} = \left[Ln(sin(\frac{\pi}{2}))\right]-\left[Ln(sin(\frac{\pi}{6}))\right] = Ln(2)$

17. $\int_0^{\frac{1}{6}} \frac{1}{\sqrt{1-9x^2}}dx \approx 0.175$

18. $\int_{\sqrt{3}}^{3} \frac{1}{9+x^2}dx \approx 0.0873$

19. $\int_1^{e^2} \frac{3}{x}dx = \left[3Ln(x)\right]_1^{e^2} = \left[3Ln(e^2)\right]-\left[3Ln(1)\right] = 6$

BOUNDARY CONDITION

20. Given that $\int \frac{1}{x}dx = F(x)$ and that $F(1)=2$ find $F(x)$.

$$\int \frac{1}{x}dx = Ln(x)+C; Ln(1)+C=2; C=2; F(x)=Ln(x)+2$$

21. Given that $\int \sin(2x)dx = F(x)$ and that $F(\pi)=1$ find $F(x)$.

$$\int \sin(2x)dx = \frac{-\cos(2x)}{2}+C; \frac{-\cos(2\pi)}{2}+C=1; C=\frac{3}{2}; F(x)=\frac{-\cos(2x)}{2}+\frac{3}{2}$$

22. Given that $\int e^{2x}+(x-1)^6dx = F(x)$ and that $F(0)=1$ find $F(x)$.

$$\int e^{2x}+(x-1)^6dx = \frac{e^{2x}}{2}+\frac{(x-1)^7}{7}+C; \frac{e^0}{2}-\frac{1}{7}+C=1; F(x)=\frac{e^{2x}}{2}+\frac{(x-1)^7}{7}+\frac{9}{14}$$

23. Given that $\int \sqrt{x}+xdx = F(x)$ and that $F(1)=1$ find $F(x)$.

$$\int \sqrt{x}+xdx = \frac{2x^{\frac{3}{2}}}{3}+\frac{x^2}{2}+C; \frac{2}{3}+\frac{1}{2}+C=1; C=-\frac{1}{6}; F(x)=\frac{2x^{\frac{3}{2}}}{3}+\frac{x^2}{2}-\frac{1}{6}$$

FINDING AREAS

24. Find the area enclosed between the functions f(x) = $x^2 - x$ and the x axis. Make a sketch to show the mentioned area.

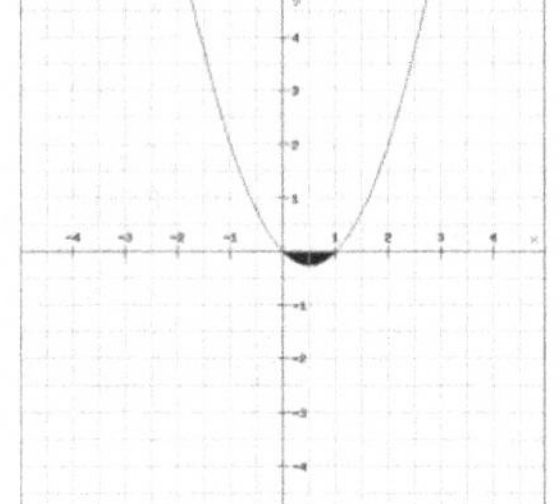

$$\int_0^1 x^2 - xdx = \left[\frac{1}{3}-1\right]-[0] = -\frac{2}{3}$$

So area enclosed is $\frac{2}{3}$

25. Find the area enclosed between the function $f(x) = x^3 - 6x^2 + 8x$ and the x axis. Make a sketch to show the mentioned area.

$$\int_0^2 x^3 - 6x^2 + 8x dx = \left[\frac{16}{4} - 16 + 16\right] - [0] = 4$$

$$\int_2^4 x^3 - 6x^2 + 8x dx = \left[\frac{256}{4} - 128 + 64\right] - \left[\frac{16}{4} - 16 + 16\right] = -4$$

So area enclosed is 8

26. Find the area enclosed between the function $f(x) = -x^3 + 3x^2 - 4$ and the axes Make a sketch to show the mentioned area.

$$-x^3 + 3x^2 - 4 = 0; x = -1, 2$$

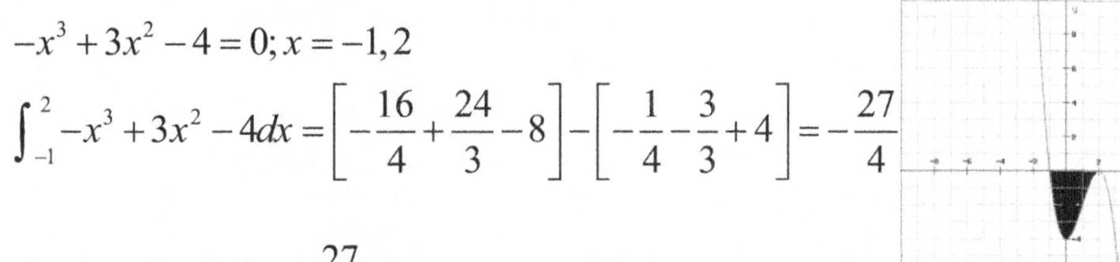

$$\int_{-1}^{2} -x^3 + 3x^2 - 4dx = \left[-\frac{16}{4} + \frac{24}{3} - 8\right] - \left[-\frac{1}{4} - \frac{3}{3} + 4\right] = -\frac{27}{4}$$

So area enclosed is $\frac{27}{4}$

27. Find the area enclosed between the functions $f(x) = x^2 + x$ and $g(x) = x + 2$. Make a sketch to show the mentioned area.

$$x^2 + x = x + 2; x = \pm\sqrt{2}$$

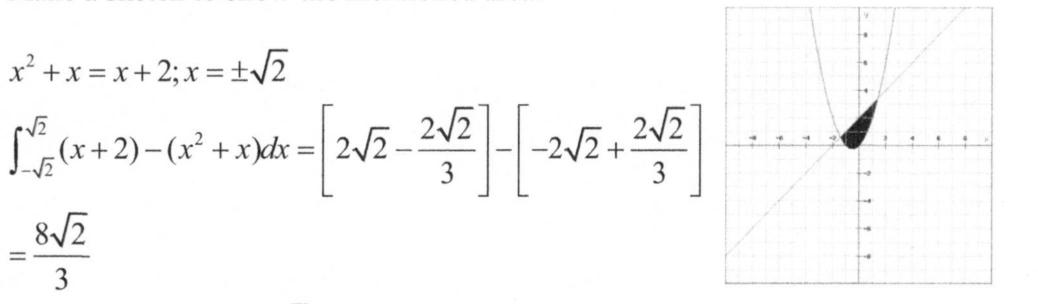

$$\int_{-\sqrt{2}}^{\sqrt{2}} (x+2) - (x^2 + x)dx = \left[2\sqrt{2} - \frac{2\sqrt{2}}{3}\right] - \left[-2\sqrt{2} + \frac{2\sqrt{2}}{3}\right]$$

$$= \frac{8\sqrt{2}}{3}$$

So area enclosed is $\frac{8\sqrt{2}}{3}$

28. Find the area enclosed between the functions $f(x) = x^2 + 2$ and $g(x) = -x^2 + 3$. Make a sketch to show the mentioned area.

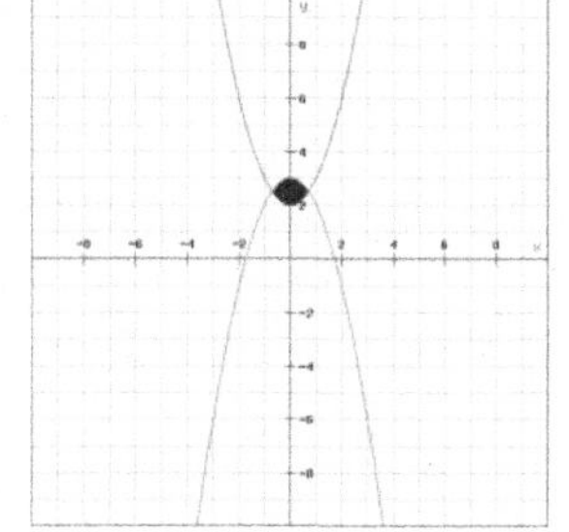

$$x^2 + 2 = -x^2 + 3; x = \pm\sqrt{\frac{1}{2}}$$

$$\int_{-\sqrt{\frac{1}{2}}}^{\sqrt{\frac{1}{2}}} (-x^2 + 3) - (x^2 + 2)dx = \frac{2\sqrt{2}}{3}$$

So area enclosed is $\frac{2\sqrt{2}}{3}$

29. Find the area enclosed between the functions $f(x) = x^4 - 2x + 1$ and $g(x) = -x^2 + 1$. Make a sketch to show the mentioned area.

$$x^4 - 2x + 1 = -x^2 + 1; x = 0,1$$

$$\int_0^1 (-x^2+1) - (x^4 - 2x + 1)dx = \left[-\frac{1}{5} - \frac{1}{3} + 1\right] - [0] = \frac{7}{15}$$

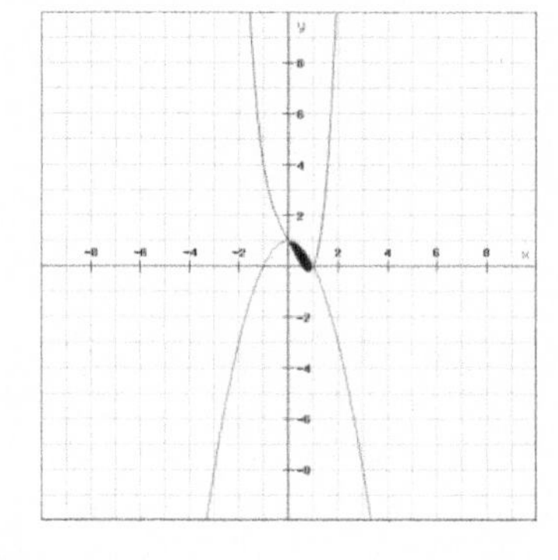

So area enclosed is $\frac{7}{15}$

30. Find the area enclosed between the functions $f(x) = 2 - x^2$ and $g(x) = |x|$. Make a sketch to show the mentioned area.

$$2 - x^2 = x; x = 1(other \quad solution \quad irrelevant)$$

$$\int_0^1 (2 - x^2) - (x)dx = \left[2 - \frac{1}{3} - 1\right] - [0] = \frac{2}{3}$$

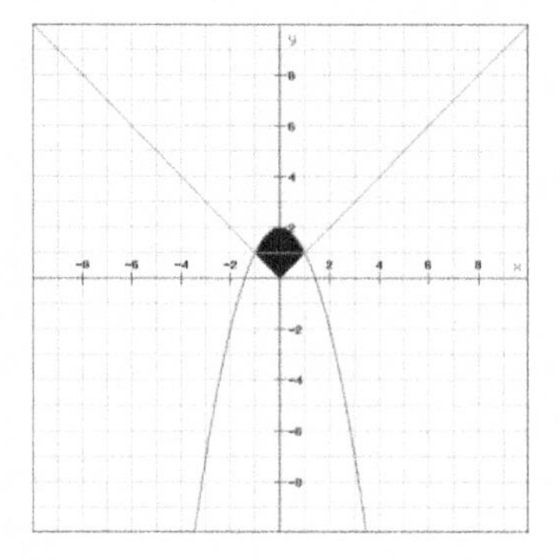

So area enclosed is trice as big (because of symmetry)

$$2 \cdot \frac{2}{3} = \frac{4}{3}$$

31. Find the area enclosed between the function $f(x) = x^2 + 2x + 2$, the tangent to $f(x)$ at its extrema and the tangent to $f(x)$ with a slope 6. Make a sketch to show the mentioned area.

$$f'(x) = 2x + 2 = 0; x = -1; f(-1) = 1; y = 1(Tangent)$$

$$f'(x) = 2x + 2 = 6; x = 2; f(2) = 10; y = 6x + b; y = 6x - 2(Tangent)$$

$$6x - 2 = 1; x = \frac{1}{2}$$

$$\int_{-1}^{\frac{1}{2}} (x^2 + 2x + 2) - (1)dx = \frac{9}{8}$$

$$\int_{\frac{1}{2}}^{2} (x^2 + 2x + 2) - (6x - 2)dx = \frac{9}{8}$$

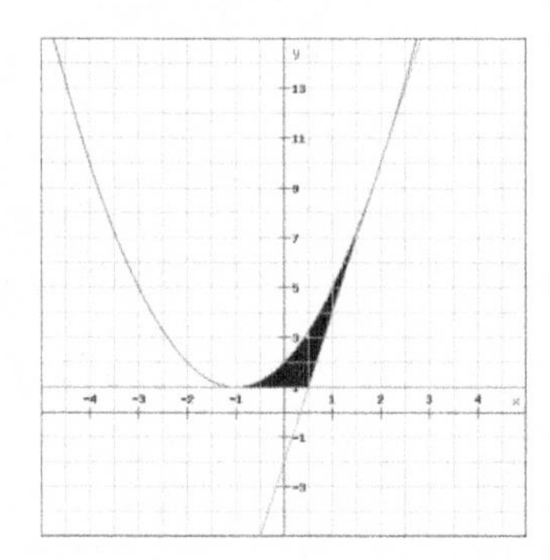

So area enclosed is $\frac{18}{8} = \frac{9}{4}$

32. Find the area enclosed between the functions $f(x) = 5 - x^2 + 4x$ and $g(x) = 5$. Make a sketch to show the mentioned area.

$5 - x^2 + 4x = 5; x = 0, 4$

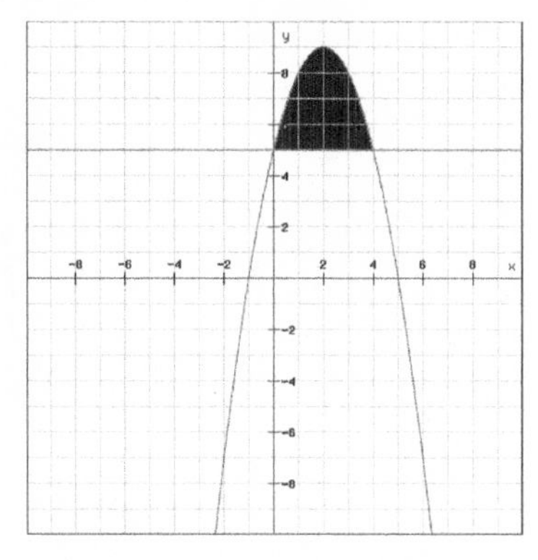

$$\int_0^4 (5 - x^2 + 4x) - (5)dx = \frac{32}{3}$$

So area enclosed is $\frac{32}{3}$

33. Find the area enclosed between the functions $f(x) = x^2 - 2x$ and $g(x) = x$. Make a sketch to show the mentioned area.

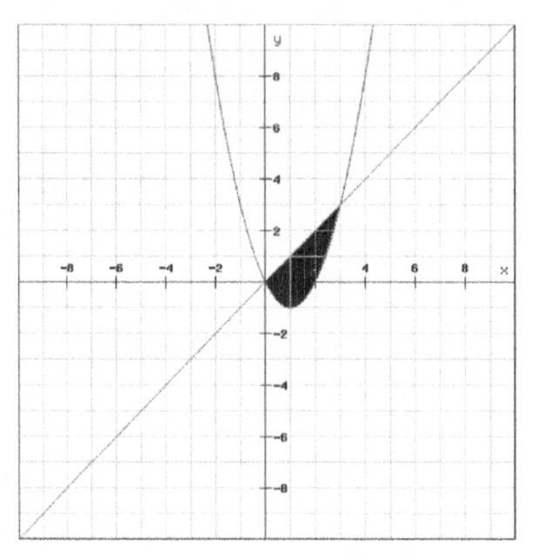

$x^2 - 2x = x; x = 0, 3$

$$\int_0^3 (x) - (x^2 - 2x)dx = \frac{9}{2}$$

So area enclosed is $\frac{9}{2}$

34. The area enclosed between the curve $y = a(1 - (x - 2)^2)$ with $a > 0$ and the x axis is 12. Find a. Make a sketch to show the mentioned area.

$y = -a(x-2)^2 + a = 0; x = 1, 3$

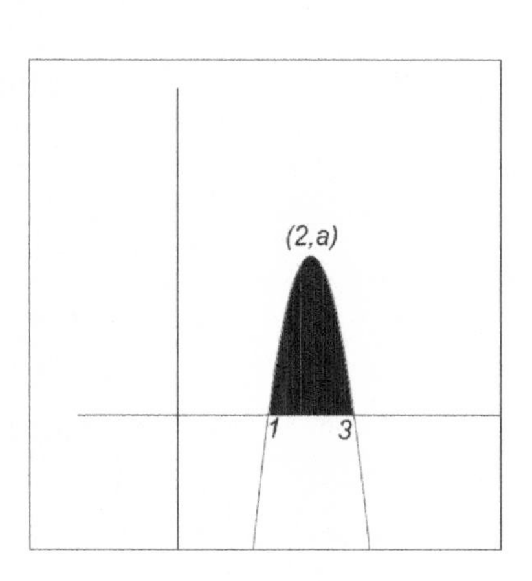

$$\int_1^3 (-a(x-2)^2 + a)dx = \left[-\frac{a(x-2)^3}{3} + ax \right]_1^3 =$$

$$= \left[-\frac{a}{3} + 3a \right] - \left[\frac{a}{3} + a \right] = \frac{4a}{3} = 12; a = 9$$

35. Given the function $f(x) = ae^{\frac{x}{3}} + \frac{1}{x^2}, x \neq 0$, find:

a. $\int_1^2 f(x)dx$ in terms of a.

$$\int_1^2 ae^{\frac{x}{3}} + \frac{1}{x^2}dx = \left[3ae^{\frac{x}{3}} - \frac{1}{x}\right]_1^2 = \left[3ae^{\frac{2}{3}} - \frac{1}{2}\right] - \left[3ae^{\frac{1}{3}} - \frac{1}{1}\right] = 3ae^{\frac{1}{3}}(e^{\frac{1}{3}} - 1) + \frac{1}{2}$$

b. If F(x) is a primitive of f(x) find a knowing that F(1) = 0 and F(2) = $\frac{1}{2}$

$F(x) = 3ae^{\frac{x}{3}} - \frac{1}{x} + C;$ $\quad I)F(1) = 3ae^{\frac{1}{3}} - 1 + C = 0$

$II) - I)\ 3a(e^{\frac{2}{3}} - e^{\frac{1}{3}}) = \frac{1}{2}; a = \frac{1}{6}(e^{\frac{2}{3}} - e^{\frac{1}{3}})^{-1}$ $\quad II)F(2) = 3ae^{\frac{2}{3}} - \frac{1}{2} + C = \frac{1}{2}$

36. Find the area bounded by: $y = e^{-x}$; $x = 0$; $y = 0$ and $x = 1$. Make a sketch to show the mentioned area.

$\int_0^1 (e^{-x})dx = \left[-e^{-1}\right] - [1] = 1 - \frac{1}{e}$

So area enclosed is $1 - \frac{1}{e}$

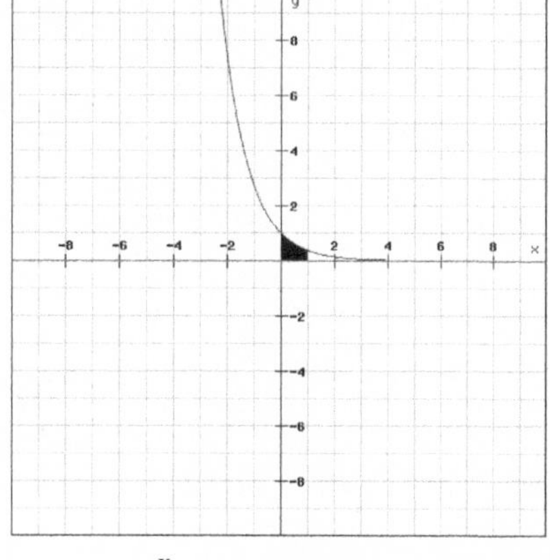

37. Find the area enclosed between the function f(x) = 1 – e^{-x}, the tangent to f(x) at the point where x = 0 and the line x = 2. Make a sketch to show the mentioned area.

$f'(x) = e^{-x}; f'(0) = 1; f(0) = 0; y = x(Tangent)$

$\int_0^2 (x) - (1 - e^{-x})dx = 1 - \frac{1}{e^2}$

So area enclosed is $1 - \frac{1}{e^2}$

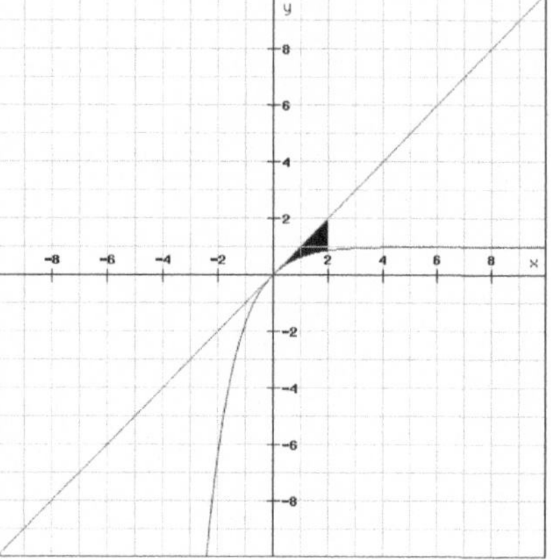

VOLUMES OF REVOLUTION

$V = \int_a^b \pi\left(f(x)\right)^2 dx$ (spinning around the x axis)

1. Find the volume of revolution formed by the function $f(x) = x+1, x \in [0,5]$

$$V = \int_0^5 \pi\left(x+1\right)^2 dx = \pi\left[\frac{\left(x+1\right)^3}{3}\right]_0^5 = \pi\left[\left[\frac{216}{3}\right]-\left[\frac{1}{3}\right]\right] = \frac{215\pi}{3}$$

2. Find the volume of revolution formed by the function $f(x) = e^x, x \in [0,1]$

$$V = \int_0^5 \pi e^{2x} dx = \pi\left[\frac{e^{2x}}{2}\right]_0^1 = \pi\left[\left[\frac{e^2}{2}\right]-\left[\frac{1}{2}\right]\right] = \frac{\pi\left(e^2-1\right)}{2}$$

3. Find the volume of revolution formed by the function $f(x) = \sqrt{\sin(2x)}, x \in [0,\frac{\pi}{6}]$.

$$V = \int_0^{\frac{\pi}{6}} \pi\sin(2x)dx = \pi\left[\frac{-\cos(2x)}{2}\right]_0^{\frac{\pi}{6}} = \pi\left[\left[-\frac{1}{4}\right]-\left[-\frac{1}{2}\right]\right] = \frac{\pi}{4}$$

4. Find the volume of revolution formed by the function $f(x) = \sqrt{x-1}, x \in [2,3]$

$$V = \int_2^3 \pi(x-1)dx = \pi\left[\frac{x^2}{2}-x\right]_2^3 = \pi\left[\left[\frac{9}{2}-3\right]-\left[\frac{4}{2}-2\right]\right] = \frac{3\pi}{2}$$

1.12. – KINEMATICS

1. The displacement of an object is measured in meters.
2. The velocity of an object is the change in the position per unit of time and it is measured in meters/second. Mathematically it is the derivative of the displacement.
3. The acceleration of an object is the and it is change in the velocity per unit of time measured in meters/second^2. Mathematically it is the derivative of the velocity or the 2nd derivative of the displacement.
4. An object accelerates from rest with a = 2 m/s^2 during 4 seconds, write down its velocity: 8 m/s
5. An object moves at 12 m/s and accelerates with a = –3 m/s^2 during 2 seconds, write down its final velocity: 6 m/s
6. If the distance run by an object after t seconds is given by $d(t) = 2t^2 + 3t + 5$, find:

   a. Its initial position: d(0) = 5m
   b. Its position after 2 seconds: d(2) = 19m
   c. Its velocity after 2 seconds: $v(t) = d'(t) = 4t + 3; v(2) = 11m/s$,
   d. Its acceleration after 2 seconds: $a(t) = v'(t) = 4; a(2) = 4m/s^2$

7. The velocity of an object after t seconds is given by $v(t) = 2s\text{in}(3t)$, find:

   a. Its initial velocity: $v(0) = 2s\text{in}(0) = 0m/s$
   b. Its initial acceleration: $a(t) = v'(t) = 6\cos(3t); a(0) = 6m/s^2$
   c. The period of its motion: $d(t) = \int 2s\text{in}(3t)dt = -\frac{2\cos(3t)}{3} + C; T = \frac{2\pi}{3}s$

8. The velocity of an object after t seconds is given by $v(t) = e^{-\frac{t}{a}}$, find:

   a. Its initial velocity: $v(0) = e^0 = 1m/s$

   b. Given that its initial acceleration is –3 m/s^2, find a:

   $$a(t) = v'(t) = \frac{-e^{-\frac{t}{a}}}{a}; a(0) = \frac{-1}{a} = -3; a = \frac{1}{3}s$$

   c. Given that the initial displacement of the object is 2m, find its displacement after 3 seconds.

   $$d(t) = \int e^{-3t}dt = \frac{-e^{-3t}}{3} + C; d(0) = \frac{-1}{3} + C = 2; C = \frac{7}{3}$$

   $$d(t) = \frac{-e^{-3t}}{3} + \frac{7}{3}; d(3) = \frac{7 - e^{-9}}{3}m$$

9. The acceleration of an object is given by $a(t) = \frac{1}{(t+1)^2}$, find:

   a. Given that v(0) = 0, find its velocity as a function time.

$$v(t) = \int \frac{1}{(t+1)^2} dt = -(t+1)^{-1} + C; v(0) = -1 + C = 0; C = 1$$
$$v(t) = -(t+1)^{-1} + 1$$

   b. Given that d(0) = 0, find its displacement as a function time.

$$d(t) = \int (-(t+1)^{-1} + 1) dt = -Ln(t+1) + t + K; d(0) = K = 0;$$
$$d(t) = -Ln(t+1) + t$$

   c. Write the acceleration and the velocity of the object after a long period

$$a(t \to \infty) \approx 0m/s^2$$
$$v(t \to \infty) \approx 1m/s$$

10. The acceleration of an object is given by $a(t) = 3\cos(2t)$, find:

   a. Given that v(0) = 0, find its velocity as a function time.

$$v(t) = \int 3\cos(2t) dt = \frac{3\sin(2t)}{2} + C; v(0) = 0 + C = 0; C = 0$$
$$v(t) = \frac{3\sin(2t)}{2}$$

   b. Given that d(0) = 0, find its displacement as a function time.

$$d(t) = \int \frac{3\sin(2t)}{2} dt = -\frac{3cos(2t)}{4} + K; d(0) = -\frac{3}{4} + K = 0; K = \frac{3}{4}$$
$$d(t) = -\frac{3cos(2t)}{4} + \frac{3}{4}$$

2.1. – INTRODUCTION TO STATISTICS

In Statistics we try to obtain some conclusions by observing and/or analyzing data.

1. The set of objects that we are trying to study is called Population, the number of elements in the population can be finite or infinite.
2. Usually the population is too big and therefore we obtain a sample. This process is called Sampling.
3. We use the sample to obtain conclusions about the population.

Types of DATA

1. Categorical data.
2. Numerical data that can be divided to discrete or continuous
3. Discrete data can be counted while continuous data can be measured.
4. 5 examples of Categorical data: eye color, favorite food, type of car, type of sport, name of child etc.
5. 3 examples of Numerical discrete data: shoe size, number of students in the classroom, number of cars in a parking lot.
6. 3 examples of Numerical continuous data: height, weight, value of a stock.

OUTLIERS

7. An outlier is a data item which is more than $1.5 \times IQR$ away from the nearest quartile.
8. $Q_1 = 10$, $Q_3 = 22$. The range of values for k so that k is considered an outlier.
   $1.5 \times IQR = 1.5(22-10) = 18$ $\quad 22+18=40 \quad 10-18=-8$
   If $k \le -8$ or $k \ge 40$ k is considered an outlier.
9. Given that for certain data $Q_1 = 7$, $Q_3 = 11$. Find the range of values for k so that k is considered an outlier.
   $1.5 \times IQR = 1.5(11-7) = 6$ $\quad 11+6=17 \quad 7-6=1$
   If $k \le 1$ or $k \ge 17$ k is considered an outlier.
10. Given that for certain data $Q_1 = p$, $Q_3 = 20$. It is known that k = 28 is an outlier. Find the possible values for p.
    $20 + 1.5 \times IQR = 20 + 1.5(20-p) < 28 \Rightarrow$
    $50 - 1.5p < 28 \Rightarrow 1.5p > 22 \Rightarrow p > \frac{44}{3} \approx 14.7$
    $20 \ge p > \frac{44}{3}$ for k to be considered an outlier
11. Given that for certain data $Q_1 = 5$ $Q_3 = c$ It is known that k = 1 is an outlier. Find the possible values for c.
    $5 - 1.5 \times IQR = 5 - 1.5(c-5) > 1 \Rightarrow 5 - 1.5c + 7.5 > 1 \Rightarrow 1.5c > 11.5 \Rightarrow c < \frac{23}{3} \approx 7.7$
    $\frac{23}{3} > c \ge 5$ for k to be considered an outlier

2.2. – FREQUENCY DIAGRAMS

1. In a certain math class the following grades were obtained:
   68, 79, 75, 89, 54, 81, 88, 62, 67, 75, 64, 85, 97, 77, 79, 90, 75, 89, 76, 68
   a. State the number of elements in the set: 20
   b. What kind of data is this? Numerical discrete
   c. Fill the table:

Grade	Mid – Grade (Mi)	Frequency (fi)	fi · Mi	Cumulative Frequency (Fi)	Fi (%)
51 – 60	55.5	1	55.5	1	5
61 – 70	65.5	5	327.5	6	30
71 – 80	75.5	7	528.5	13	65
81 – 90	85.5	6	513	19	95
91 – 100	95.5	1	95.5	20	100
Total		20	1520		

   d. Is this the only possible choice for the left column of the table? Why? Discuss the advantages and disadvantages of organizing information in such a way.
   No it is not the only possibility. Narrower or wider intervals can be chosen. Narrower interval implies higher accuracy but information may be harder to understand and/or analyze. It also implies more work. Wider interval implies lower level of accuracy but information may be easier to understand and/or analyze. It also implies less work.
   e. Design a new table with a different interval width

Grade	Mid – Grade (Mi)	Frequency (fi)	fi · Mi	Cumulative Frequency (Fi)	Fi (%)
51 – 55	53	1	53	1	5
56 – 60	58	0	0	1	5
61 – 65	63	2	126	3	15
66 – 70	68	3	204	6	30
71 – 75	73	3	219	9	45
76 – 80	78	4	312	13	65
81 – 85	83	2	166	15	75
86 – 90	88	4	352	19	95
91 – 95	93	0	0	19	95
96 – 100	98	1	98	20	100
Total		20	1530		

f. The mean in both cases: Table 1 $\mu = \frac{1520}{20} = 76$ Table 2 $\mu = \frac{1530}{20} = 76.5$

g. State a formula for the mean: $\mu = \frac{\sum_n M_i f_i}{n}$

h. The mean of the population is denoted with the Greek letter mu: μ and typically it is unknown. The mean of the sample is denoted by $\overline{x}$

i. State the mode of the set: 75

j. Find the modal interval in both cases:
Table 1: 71 – 80 Table 2: 76 – 80, 86 – 90 (Bimodal)

k. Find the Median using the original data: 76.5
Since there are 20 elements, the mean of elements 10 and 11 is the median. First elements must be put in order:
54 62 64 67 68 68 75 75 75 **76 77** 79 79 81 85 88 89 89 90 97
So median is 76.

l. Find the median using the tables, discuss your answer.
The median is the center of interval where F% ≥ 50% for the first time.
Table 1: 75.5 Table 2: 78

m. In general this method of organizing information is called grouping

n. The 1st column is called class with upper interval boundary and lower interval boundary.

o. The 2nd column is called Mid - Class

p. On the following grid paper sketch the corresponding points.

Cumulative frequency **GIVE**

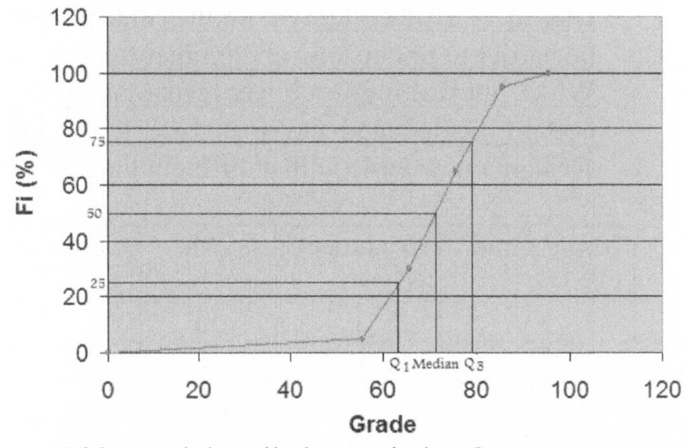

q. This graph is called cumulative frequency curve or Ogive

r. Find the median using the graph: ≈ 72

s. Find the first quartile (Q_1) using the graph: Q_1 = ≈ 64

t. Find the first quartile (Q_1) using the original data: Q_1 = 68

u. Find the third quartile (Q_3) using the graph: Q_3 = ≈ 79

v. Find the first quartile (Q_3) using the original data: Q_3 = 86.5

w. Find P_{30} using the graph: ≈ 67 Find P_{65} using the graph: ≈ 75

x. The Inter Quartile Range is in general $Q_3 - Q_1$ in this case 86.5–68= 18.5

2. In a certain class the following heights (in m) of students were collected: 1.77, 1.60, 1.89, 1.54, 1.77, 1.65, 1.86, 1.51, 1.67, 1.94, 1.73, 1.70, 1.66
   a. State the number of elements in the set: 13
   b. What kind of data is this? Numerical continuous
   c. Fill the table:

Height	Mid – Height (Mi)	Frequency (fi)	fi · Mi	Cumulative Frequency (Fi)	Fi (%)
[1.50 , 1.60)	1.55	2	3.1	2	15.4
[1.60 , 1.70)	1.65	4	6.6	6	46.2
[1.70 , 1.80)	1.75	4	7	10	76.9
[1.80 , 1.90)	1.85	2	3.7	12	92.3
[1.90 , 2.00)	1.95	1	1.95	13	100
Total			22.35		

   d. Obtain the mean: $\mu = \dfrac{22.35}{13} \approx 1.72m$
   e. State the mode of the set: 1.77m
   f. Find the modal interval: bimodal, [1.60 – 1.70), [1.70– 1.80)
   g. Find the Median using the original data: We order the data:
      1.51 1.54 1.60 1.65 1.66 1.67 **1.70** 1.73 1.77 1.77 1.86 1.89 1.94
      There are 13 terms so the median is the 7th, 1.70m
   h. Find the median using the table, discuss your answer.
      The median according to table is the centre of the interval in which Fi% is greater than 50% for the first time. The interval is [1.70– 1.80) so median 1.75.
   i. On the following grid paper sketch the corresponding points.

Cumulative frequency

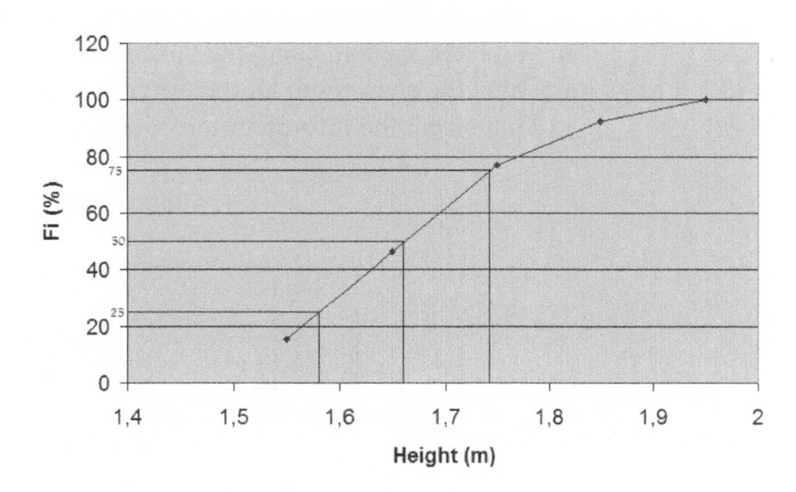

j. This graph is called cumulative frequency curve or ogive
k. Find the median using the graph: □ $1.66m$
l. Find the first quartile (Q_1) using the graph: Q_1 = □ $1.58m$
m. Find the first quartile (Q_1) using the original data: Q_1 = 1.625m
We use the ordered data; the middle of the first half of data is 1.625m
1.51 1.54 **1.60 1.65** 1.66 1.67 1.70 1.73 1.77 1.77 1.86 1.89 1.94
n. Find the third quartile (Q_3) using the graph: Q_3 = □ $1.74m$
o. Find the first quartile (Q_3) using the original data: Q_3 = 1.815m
We use the ordered data; the middle of the second half of data is 1.815m
1.51 1.54 1.60 1.65 1.66 1.67 1.70 1.73 1.77 **1.77 1.86** 1.89 1.94
p. Find P_{20} using the graph: □ $1.67m$ Find P_{80} using the graph: □ $1.78m$
q. The Inter Quartile Range is in general $Q_3 - Q_1$ in this case 1.815 – 1.625 = 0.190m

3. In a certain class students eye color was collected:
Brown, Black, Brown, Blue, Brown, Blue, Green, Brown, Black, Green
a. State the number of elements in the set: 10
b. What kind of data is this? Categorical
c. Fill the table:

Eye Color	Mid – Color (Mi)	Frequency (fi)	Fi x Mi	Cumulative Frequency (Fi)	Fi (%)
Brown	N/A	4	N/A	N/A	N/A
Blue	N/A	2	N/A	N/A	N/A
Green	N/A	2	N/A	N/A	N/A
Black	N/A	2	N/A	N/A	N/A
Total	N/A	10	N/A	N/A	N/A

d. Obtain the mean: N/A
e. State the mode of the set: Brown
f. Find the modal interval: N/A
g. Find the Median using the original data: N/A
h. Find the median using the table, discuss your answer. N/A
i. Find the answers to all the different parts using your GDC. N/A
j. Represent the information in a histogram:

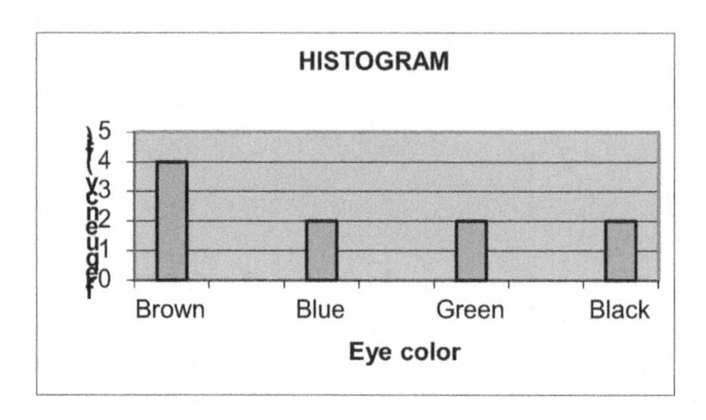

BOX AND WHISKER DIAGRAM

1. N/A
2. The results for 100 m dash competition are displayed in the following diagram: Use the Box and Whisker diagram to answer:

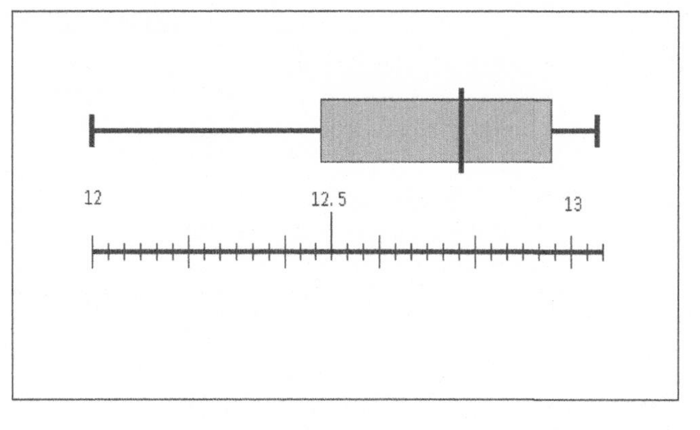

a. Min = 12
b. Max = 13.1
c. $Q_1 = 12.5$
d. Q_2 = Med = 12.8
e. $Q_3 = 13$
f. Range = 13.1 – 12 = 1.1
g. Inter quartile range = 13 – 12.5 = 0.5

3. Use the Box and Whisker diagram to answer:

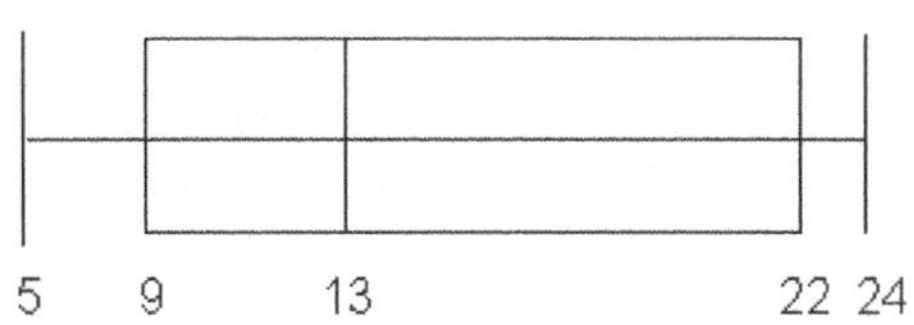

Use the Box and Whisker diagram to answer:

a. Min = 5 Max = 24
b. $Q_1 = 9$ Q_2 = Med = 13 $Q_3 = 22$
c. Range = 24 – 5 = 19
d. Inter quartile range = 22 – 9 = 13

Given that in a certain classroom the heights of the students in cm are: 168, 178, 166, 191, 188, 181, 174, 159, 179, 173, 171, 166, 185, 184, 169. Draw a box-and-whisker Diagram.

Population size: 15 Median: 174 Minimum: 159 Maximum: 191
First quartile: 168 Third quartile: 184 Interquartile Range: 16
Outliers: none

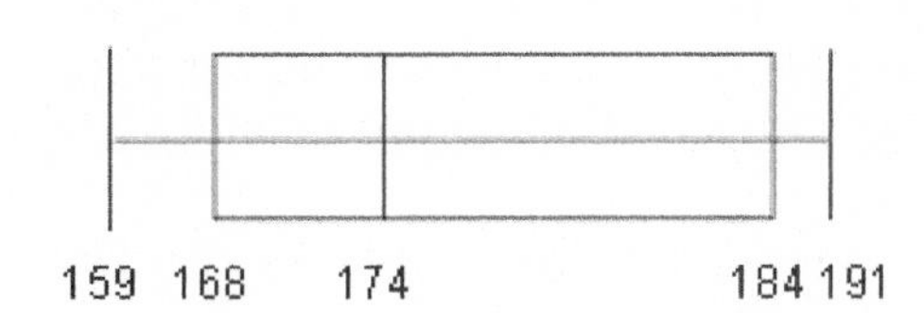

2.3. – MEASURES OF DISPERSION

1. In a certain Biology test the following results were obtained: 80, 80, 80, 80,

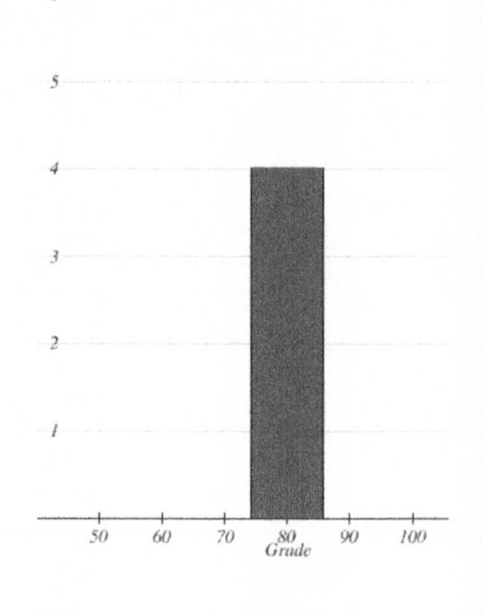

   a. Obtain the mean: m $= \underline{80}$
   b. Represent the results using a histogram:
   c. The standard deviation of a set of numbers is defined by:

$$\sigma = \sqrt{\frac{\sum_i f_i (x_i - \mu)^2}{n}} = \sqrt{\frac{f_1(x_1-\mu)^2 + f_2(x_2-\mu)^2 + \ldots}{n}}$$

   In this case

$$\sigma = \sqrt{\frac{1(80-80)^2 + 1(80-80)^2 + 1(80-80)^2 + 1(80-80)^2}{4}} = 0$$

   d. How spread is this group of grades? It is not spread at all, that means 0 standard deviation.

2. In a certain Physics test the following results were obtained: 70, 80, 80, 90

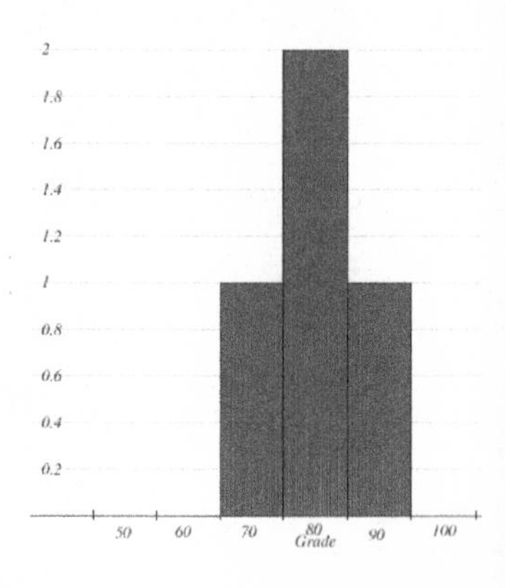

   a. Obtain the mean: m $= \underline{80}$
   b. Represent the results using a histogram:
   c. The standard deviation of a set of numbers is defined by:

$$\sigma = \sqrt{\frac{\sum_i f_i (x_i - \mu)^2}{n}} = \sqrt{\frac{f_1(x_1-\mu)^2 + f_2(x_2-\mu)^2 + \ldots}{n}}$$

   In this case

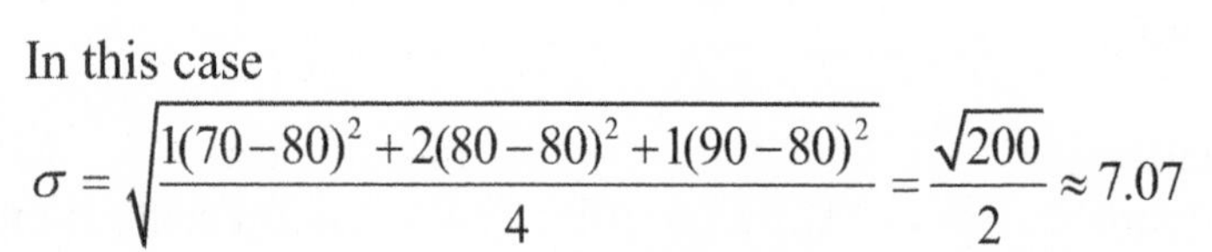

$$\sigma = \sqrt{\frac{1(70-80)^2 + 2(80-80)^2 + 1(90-80)^2}{4}} = \frac{\sqrt{200}}{2} \approx 7.07$$

   d. How spread is this group of grades? Is it more spread than the previous one? As can be seen both distributions have the same mean but the 2nd one is more spread, its S.D. is approximately 7.07.

3. The weights in kg of 6 different classes (A, B, C, D, E, F) was collected and represented in the following histograms:

   a. Find the number of students in the sample: 27

$\bar{x}$ and σ	Class
1	C
2	D

3	E
4	B
5	A
6	F

b. Which distribution has the highest SD: E
c. Which distribution has the lowest SD: F
d. Match between the histograms and the numerical results. Use the table:

4. In a certain math class the following grades were obtained:
68, 79, 75, 89, 54, 81, 88, 62, 67, 75, 64, 85, 97, 77, 79, 90, 75, 89, 76, 68
   a. State the number of elements in the set: 20
   b. What kind of data is this? Numerical discrete
   c. Fill the table:

Grade	Mid – Grade (Mi)	Frequency (fi)	fi · Mi	$(Mi - m)^2$	$fi(Mi - m)^2$
51 – 60	55.5	1	55.5	$(55.5-76)^2$	$1(55.5-76)^2$
61 – 70	65.5	5	327.5	$(65.5-76)^2$	$5(65.5-76)^2$
71 – 80	75.5	7	528.5	$(75.5-76)^2$	$7(75.5-76)^2$
81 – 90	85.5	6	513	$(85.5-76)^2$	$6(85.5-76)^2$
91 – 100	95.5	1	95.5	$(95.5-76)^2$	$1(95.5-76)^2$
Total		20	1520		1895

   d. Obtain the mean: m = 76
   e. The numbers in the 6th column give us an idea about the contribution of each interval to the spread of the data.
   f. The sum of the numbers in the 6th column gives us an idea about the total spread of the data. In case this number is 0 it means that the data is not spread at all (like in example 1) for example:
   g. The Variance: $Variance = \sigma^2 = \frac{\sum_i f_i(x_i - \mu)^2}{n} = \frac{1895}{20} = 94.75$

   The Standard Deviation: $S.D. = \sigma = \sqrt{\frac{\sum_i f_i(x_i - \mu)^2}{n}} = \sqrt{\frac{1895}{20}} \approx 9.73$

   h. Write down the formula for the Variance of a population (s^2): see part g.
   i. Write down the formula for the SD of a population (s) : see part g.

5. In a certain class the following heights (in m) of students were collected:
1.77, 1.60, 1.89, 1.54, 1.77, 1.65, 1.86, 1.51, 1.67, 1.94, 1.73, 1.70, 1.66
   a. State the number of elements in the set: 13
   b. What kind of data is this? Numerical continuous
   c. Fill the table:

Height	Mid – Height (Mi)	Frequency (fi)	Fi · Mi	$(Mi - m)^2$	$fi(Mi - m)^2$
[1.50 – 1.60)	1.55	2	3.1	$(1.55 - 1.72)^2$	$2(1.55 - 1.72)^2$
[1.60 – 1.70)	1.65	4	6.6	$(1.65 - 1.72)^2$	$4(1.65 - 1.72)^2$
[1.70– 1.80)	1.75	4	7	$(1.75 - 1.72)^2$	$4(1.75 - 1.72)^2$
[1.80 – 1.90)	1.85	2	3.7	$(1.85 - 1.72)^2$	$2(1.85 - 1.72)^2$
[1.90 – 2.00)	1.95	1	1.95	$(1.95 - 1.72)^2$	$1(1.95 - 1.72)^2$
Total			22.35		0.1677

d. Obtain the mean: $m = \dfrac{22.35}{13} \approx 1.72m$

e. The numbers in the 6th column give us an idea about the contribution of each interval to the spread of the data.

f. The sum of the numbers in the 6th column gives us an idea about the total spread of the data. In case this number is 0 it means that the data is not spread at all (like in example 1) for example:

g. Find the Variance (assuming population):

$$Variance = \sigma^2 = \frac{\sum_i f_i(x_i - \mu)^2}{n} = \frac{0.1677}{13} = 0.0129m^2$$

h. Find the Standard Deviation S.D. (assuming population):

$$S.D. = \sigma = \sqrt{\frac{\sum_i f_i(x_i - \mu)^2}{n}} = \sqrt{\frac{0.1677}{13}} \approx 0.114m$$

6. In a certain class students eye color was collected: Brown, Black, Brown, Blue, Brown, Blue, Green, Brown, Black, Green
   a. State the number of elements in the set: 10
   b. What kind of data is this? Categorical
   c. Fill the table:
   d. What can you say about the measures of spread in this case? There is no meaning to spread in case of categorical data

Eye Color	Mid – Color (Mi)	Frequency (fi)	Fi · Mi
Brown	N/A	4	N/A
Blue	N/A	2	N/A

Green	N/A	2	N/A
Black	N/A	2	N/A
Total	N/A	10	N/A

7. The sum of the grades of a group of 3 students is 240. Given that the grades for an arithmetic sequence and that its standard deviation is $\sqrt{128}$:
   a. The mean grade: $\mu = \frac{240}{3} = 80$
   b. The grades of the students: 66.1, 80, 93.9

$I) x + x + d + x + 2d = 240; x + d = 80$

$II) \sqrt{128} = \sqrt{\frac{(x-80)^2 + (x+d-80)^2 + (x+2d-80)^2}{3}}$

$II) \sqrt{128} = \sqrt{\frac{2(x-80)^2}{3}}; x = 93.9; d = -13.9$

8. The time it takes a pool to be filled was measured by using a sample of 80 pools and the following results were obtained Find
   a. The mean: $\mu = \frac{326}{44} \approx 7.41h$
   b. The standard deviation: $\sigma \approx 1.39h$
   c. Later it was discovered that one more pool was tested. If the standard deviation has not changed by adding it to the sample, find out how much time it took to fill this pool.

Time (hours)	Number of pools
$3 \le t \le 4$	1
$4 < t \le 5$	2
$5 < t \le 6$	3
$6 < t \le 7$	9
$7 < t \le 8$	12
$8 < t \le 9$	13
$9 < t \le 10$	4
Total	

Before: $1.39 = \sqrt{\frac{\sum_i f_i (x_i - \mu)^2}{44}}; \sum_i f_i (x_i - \mu)^2 = 85.0124$

After: $1.39 = \sqrt{\frac{85.0124 + (x_{newPool} - 7.41)^2}{45}}; x_{newPool} = 8.8h \quad or \quad 6.02h$

9. A group of students obtained the following grades: 60, x, y, 50, 80. The mean of the sample is 68 and its variance is 136. Find x and y.

$$\mu = \frac{x + y + 190}{5} = 68; x + y = 150$$

$$\sigma^2 = \frac{(x-68)^2 + (y-68)^2 + (60-68)^2 + (50-68)^2 + (80-68)^2}{5} = 136$$

$$x = 70, y = 80 \quad or \quad x = 80, y = 70$$

2.4. – CORRELATION

1. In many occasions variables may be related to each other, for example: Give 3 other examples; discuss the kind of relation that exists between the variables:

    Year – mean temperature
    Humidity level – wind speed
    Name of a student – shoe size
2. The relation between variables is called: correlation and if it is linear it can be classified in the following way:
3. This correlation is characterized by a certain number called correlation coefficient (r).
4. In case of a perfect positive correlation the value of r is 1
5. In case of a perfect negative correlation the value of r is –1
6. In case of a no correlation the value of r is 0
7. Finally r is between –1 and 1
8. All of the correlations above mentioned are linear. There can be other kinds of correlation for example logarithmic, exponential, quadratic etc.
9. The full name of r is Pearson product–moment correlation coefficient
10. If $r \in [0.75, 1)$ we say there is a strong positive Correlation.
11. If $r \in [0.5, 0.75)$ we say there is a moderate positive Correlation.
12. If $r \in [0.25, 0.5)$ we say there is a weak positive Correlation.
13. If $r \in (-0.25, 0.25)$ we say there is a no Correlation.
14. If $r \in (-0.5, -0.25]$ we say there is a weak negative Correlation.
15. If $r \in (-0.75, -0.5]$ we say there is a moderate negative Correlation.

Name	John	Dean	Elisa	Marc	Heather	Alicia	Raquel	Kevin	Alex	Deena
HW Done (%)	58	90	75	50	40	95	100	85	75	82
Grade (%)	70	80	80	65	55	78	86	89	82	70

16. If $r \in (-1, -0.75]$ we say there is a strong negative Correlation.
17. In a certain math class the following data about students was found:

    a. Represent the data on a graph:

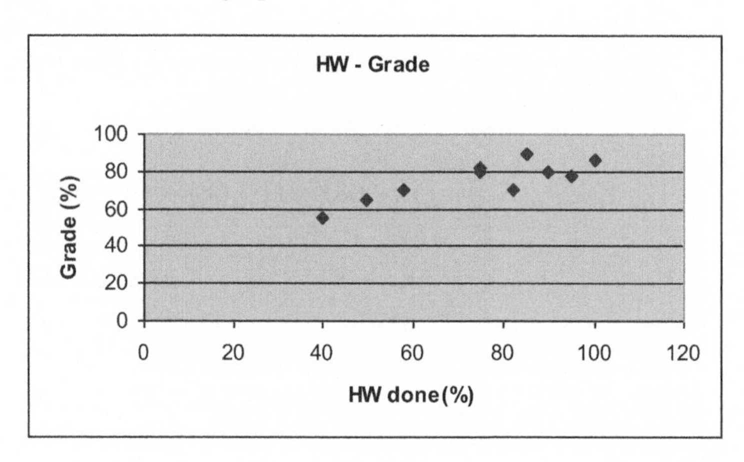

b. Is there correlation? It seems strong positive correlation
c. Try to predict the value of r: 0.85? guessing..
d. In order to calculate the value of r first find: $\bar{x} = 75$ $\bar{y} = 75.5$
Complete the table:

Name	x_i	$(x_i - \bar{x})^2$	y_i	$(y_i - \bar{y})^2$	$x_i y_i$
John	58	289	70	30.25	4060
Dean	90	225	80	20.25	7200
Elisa	75	0	80	20.25	6000
Marc	50	625	65	110.25	3250
Heather	40	1225	55	420.25	2200
Alicia	95	400	78	6.25	7410
Raquel	100	625	86	110.25	8600
Kevin	85	100	89	182.25	7565
Alex	75	0	82	42.25	6150
Deena	82	49	70	30.25	5740
Total		3538		972.5	58175

Use the table to find Sx, Sy and Sxy using the following formulas taken from IB information booklet:

$$S_x = \sqrt{\frac{3538}{10}} \approx 18.8, S_y = \sqrt{\frac{972.5}{10}} \approx 9.86, S_{xy} = \frac{\left(58175 - \frac{750 \cdot 755}{10}\right)}{10} \approx 155$$

Find r using $r = \frac{S_{xy}}{S_x S_y} = \frac{155}{(18.8)(9.86)} \approx 0.836$

e. Was your prediction accurate? Not bad...
f. Find r using your GDC
g. $r = \frac{S_{xy}}{S_x S_y} = \frac{155}{(18.8)(9.86)} \approx 0.836$ r has the same value.

LINE OF BEST FIT

18. The line of best fit is the straight line that most approximates to the scatter diagram obtained. The equation of the line is given by: $y - \bar{y} = \frac{S_{xy}}{(S_x)^2}(x - \bar{x})$

19. Write this expression in the forma y = mx + b $y = \frac{S_{xy}}{(S_x)^2}x + \bar{y} - \frac{S_{xy}}{(S_x)^2}\bar{x}$

20. The slope of the line is m = $\frac{S_{xy}}{(S_x)^2}$

Name	John	Dean	Elisa	Marc	Heather	Alicia	Raquel	Kevin	Alex	Deena
HW Done (%)	58	90	75	50	40	95	100	85	75	82
Grade (%)	70	80	80	65	55	78	86	89	82	70

21. Given the data:

Using your GDC find:

a. $r \approx 0.836$

b. $\bar{x} = 75$ $\bar{y} = 75.5$

c. The line of best fit y on x: $y = 0.438101x + 42.642453$

d. The line of best fit x on y: $x = 1.59383y - 45.33419$

e. The point of intersection is $(75, 75.5)$, the intersect at $(\bar{x}, \bar{y})$

22. In a group of students height and weight correlation was studies. The results are given by the table below.

a. $\bar{x} = 174.375$ $\bar{y} = 71.5$

b. The equation of the regression line $y = 1.438757x - 179.383173$

c. The weight of a student who is 174cm tall. $y = 1.438757(174) - 179.383173 = 71.0$kg

d. The correlation coefficient and the kind of correlation that exists. R = 0.941, strong positive correlation

e. Draw

f. $x = 0.668656y + 126.566112$

g. $(174.375, 71.5)$ $(\bar{x}, \bar{y})$

Height (cm)	Weight (kg)
165	58
170	62
172	80
169	65
188	88
163	52
191	95
177	72

23. In a group of students the reading speed was studied in relation to age of the student. The results are given by the table below.

Age (years)	Reading speed (words per minute)
15	98
12	65
17	111
19	120
18	122
16	102
19	143
17	100
13	80
14	85
14	95
15	90

a. The equation of the regression line in the

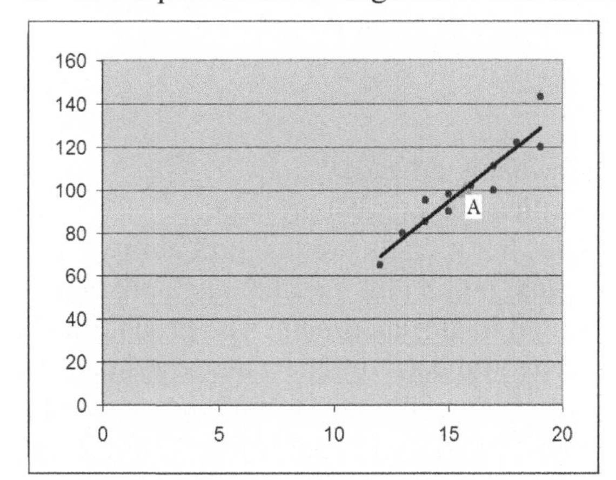

form y = mx + c   y = 8.56x – 33.9

b. Reading speed of a student who is 11 years old:
y = (8.56)11 – 33.9 = 60.26 words/min

c. Write down the correlation coefficient and the kind of correlation that exists: R = 0.941

d. Draw a scatter diagram to show the data: $\bar{x} = \frac{89}{12} \approx 15.8$ $\bar{y} = \frac{1211}{12} \approx 101$

e. Plot the point ($\bar{x}$, $\bar{y}$) on your scatter diagram. Label this point as A.

f. Draw the regression line on the diagram.

2.5. – PROBABILITY

Probability is the science of chance or likelihood of an event happening. If a random experiment is repeated n times in such a way that each of the trials is identical and independent, where n(A) is the number of times event A occurred, then:

$$\text{Relative frequency of event A} = P(A) = \frac{n(A)}{N} \qquad (N \to \infty)$$

Exercises

1. In an unbiased coin what is P(head) ?
   This probability is called "theoretical probability"
2. Explain the difference between theoretical probability and "regular" probability. Theoretical probability is calculated, predicted. "regular" probability is measured in an experiment. The probability for head is theoretically 0.5, we would need to repeat an experiment an infinite number of times to make sure it is. In reality the coin has some small probability to lend on its thin side (more than 0) so it is not really 0.5 for head…
3. Throw a drawing pin, fill the table: This experiment should be done in class
4. The definition of probability ("***Laplace law***")is:

$$P(A) = \frac{\text{Number of times A ocurred}}{\text{Total numberof times experiment repeated}}$$

Venn diagrams

Event	**Set Language**	**Venn diagram**	**Probability result**
Complementary event (A')	Not A	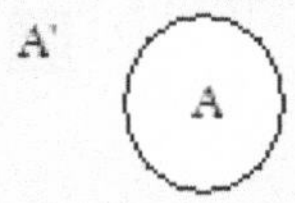 A' A	P(A') =1 – P(A)
The intersection of A and B $(A \cap B)$	Set of elements that belongs to A and B	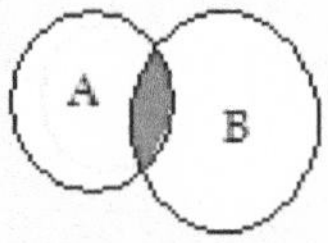 A B	$P(A \cup B) = P(A) + P(B) - P(A \cup B)$
The union of A and B $(A \cup B)$	Set of elements that belongs to A or B or both	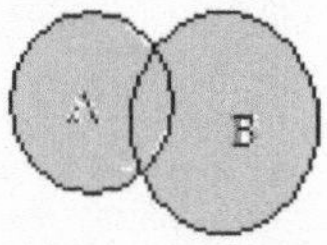 A B	
If $(A \cap B) = \varnothing$ A and B are said to be: mutually exclusive	The sets A and B are Mutually exclusive	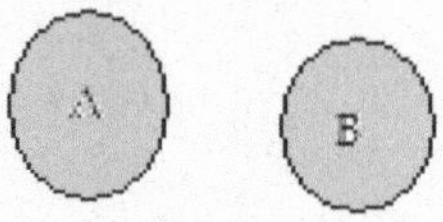 A B	$P(A \cup B) = P(A) + P(B)$ $P(A \cap B) = 0$

1. Given the Venn diagram. Shade $A \cap B$

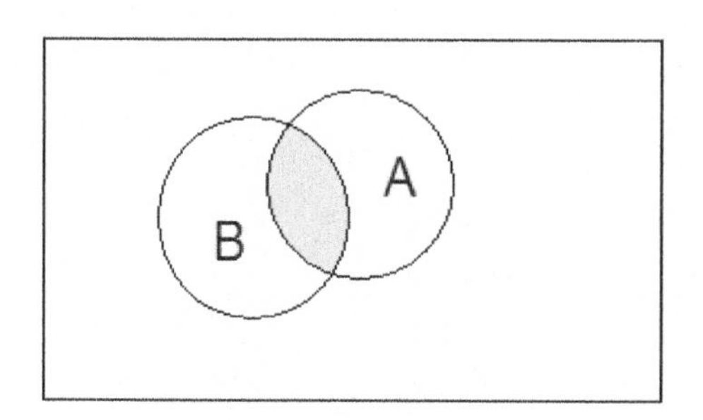

2. Given the Venn diagram. Shade $A \cap B'$

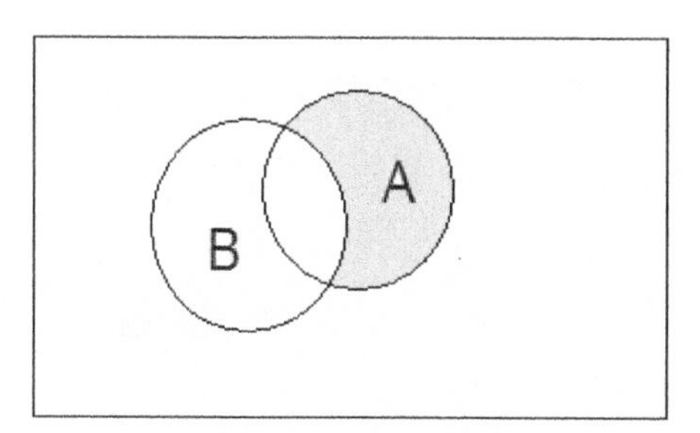

3. Given the Venn diagram. Shade B'

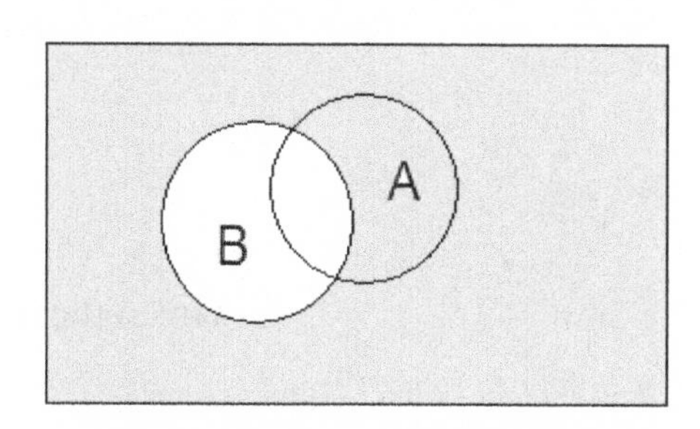

4. Given the Venn diagram. Shade $A' \cap B'$

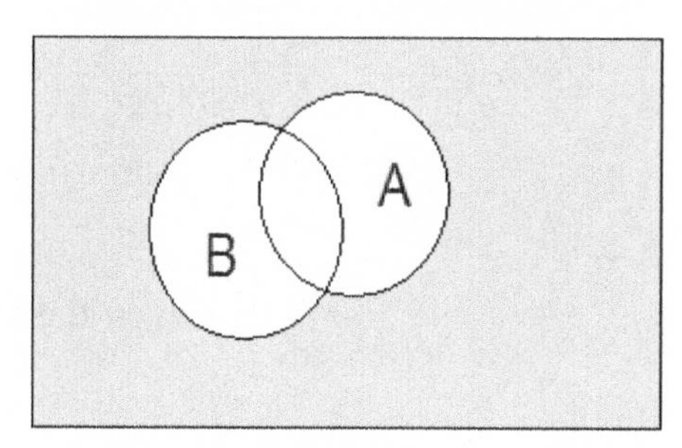

5. Given the Venn diagram. Shade $A \cup B$

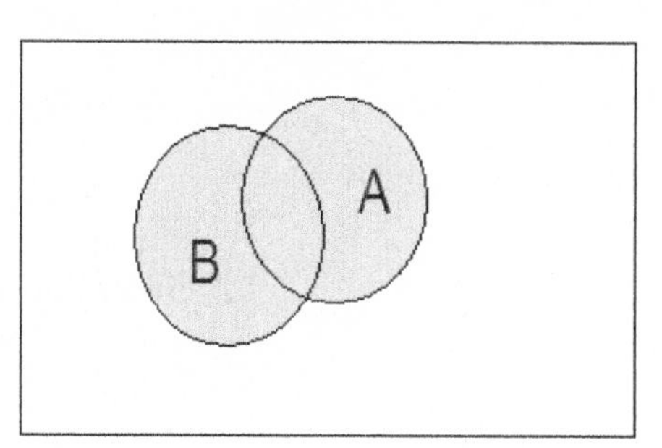

6. Given the Venn diagram. Shade A' ∪ B

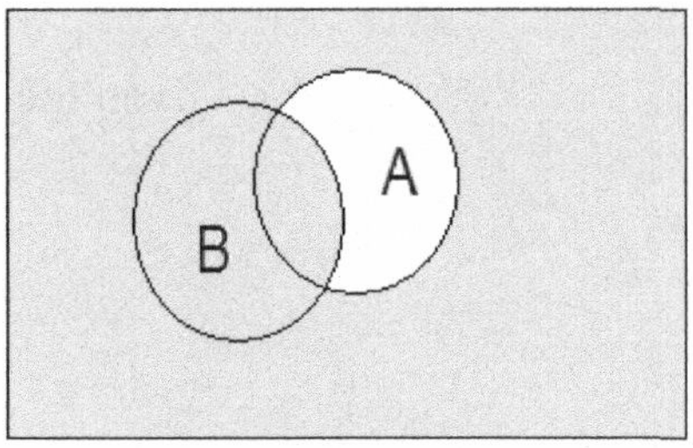

7. Given the Venn diagram. Shade A' ∪ B'

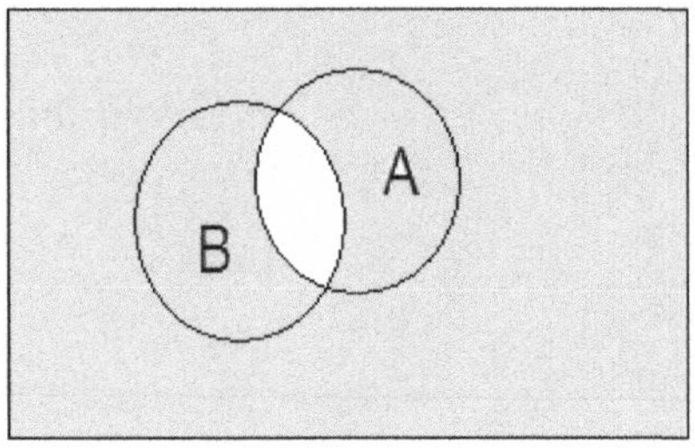

8. Given the Venn diagram. Shade A ∪ B

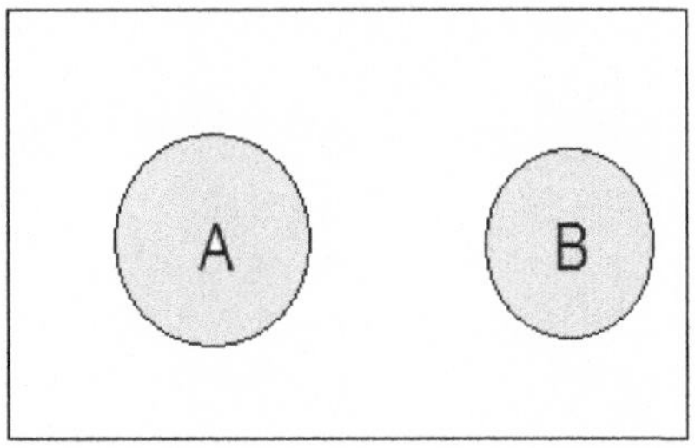

9. Given the Venn diagram. Shade A ∪ B'

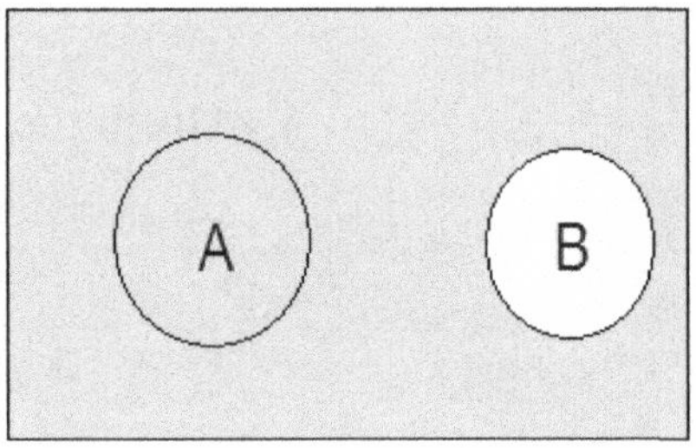

10. Given the Venn diagram. Shade A ∩ B'

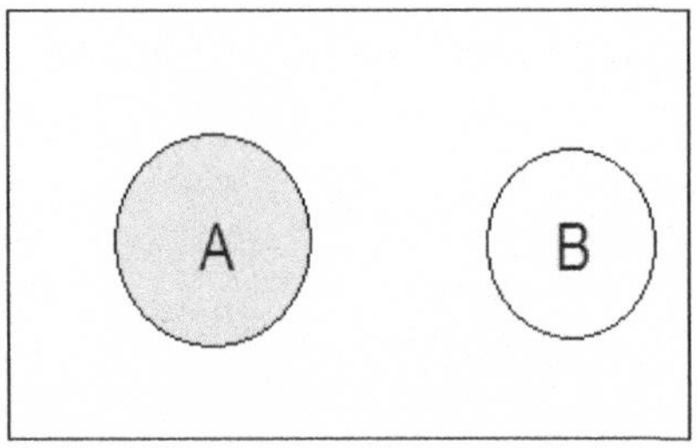

11. Given the Venn diagram. Shade A ∩ B(None - Empty)

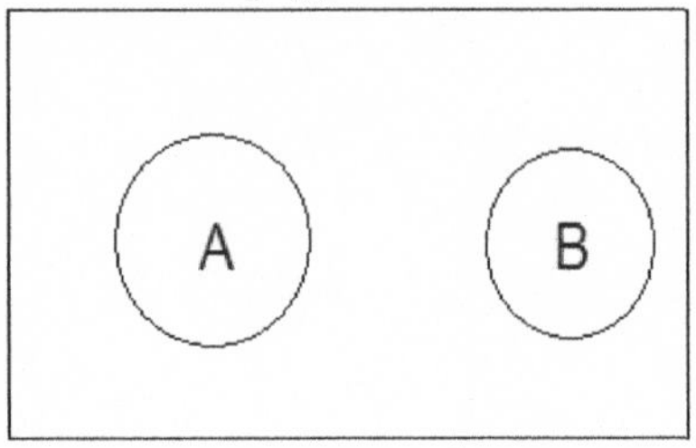

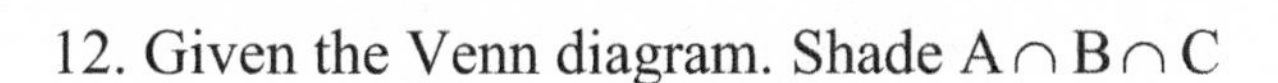

12. Given the Venn diagram. Shade $A \cap B \cap C$ (None - Empty)

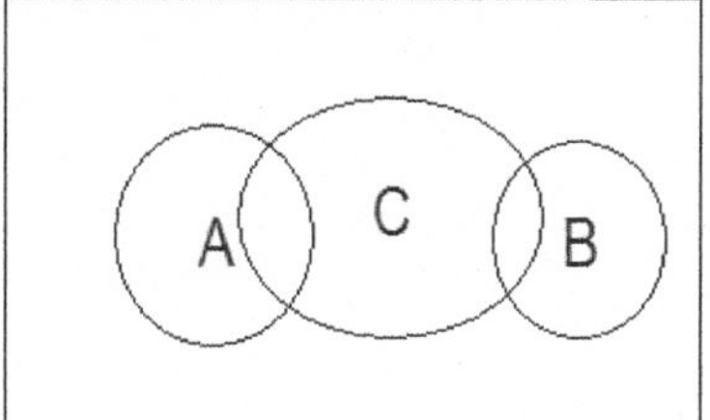

13. Given the Venn diagram. Shade $(A \cup B) \cap C$

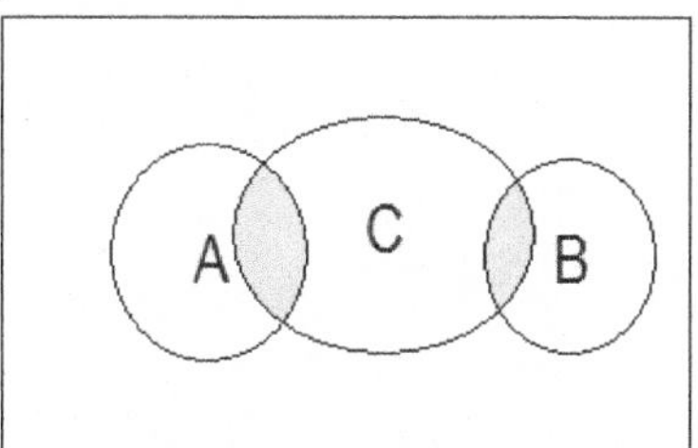

14. Given the Venn diagram. Shade $(A' \cup B) \cap C$

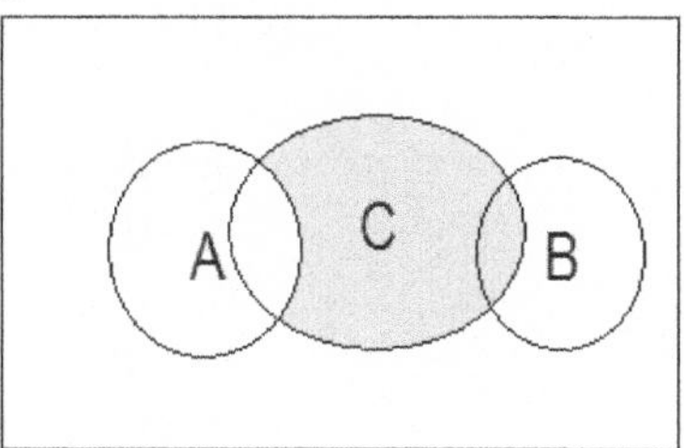

15. Given the Venn diagram. Shade $(A \cup B) \cap C'$

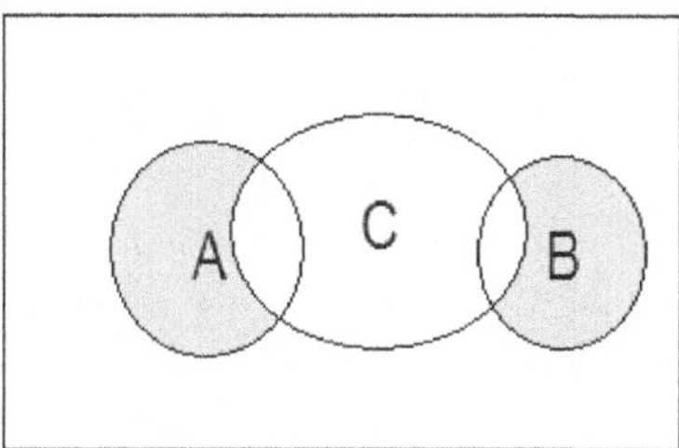

16. Given the Venn diagram. Shade $A \cap B \cap C$

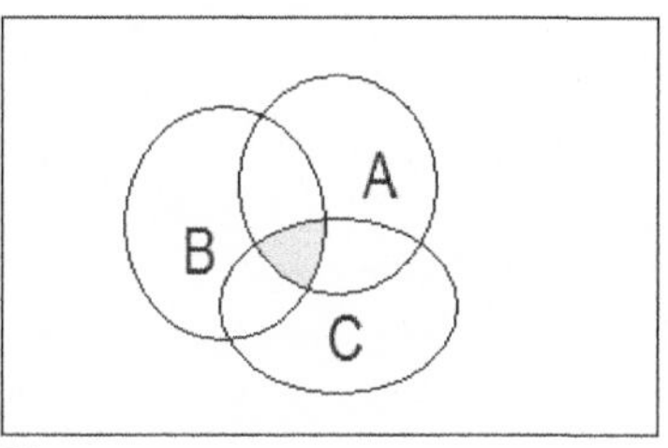

17. Given the Venn diagram. Shade $(A \cap B) \cap C'$

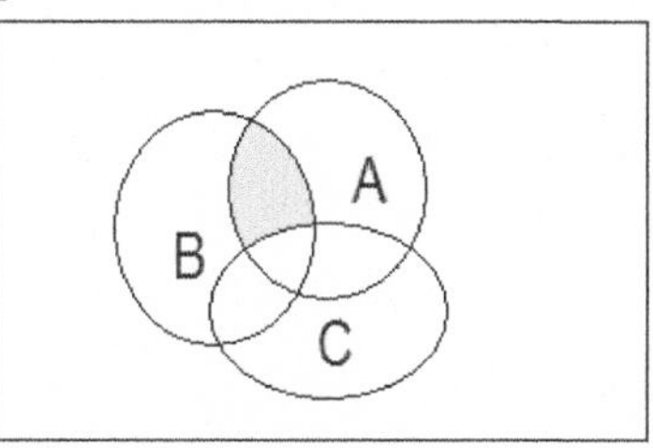

18. Given the Venn diagram. Shade $(A' \cap B) \cap C$

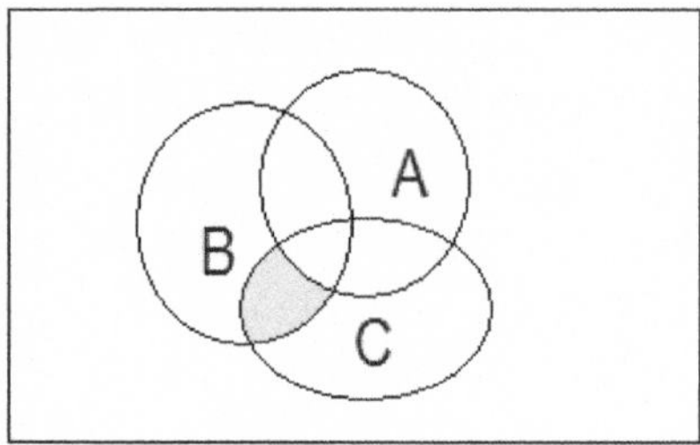

19. Given the Venn diagram. Shade $(A \cap B') \cap C$

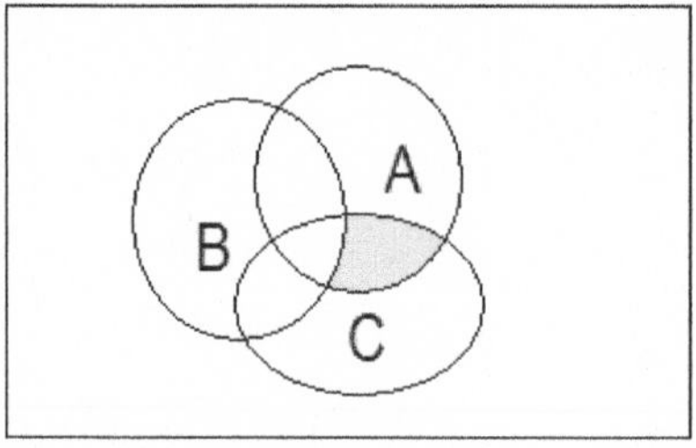

20. The events A and B are such $P(A) = 0.2$, $P(B) = 0.4$ and $P(A \cup B) = 0.5$. Find:

a. $P(A \cup B) = P(A) + P(B) - P(A \cap B)$
   $0.5 = 0.2 + 0.4 - P(A \cap B)$; $P(A \cap B) = 0.1$
b. $P(B') = 1 - P(B) = 0.6$
c. Sketch the corresponding Venn diagram.
d. $P(A' \cap B)$ is the size of the shaded area so 0.3

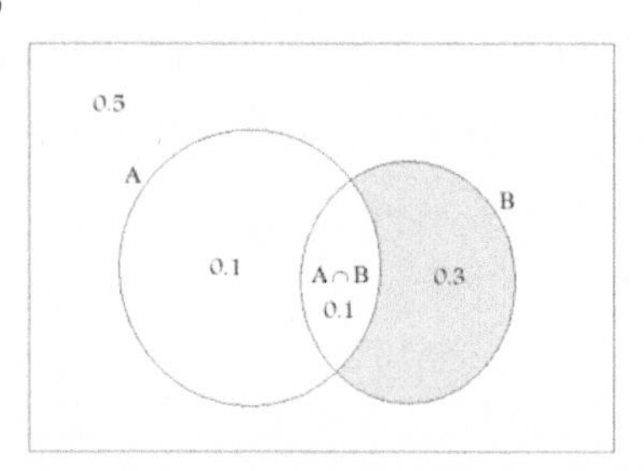

e. $P(A' \cap B')$ is the size of the shaded area so 0.5
f. Are the events A and B Independent? Explain. <u>In case events are independent $P(A \cap B) = P(A)\,P(B)$, in this case $0.1 \neq (0.2)(0.4)$ therefore these events are not independent.</u>

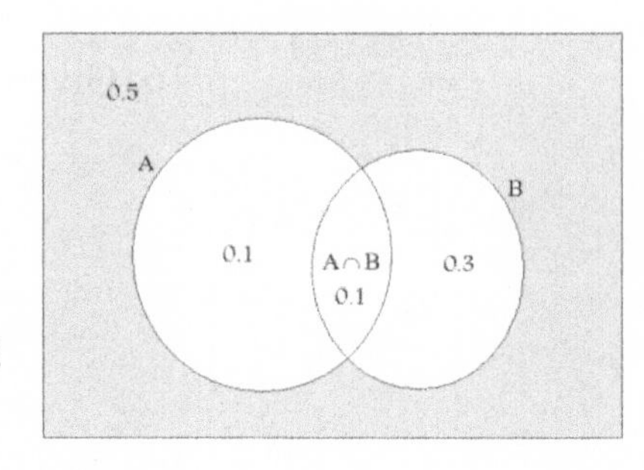

21. The events A and B are such $P(A) = 0.15$, $P(B) = 0.3$ and $P(A \cup B) = 0.4$, find:

a. $P(A \cap B) =$;$P(A \cup B) = P(A) + P(B) - P(A \cap B)$
   $0.4 = 0.15 + 0.3 - P(A \cap B)$; $P(A \cap B) = 0.05$
b. $P(B') = 1 - P(B) = 0.7$
c. Sketch the corresponding Venn diagram.

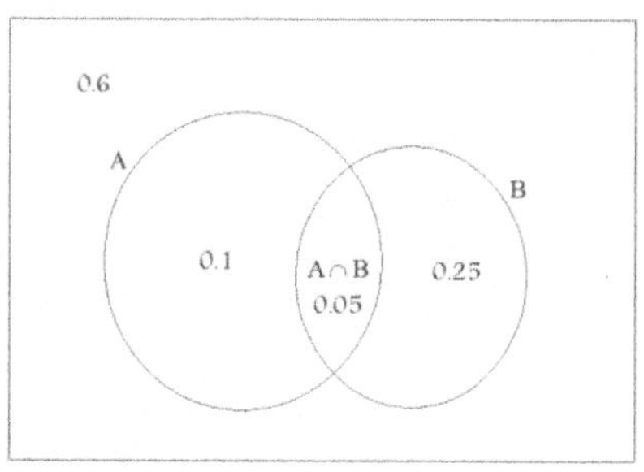

d. $P(A' \cap B)$ is the size of the shaded area so 0.25

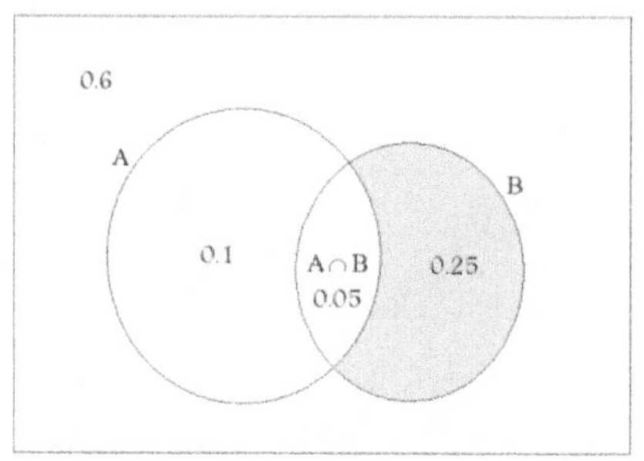

e. $P(A' \cap B')$ is the size of the shaded area so 0.6
f. Are the events A and B Independent? Explain.
   In case events are independent $P(A \cap B) = P(A)\,P(B)$, in this case $0.05 \neq (0.15)(0.3)$ therefore these events are not independent.

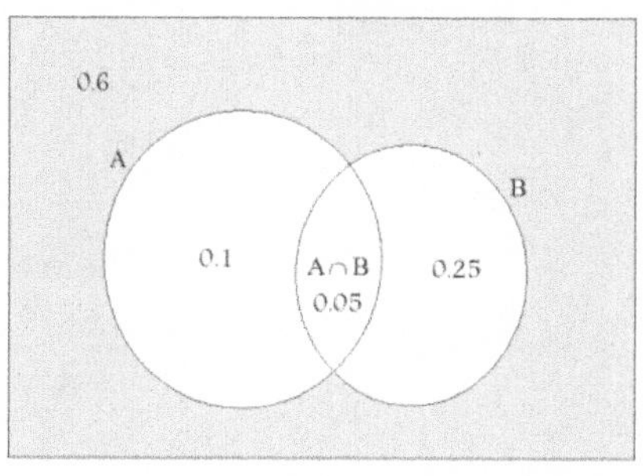

22. The events A and B are such $P(A) = 0.3$, $P(B) = 0.6$ and $P(A \cup B) = 0.9$, Find:

a. $P(A \cap B)$
   $P(A \cup B) = P(A) + P(B) - P(A \cap B)$
   $0.9 = 0.6 + 0.3 - P(A \cap B)$; $P(A \cap B) = 0$ That means no intersection
   So events are mutually exclusive.
b. $P(B') = 1 - P(B) = 0.4$
c. Sketch the corresponding Venn diagram.

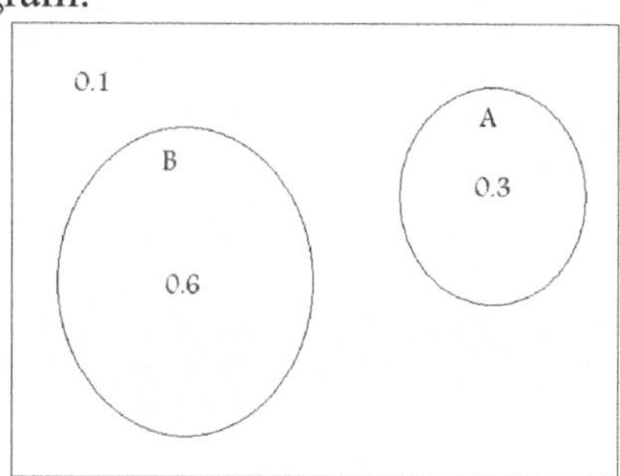

d. $P(A' \cap B) = P(B) = 0.6$ (the size of the shaded area)

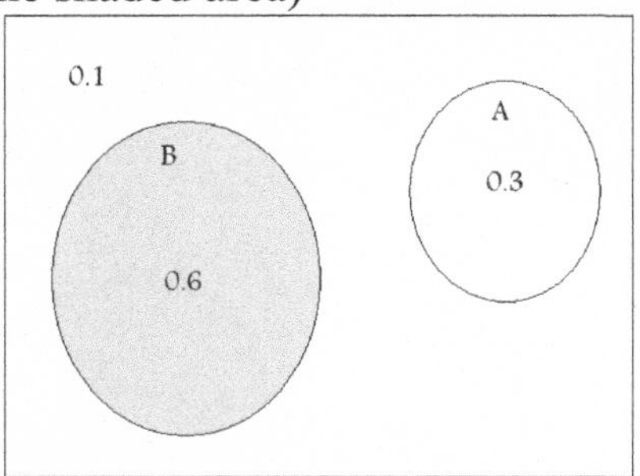

e. $P(A' \cap B') = 0.1$ (the size of the shaded area)

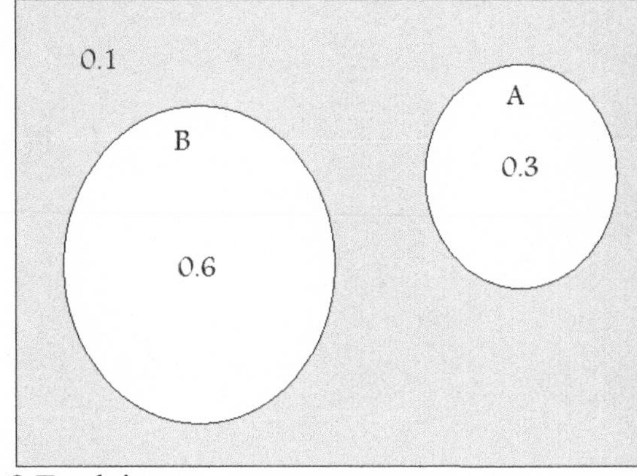

f. Are the events A and B Independent? Explain.
In case events are independent $P(A \cap B) = P(A)\,P(B)$, in this case $0 \neq (0.3)(0.6)$ therefore these events are not independent.

23. The events A and B are such $P(A) = 0.2$, $P(B) = 0.9$ and $P(A \cap B) = 0.1$, Find:

a. $P(A \cup B)$
$P(A \cup B) = P(A) + P(B) - P(A \cap B)$
$P(A \cup B) = 0.2 + 0.9 - 0.1$; $P(A \cup B) = 1$, that means there is no "outside" the events "fill" the entire rectangle.

b. $P(B') = 1 - P(B) = 0.1$

c. Sketch the corresponding Venn diagram.

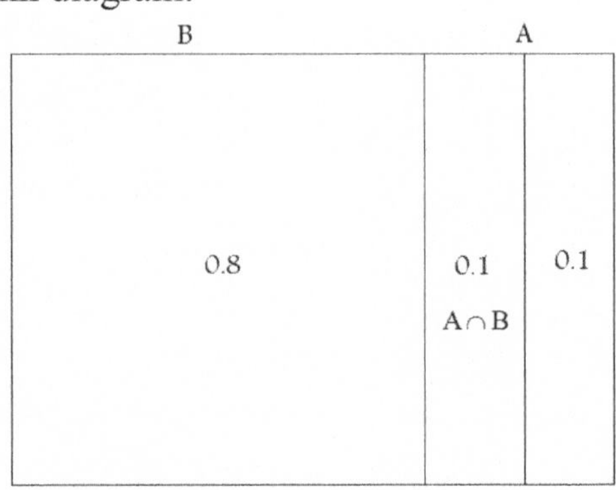

d. $P(A' \cap B) = 0.8$(the size of the shaded area)

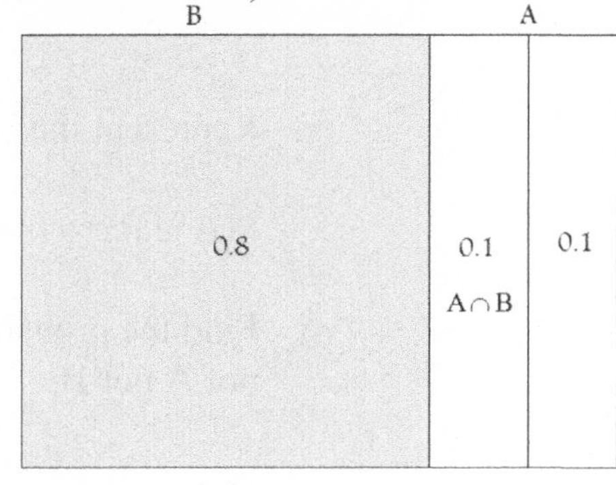

e. $P(A' \cap B') = 0$, there is no "outside"

f. Are the events A and B Independent? Explain.
<u>In case events are independent $P(A \cap B) = P(A)\,P(B)$, in this case $0.1 \neq (0.2)(0.9)$ therefore these events are not independent.</u>

24. 20% of certain city census consume alcohol regularly, 40% do sport regularly and 10% do both.
    a. Represent the information in a diagram.

    $P(A \cup S) = P(A) + P(S) - P(A \cap S)$
    $P(A \cup S) = 0.2 + 0.4 - 0.1$; $P(A \cup S) = 0.5$

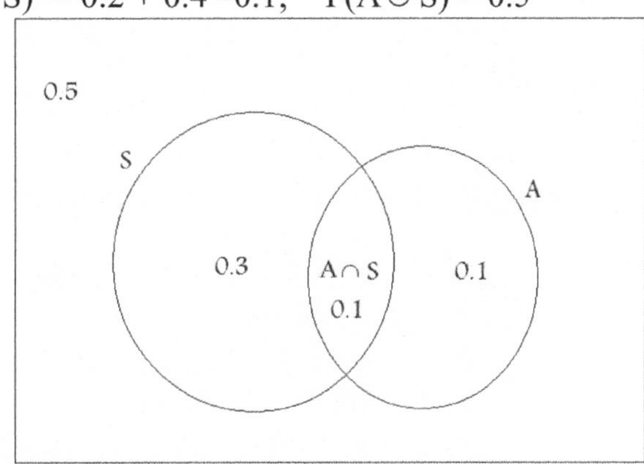

    b. Calculate the probability that someone chosen at random only drinks alcohol regularly.
    P(A only) = 0.1 (see venn diagram)

    c. Calculate the probability that someone chosen at random only drink alcohol regularly or only practices sport regularly (but not both).
    P(A or S but not both) = 0.1 + 0.3 = 0.4 (see venn diagram)

    d. Calculate the probability that someone picked at random does not drink alcohol nor practices sport regularly.
    $P(A' \cap S') = 0.5$ (The "outside")

25. $P(A) = 0.46$, $P(B) = 0.33$, $P(A \cap B) = 0.15$.

a. Represent the information in a diagram.

$P(A \cup B) = 0.46 + 0.33 - 0.15 = 0.64$

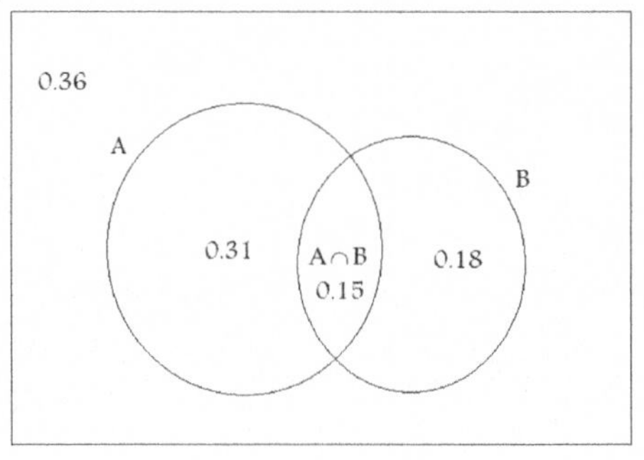

b. Find the probability that an event is not A nor B.

$P(A' \cap B') = 1 - 0.64 = 0.36$

INDEPENDENT EVENTS

Exercises

1. What is the difference between independent events and mutually exclusive events?
   In case of independent events $P(A \cap B) = P(A)P(B)$
   In case of mutually exclusive events $P(A \cap B) = 0$
2. Give an example of independent events:
   - Tossing a coin, the probability of obtaining a head or tail is independent of previous times the coin was tossed.
   - Each time the ball of casino roulette is launched is an independent event of previous launches.

3. In a certain town the probability of a rainy day is 0.58 and the probability of strong wind is 0.76. If these are independent events, find the probability of:
   a. A rainy windy day.
      $P(R \cap W) = P(R)P(W) = (0.58)(0.76) = 0.4408$
   b. A dry windy day.
      $P(R' \cap W) = P(R')P(W) = (0.42)(0.76) = 0.3192$
   c. A dry and not windy day.
      $P(R' \cap W') = P(R')P(W') = (0.42)(0.24) = 0.1008$
   d. 2 consecutive rainy days.
      $P(R \cap R) = P(R)P(R) = (0.58)(0.58) = 0.3364$
   e. 2 consecutive windy rainy days.
      $P(R \cap W)\, P(R \cap W) = (0.4408)(0.4408) = 0.194$

CONDITIONAL PROBABILITY

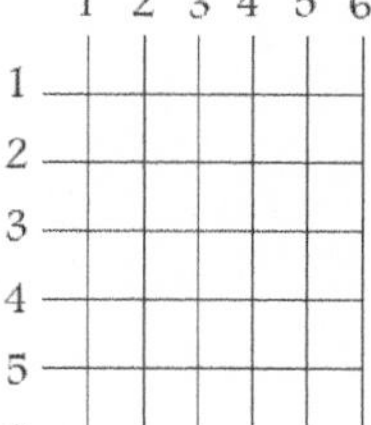

4. Two dice numbered one to six are rolled onto a table.

   a. Sketch a corresponding diagram.

   b. Find the probability that the sum is 7.

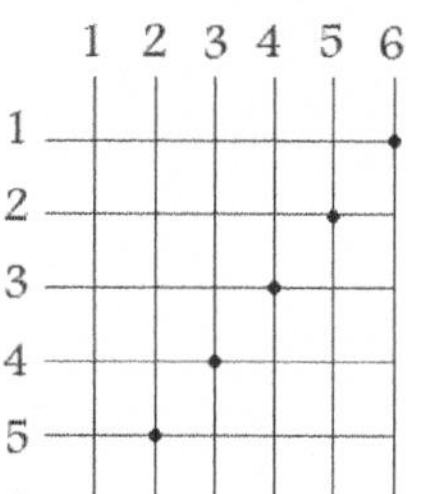

$$P(\text{Sum} = 7) = \frac{6}{36}$$

   c. Find the probability that the sum is more than 7.

$$P(\text{Sum} > 7) = \frac{15}{36}$$

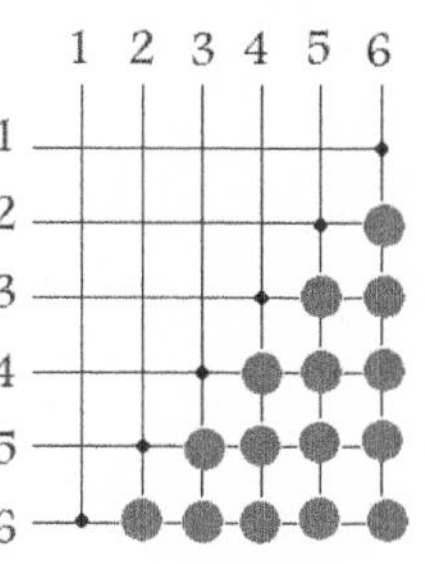

   d. Find the probability that the sum is less than 4.

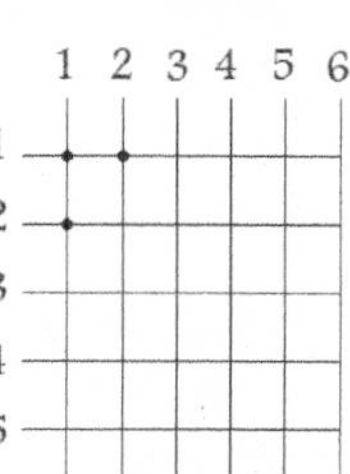

$$P(\text{Sum} < 4) = \frac{3}{36}$$

   e. Find the probability that the sum is even.

$$P(\text{Sum} = \text{even}) = \frac{18}{36}$$

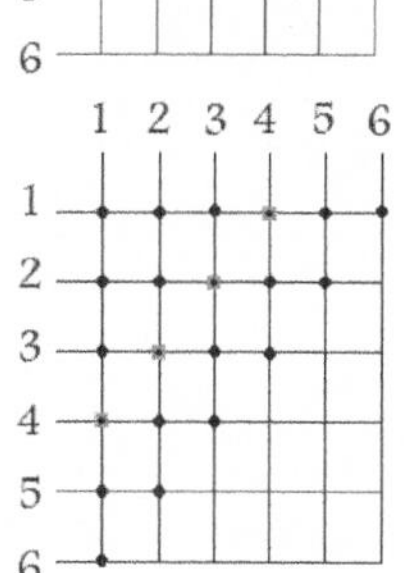

   f. Find the probability of obtaining a sum of five <u>given</u> that the sum is seven or less.

      Conditional probability: $P(A|B) = \frac{P(A \cap B)}{P(B)}$ in this case:

$$P(sum = 5 | sum \leq 7) = \frac{P(sum = 5 \cap sum \leq 7)}{P(sum \leq 7)} = \frac{\left(\frac{4}{36}\right)}{\left(\frac{21}{36}\right)} = \frac{4}{21}$$

   g. Find the probability of obtaining a sum of 4 <u>given</u> that the sum is even.

      Conditional probability: $P(A|B) = \frac{P(A \cap B)}{P(B)}$ in this case:

$$P(sum = 4 | sum = even) = \frac{P(sum = 4 \cap sum = even)}{P(sum = even)} = \frac{\left(\frac{3}{36}\right)}{\left(\frac{18}{36}\right)} = \frac{3}{18}$$

5. A regular and special dice rolled on a table. The special is a 4 sided pyramid numbered with the numbers 1,3,5,7.

   a. Sketch a corresponding diagram.

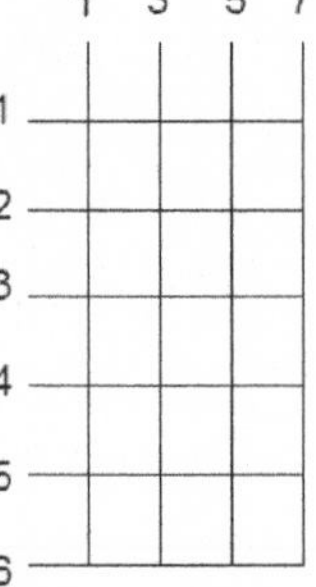

   b. Find the probability that the sum of the dice will be odd.

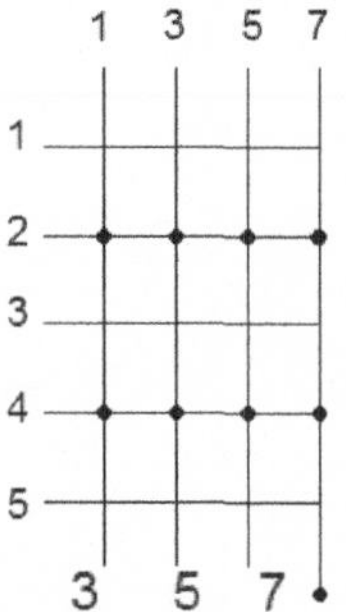

$$P(sum = Odd) = \frac{12}{24} = \frac{1}{2}$$

   c. Find the probability that the sum of the dice will be 8.

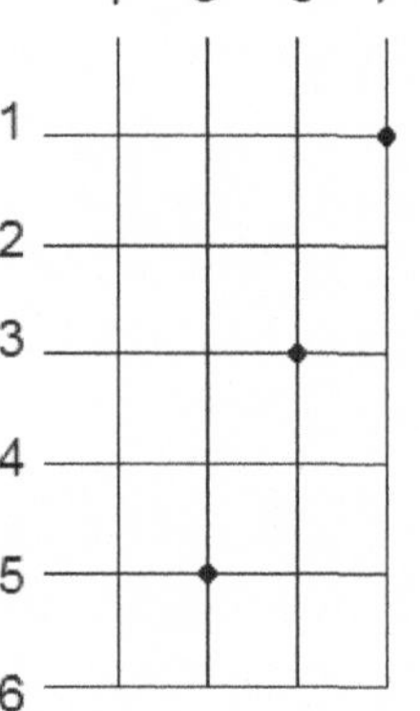

$$P(sum = 8) = \frac{3}{24} = \frac{1}{8}$$

   d. Find the probability that the sum of the dice will be less than 9.

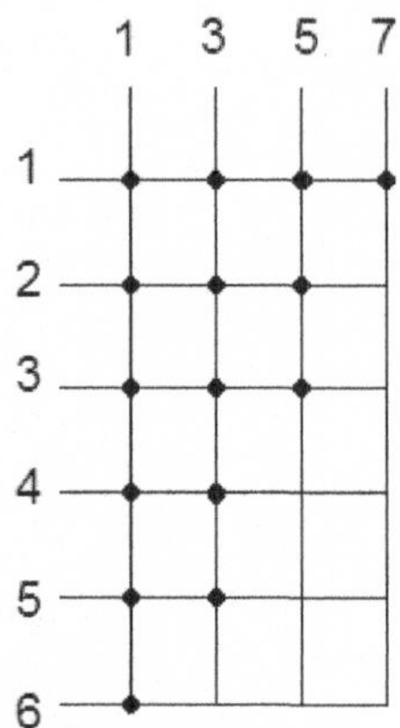

$$P(sum < 9) = \frac{15}{24}$$

   e. Find the probability of obtaining a sum of 10 knowing that the sum was more or equal to 6.

$$P(sum=10|sum\geq 6)=\frac{P(sum=10\cap sum\geq 6)}{P(sum\geq 6)}=\frac{\left(\frac{2}{24}\right)}{\left(\frac{18}{24}\right)}=\frac{2}{18}=\frac{1}{9}$$

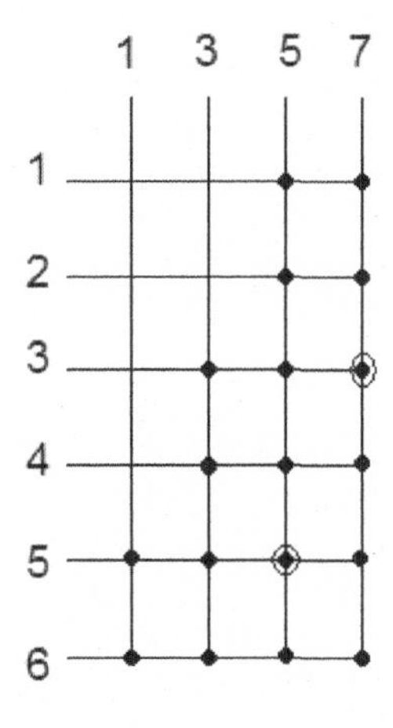

6. Two special dice numbered one to seven are rolled onto a table.

h. Sketch a corresponding diagram.

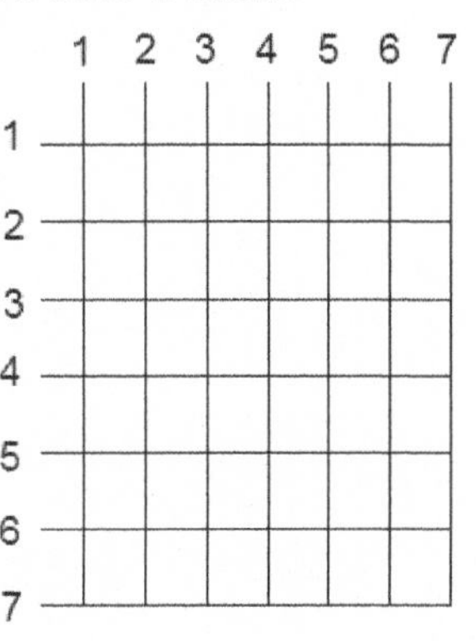

i. Find the probability that the product is 6.

$$P(product=9)=\frac{4}{49}$$

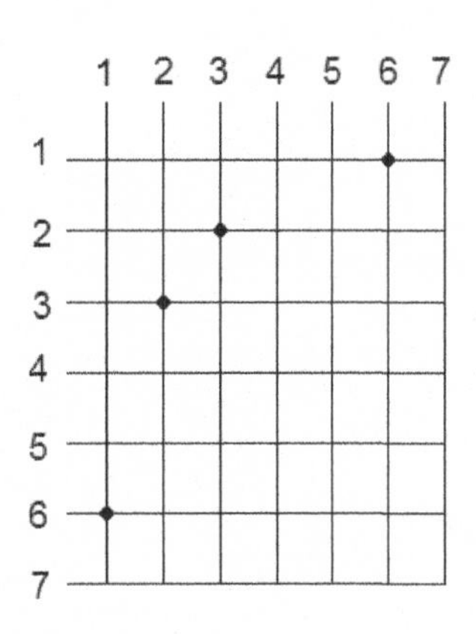

j. Find the probability that the quotient is more than 3.

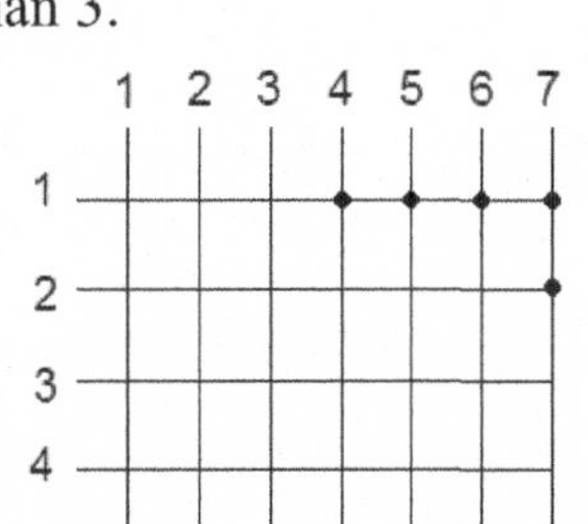

$$P(quotient > 3) = \frac{5}{49}$$

k. Find the probability that the sum is a prime number.

$$P(sum = prime) = \frac{19}{49}$$

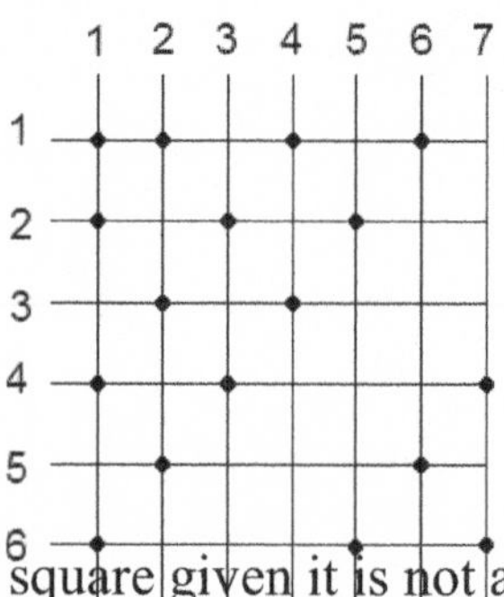

l. Find the probability that the sum is a perfect square given it is not a prime number.

$$P(sum = perfectSquare | sum \neq prime) =$$

$$= \frac{P(sum = perfectSquare \cap sum \neq prime)}{P(sum \neq prime)} =$$

$$\frac{\left(\frac{9}{24}\right)}{\left(\frac{30}{49}\right)} = \frac{9}{30} = \frac{3}{10}$$

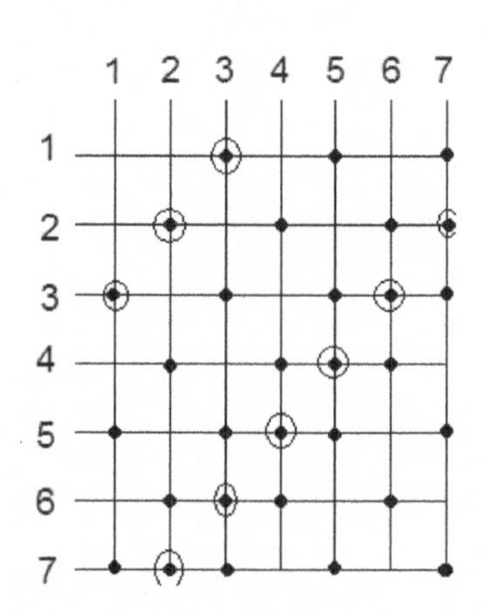

m. Find the probability of obtaining an even sum given that the sum is six or less.

$$P(sum = even | sum \leq 6) =$$

$$= \frac{P(sum = even \cap sum \leq 6)}{P(sum \leq 6)} =$$

$$\frac{\left(\frac{9}{49}\right)}{\left(\frac{15}{49}\right)} = \frac{9}{15} = \frac{3}{5}$$

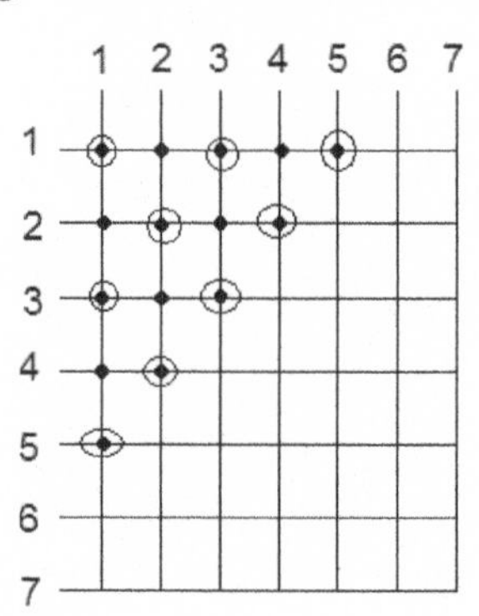

2. A die and coin are rolled on a table.

a. Sketch a corresponding diagram.

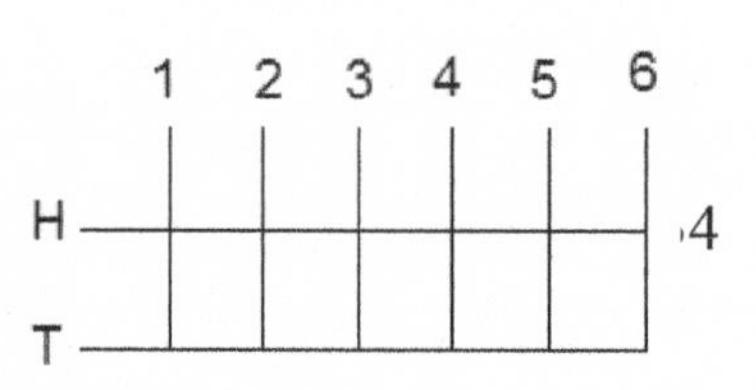

b. Find the probability of getting Tail and an even number.

$$P(Tail \cap even) = \frac{3}{12} = \frac{1}{4}$$

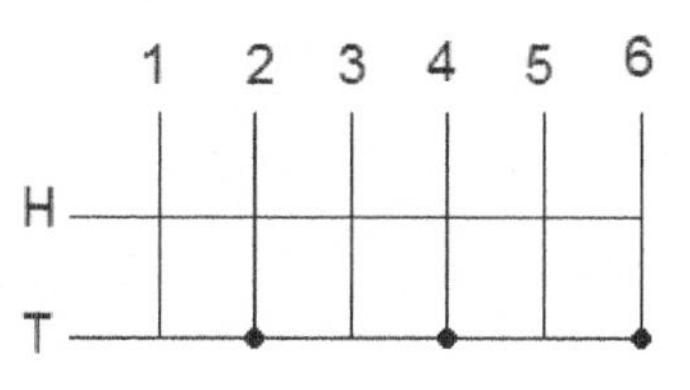

c. Find the probability of getting Tail and a 4.

$$P(Tail \cap 4) = \frac{1}{12}$$

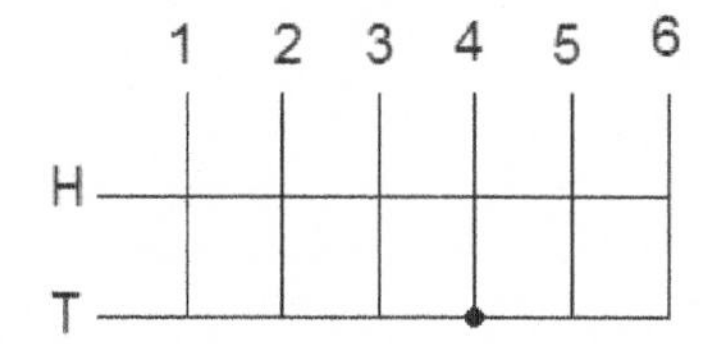

TREE DIAGRAMS

7. If the probability of tail is 0.53, find the probability of at least one tail in 2 throws.

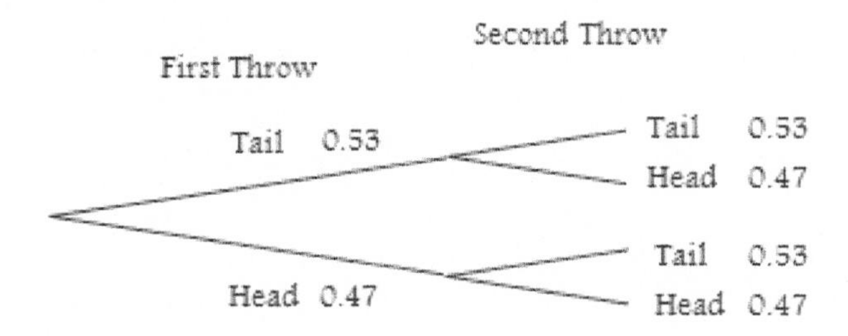

$$P(T \cap T) + P(T \cap H) + P(H \cap T) = (0.53)^2 + (0.53)(0.47) + (0.47)(0.53) = 0.7791$$

Can be done easier:

$$1 - P(H \cap H) = 1 - (0.47)^2 = 0.7791$$

8. An urn contains 8 cubes of which 5 are black and the rest are white.

a. What is the probability to draw a white cube? $P(W) = \frac{3}{8}$

b. Draw a tree diagram in case a 1st cube is drawn, it is **NOT** **replaced** and then another cube is drawn. Indicate all the probabilities on the tree diagram.

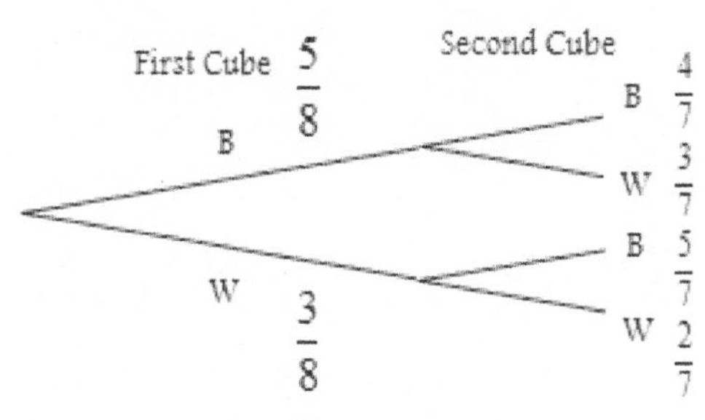

c. Calculate the probability to draw 2 consecutive black cubes.

$$P(B \cap B) = \frac{5}{8} \cdot \frac{4}{7} = \frac{20}{56}$$

d. Calculate the probability to draw **at least** 1 black cube.

$$P(B\cap B)+P(B\cap W)+P(W\cap B)=\frac{50}{56}$$

Can be done easier:

$$1-P(W\cap W)=1-\frac{3}{8}\cdot\frac{2}{7}=1-\frac{6}{56}=\frac{50}{56}$$

e. Given that the first cube drawn was white, calculate the probability that the 2nd is black.

Conditional probability: $P(A|B)=\frac{P(A\cap B)}{P(B)}$ in this case:

$$P(2ndB|1stW)=\frac{P(2ndB\cap 1stW)}{P(1stW)}=\frac{\left(\frac{3}{8}\cdot\frac{5}{7}\right)}{\left(\frac{3}{8}\right)}=\frac{5}{7}$$

9. A bag contains 3 red balls, 4 blue balls and 5 green balls. A ball is chosen at random from the bag and is not replaced. A second ball is chosen. Find the probability of choosing one green ball and one blue ball in any order.

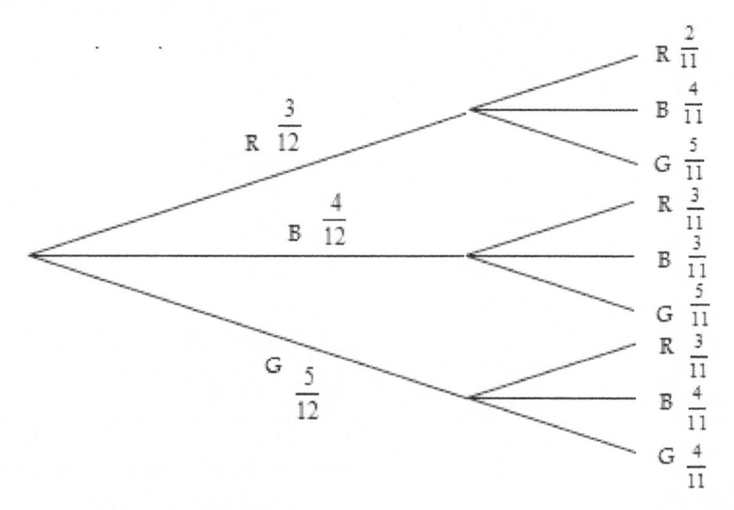

$$P(B\cap G)+P(G\cap B)=\frac{4}{12}\cdot\frac{5}{11}+\frac{5}{12}\cdot\frac{4}{11}=\frac{40}{132}$$

10. Given that events A and B are independent with $P(A\cap B)=0.4$ and $P(A\cap B')=0$. Find $P(A\cup B)$.

P($A \cap B'$) = 0 means that A is inside B (it has no intersection with the "outside" of B), the Venn diagram is:

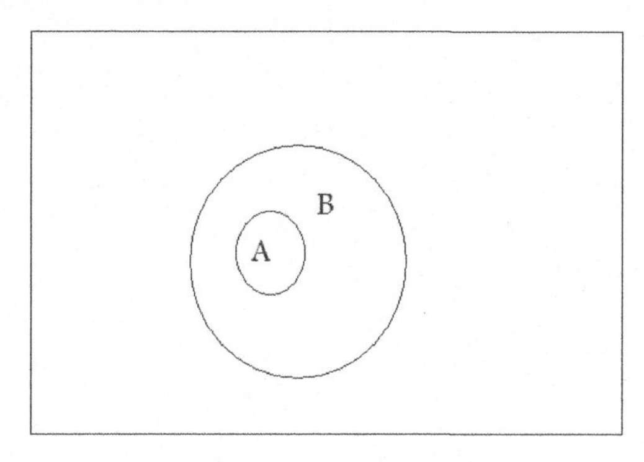

In consequence:
$P(A \cup B) = P(B)$
$P(A \cap B) = P(A) = 0.4$

Since events are independent
$P(A \cap B) = P(A)\,P(B)$
$0.4 = (0.4)P(B)$
$P(B) = 1 = P(A \cup B)$.

11. Given that P(A) = 0.4, P(B) = 0.7 and P($A \cup B$) = 0.8. Find:

   a. $P(A \cap B)$
   $P(A \cup B) = P(A) + P(B) - P(A \cap B)$
   $0.8 = 1.1 - P(A \cap B)$; $P(A \cap B) = 0.3$
   b. P(A | B)
   $$P(A|B) = \frac{P(A \cap B)}{P(B)} = \frac{0.3}{0.7} = \frac{3}{7}$$

   c. Determine if A and B are independent events.
   Check if $P(A \cap B) = P(A)\,P(B)$ is satisfied:
   $0.3 \neq (0.4)(0.7)$ so events are not independent.
12. Given that P(A) = 0.4, P(B) = 0.6 and P($A \cup B$) = 0.76.

   a. Find $P(A \cap B)$
   $P(A \cup B) = P(A) + P(B) - P(A \cap B)$
   $0.76 = 0.4 + 0.6 - P(A \cap B)$; $P(A \cap B) = 0.24$

   b. Are events A and B mutually exclusive? Explain.
   The events are not mutually exclusive since their intersection exists and it is bigger than 0.

   c. Are events A and B independent?
   Check if $P(A \cap B) = P(A)\,P(B)$ is satisfied:
   $0.24 = (0.4)(0.6)$ so events are independent.

13. The events A and B are independent, where A is the event "it will rain today" and B is the event "We will go out for pizza". It is known that

$P(B) = 0.3$, $P(A \mid B) = 0.6$, $P(A \mid B') = 0.5$.

a. Complete the following tree diagram.

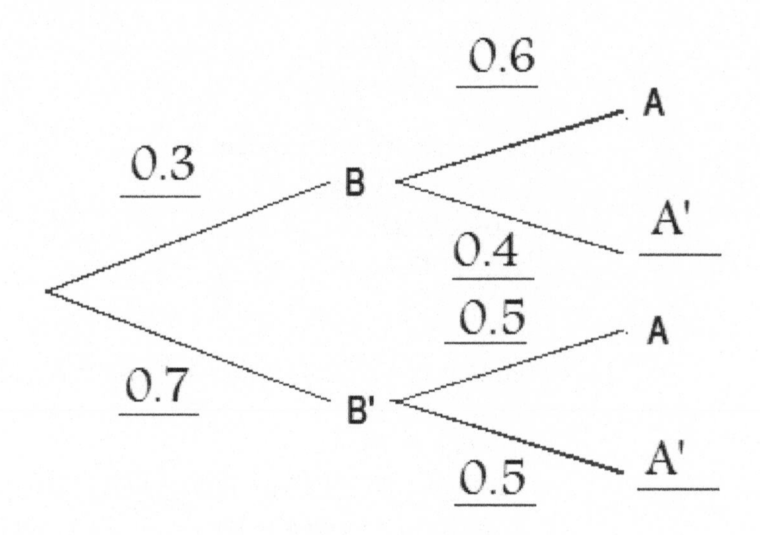

b. Calculate the probability that it rains knowing we went out for pizza.

$P(A \mid B) = 0.6$

2.6. – DISCRETE RANDOM VARIABLES

1. A Discrete Random Variable takes exactly n numerical values and each of these values corresponds to a single event in the sample space.
2. For example in rolling a die the possible values of X are: {1,2,3,4,5,6}
3. A discrete random variable is one in which we can produce a countable number of events.
4. If we roll 2 dice the possible values of X are: {2,3,4,5,6,7,8,9,10,11,12}
   a. Fill the following table:

x	2	3	4	5	6	7	8	9	10	11	12
P(X = x)	$\frac{1}{36}$	$\frac{2}{36}$	$\frac{3}{36}$	$\frac{4}{36}$	$\frac{5}{36}$	$\frac{6}{36}$	$\frac{5}{36}$	$\frac{4}{36}$	$\frac{3}{36}$	$\frac{2}{36}$	$\frac{1}{36}$

   b. Represent the information in the table graphically:

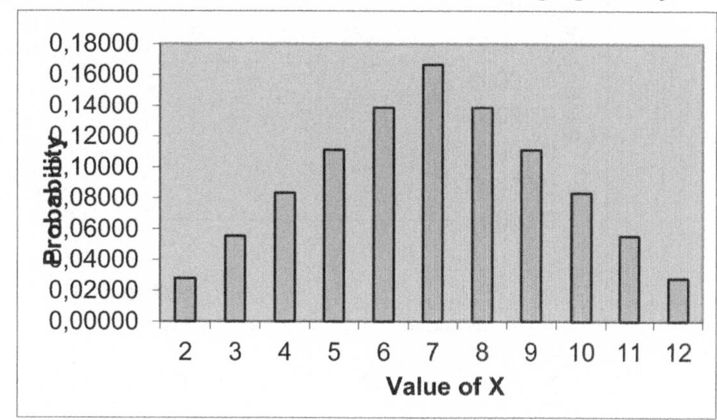

   c. $\sum_{i=1}^{i=n} P(X=x_i) = P(X=x_1)+P(X=x_2)+...+P(X=x_n)=1$

   d. Show that the last statement is satisfied in the problem mentioned:

$$\frac{1}{36}+\frac{2}{36}+\frac{3}{36}+\frac{4}{36}+\frac{5}{36}+\frac{6}{36}+\frac{5}{36}+\frac{4}{36}+\frac{3}{36}+\frac{2}{36}+\frac{1}{36}=1$$

Mean value or Expected of value

   e. Find the mean value of the distribution E(X) = m.

$$E(x)=2\cdot\frac{1}{36}+3\cdot\frac{2}{36}+4\cdot\frac{3}{36}+5\cdot\frac{4}{36}+6\cdot\frac{5}{36}+7\cdot\frac{6}{36}+8\cdot\frac{5}{36}+9\cdot\frac{4}{36}+10\cdot\frac{3}{36}+11\cdot\frac{2}{36}+12\cdot\frac{1}{36}=$$

$$\frac{252}{36}=7$$

Deduce the general expression for the mean E(X) discrete probability distribution:

$$E(X)=\sum_{i=1}^{i=n} x_i \cdot P(X=x_i)$$

   f. This mean is usually called "the expected value of X".
   g. This number, E(X) can be interpreted in 2 ways:
   A Weighted Average.
   A long-term Average.

5. The number of customers entering a shop during 1 hour follows the following table:

x	0	1	3	4	5
P(X = x)	$\frac{1}{6}$	$\frac{1}{12}$	$\frac{5}{12}$	$\frac{1}{6}$	$\frac{1}{6}$

a. Fill the blank in the table.

b. Represent the information in the table graphically:

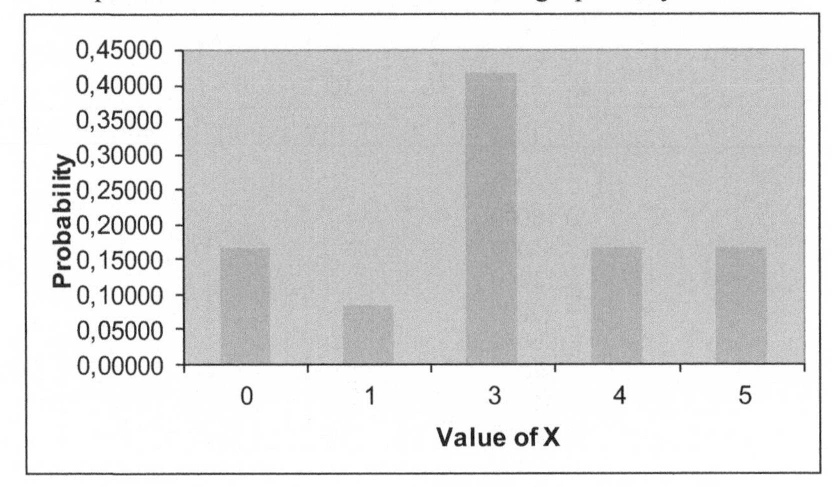

c. $\sum_{i=1}^{i=n} P(X = x_i) = P(X = x_1) + P(X = x_2) + \ldots + P(X = x_n) = 1$

d. Show that the last statement is satisfied in the problem mentioned:

$$\frac{1}{6} + \frac{1}{12} + \frac{5}{12} + \frac{1}{6} + \frac{1}{6} = 1$$

e. Find the mean value of the distribution E(X).

$$E(X) = 0 \cdot \frac{1}{6} + 1 \cdot \frac{1}{12} + 3 \cdot \frac{5}{12} + 4 \cdot \frac{1}{6} + 5 \cdot \frac{1}{6} = 1$$

6. Fill the blanks:

a. E(a) = a (a is a constant). Give an example:

b. E(aX) = aE(X)

c. E(f(X)) = $\sum_{i=i}^{i=n} f(x_i) \times P(X = x_i)$. An example would be:

$$E(aX + b) = \sum_{i=i}^{i=n} (ax_i + b) \times P(X = x_i) = \sum_{i=i}^{i=n} ax_i \times P(X = x_i) + b \times P(X = x_i) =$$

$$a \sum_{i=i}^{i=n} x_i \times P(X = x_i) + b \sum_{i=i}^{i=n} P(X = x_i) = aE(X) + b$$

x	2	3	5	6	10

7. Given the following probability distribution

P(X = x)	$\frac{1}{6}$	$\frac{1}{12}$	$\frac{5}{12}$	0	$\frac{4}{12}$

a. Fill the blank.

b. E(X) = $2\cdot\frac{1}{6}+3\cdot\frac{1}{12}+5\cdot\frac{5}{12}+6\cdot 0+10\cdot\frac{4}{12}=\frac{72}{12}=6$ (Expected value never occurs)

c. E(2X) = $2E(X)=12$

d. E(4X) = $4E(X)=24$

e. 2E(X) = 12

f. 4E(X) = 24

g. $(E(X))^2 = 36$

h. $E(X^2) = 4\cdot\frac{1}{6}+9\cdot\frac{1}{12}+25\cdot\frac{5}{12}+36\cdot 0+100\cdot\frac{4}{12}=\frac{542}{12}\approx 45.2$

i. $E(X^3) = 8\cdot\frac{1}{6}+27\cdot\frac{1}{12}+125\cdot\frac{5}{12}+216\cdot 0+1000\cdot\frac{4}{12}=\frac{4668}{12}=389$

j. $E(\sqrt{X}) = \sqrt{2}\cdot\frac{1}{6}+\sqrt{3}\cdot\frac{1}{12}+\sqrt{5}\cdot\frac{5}{12}+\sqrt{6}\cdot 0+\sqrt{10}\cdot\frac{4}{12}\approx 2.37$

k. Repeat the process using your GDC.

l. In general is $(E(X))^2 = E(X^2)$? No Is it possible in a specific case? Yes

Variance and standard deviation

a. The Variance measures the spread of the distribution

b. Variance is defined as:

$$Var(X) = E((X-\mu)^2) = \sum_{i=i}^{i=n}(x-\mu)^2 P(X=x) \qquad \text{Or}$$

$$Var(X) = E(X^2)-(E(X))^2 = E(X^2)-\mu^2$$

Use the data from exercise 7 to find:

Find Var(X) = $E(X^2)-\mu^2 = 45.2-36 = 9.2$

c. Standard deviation is defined as Sd(X) = $\sqrt{Var(X)} = \sqrt{E(X^2)-\mu^2}$

d. In this case Sd(X) = $\sqrt{45.2-36} = \sqrt{9.2} \approx 3.03$. We use the Sd(X) and not the variance because Sd has the same units as the original distribution.

e. Calculate Var(2X) =

$E((2X)^2)-(E(2x))^2 = 4E(X^2)-(E(2x))^2 = 4\cdot 45.2-144 = 36.8$

How is it related to Var(X)? Var(2X) = 2^2Var(X) = 4 Var(X) = $4\cdot 9.2 = 38.4$

f. Var(aX) = $a^2 Var(X)$

g. Var(a) = 0 (a is a constant)

Given 2 distributions:

x	1	2	3	4
P(X = x)	$\frac{1}{6}$	$\frac{2}{6}$	$\frac{1}{6}$	$\frac{2}{6}$

x	7	8	9	10
P(X = x)	$\frac{1}{6}$	$\frac{2}{6}$	$\frac{1}{6}$	$\frac{2}{6}$

h. Represent them both on the same graph:

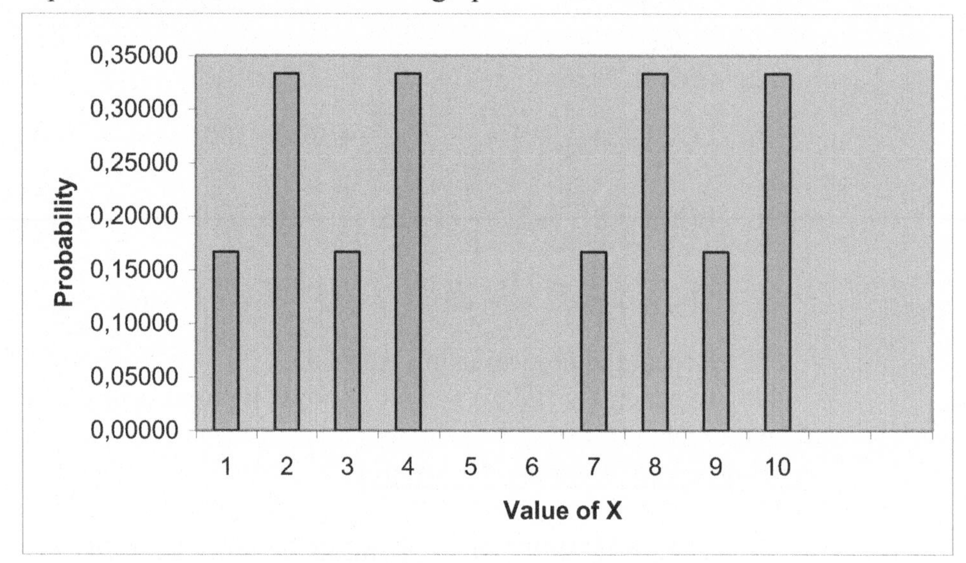

i. The 2nd distribution is <u>the same</u> as the 1st one only <u>shifted 6 to the right</u>

j. $E(X_{\text{first}}) = 1\cdot\frac{1}{6}+2\cdot\frac{2}{6}+3\cdot\frac{1}{6}+4\cdot\frac{2}{6}=\frac{16}{6}=\frac{8}{3}$

k. $E(X_{\text{second}}) = 7\cdot\frac{1}{6}+8\cdot\frac{2}{6}+9\cdot\frac{1}{6}+10\cdot\frac{2}{6}=\frac{52}{6}=\frac{26}{3}=\frac{8}{3}+6$ (expected value suffered the same translation)

l. $E(X^2_{\text{first}}) = 1\cdot\frac{1}{6}+4\cdot\frac{2}{6}+9\cdot\frac{1}{6}+16\cdot\frac{2}{6}=\frac{50}{6}=\frac{25}{3}$

m. $E(X^2_{\text{second}}) = 49\cdot\frac{1}{6}+64\cdot\frac{2}{6}+81\cdot\frac{1}{6}+100\cdot\frac{2}{6}=\frac{458}{6}=\frac{229}{3}$

n. $\text{Var}(X_{\text{first}}) = E(X^2)-(E(X))^2=\frac{25}{3}-\frac{64}{9}=\frac{11}{9}$

o. $\text{Var}(X_{\text{second}}) = E(X^2)-(E(X))^2=\frac{229}{3}-\frac{676}{9}=\frac{11}{9}$

p. Your conclusions: As can be seen translating a distribution left or right does not change its spread and variance and SD therefore stay invariant.

q. $\text{Var}(X + b) = \text{Var}(X)$

r. $\text{Var}(a(X + b)) = \text{Var}(aX) = a^2\, \text{Var}(X)$

s. $\text{Var}(aX + c) = a^2\, \text{Var}(X)$

2.7. – THE BINOMIAL DISTRIBUTION

1. Dichotomous Experiment – An experiment with two possible results: heads or tail male or female, adult or child etc.
2. The probabilities of the results are P(A) and P(A') = 1 – P(A)
3. The variable X is discrete. It is called a Binomial Distribution to B(n, p). n is the number of times the experiment took place. p is the probability for "success"and q is 1 – p
4. The probability that X would have the value k is given by:

$$P(X = k) = \binom{n}{k} p^k q^{n-k}, k = 0,1,2...n$$

$$E(x) = \mu = np$$

$$Var(X) = \sigma^2 = npq$$

$$Sd(X) = \sigma = \sqrt{npq}$$

The mode of X is the value of x with the largest probability.

5. If B(1, $\frac{1}{2}$) find: (this experiment is similar to tossing a coin once)

a. $P(X = 0) = \binom{1}{0}(\frac{1}{2})^0(\frac{1}{2})^1 = \frac{1}{2}$

b. $P(X = 1) = \binom{1}{1}(\frac{1}{2})^1(\frac{1}{2})^0 = \frac{1}{2}$

c. P(X = 2) = Not possible, if the experiment took place once, "success" cannot be obtained twice.

d. Mode of X is 0, 1 both have the same probability

e. $E(X) = np = 1 \cdot \frac{1}{2} = \frac{1}{2}$ $Var(X) = npq = 1 \cdot \frac{1}{2} \cdot \frac{1}{2} = \frac{1}{4}$ $Sd(X) = \sqrt{\frac{1}{4}} = \frac{1}{2}$

f. Write down the probability of the expected value: 0 ($\frac{1}{2}$ will never be obtained)

6. If B(3, $\frac{1}{2}$) find:

a. $P(X = 0) = \binom{3}{0}(\frac{1}{2})^0(\frac{1}{2})^3 = \frac{1}{8}$

b. $P(X = 1) = \binom{3}{1}(\frac{1}{2})^1(\frac{1}{2})^2 = \frac{3}{8}$

c. $P(X = 2) = \binom{3}{2}(\frac{1}{2})^2(\frac{1}{2})^1 = \frac{3}{8}$

d. $P(X=3)=\binom{3}{3}(\frac{1}{2})^3(\frac{1}{2})^0=\frac{1}{8}$

e. $P(X=2)=\frac{3}{8}$ means that there is a probability of $\frac{3}{8}$ that success will occur twice if the experiment takes place 3 times (n = 3)

f. Mode of X is 1, 2, both have the same highest probability

g. $P(X<2)=P(X=0)+P(X=1)=\frac{4}{8}$

h. $P(X\geq 2)=P(X=2)+P(X=3)=\frac{4}{8}$

i. $E(X)=np=3\cdot\frac{1}{2}=\frac{3}{2}$ $Var(X)=npq=3\cdot\frac{1}{2}\cdot\frac{1}{2}=\frac{3}{4}$ $Sd(X)=\sqrt{\frac{3}{4}}$

j. The probability of the expected value: 0 ($\frac{3}{2}$ will never be obtained)

7. If $B(3,\frac{1}{6})$ find:

a. $P(X=0)=\binom{3}{0}(\frac{1}{6})^0(\frac{5}{6})^3=\frac{125}{216}$

b. $P(X=1)=\binom{3}{1}(\frac{1}{6})^1(\frac{5}{6})^2=\frac{75}{216}$

c. $P(X=2)=\binom{3}{2}(\frac{1}{6})^2(\frac{5}{6})^1=\frac{15}{216}$

d. $P(X=3)=\binom{3}{3}(\frac{1}{6})^3(\frac{5}{6})^0=\frac{1}{216}$

e. $P(X=2)=\frac{15}{216}$ means that there is a probability of $\frac{15}{216}$ that success will occur twice if the experiment takes place 3 times (n = 3)

f. Mode of X is 0, the value with highest probability

g. $P(X<2)=P(X=0)+P(X=1)=\frac{200}{216}$

h. $P(X\geq 2)=P(X=2)+P(X=3)=\frac{16}{216}$

i. $E(X)=np=3\cdot\frac{1}{6}=\frac{1}{2}$ $Var(X)=npq=3\cdot\frac{1}{6}\cdot\frac{5}{6}=\frac{15}{36}$ $Sd(X)=\sqrt{\frac{15}{36}}$

j. Write down the probability of the expected value: : 0 ($\frac{1}{2}$ will never be obtained)

8. If B(20, $\frac{1}{2}$) Using GDC binompdf(n,p,x), binompdf(n,p,(x_1,x_n)), binomcdf(n,p,x) for $P(X \le x)$
   a. $P(X = 5)$ = binompdf(20,0.5,5) = 0.148
   b. $P(X = 10)$ = binompdf(20,0.5,10) = 0.176
   c. $P(X = 18)$ = binompdf(20,0.5,18) = 0.000181
   d. $P(X < 8)$ = binomcdf(20,0.5,7) = 0.132
   e. $P(X \le 8)$ = binomcdf(20,0.5,8) = 0.252
   f. $P(X \ge 13)$ = 1 – binomcdf(20,0.5,12) = 0.132
   g. $P(X > 13)$ = 1 – binomcdf(20,0.5,13) = 0.0577
   h. E(X) = $np = 20 \cdot \frac{1}{2} = 10$ Var(X) = $npq = 20 \cdot \frac{1}{2} \cdot \frac{1}{2} = 5$ Sd(X) = $\sqrt{5}$
   i. Write down the probability of the expected value: 0.176
9. If B(70, 0.2) Find:
   a. $P(X = 17)$ = binompdf(70,0.2,17) = 0.0755
   b. $P(X = 36)$ = binompdf(70,0.2,36) = $3.80 \cdot 10^{-9}$
   c. $P(X = 28)$ = binompdf(70,0.2,28) = $6.39 \cdot 10^{-5}$
   d. $P(X < 50)$ = binomcdf(70,0.2,49) ≈ 1 (limitations of GDC are seen)
   e. $P(X \le 70) = 1$
   f. $P(X \ge 38)$ = 1 – binomcdf(70,0.2,37) = $2.38 \cdot 10^{-10}$
   g. $P(X > 10)$ = 1 – binomcdf(70,0.2,10) = 0.853
   h. E(X) = $np = 70 \cdot \frac{1}{5} = 14$ Var(X) = $npq = 70 \cdot \frac{1}{5} \cdot \frac{4}{5} = \frac{56}{5}$ Sd(X) = $\sqrt{\frac{56}{5}}$
   i. Write down the probability of the expected value: 0.118

10. A machine that makes products has a probability of 0.03 to build a defective product. The machine produces 500 products B(500, 0.03)
    a. The most probable number of defective products, its probability $E(X) = np = 500 \cdot 0.03 = 15$, binompdf(500,0.03,15) = 0.104
    b. Probability for 10 defective products: binompdf(500,0.03,10) = 0.0479
    c. Less than 12 defective products: binomcdf(500,0.03,11) = 0.181
    d. Probability for more than 18 defective products: 1 – binomcdf(500,0.03,18) = 0.177
11. A die it thrown 50 times.
    a. B(50, $\frac{1}{6}$) Probability 5 "ones": binompdf(50,1/6,5) = 0.0745
    a. B(50, $\frac{1}{2}$) Probability 20 even: binompdf(50,1/2,20) = 0.0419
    b. B(50, $\frac{1}{6}$) Probability less than 12 "ones" binomcdf(50,1/6,11) = 0.883
    c. B(50, $\frac{1}{3}$) Probability more than 17 times a "six" or "five"

       1 – binomcdf(50,1/3,17) = 0.395

2.8. – NORMAL DISTRIBUTION

What do you observe? Can you guess how would a bigger sample look like? It will become more and more similar to a "bell" shaped distribution, this distribution is called the "normal distribution".

1. The normal distribution is characterized by two numbers: The mean μ and the standard deviation σ
2. Fill the missing data for the following distributions:

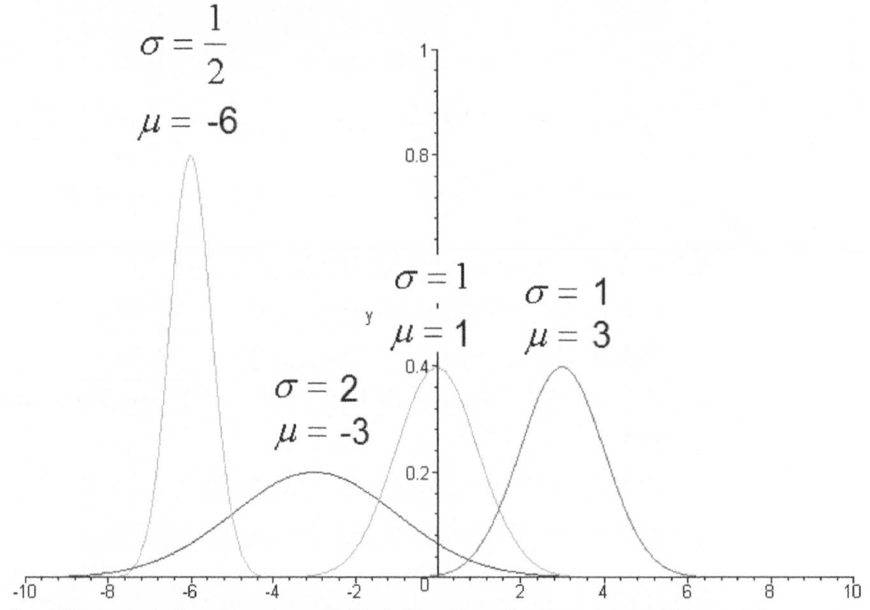

3. **The standard normal distribution** is the one with $\mu = 0$ y $\sigma = 1$ (Green)
4. The mean μ is located at the centre of the distribution.
5. The standard deviation σ represents the distance between the mean and the inflection point

Properties of the normal distribution

6. The area under the curve from negative infinity to plus infinity is 1
7. The normal distribution is symmetrical that means that the area under the graph on each side of the mean is 0.5.
8. The shape and position of a normal distribution depend on the parameters μ and σ therefore there is an infinite number of normal distributions. The distribution gets will narrower and taller as σ gets smaller
9. In general the area under the curve in the interval $\mu \pm 1\sigma$ is $\approx 68\%$
10. In general the area under the curve in the interval $\mu \pm 2\sigma$ is $\approx 95\%$
11. In general the area under the curve in the interval $\mu \pm 3\sigma$ is $\approx 99.7\%$

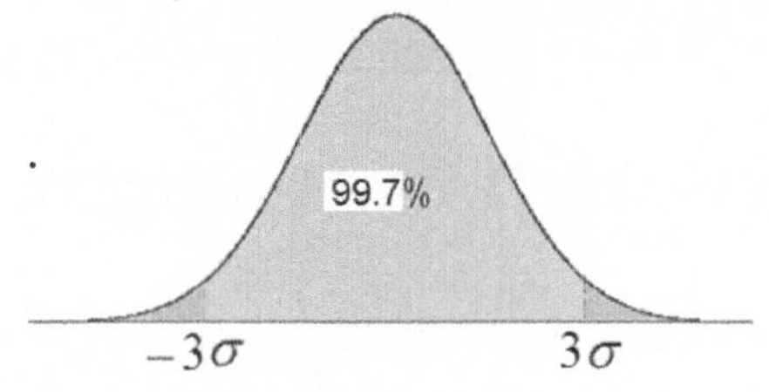

12. σ (the standard deviation) gives us an idea about the spread of the distribution
13. μ (the mean) indicates the centre of the distribution
14. Normally the normal distribution is written as N(μ , σ^2), that means that a distribution N(28, 4) will have a mean of 28 and a SD of 2

FINDING PROBABILIT OF $a < Z < b$

Shade and calculate use **GDC**: ShadeNorm(a, b) or ShadeNorm(a, b, μ , σ)
(Use large numbers for ∞ or $-\infty$)

15. **All Diagrams not to scale**

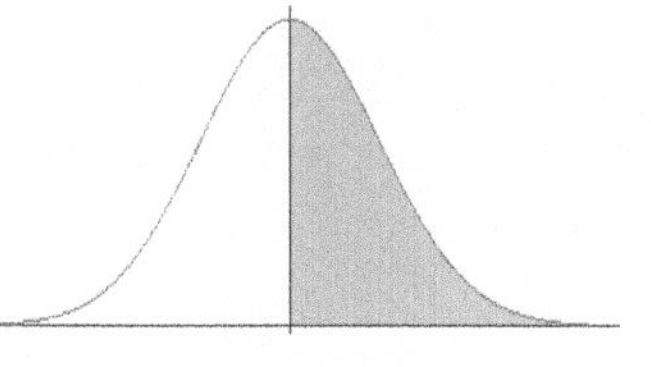

a. $P(Z \geq 0) = 0.5$
b. $P(Z = 1) = 0$ (the corresponding area is 0)
c. $P(Z < 1)$ = ShadeNorm(–1000, 1) = 0.841

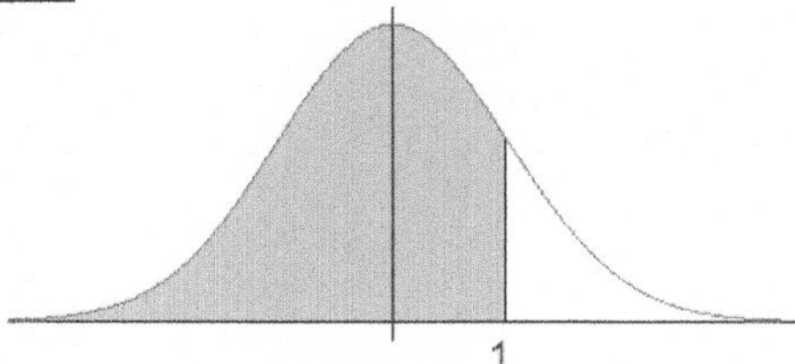

d. $P(Z \geq 2)$ = ShadeNorm(2,1000) = 0.0228

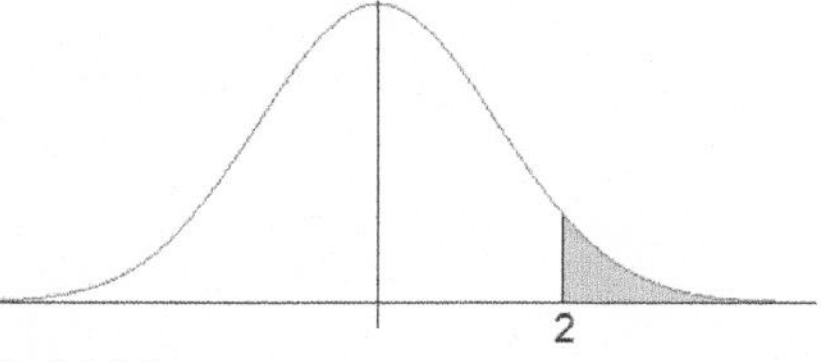

e. $P(Z \geq 2.23)$ = ShadeNorm(2.23,1000) = 0.0129

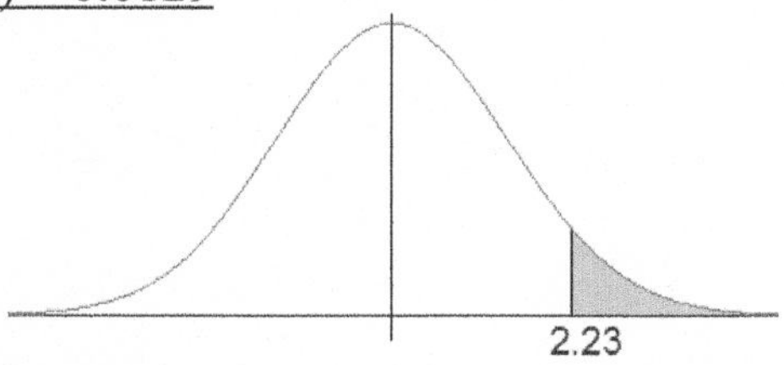

f. $P(Z \geq 1.57)$ = ShadeNorm(1.57,1000) = 0.0582

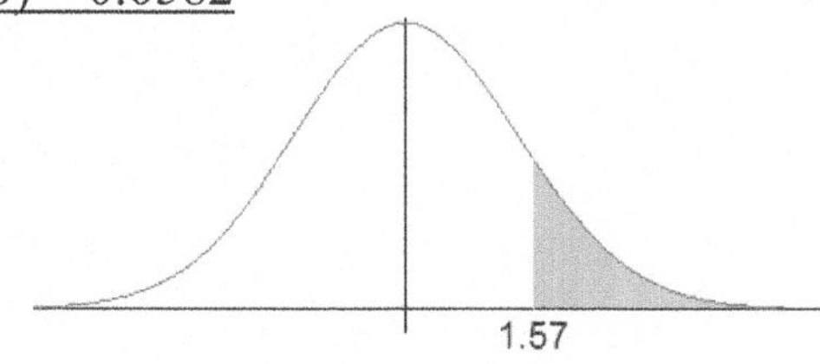

g. P(Z ≤ 1.86) = ShadeNorm(–1000, 1.86) = 0.967

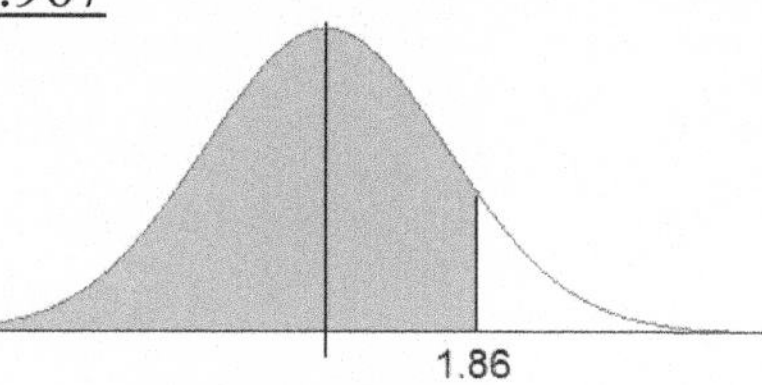

h. P(Z ≤ –2) = ShadeNorm(–1000,2) = 0.0228

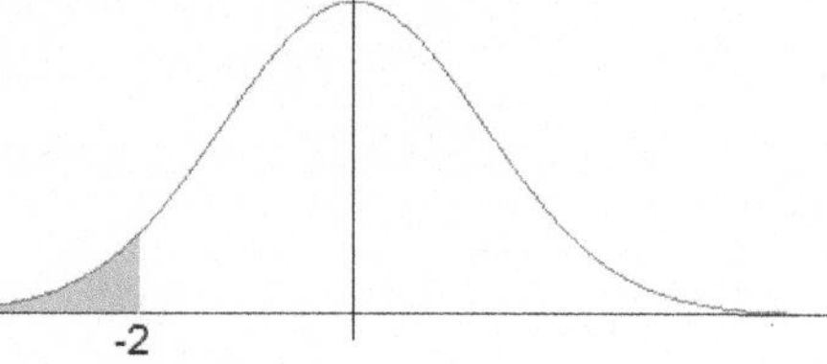

i. P(Z ≤ –2.1) = ShadeNorm(–1000, –2.1) = 0.0179

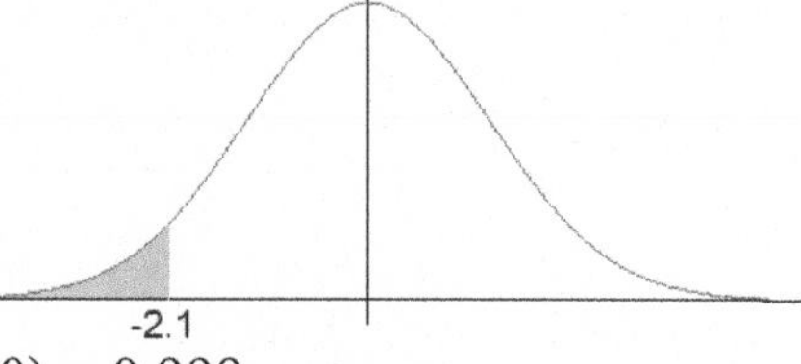

j. P(Z ≥ –3.11) = ShadeNorm(–3.11, 1000) = 0.999

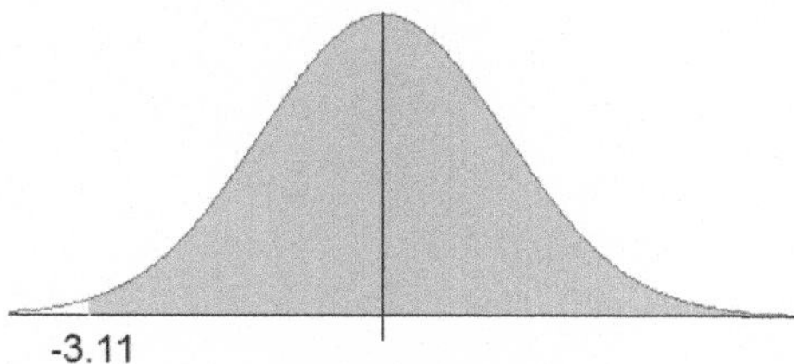

k. P(Z ≥ –2) = ShadeNorm(–2,1000) = 0.977

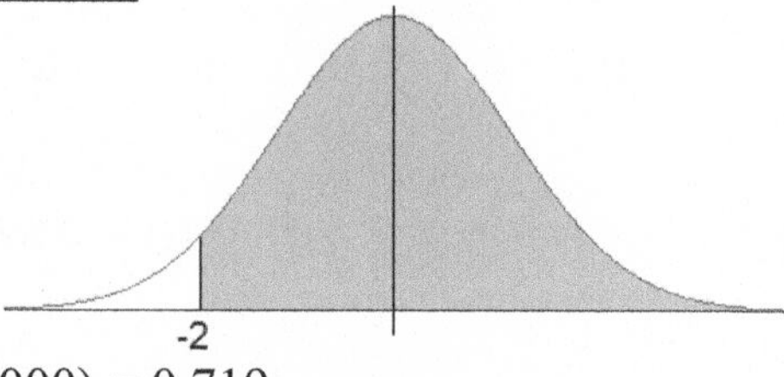

l. P(Z ≥ –0.58) = ShadeNorm(–0.58,1000) = 0.719

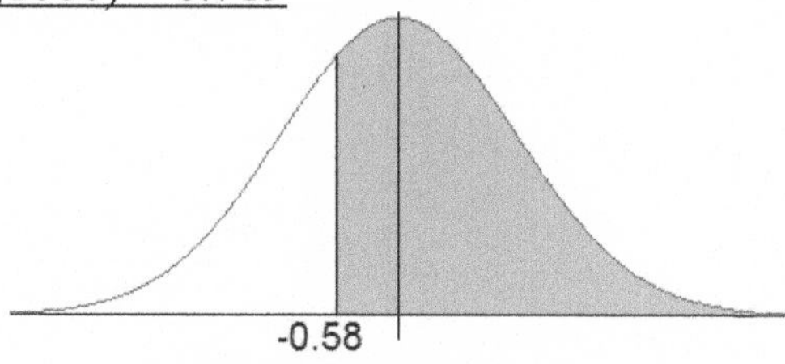

m. P(Z ≤ –2.7) = ShadeNorm(–1000, –2.7) = 0.00347

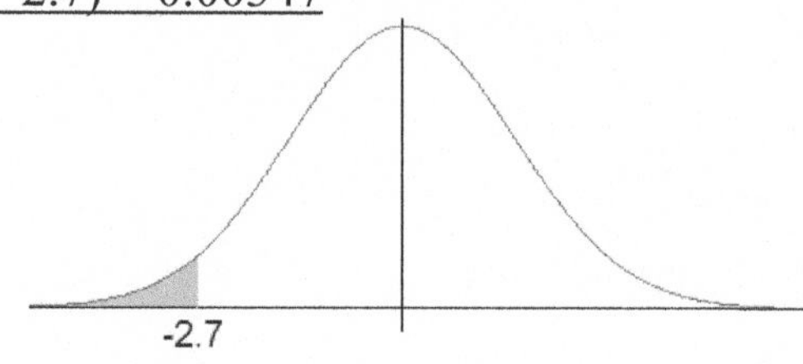

n. $P(-\infty \le Z \le -2.7)$ = <u>ShadeNorm(–1000, –2.7) = 0.00347 (same as previous example)</u>

o. $P(3 \le Z \le -2.7)$ = Not possible, the number on the left is bigger than the number on the right.

p. $P(1 \le Z \le 2)$ = <u>ShadeNorm(1,2) = 0.136</u>

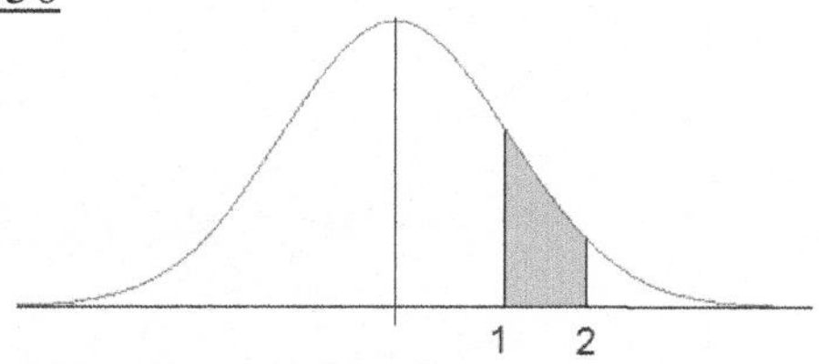

q. $P(-1.25 \le Z \le 0)$ = <u>ShadeNorm(–1.25,0) = 0.394</u>

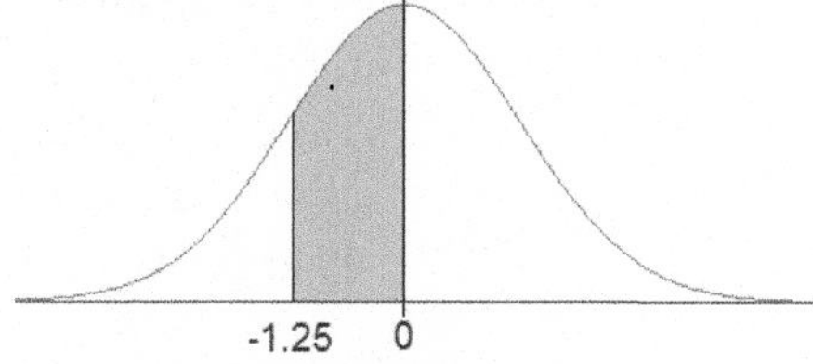

r. $P(-2.12 \le Z \le 1.65)$ = <u>ShadeNorm(–2.12,1.65) = 0.934</u>

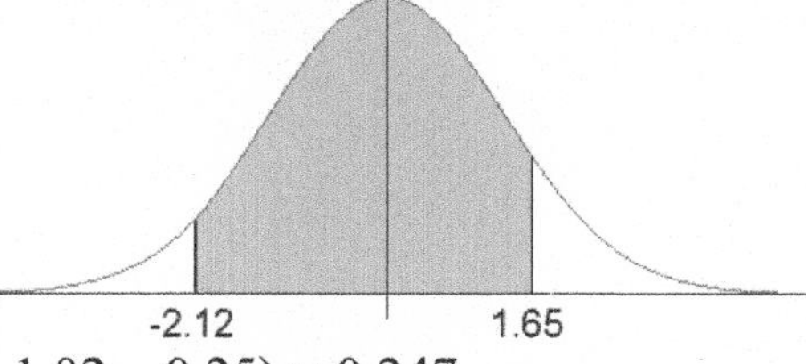

s. $P(-1.02 \le Z \le -0.25)$ = <u>ShadeNorm(–1.02, –0.25) = 0.247</u>

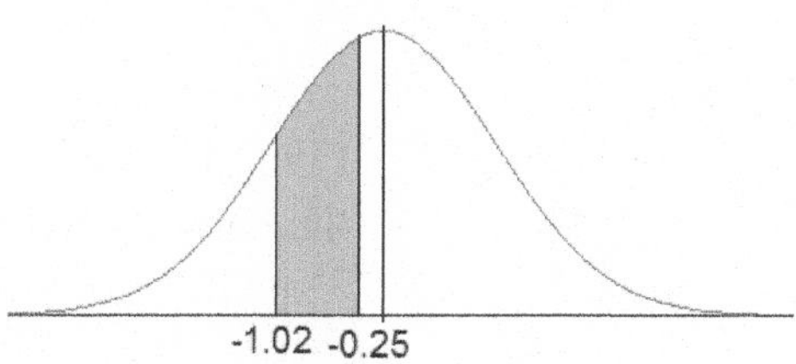

t. $P(0.97 \le Z \le 1.76)$ = <u>ShadeNorm(0.97,1.76) = 0.127</u>

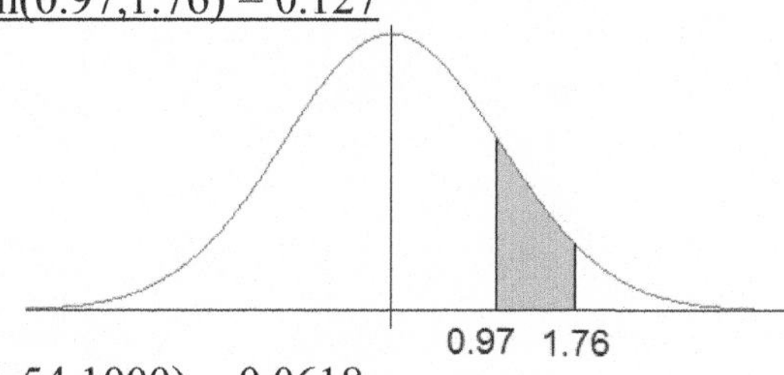

u. $P(1.54 \le Z \le \infty)$ = <u>ShadeNorm(1.54,1000) = 0.0618</u>

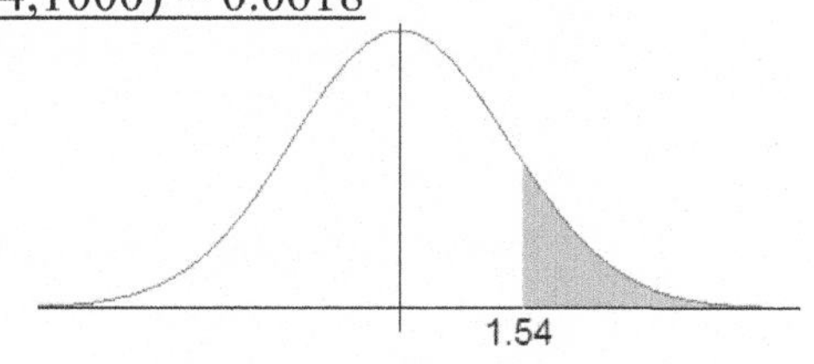

v. $P(1.31 \le Z \le 3.06) =$ ShadeNorm(1.31,3.06) = 0.0940

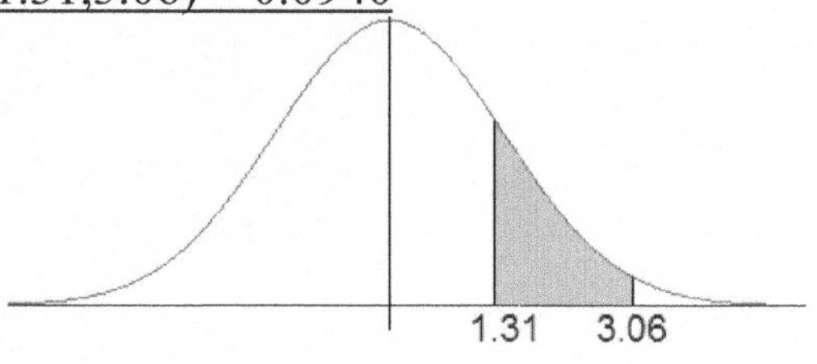

FINDING PROBABILITY FOR $a < X < b$

The amount of time to produce a product follows a normal distribution with mean of 40 minutes and S. D. of 8 minutes.

16. Find the probability that the product is produced between 35 and 50 minutes. Shade the corresponding area on the following diagram.
    Use **GDC** to find your answer: normalcdf(35, 50, 40, 8) = 0.628

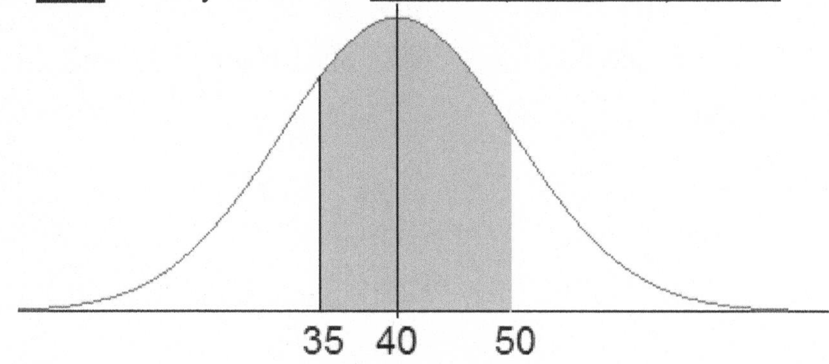

17. Find the probability that the product is produced in more than 38 minutes. Shade the corresponding area on the following diagram.
    Use GDC to find your answer: normalcdf(38, 1000, 40, 8) = 0.599

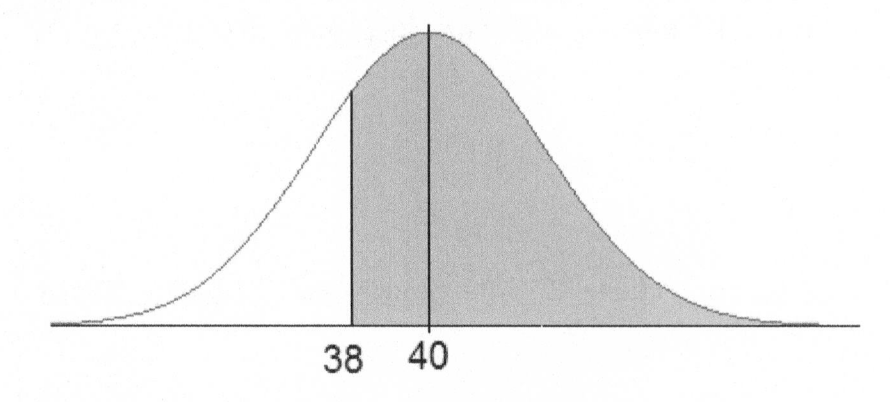

18. Find the probability that the product is produced in less than 34 minutes. Shade the corresponding area on the following diagram.
    Use GDC to find your answer: normalcdf(–1000,34, 40, 8) 0 0.227

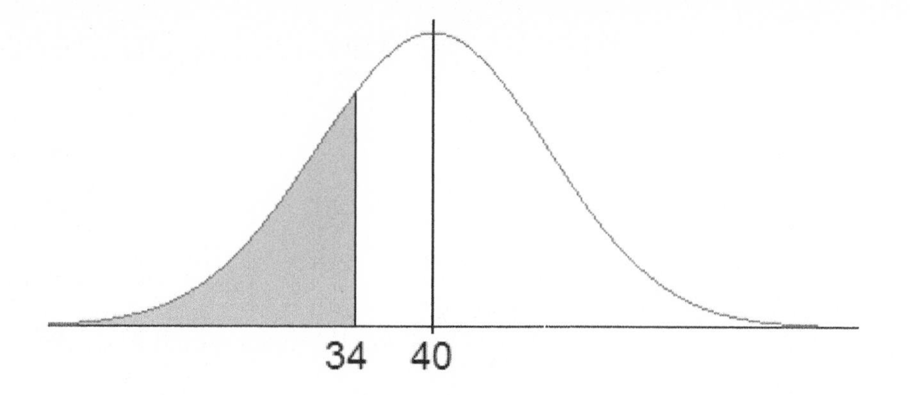

Exercises

19. In a normal distribution N(24, 6) Find and shade:

    a. P(X = 25) = 0 (No area)

    b. P(X ≥ 25) = normalcdf(25,1000, 24, 6) = 0.434

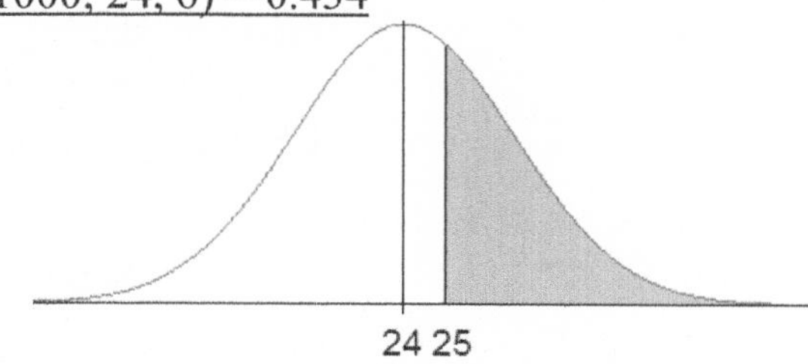

    c. P(X ≤ 25) = normalcdf(–1000, 25,24,6) = 0.566

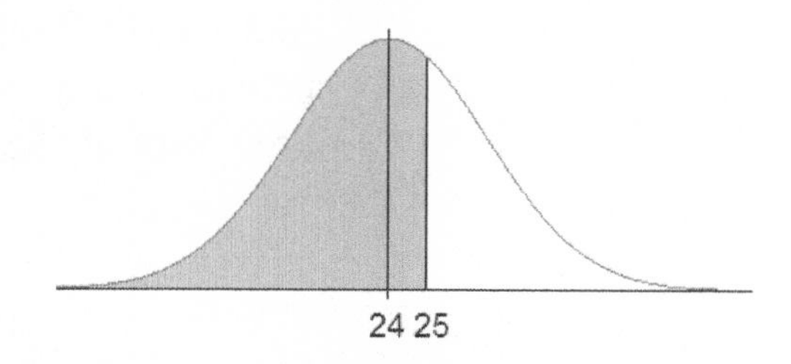

    d. P(X ≥ 15) = normalcdf(15,1000, 24, 6) = 0.933

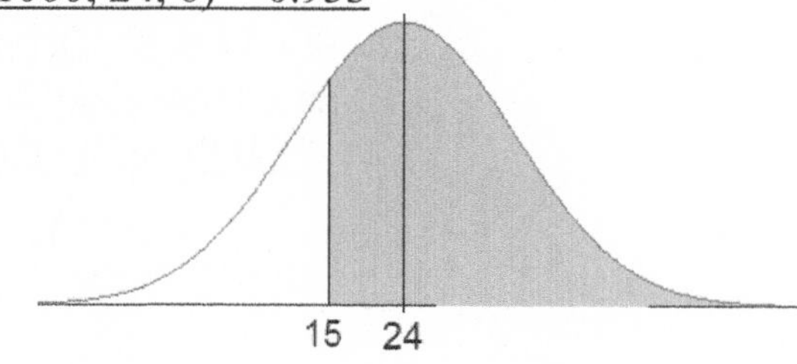

e. $P(14 \leq X \leq 20)$ = normalcdf(14,20, 24, 6) = 0.205

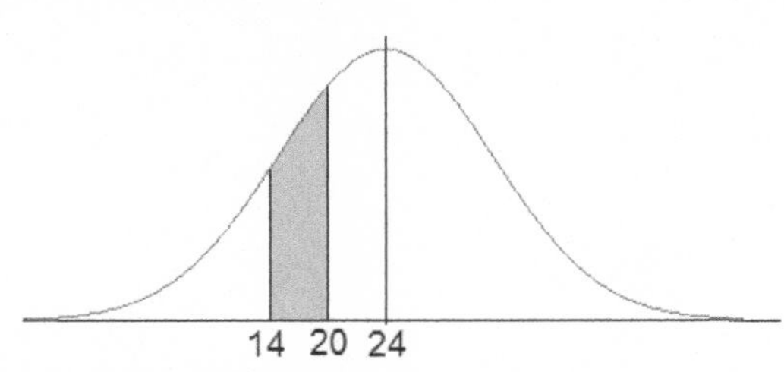

f. $(19 \leq X \leq 31)$ = normalcdf(19,31, 24, 6) = 0.676

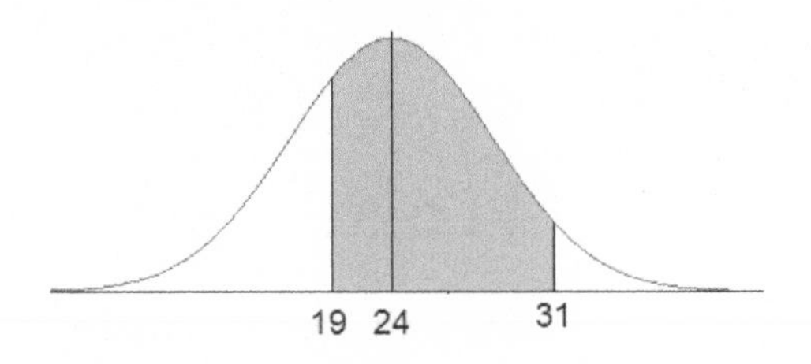

20. In a lake there are 3000 fish distributed according to a normal distribution with a mean of 26cm and a standard deviation of 7cm.

a. Find and shade on the graph the interval in which 68% of the fish lengths are. How many fish in this case? This exactly the percentage the corresponds 1 SD therefore the interval is (19, 33) cm, 68% of 3000 is 2040 Fish.

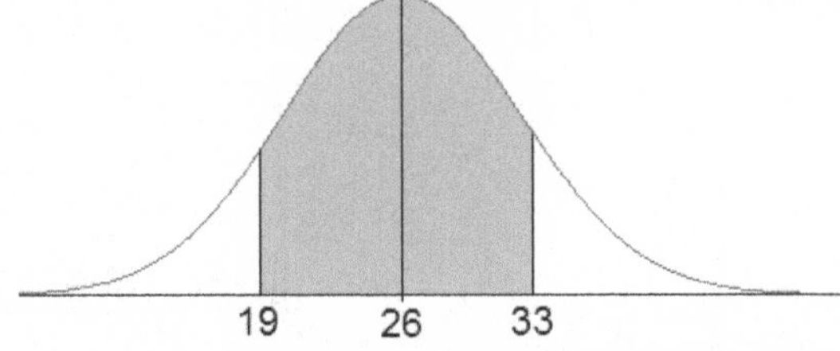

b. Find and shade on the graph the interval in which 95% of the fish lengths are. How many fish in this case? This exactly the percentage the corresponds 2 SD therefore the interval is (12, 40) cm, 95% of 3000 is 2850 Fish.

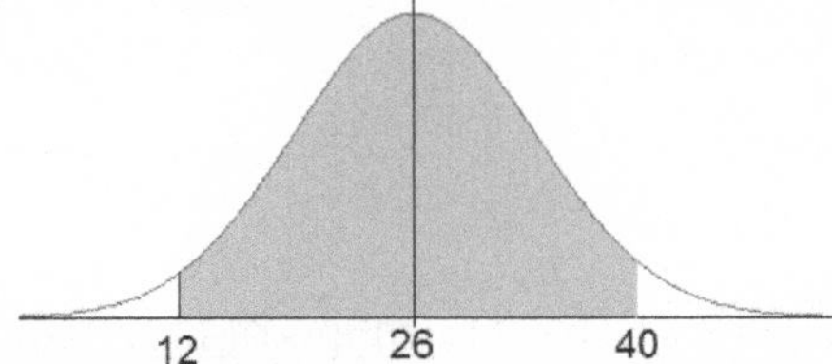

c. Find and shade on the graph the interval in which 99.7% of the fish lengths are. How many fish in this case? This exactly the percentage the corresponds 3 SD therefore the interval is (5, 47) cm, 99.7% of 3000 is 2991 Fish.

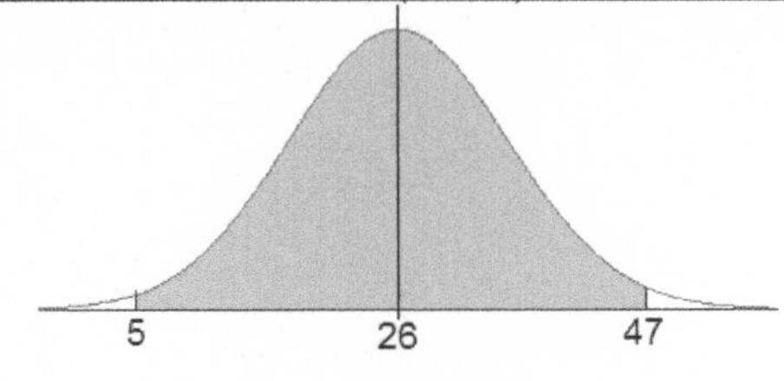

d. Find and the probability for a fish to measure between 23 and 28 cm. Shade on graph. How many fish in this would you expect in this case to be in this interval? normalcdf(23,28, 26, 7) = 0.278, $0.278 \times 3000 = 834$ fish

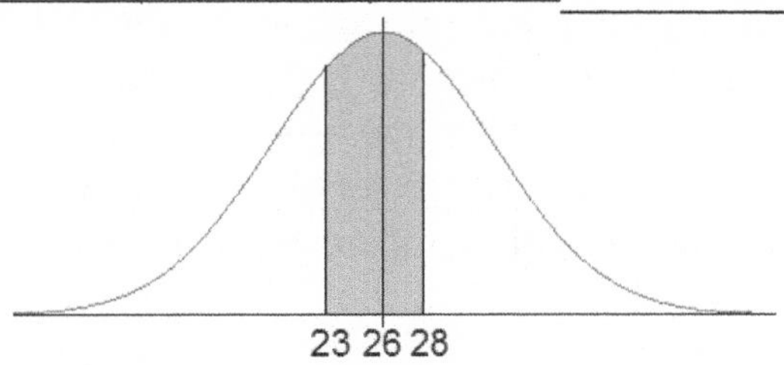

e. Find and the probability for a fish to measure between 12 and 24 cm. Shade on graph. How many fish in this would you expect in this case to be in this interval? normalcdf(12,24, 26, 7) = 0.365, $0.365 \times 3000 = 1095$ fish

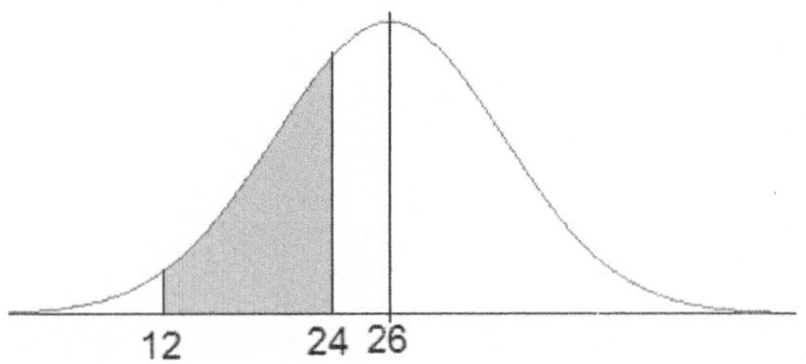

f. Find and the probability for a fish to measure between 27 and 28 cm. Shade on graph. How many fish in this would you expect in this case to be in this interval? normalcdf(27,28, 26, 7) = 0.0557, $0.0557 \times 3000 = 167$ fish

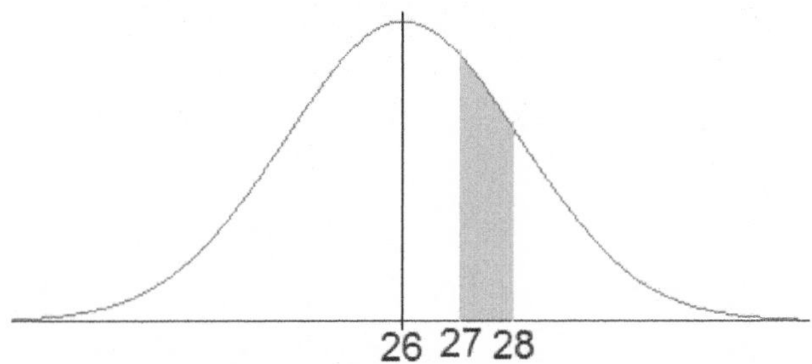

g. Find and shade on graph the probability for a fish to measure more than 26 cm. How many fish in this case? normalcdf(26,1000, 26, 7) = 0.5, 1500 fish

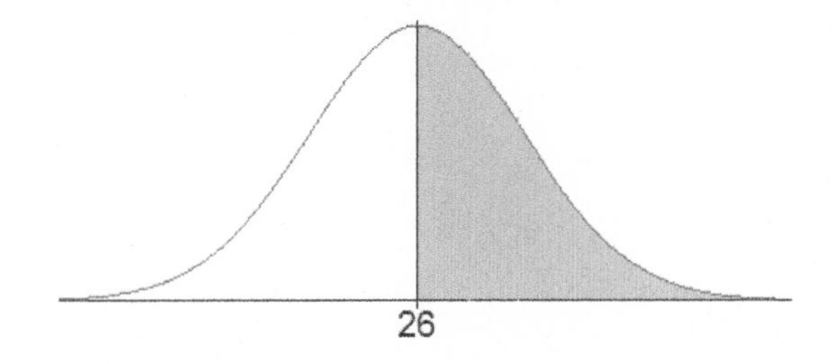

h. Find and shade on graph the probability for a fish to measure exactly 27 cm. 0, no corresponding area

i. Find and shade on graph the probability for a fish to measure exactly 20 cm 0, no corresponding area

STANDARDIZATION OF THE NORMAL DISTRIBUTION

21. As we already know there is an infinite number of normal distributions, depending on mean and Standard Deviation. The standard distribution is one of them, the distribution in which the mean is 0 and the SD is 1.
22. Usually in a problem the distribution is not the standard therefore the mean is not 0 and the Standard Deviation is not 1. The way to transform any normal distribution to the standard one is the following: $Z = \frac{X - \mu}{\sigma}$
23. In reality what this expression means is rescaling the variable. And Z is the number of Standard Deviations away from the mean.

24. Given a distribution N(22, 5) , find the standard variable Z, shade and calculate:
    a. $P(X \geq 22) = P(Z \geq 0) = 0.5$

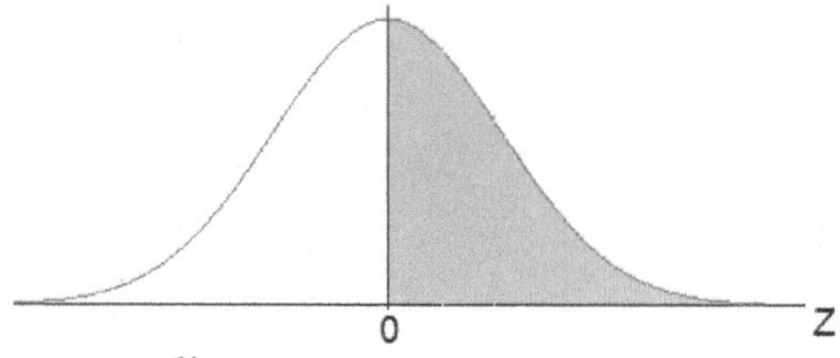

b. $P(X = 27) = P(Z = 1) = 0$, no corresponding area.

c. $P(X < 20) = P(Z < \frac{20-22}{5}) = P(Z < -0.2) = $ normalcdf(–1000, –0.2) = 0.421

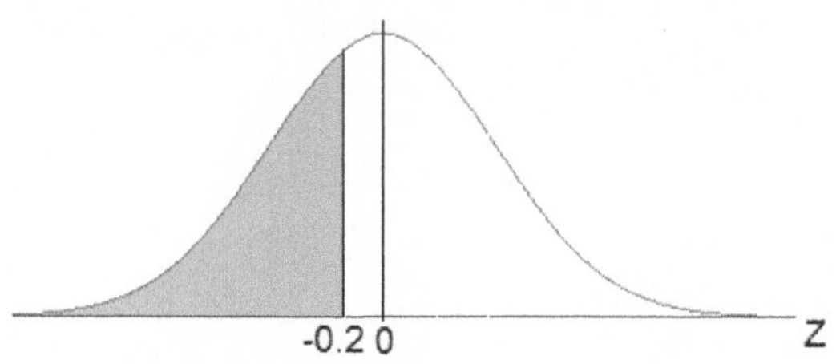

d. $P(X \geq 25) = P(Z > \frac{25-22}{5}) = P(Z > 0.6) = $ normalcdf(0.6, 1000) = 0.274

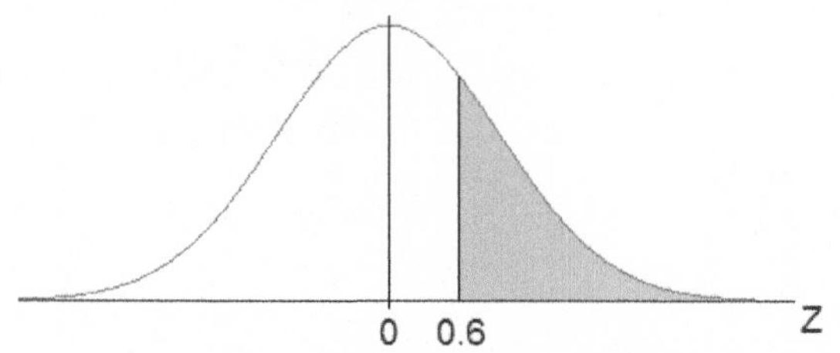

e. $P(X \geq 15) = P(Z > \frac{15-22}{5}) = P(Z > -1.4) = $ normalcdf(–1.4, 1000) = 0.919

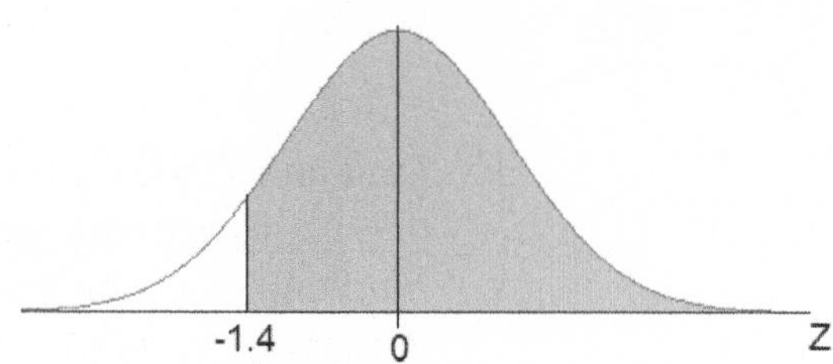

f. $P(X \geq 0) = P(Z > \frac{0-22}{5}) = P(Z > -4.4) =$ normalcdf(–4.4, 1000) ≈ 1

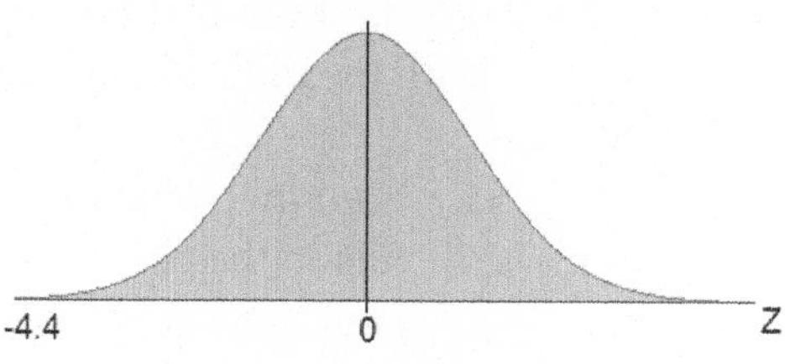

g. $P(X \leq 18) = P(Z < \frac{18-22}{5}) = P(Z < -0.8) =$ normalcdf(–1000, –-0.8) = 0.219

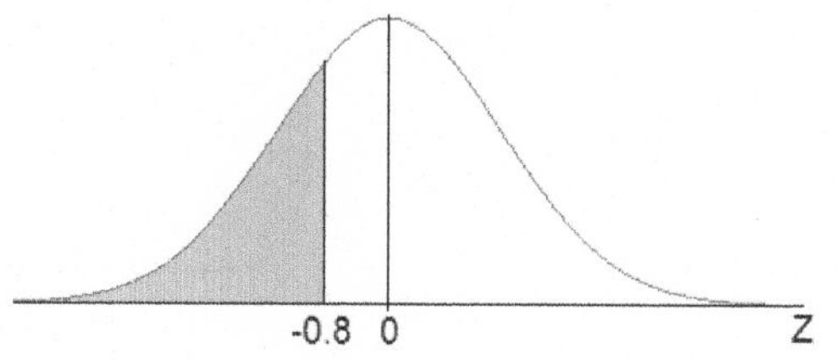

h. $P(-\infty \leq X \leq 27) = P(Z < \frac{27-22}{5}) = P(Z < 1) =$ normalcdf(–1000, 1) = 0.841

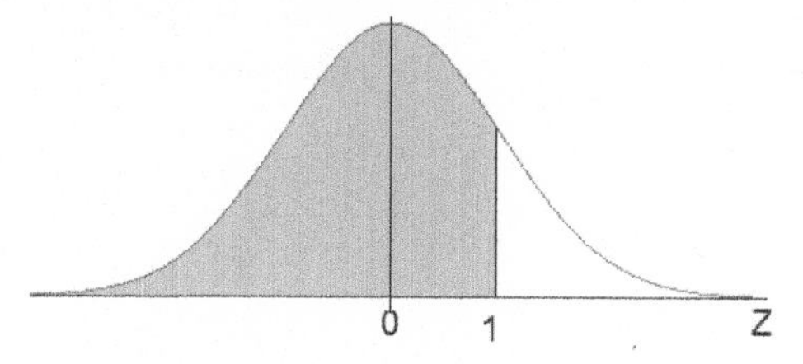

i. $P(20 \leq X \leq 25) = P(\frac{20-22}{5} < Z < \frac{25-22}{5}) = P(-0.2 < Z < 0.6) =$
normalcdf(–0.2, 0.6) = 0.305

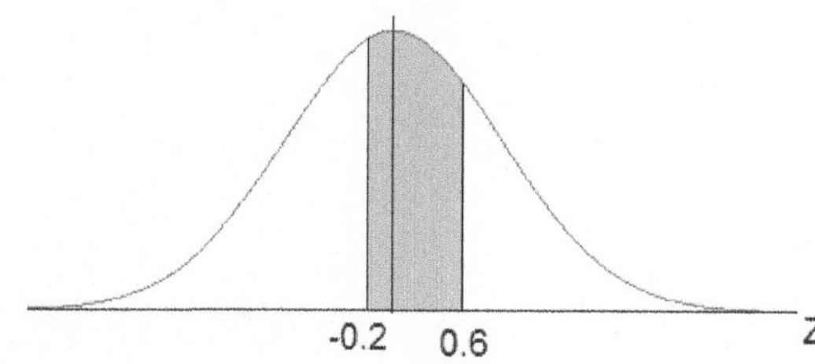

j. $P(12 \leq X \leq 18) = P(\frac{12-22}{5} < Z < \frac{18-22}{5}) = P(-2 < Z < -0.8) =$
normalcdf(–2, –0.8) = 0.189

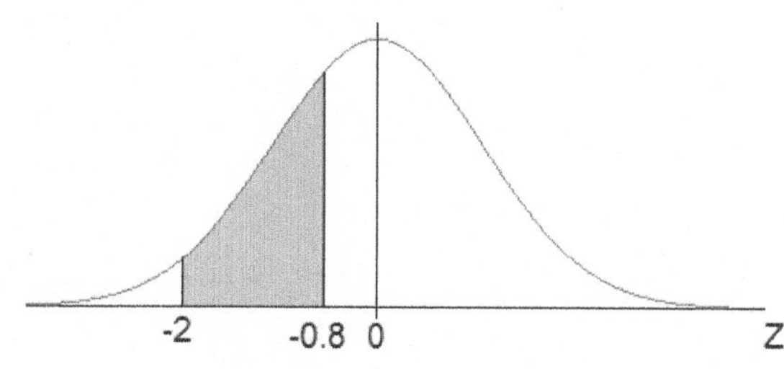

FINDING INVERSE NORMAL PROBABILITIES

25. The amount of time (X) to produce a product follows a normal distribution with mean of 40 minutes and S. D. of 8 minutes.

    a. Find the value of a, if 6% of the products are produced in less than a min. Shade the corresponding area on the following diagram. Use GDC to find your answer: invNorm(0.06, 40, 8) = 27.6min

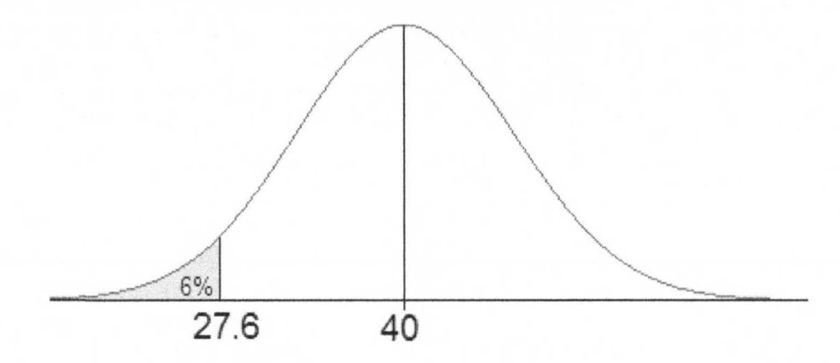

    b. Find the value of a, if 13% of the products are produced in more than a min. Shade the corresponding area on the following diagram. Use GDC to find your answer: invNorm(0.87, 40, 8) = 49.0

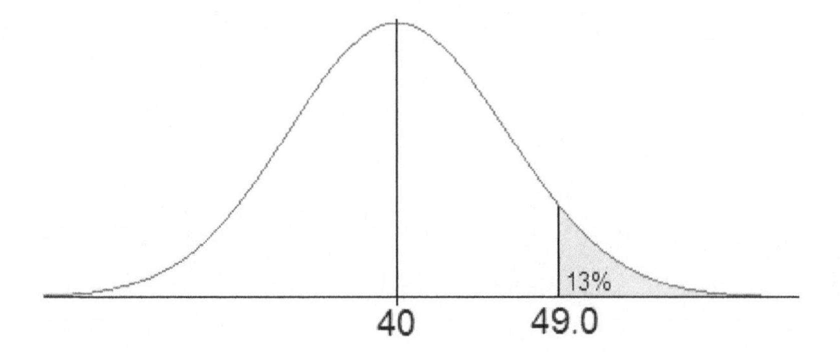

    c. Find the value of a and b if the middle 50% of the products are produced in between a and b min. Shade the corresponding area on the following diagram. Use GDC to find your answer: , invNorm(0.25, 40, 8) = 34.6 invNorm(0.75, 40, 8) = 45.4

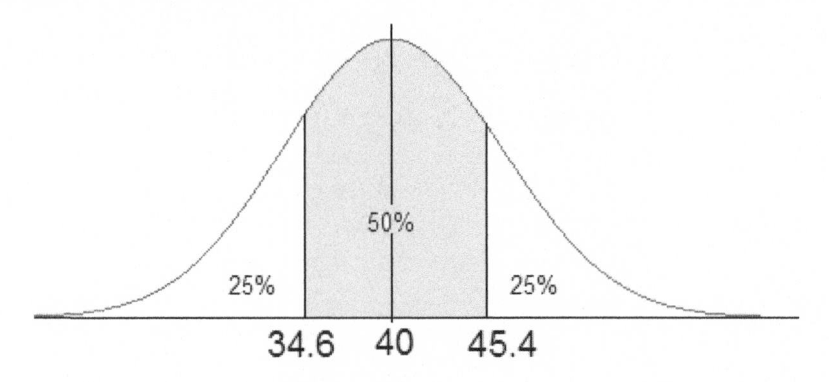

26. In a lake there are 2000 fish distributed according to a normal distribution with a mean of 26cm and a standard deviation of 7cm.

a. Find and shade the length interval for 80% of the fish. How many fish are expected to be in the interval in this case? invNorm(0.1, 26, 7) = 17.0 invNorm(0.9, 26, 7) = 35.0

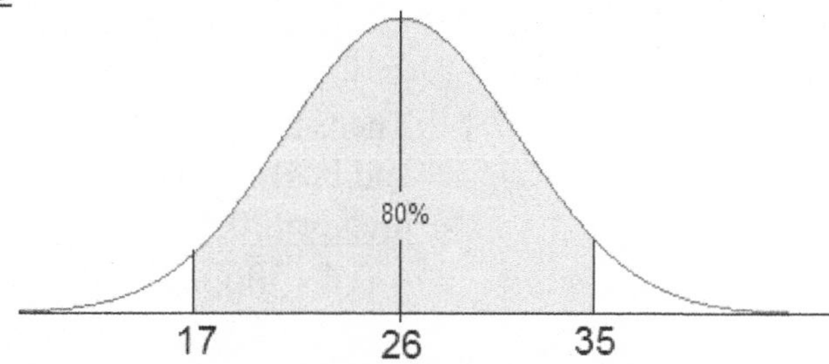

b. Find and shade the length interval for 90% of the fish. How many fish are expected to be in the interval in this case? invNorm(0.05, 26, 7) = 14.5 invNorm(0.95, 26, 7) = 37.5

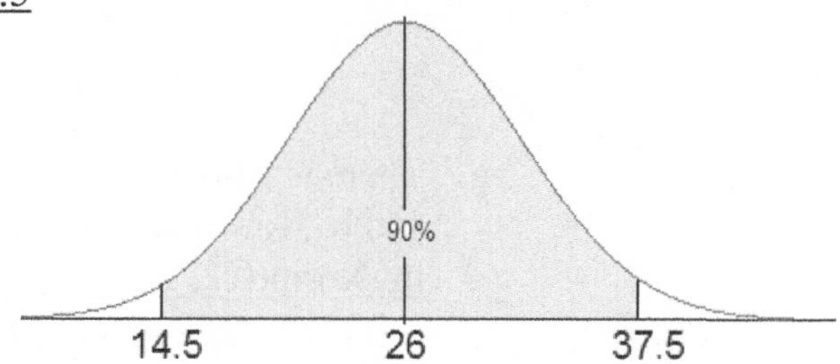

c. Find and shade the length interval for 75% of the fish. How many fish are expected to be in the interval in this case? invNorm(0.125, 26, 7) = 17.9 invNorm(0.875, 26, 7) = 34.1

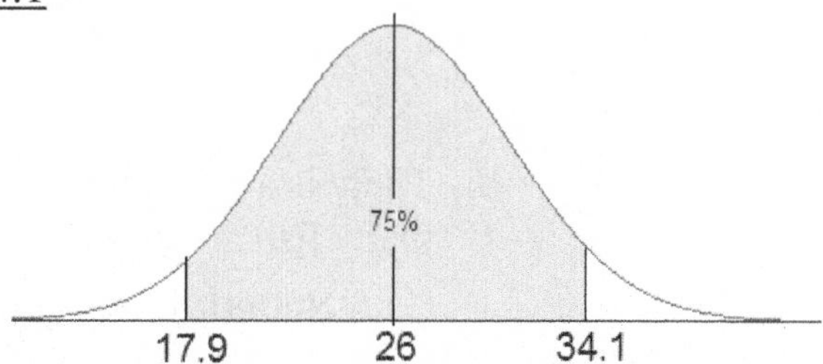

d. There is a probability of 0.2 that a fish's length is more than q, find q. How many fish are expected to be in the interval in this case?

q = invNorm(0.8, 26, 7) = 31.9, $0.2 \times 3000 = 600$ fish

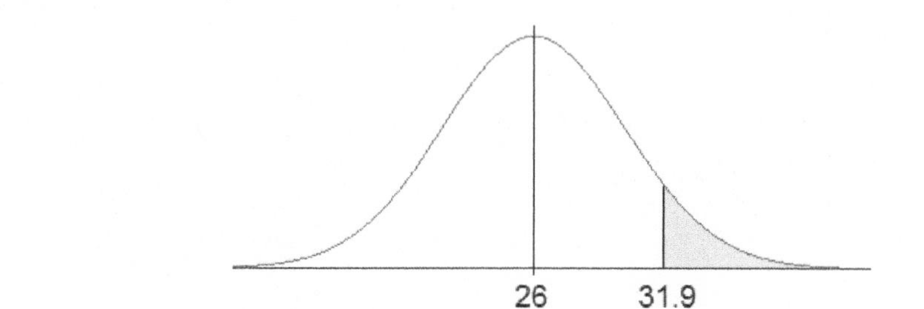

e. There is a probability of 0.32 that a fish's length is less than w, find w. How many fish are expected to be in the interval in this case?
w = invNorm(0.32, 26, 7) = 22.7, $0.32 \times 3000 = 960$ fish

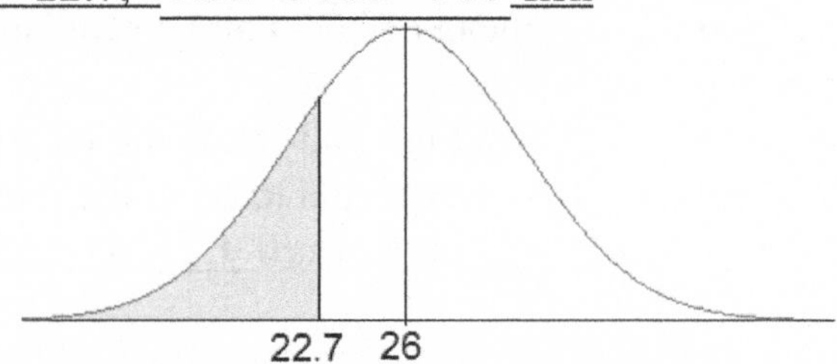

f. There is a probability of 0.4 that a fish's length is between a and b, find a and b. How many fish are expected to be in the interval in this case?
invNorm(0.3, 26, 7) = 22.3, invNorm(0.7, 26, 7) = 29.7
$0.4 \times 3000 = 1200$ fish

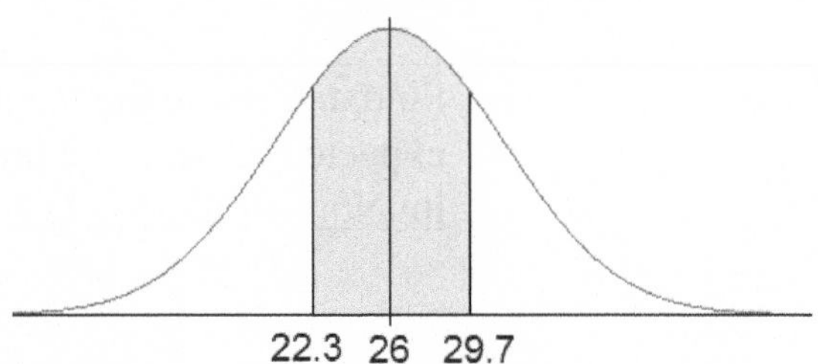

g. There is a probability of 0.6 that a fish's length is between a and b, find a and b. How many fish are expected to be in the interval in this case?
invNorm(0.2, 26, 7) = 20.1, invNorm(0.8, 26, 7) = 31.9
$0.6 \times 3000 = 1800$ fish

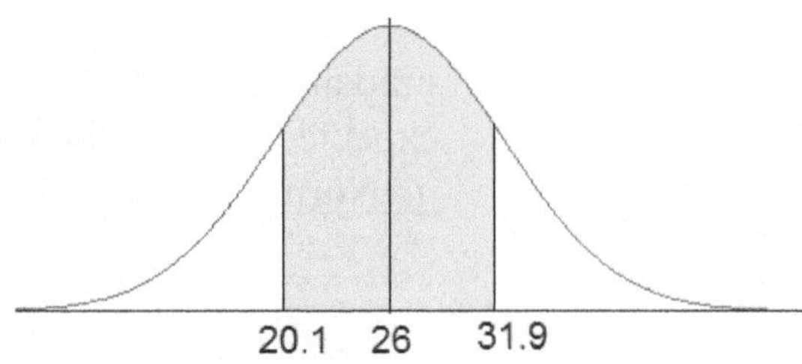

h. There is a probability of 0.1 that a fish's length is less than t, find t. How many fish are expected to be in the interval in this case?
t=invNorm(0.1, 26, 7) = 17.0, $0.1 \times 3000 = 300$ fish

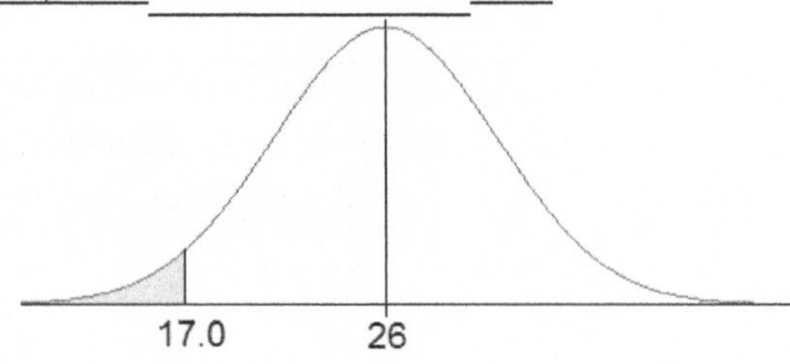

i. Find and shade the interval in which 65% of the fish measure. How many fish are expected to be in the interval in this case?
invNorm(0.175, 26, 7) = 19.5, invNorm(0.825, 26, 7) = 32.5
$0.65 \times 3000 = 1950$ fish

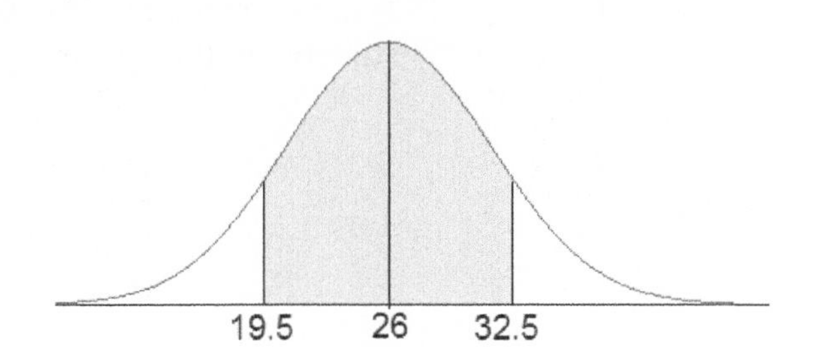

25. Calculate k if P(X ≤ k) = 0.6103 and X is a normal distribution N(15, 4)
k = invNorm(0.6103, 15, 4) = 16.1

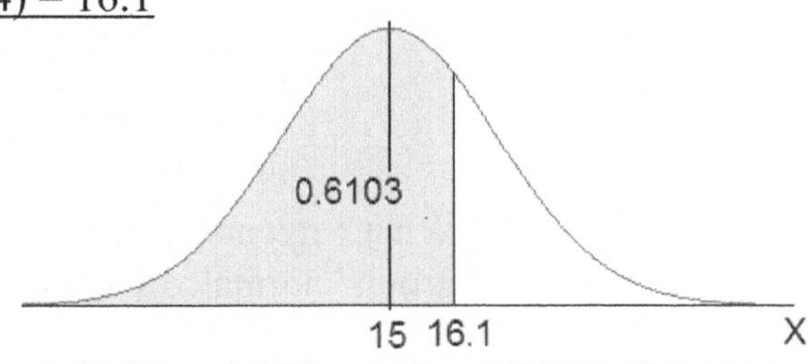

26. It is known that P(X ≤ 7) = 0.9147 and P(X ≤ 6.5) = 0.7517. Calculate

a. μ and σ

invNorm(0.9147, 0, 1) = 1.37, invNorm(0.7517, 0, 1) = 0.680

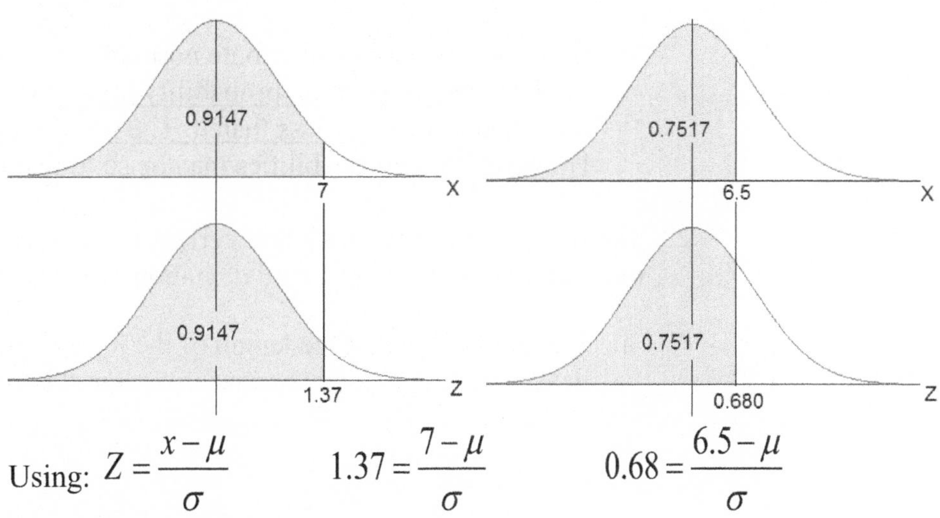

Using: $Z = \dfrac{x-\mu}{\sigma}$ $\quad 1.37 = \dfrac{7-\mu}{\sigma}$ $\quad 0.68 = \dfrac{6.5-\mu}{\sigma}$

Solving the system gives: $\mu = 6.01$ $\quad \sigma = 0.725$

b. k so that P(X ≥ k) = 0.3
invNorm(0.7, 6.01, 0.725) = 6.39

27. 500 high school students' grades are distributed normally with a mean of 72 and a standard deviation of 6.
    a. Find the interval mean plus/minus 2 standard deviations: (60, 84)
    b. What percentage of scores are between scores 60 and 70? How many students in this group? normalcdf(60, 70, 72, 6) = 0.345 = 34.5%

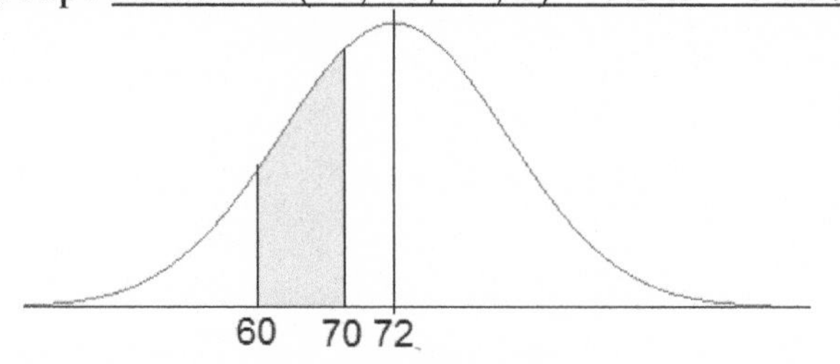

    c. What percentage of scores are more than 88? How many students in this group? normalcdf(88, 1000, 72, 6) = 0.00383 = 0.383%

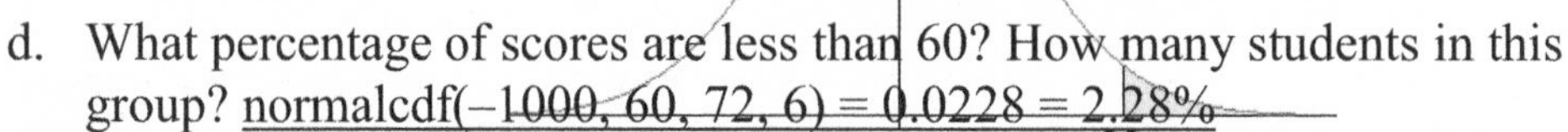

    d. What percentage of scores are less than 60? How many students in this group? normalcdf(−1000, 60, 72, 6) = 0.0228 = 2.28%

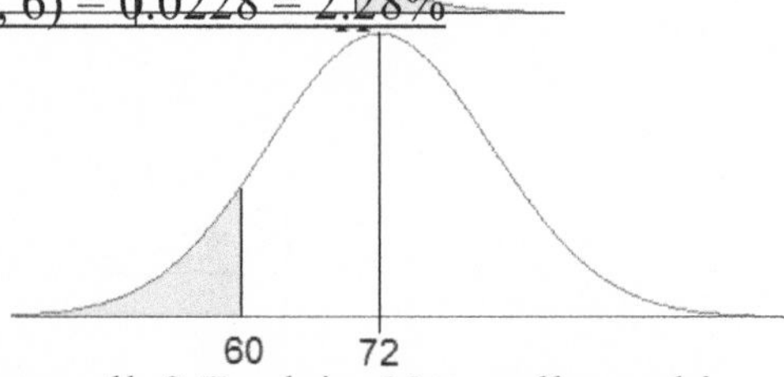

    e. Can students' grades distribute normally? Explain. Not really as this implies there is a certain probability (more than 0) of obtaining a grade of more than a 100% or less than 0. The same happens with height or weight. However, these probabilities may be so lo that the error is very small.

28. The time it takes to complete a certain journey is normally distributed with a mean of 50 days and a standard deviation of 4 days.

    a. The probability that the length of the journey lies between 53 and 60 days is represented by the shaded area in the following diagram.

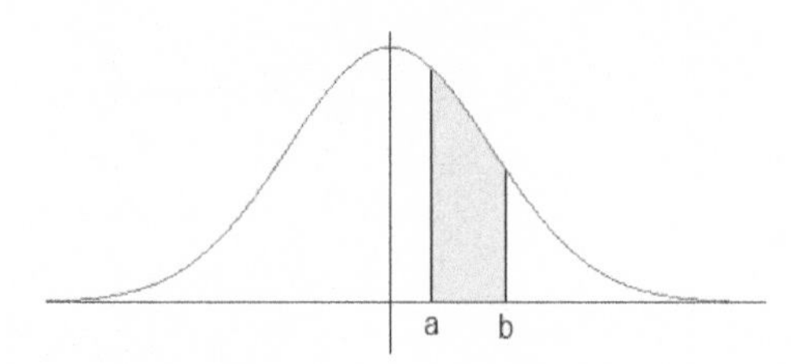

Write down the values of a and b. $a = 53$ $b = 60$

    b. Find the probability that the length of the journey is more than 57 days. normalcdf(57, 1000, 50, 4) = 0.401

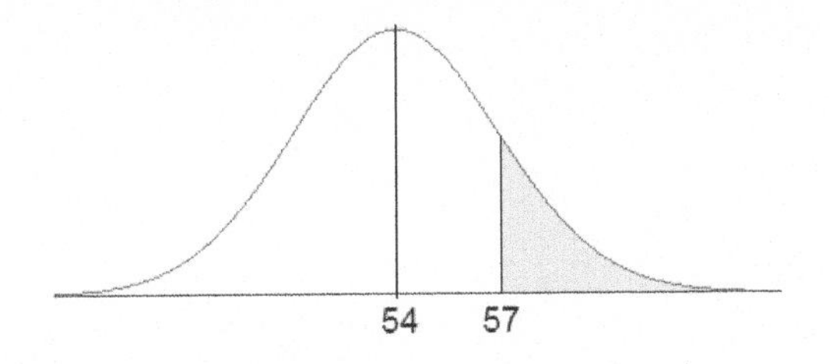

c. Find the probability that the length of the journey is between 56 and 61 days. normalcdf(56, 61, 50, 4) = 0.0638

d. 80% of the travellers complete the journey after x days. Find x. x = invNorm(0.8, 50, 4) = 53.4 days

29. The weight of a certain animal is normally distributed with mean of 150 kg and standard deviation of 12 kg. We classify the animals in the following way:
   a. Find the probability for each one the cases described.
      P(weight < 130) = normalcdf(−1000, 130, 150, 12) = 0.0478
      P(130 < weight < 170) = normalcdf(130, 170, 150, 12) = 0.904
      P(weight > 170) = normalcdf(170, 1000, 150, 12) = 0.0478
   b. There is a probability of 0.2 for an animal to have a weight bigger than q. Find q. P(weight > q) = 0.2 q = invNorm(0.8, 150, 12) = 160 kg
   c. In a jungle with 3000 animals how many are expected to have a weight bigger than q? $0.2 \times 3000 = 600$ animals

Made in the USA
Monee, IL
18 November 2020